Discovering
Geometry

FIFTH EDITION

Michael Serra

Kendall Hunt
publishing company

Project Director
Tim Pope

Project Editor
Holly Paige

Developmental Editors
Jennifer North Morris
Dr. Sandy Berger, Ph.D

Consulting Editor
Dr. Karen M. Greenhaus, Ed.D

Permissions Editor
Tammy Hunt

Cover Designers
Janell Cannavo
Suzanne Millius

Cover image © Shutterstock

Chairman and Chief Executive Officer Mark C. Falb
President and Chief Operating Officer Chad M. Chandlee
Vice President, PreK-12 Division Charley Cook

www.kendallhunt.com
Send all inquiries to:
4050 Westmark Drive
Dubuque, IA 52004-1840
1-800-542-6657

Printed in the United States of America
4 5 6 7 8 9 10

CONTENTS

CHAPTER 3

Using Tools of Geometry 149

CHAPTER 6

Applications of Transformations 317

CHAPTER 11

Volume 533

CHAPTER 12

Trigonometry 583

CHAPTER 13 Geometry as a Mathematical System 621

Geometric Art

A work by Dutch graphic artist M. C. Escher (1898–1972) opens each chapter in this book. Escher used geometry in creative ways to make his interesting and unusual works of art. As you come to each new chapter, see whether you can connect the Escher work to the content of the chapter.

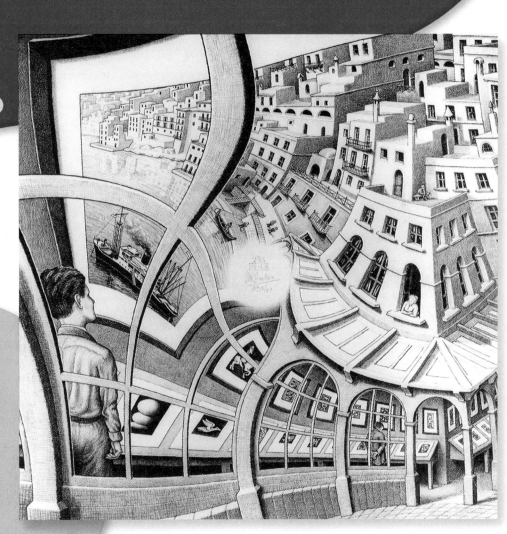

"My subjects are often playful. . . . It is, for example, a pleasure to deliberately mix together objects of two and of three dimensions, surface and spatial relationships, and to make fun of gravity."

M. C. ESCHER

OBJECTIVES

In this chapter you will

- see examples of geometry in nature
- study geometric art forms of cultures around the world
- study the symmetry in flowers, crystals, and animals
- see geometry as a way of thinking and of looking at the world
- practice using a compass and straightedge

Geometry in Nature and in Art

Nature displays a seemingly infinite variety of geometric shapes, from tiny atoms to great galaxies. Crystals, honeycombs, snowflakes, spiral shells, spiderwebs, and seed arrangements on sunflowers and pinecones are just a few of nature's geometric masterpieces.

Circle

Hexagon

Pentagon

Geometry includes the study of the properties of shapes such as circles, hexagons, and pentagons. Outlines of the sun, the moon, and the planets appear as circles. Snowflakes, honeycombs, and many crystals are hexagonal (6-sided). Many living things, such as flowers and starfish, are pentagonal (5-sided).

People observe geometric patterns in nature and use them in a variety of art forms. Basket weavers, woodworkers, and other artisans often use geometric designs to make their works more interesting and beautiful. You will learn some of their techniques in this chapter.

In the Celtic knot design above, the curves seem to weave together.

This Islamic tile design uses 5, 8, and 12-pointed stars in addition to 4, 6, and 8-sided shapes. Can you identify them all?

Artists rely on geometry to show perspective and proportion, and to produce certain optical effects. Using their understanding of lines, artists can give depth to their drawings. Or they can use lines and curves to create designs that seem to pop out of the page.

3-D street painting in Bangkok, Thailand.

Symmetry is a geometric characteristic of both nature and art. You may already know the two basic types of symmetry, reflectional symmetry and rotational symmetry. A design has **reflectional symmetry** if you can fold it along a **line of symmetry** so that all the points on one side of the line exactly coincide with (or match) all the points on the other side of the line.

This leaf and butterfly both have one line of reflectional symmetry.

Line of symmetry

You can place a mirror on the line of symmetry so that half the figure and its mirror image re-create the original figure. So, reflectional symmetry is also called *line symmetry* or *mirror symmetry*. Biologists say an organism with just one line of symmetry, like the human body or a butterfly, has *bilateral symmetry*. An object with reflectional symmetry looks balanced.

A design has **rotational symmetry** if it looks the same after you turn it around a point by less than a full circle. The number of times that the design looks the same as you turn it through a complete 360° circle determines the type of rotational symmetry. The Apache basket has 5-fold rotational symmetry because it looks the same after you rotate it 72°(a fifth of a circle, 144° (two-fifths of a circle), 216° (three-fifths of a circle), 288° (four-fifths of a circle), and 360° (one full circle).

This Apache basket has 5-fold rotational symmetry.

Other examples of 5-fold symmetry include the flower on page 2, the starfish below, and the star in Exercise 5. Does the sand dollar in Exercise 5 have 5-fold symmetry?

Consumer
CONNECTION

Many products have eye-catching labels, logos, and designs. Have you ever paid more attention to a product because the geometric design of its logo was familiar or attractive to you?

GEO ART
Graphic Designs

Countries throughout the world use symmetry in their national flags. Notice that the Jamaican flag has rotational symmetry in addition to two lines of reflectional symmetry. You can rotate the flag 180° without changing its appearance. The origami boxes, however, have rotational symmetry, but not reflectional symmetry.

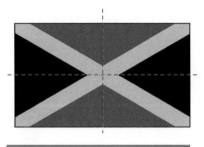

The Jamaican flag has two lines of reflectional symmetry.

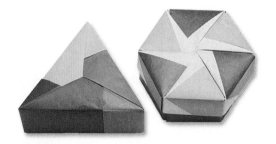

If you ignore colors, the Japanese origami box on the left has 3-fold rotational symmetry. What type of symmetry does the other box have?

0.1 Exercises

1. Name two objects from nature whose shapes are hexagonal. Name two living organisms whose shapes have five-fold rotational symmetry.

2. Describe some ways that artists use geometry.

3. Name some objects with only one line of symmetry. What is the name for this type of symmetry?

4. Which of these playing cards have rotational symmetry? Which ones have reflectional symmetry? Explain.

5. Which of these objects have reflectional symmetry (or approximate reflectional symmetry)?

a.

b.

c.

d.

e.

f.

6. Which of the objects in Exercise 5 have rotational symmetry (or approximate rotational symmetry)?

7. British artist Andy Goldsworthy (b 1956) uses materials from nature to create beautiful outdoor sculptures. The artful arrangement of sticks below might appear to have rotational symmetry, but instead it has one line of reflectional symmetry. Can you find the line of symmetry? *(h)*

> If an exercise has an *(h)* at the end, you can find a hint to help you in Hints for Selected Exercises at the back of the book.

Early morning calm
knotweed stalks
pushed into lake bottom
made complete by their own reflections

**DERWENT WATER CUMBRIA
20 FEBRUARY & 8-9 MARCH**

For the title of this outdoor sculpture by Andy Goldsworthy, see the hint to Exercise 7 in the Hints section.

8. Create a simple design that has two lines of reflectional symmetry. Does it have rotational symmetry? Next, try to create another design with two lines of reflectional symmetry, but without rotational symmetry. Any luck?

9. Bring to class an object from nature that shows geometry. Describe the geometry that you find in the object as well as any symmetry the object has.

10. Bring an object to school or wear something that displays a form of handmade or manufactured geometric art. Describe any symmetry the object has.

11. Shah Jahan, Mughal emperor of India from 1628 to 1658, had the beautiful Taj Mahal built in memory of his wife, Mumtaz Mahal. Its architect, Ustad Ahmad Lahori, designed it with perfect symmetry. Describe two lines of symmetry in this photo. How does the design of the building's grounds give this view of the Taj Mahal even more symmetry than the building itself has?

Architecture CONNECTION

The Taj Mahal in Agra, India, was described by the poet Rabindranath Tagore as "rising above the banks of the river like a solitary tear suspended on the cheek of time."

DEVELOPING MATHEMATICAL REASONING

Pickup Sticks

Pickup sticks is a good game for developing motor skills, but you can turn it into a challenging visual puzzle. In what order should you pick up the sticks so that you are always removing the top stick?

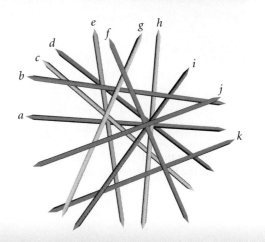

Line Designs

The symmetry and patterns in geometric designs make them very appealing. You can make many designs using the basic tools of geometry—**compass** and **straightedge**.

You'll use a straightedge to construct straight lines and a compass to construct circles and to mark off equal distances. A straightedge is like a ruler but it has no marks. You can use the edge of a ruler as a straightedge. The straightedge and the compass are the classical construction tools used by the ancient Greeks, who laid the foundations of the geometry that you are studying.

"We especially need imagination in science. It is not all mathematics, nor all logic, but it is somewhat beauty and poetry."

MARIA MITCHELL

Japanese design is known for its simple, clean lines.

The line designs on the ceiling of the Vatican museum make the hall look grandiose.

Some of the lines in this mosaic appear to be tied in knots!

You can create many types of designs using only straight lines. Here are two line designs and the steps for creating each one.

The Astrid

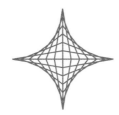

The 8-Pointed Star

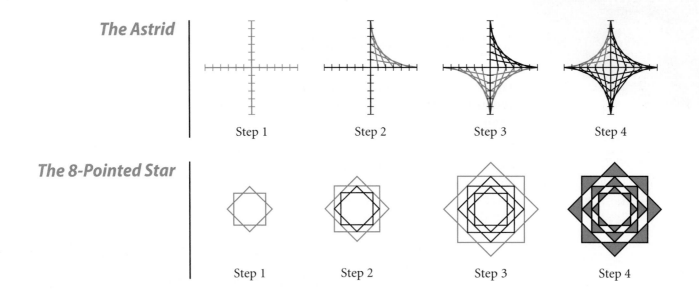

The Astrid

Step 1   Step 2   Step 3   Step 4

The 8-Pointed Star

Step 1   Step 2   Step 3   Step 4

0.2 Exercises

1. What are the classical construction tools of geometry?

2. Create a line design from this lesson. Color your design.

3. Each of these line designs uses straight lines only. Select one design and re-create it on a sheet of paper. ⓗ

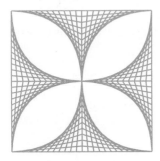  

4. Describe the symmetries of the three designs in Exercise 3. For the third design, does color matter?

5. Many quilt designers create beautiful geometric patterns with reflectional symmetry. One-fourth of a 4-by-4 quilt pattern and its reflection are shown at right. Copy the designs onto graph paper, and complete the 4-by-4 pattern so that it has two lines of reflectional symmetry. Color your quilt.

6. Geometric patterns seem to be in motion in a quilt design with rotational symmetry. Copy the quilt piece shown in Exercise 5 onto graph paper, and complete the 4-by-4 quilt pattern so that it has 4-fold rotational symmetry. Color your quilt.

7. Organic molecules have geometric shapes. How many different lines of reflectional symmetry does this benzene molecule have? Does it have rotational symmetry? Sketch your answers.

Benzene molecule

Circle Designs

People have always been fascinated by circles. Circles are used in the design of mosaics, baskets, and ceramics, as well as in the architectural design of buildings.

"It's where we go, and what we do when we get there, that tells us who we are."
JOYCE CAROL OATES

Rosette

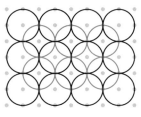

Circular window

Lace pattern

You can make circle designs with a compass as your primary tool. For example, here is a design you can make on a square dot grid.

Overlapping Circles

Begin with a 7-by-9 square dot grid. Construct three rows of four circles.

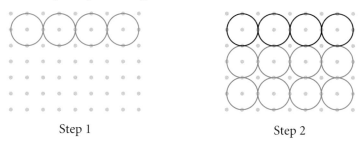

Step 1

Step 2

Construct two rows of three circles using the points between the first set of circles as centers. The result is a set of six circles overlapping the original 12 circles. Decorate your design.

Step 3

Step 4

The Daisy

Here is another design that you can make using only a compass. Start by constructing a circle, then select any point on it. Without changing your compass setting, swing an arc centered at the selected point. Swing an arc with each of the two new points as centers, and so on.

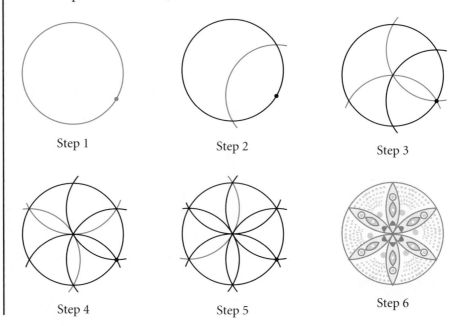

Step 1   Step 2   Step 3

Step 4   Step 5   Step 6

Notice the shape you get by connecting the six petal tips of the daisy. This is a **regular hexagon**, a 6-sided figure whose sides are the same length and whose angles are all the same size. If you connect every other petal tip, you get a regular triangle, with all the sides the same length and whose angles are all the same size, more commonly called an **equilateral triangle**.

Instead of stopping at the perimeter of the first circle, you can continue to swing full circles. Then you get a "field of daisies," as shown above.

You can do many variations on a daisy design.

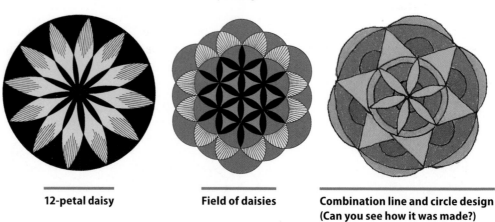

12-petal daisy   **Field of daisies**   **Combination line and circle design (Can you see how it was made?)**

Schuyler Smith, former geometry student

0.3 Exercises

YOU WILL NEED

Construction tools for Exercises **1–5**

For Exercises 1–5, use your construction tools.

1. Use square dot paper to create a 4-by-5 grid of 20 circles, and then make 12 circles overlapping them. Color or shade the design so that it has reflectional symmetry.

2. Use your compass to create a set of seven identical circles that touch but do not overlap. Draw a larger circle that encloses the seven circles. Color or shade your design so that it has rotational symmetry. ⓗ

3. Create a 6-petal daisy design and color or shade it so that it has rotational symmetry, but not reflectional symmetry.

4. Make a 12-petal daisy by drawing a second 6-petal daisy between the petals of the first 6-petal daisy. Color or shade the design so that it has reflectional symmetry, but not rotational symmetry.

5. Using a 1-inch setting for your compass, construct a central regular hexagon and six regular hexagons that each share one side with the original hexagon. Your hexagon design should look similar to, but larger than, the figure at right. This design is called a tessellation, or tiling, of regular hexagons.

This rose window at the National Cathedral in Washington, D.C., has a central design of seven circles enclosed in a larger circle.

DEVELOPING MATHEMATICAL REASONING

Magic Squares I

A magic square is an arrangement of numbers in a square grid. The numbers in every row, column, or diagonal add up to the same number. For example, in the magic square on the left, the sum of each row, column, and diagonal is 18.

Complete the 5-by-5 magic square on the right. Use only the numbers in this list: 6, 7, 9, 13, 17, 21, 23, 24, 27, and 28.

5	10	3
4	6	8
9	2	7

20			8	14
	19	25	26	
	12	18		30
29	10	11		
22			15	16

Op Art

Op art, or optical art, is a form of abstract art that uses lines or geometric patterns to create a special visual effect. The contrasting dark and light regions sometimes appear to be in motion or to represent a change in surface, direction, and dimension.

Victor Vasarely, widely accepted as the grandfather of the op art movement, had a strong interest in geometry, which was reflected in his work. Vasarely was one artist who transformed grids so that spheres seem to bulge from them.

"Everything is an illusion, including this notion."

STANISLAW J. LEC

You can see Vasarely's trademark bulging sphere in the designs on the stamps.

Hungarian artist Victor Vasarely (1908–1997)

The Wavy Letter

Op art is fun and easy to create. To create one kind of op art design, first make a design in outline. Next, draw horizontal or vertical lines, gradually varying the space between the lines or each pair of lines, as shown below, to create an illusion of hills and valleys. Finally, color in or shade alternating spaces.

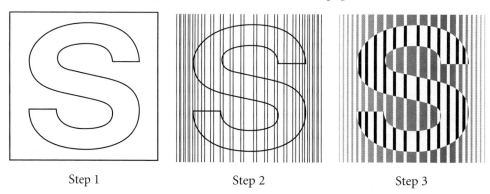

Step 1   Step 2   Step 3

The Square Spiral

To create the next design, first locate a point on each of the four sides of a square. Each point should be the same distance from a corner, as shown. Your compass is a good tool for measuring equal lengths. Connect these four points to create another square within the first. Repeat the process until the squares appear to converge on the center. Be careful that you don't fall in!

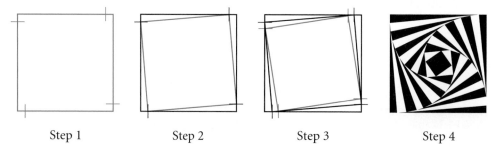

Step 1   Step 2   Step 3   Step 4

Here are some other examples of op art.

Square tunnel or top of pyramid?

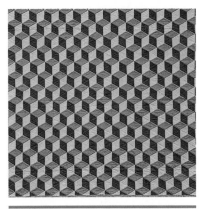

Amish quilt, tumbling block design

Are the designs burrowing down or climbing up?

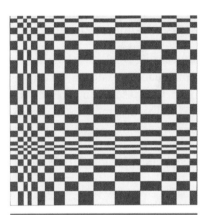

Op art by Carmen Apodaca, geometry student

You can create any of the designs on this page using just a compass and straightedge (and doing some careful coloring). Can you figure out how each of these op art designs was created?

→*Architecture*
CONNECTION

Frank Lloyd Wright (1867–1959) is often called America's favorite architect. He built homes in 36 states—sometimes in unusual settings.

Fallingwater, located in Pennsylvania, is a building designed by Wright that displays his obvious love of geometry. Can you describe the geometry you see?

Exercises

1. What is the optical effect in each piece of art in this lesson?

2. Nature creates its own optical art. At first the black and white stripes of a zebra appear to work against it, standing out against the golden brown grasses of the African plain. However, the stripes do provide the zebras with very effective protection from predators. When and how?

3. Select one type of op art design from this lesson and create your own version of it.

4. Create an op art design that has reflectional symmetry, but not rotational symmetry.

5. Antoni Gaudí (1852–1926) designed the Bishop's Palace in Astorga, Spain. List as many geometric shapes as you can recognize on the palace (flat, two-dimensional shapes such as rectangles as well as solid, three-dimensional shapes such as cylinders). What type of symmetry do you see on the palace?

Bishop's Palace, Astorga, Spain

DEVELOPING MATHEMATICAL REASONING

Bagels

In the original computer game of bagels, a player determines a three-digit number (no digit repeated) by making educated guesses. After each guess, the computer gives a clue about the guess. Here are the clues.

bagels: no digit is correct
pico: one digit is correct but in the wrong position
fermi: one digit is correct and in the correct position

In each of the games below, a number of guesses have been made, with the clue for each guess shown to its right. From the given set of guesses and clues, determine the three-digit number. If there is more than one solution, find them all.

Game 1:
1 2 3	*bagels*
4 5 6	*pico*
7 8 9	*pico*
0 7 5	*pico fermi*
0 8 7	*pico*
? ? ?	

Game 2:
9 0 8	*bagels*
1 3 4	*pico*
3 8 7	*pico fermi*
2 5 6	*fermi*
2 3 7	*pico pico*
? ? ?	

Knot Designs

Knot designs are geometric designs that appear to weave or to interlace like a knot. Some of the earliest known designs are found in Celtic art from the northern regions of England and Scotland. In their carved stone designs, the artists imitated the rich geometric patterns of three-dimensional crafts such as weaving and basketry. The *Book of Kells* (8th and 9th centuries) is the most famous source of Celtic knot designs.

"In the old days, a love-sick sailor might send his sweetheart a length of fishline loosely tied in a love knot. If the knot was returned pulled tight, it meant the passion was strong. But if the knot was returned untied—ah, matey, time to ship out."

OLD SAILOR'S TALE

Celtic knot design

Carved knot pattern from Nigeria

Today a very familiar knot design is the set of interconnected rings used as the logo for the Olympic Games.

Knot Designs

Here are the steps for creating two examples of knot designs. Look them over before you begin the exercises.

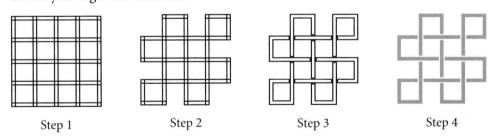

Step 1　　　　Step 2　　　　Step 3　　　　Step 4

You can use a similar approach to create a knot design with rings.

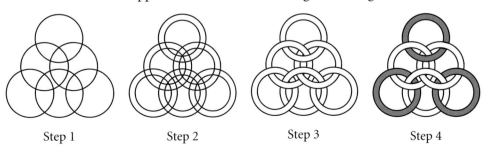

Step 1　　　　Step 2　　　　Step 3　　　　Step 4

Here are some more examples of knot designs.

Knot design by Scott Shanks, former geometry student

Tiger Tail **by Diane Cassell, parent of former geometry student**

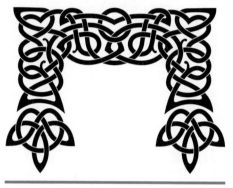

Nordic frame with knot design and floral sprouts

Chinese knot design

The last woodcut made by M. C. Escher is a knot design called *Snakes*. **The rings and the snakes interlace, and the design has 3-fold rotational symmetry.**

M. C. Escher's *Snakes* ©2014 The M.C. Escher Company— The Netherlands. All rights reserved. www.mcescher.com

 **Exercises**

1. Name a culture or country whose art uses knot designs.

2. Create a knot design of your own, using only straight lines on graph paper.

3. Create a knot design of your own with rotational symmetry, using a compass or a circle template.

4. Sketch five rings linked together so that you could separate all five by cutting open one ring.

5. The coat of arms of the Borromeo family, who lived during the Italian Renaissance (ca. 15th century), showed a very interesting knot design known as the Borromean Rings. In it, three rings are linked together so that if any one ring is removed the remaining two rings are no longer connected. Got that? Good. Sketch the Borromean Rings.

6. The Chokwe storytellers of northeastern Angola are called *Akwa kuta sona* ("those who know how to draw"). When they sit down to draw and to tell their stories, they clear the ground and set up a grid of points in the sand with their fingertips, as shown below left. Then they begin to tell a story and, at the same time, trace a finger through the sand to create a *lusona* design with one smooth, continuous motion. Try your hand at creating *sona* (plural of *lusona*). Begin with the correct number of dots. Then, in one motion, re-create one of the *sona* below. The initial dot grid is shown for the rat.

Initial dot grid   Rat   Mbemba bird   Scorpion

7. In Greek mythology, the Gordian knot was such a complicated knot that no one could undo it. Oracles claimed that whoever could undo the knot would become the ruler of Gordium. When Alexander the Great (356–323 B.C.E.) came upon the knot, he simply cut it with his sword and claimed he had fulfilled the prophecy, so the throne was his. The expression "cutting the Gordian knot" is still used today. What do you think it means?

8. The square knot and granny knot are very similar but do very different things. Compare their symmetries. Use string to re-create the two knots and explain their differences.

Square knot   Granny knot

9. Cut a long strip of paper from a sheet of lined paper or graph paper. Tie the strip of paper snugly, but without wrinkles, into a simple knot. What shape does the knot create? Sketch your knot.

Islamic Tile Designs

Islamic art is rich in geometric forms. Early Islamic, or Muslim, artists became familiar with geometry through the works of Euclid, Pythagoras, and other mathematicians of antiquity, and they used geometric patterns extensively in their art and architecture.

"Patience with small details makes perfect a large work, like the universe."

JALALUDDIN RUMI

An exterior wall of the Dome of the Rock (660–750 C.E.) mosque in Jerusalem

Alcove in the Hall of Ambassadors, the Alhambra, in Granada, Spain

Islam frowned upon the representation of humans or animals in religious art. So, instead, the artists use abstract geometric patterns that are quite intricate.

One striking example of Islamic architecture is the Alhambra, a Moorish palace in Granada, Spain. Built over 600 years ago by Moors and Spaniards, the Alhambra is filled from floor to ceiling with marvelous geometric patterns. The designs you see on this page are but a few of the hundreds of intricate geometric patterns found in the tile work and the inlaid wood ceilings of buildings like the Alhambra and the Dome of the Rock.

Carpets and hand-tooled bronze plates from the Islamic world also show geometric designs. The patterns often elaborate on basic grids of regular hexagons, equilateral triangles, or squares. These complex Islamic patterns were constructed with no more than a compass and a straightedge. Repeating patterns like these are called **tessellations**. You'll learn more about tessellations in Chapter 6.

The two examples below show how to create one tile in a square-based and a hexagon-based design. The hexagon-based pattern is also a knot design.

8-Pointed Star

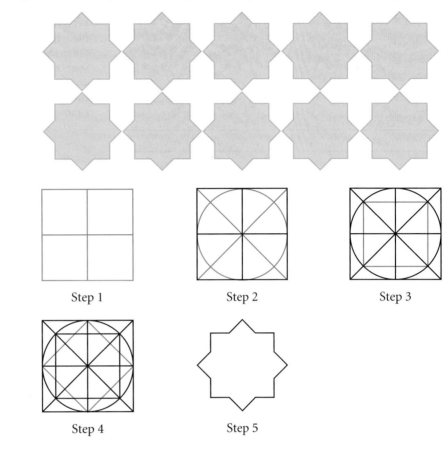

Step 1   Step 2   Step 3

Step 4   Step 5

Hexagon Tile Design

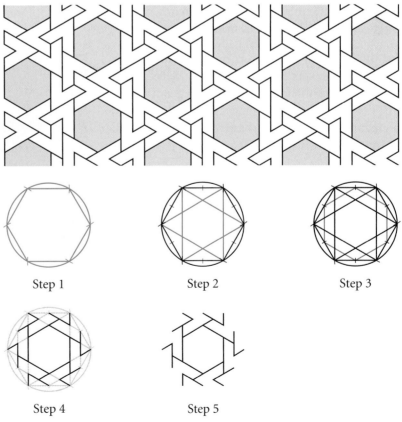

Step 1   Step 2   Step 3

Step 4   Step 5

In Morocco, *zillij*, the art of using glazed tiles to form geometric patterns, is the most common practice for making mosaics. *Zillij* artists cut stars, octagons, and other shapes from clay tiles and place them upside down into the lines of their design. When the tiling is complete, artists pour concrete over the tiles to form a slab. When the concrete dries, they lift the whole mosaic, displaying the colors and connected shapes, and mount it against a fountain, palace, or other building.

0.6 Exercises

YOU WILL NEED

Construction tools for Exercises 5–7

1. Name two countries where you can find Islamic architecture.

2. What is the name of the famous palace in Granada, Spain, where you can find beautiful examples of tile patterns?

3. Using tracing paper or transparency film, trace a few tiles from the 8-Pointed Star design. Notice that you can slide, or translate, the tracing in a straight line horizontally, vertically, and even diagonally to other positions so that the tracing will fit exactly onto the tiles again. What is the shortest translation distance you can find, in centimeters?

4. Notice that when you rotate your tracing from Exercise 3 about certain points in the tessellation, the tracing fits exactly onto the tiles again. Find two different points of rotation. (Put your pencil on the point and try rotating the tracing paper or transparency.) How many times in one rotation can you make the tiles match up again?

→Architecture CONNECTION

After studying buildings in other Muslim countries, the architect of the Petronas Twin Towers, Cesar Pelli (b 1926), decided that geometric tiling patterns would be key to the design. For the floor plan, his team used a very traditional tile design, the 8-pointed star—two intersecting squares. To add space and connect the design to the traditional "arabesques," the design team added arcs of circles between the eight points.

5. Currently the tallest twin towers in the world are the Petronas Twin Towers in Kuala Lumpur, Malaysia. The floor plans of the towers have the shape of Islamic designs. Use your compass and straightedge to re-create the design of the base of the Petronas Twin Towers, shown below right. *(h)*

6. Use your protractor and ruler to draw a square tile. Use your compass, straightedge, and eraser to modify and decorate it. See the example in this lesson for ideas, but yours can be different. Be creative!

7. Construct a regular hexagon tile and modify and decorate it. See the example in this lesson for ideas, but yours can be different.

8. Create a tessellation with one of the designs you made in Exercises 6 and 7. Trace or make several copies and paste them together in a tile pattern. (You can also create your tessellation using geometry software and print out a copy.) Add finishing touches to your tessellation by adding, erasing, or whiting out lines as desired. If you want, see if you can interweave a knot design within your tessellation. Color your tessellation.

In this chapter, you described the geometric shapes and symmetries you see in nature, in everyday objects, in art, and in architecture. You learned that geometry appears in many types of art—ancient and modern, from every culture—and you learned specific ways in which some cultures use geometry in their art. You also used a compass and straightedge to create your own works of geometric art.

> The end of a chapter is a good time to review and organize your work. Each chapter in this book will end with a review lesson.

Exercises

YOU WILL NEED

Construction tools for Exercises **4, 5,** and **10**

1. List three cultures that use geometry in their art.

2. Describe the symmetry of the Native American basket on the right.

3. Name the basic tools of geometry you used in this chapter and describe their uses.

4. With a compass, draw a 12-petal daisy.

5. You can use your 12-petal daisy from Exercise 4 to construct regular polygons inscribed in a circle. Construct a dodecagon, a regular hexagon, a square, and an equilateral triangle. For each polygon, explain how you did your construction.

6. List three things in nature that have geometric shapes. Name their shapes.

7. Draw an original knot design.

8. Which of the wheels below have reflectional symmetry? How many lines of symmetry does each have?

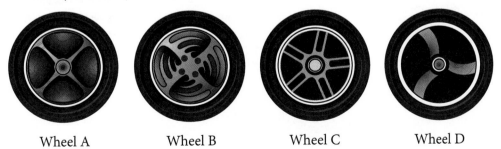

Wheel A   Wheel B   Wheel C   Wheel D

9. Which of the wheels in Exercise 8 have *only* rotational symmetry? What kind of rotational symmetry does each of the four wheels have?

10. A *mandala* is a circular design arranged in rings that radiate from the center. (See the Cultural Connection below.) Use your compass and straightedge to create a mandala. Draw several circles using the same point as the center. Create a geometric design in the center circle, and decorate each ring with a symmetric geometric design. Color or decorate your mandala. Two examples are shown below.

The first mandala uses daisy designs. The second mandala is a combination knot and Islamic design by Scott Shanks, former geometry student.

11. Create your own personal mandala. You might include your name, cultural symbols, photos of friends and relatives, and symbols that have personal meaning for you. Color it.

12. Create one mandala that uses techniques from Islamic art, is a knot design, and also has optical effects.

13. Before the Internet, "flags" was the most widely read topic of the World Book Encyclopedia. Research answers to these questions.

    a. Is the flag of Puerto Rico symmetric? Explain.

    b. Does the flag of Kenya have rotational symmetry? Explain.

    c. Name a country whose flag has both rotational and reflectional symmetry. Sketch the flag.

→ *Cultural*
CONNECTION

The word *mandala* comes from Sanskrit, the classical language of India, and means "circle" or "center." Hindus use mandala designs for meditation. The Aztec calendar stone on the left is an example of a mandala. Notice the symbols are arranged symmetrically within each circle. The rose windows in many gothic cathedrals, like the one on the right from the Chartres Cathedral in France, are also mandalas. Notice all the circles within circles, each one filled with a design or picture.

Introducing Geometry

> *"Although I am absolutely without training or knowledge in the exact sciences, I often seem to have more in common with mathematicians than with my fellow artists."*
>
> M. C. ESCHER

OBJECTIVES

In this chapter you will

- write your own definitions of many geometry terms and geometric figures
- start a notebook with a list of all the terms and their definitions
- discover some basic properties of transformations and symmetry

Building Blocks of Geometry

"Nature's Great Book is written in mathematical symbols."

GALILEO GALILEI

Three building blocks of geometry are points, lines, and planes. A **point** is the most basic building block of geometry. It has no size. It has only location. You represent a point with a dot, and you name it with a capital letter. The point shown below is called *P*.

P
●

Mathematical model of a point

A tiny seed is a physical model of a point. A point, however, is smaller than any seed that ever existed.

A **line** is a straight, continuous arrangement of infinitely many points. It has infinite length, but no thickness. It extends forever in two directions. You name a line by giving the letter names of any two points on the line and by placing the line symbol above the letters, for example, $\overleftrightarrow{AB}$ or $\overleftrightarrow{BA}$.

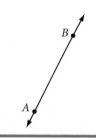

Mathematical model of a line

A piece of spaghetti is a physical model of a line. A line, however, is longer, straighter, and thinner than any piece of spaghetti ever made.

A **plane** has length and width, but no thickness. It is like a flat surface that extends infinitely along its length and width. You represent a plane with a four-sided figure, like a tilted piece of paper, drawn in perspective. Of course, this actually illustrates only part of a plane. You name a plane with a script capital letter, such as $\mathcal{P}$.

𝒫

A flat piece of rolled-out dough is a physical model of a plane. A plane, however, is broader, wider, and thinner than any piece of dough you could ever roll out.

Mathematical model of a plane

It can be difficult to explain what points, lines, and planes are even though you may recognize them. Early mathematicians tried to define these terms.

The ancient Greeks said, "A point is that which has no part. A line is breadthless length." The Mohist philosophers of ancient China said, "The line is divided into parts, and that part which has no remaining part is a point." Those definitions don't help much, do they?

A **definition** is a statement that clarifies or explains the meaning of a word or a phrase. However, it is impossible to define point, line, and plane without using words or phrases that themselves need definition. So these terms remain undefined. Yet, they are the basis for all of geometry.

Using the undefined terms *point, line,* and *plane,* you can define all other geometry terms and geometric figures. Many are defined in this book, and others will be defined by you and your classmates.

Here are your first definitions. Begin your list and draw sketches for all definitions.

> Keep a definition list in your notebook, and each time you encounter new geometry vocabulary, add the term to your list. Illustrate each definition with a simple sketch.

Collinear means on the same line.

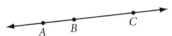

Points A, B, and C are collinear.

Coplanar means on the same plane.

Points D, E, and F are coplanar.

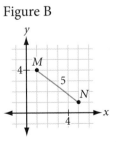

A **line segment** consists of two points called the **endpoints** of the segment and all the points between them that are collinear with the two points.

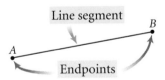

You can write line segment *AB,* using a segment symbol, as $\overline{AB}$ or $\overline{BA}$. There are two ways to write the length of a segment. You can write *AB* = 2 in., meaning the distance from *A* to *B* is 2 inches. You can also use an *m* for "measure" in front of the segment name, and write the distance as $m\overline{AB}$ = 2 in. If no measurement units are used for the length of a segment, it is understood that the choice of units is not important or is based on the length of the smallest square in the grid.

Figure A

A ———————— 2 in. ———————— *B*

AB = 2 in., or $m\overline{AB}$ = 2 in.

Figure B

MN = 5 units, or $m\overline{MN}$ = 5 units

If points A, B, and C are collinear and B is between A and C, then $AB + BC = AC$. This is called **segment addition**. Solve the following problem and explain how it represents segment addition.

EXAMPLE A

Podunkville, Smallville, and Gotham City lie along a straight highway with Smallville between the other two towns. If Podunkville and Smallville are 70 km apart and Smallville and Gotham City are 110 km apart, how far apart are Podunkville and Gotham City?

Solution

Draw a diagram that represents the relative positions of the three towns.

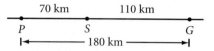

Because P, S, and G are collinear (the towns lie along a straight highway) and Smallville is between Podunkville and Gotham City, segment addition applies:

$PG = PS + SG$
$PG = 70 + 110$
$PG = 180$

That is, Podunkville and Gotham City are 180 km apart

We use the expression "is equal to" (and we use the symbol "=") when speaking of numerical expressions that have the same value. If we can move one geometric figure so that it exactly coincides with the other we say the figures are congruent (and we use the symbol "≅") instead of equal. If it is possible to move one segment to be superimposed over another segment then the two segments are congruent. What is true of congruent segments if we do not wish to copy one and see if it fits exactly on top of the other? Two segments are congruent if and only if they have equal measures, or lengths.

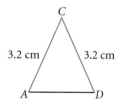

You use "is equal to" with numbers.

$AC = DC$
3.2 cm = 3.2 cm

You use "is congruent to" with figures.

$\overline{AC} \cong \overline{DC}$

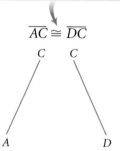

When drawing figures, you show congruent segments by making identical markings.

These single marks mean these two segments are congruent to each other.

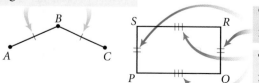

These double marks mean that $\overline{SP} \cong \overline{RQ}$.

These triple marks mean that $\overline{PQ} \cong \overline{SR}$.

The **midpoint** of a segment is the point on the segment that is the same distance from both endpoints. The midpoint **bisects** the segment, or divides the segment into two congruent segments. If a line passes through the midpoint of a segment the line bisects the segment.

EXAMPLE B

Study the diagrams below.

a. Name each midpoint and the segment it bisects.

b. Name all the congruent segments. Use the congruence symbol to write your answers.

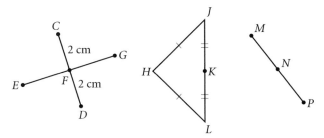

Solution

Look carefully at the markings and apply the midpoint definition.

a. $CF = FD$, so F is the midpoint of $\overline{CD}$; $\overline{JK} \cong \overline{KL}$, so K is the midpoint of $\overline{JL}$.

b. $\overline{CF} \cong \overline{FD}$, $\overline{HJ} \cong \overline{HL}$, and $\overline{JK} \cong \overline{KL}$.

Even though $\overline{EF}$ and $\overline{FG}$ appear to have the same length, you cannot assume they are congruent without the markings. The same is true for $\overline{MN}$ and $\overline{NP}$.

Ray AB is the part of $\overleftrightarrow{AB}$ that contains point A and all the points on $\overleftrightarrow{AB}$ that are on the same side of point A as point B. Imagine cutting off all the points to the left of point A.

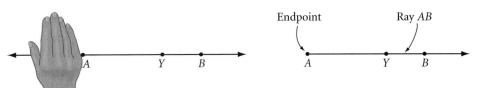

In the figure above, $\overrightarrow{AY}$ and $\overrightarrow{AB}$ are two ways to name the same ray. Note that $\overrightarrow{AB}$ is not the same as $\overrightarrow{BA}$!

A ray begins at a point and extends infinitely in one direction. You need two letters to name a ray. The first letter is the endpoint of the ray, and the second letter is any other point that the ray passes through.

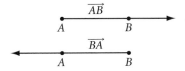

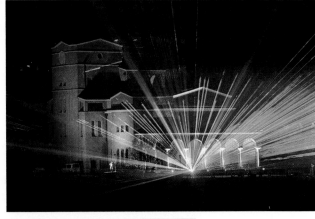

Physical model of a ray: beams of light

INVESTIGATION

Mathematical Models

In this lesson, you encountered many new geometry terms. In this investigation you will work as a group to identify models from the real world that represent these terms and to identify how they are represented in diagrams.

Step 1 Look around your classroom and identify examples of each of these terms: point, line, plane, line segment, congruent segments, midpoint of a segment, and ray.

Step 2 Identify examples of these terms in the photograph at right.

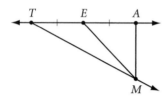

Step 3 Identify examples of these terms in the figure above.

Step 4 Explain in your own words what each of these terms means.

1.1 Exercises

1. In the photos below identify the physical models that represent a point, segment, plane, collinear points, and coplanar points.

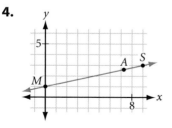

For Exercises 2–4, name each line in two different ways.

2. P ——— T

3. A R T

4.

For Exercises 5–7, draw two points and label them. Then use a ruler to draw each line. Don't forget to use arrowheads to show that the line extends indefinitely.

5. $\overleftrightarrow{AB}$

6. $\overleftrightarrow{KL}$

7. $\overleftrightarrow{DE}$ with $D(-3, 0)$ and $E(0, -3)$

For Exercises 8–10, name each line segment.

8.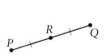

9.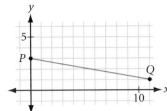

10.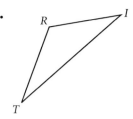

For Exercises 11 and 12, draw and label each line segment.

11. $\overline{AB}$

12. $\overline{RS}$ with $R(0, 3)$ and $S(-2, 11)$

For Exercises 13 and 14, use your ruler to find the length of each line segment to the nearest tenth of a centimeter. Write your answer in the form $m\overline{AB} = \underline{\ ?\ }$.

13. A •———————————————————————————————• B

14. C •————————————————————————• D

For Exercises 15–17, use your ruler to draw each segment as accurately as you can. Label each segment.

15. $AB = 4.5$ cm

16. $CD = 3$ in.

17. $EF = 24.8$ cm

18. Name each midpoint and the segment it bisects.

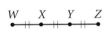

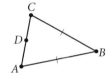

19. Draw two segments that have the same midpoint. Mark your drawing to show congruent segments.

20. Draw and mark a figure in which M is the midpoint of $\overline{ST}$, $SP = PT$, and T is the midpoint of $\overline{PQ}$.

For Exercises 21–23, name the ray in two different ways.

21. A• B• C•→

22. ←•M •N P•→

23. Z Y X

For Exercises 24–26, draw and label each ray.

24. $\overrightarrow{AB}$

25. $\overrightarrow{YX}$

26. $\overrightarrow{MN}$

27. Draw a plane containing four coplanar points A, B, C, and D, with exactly three collinear points A, B, and D.

28. Given two points A and B, there is only one segment that you can name: $\overline{AB}$. With three collinear points A, B, and C, there are three different segments that you can name: $\overline{AB}$, $\overline{AC}$, and $\overline{BC}$. With five collinear points A, B, C, D, and E, how many different segments can you name?

For Exercises 29–31, draw axes on graph paper and locate point $A(4, 0)$ as shown.

29. Draw $\overline{AB}$, where point B has coordinates $(2, -6)$.

30. Draw $\overrightarrow{OM}$ with endpoint $(0, 0)$ that goes through point $M(2, 2)$.

31. Draw $\overleftrightarrow{CD}$ through points $C(-2, 1)$ and $D(-2, -3)$.

32. If the signs of the coordinates of collinear points $P(-6, -2)$, $Q(-5, 2)$, and $R(-4, 6)$ are reversed, are the three new points still collinear? Draw a picture and explain why.

33. Draw a segment with midpoint $N(-3, 2)$. Label it $\overline{PQ}$.

34. Copy triangle TRY shown at right. Use your ruler to find the midpoint A of side $\overline{TR}$ and the midpoint G of side $\overline{TY}$. Draw $\overline{AG}$.

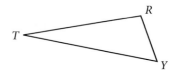

35. Use your ruler to draw a triangle with side lengths 8 cm and 11 cm. Explain your method. Can you draw a second triangle with these two side lengths that looks different from the first? Explain.

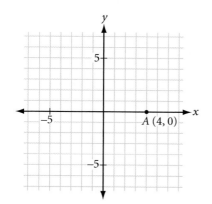

DEVELOPING MATHEMATICAL REASONING

Polyominoes

In 1953, United States mathematician Solomon Golomb introduced polyominoes at the Harvard Mathematics Club, and they have been played with and enjoyed throughout the world ever since. Polyominoes are shapes made by connecting congruent squares. The squares are joined together side to side. (A complete side must touch a complete side.) Some of the smaller polyominoes are shown below. There is only one monomino and only one domino, but there are two trominoes, as shown. There are five tetrominoes—one is shown. Sketch the other four.

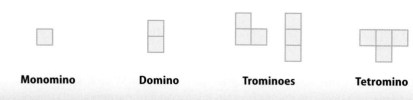

| Monomino | Domino | Trominoes | Tetromino |

The Midpoint

A midpoint is the point on a line segment that is the same distance from both endpoints.

You can think of a midpoint as being halfway between two locations. You know how to mark a midpoint. But when the position and location matter, such as in navigation and geography, you can use a coordinate grid and some algebra to find the exact location of the midpoint. You can calculate the coordinates of the midpoint of a segment on a coordinate grid using a formula.

Coordinate Midpoint Property

If (x_1, y_1) and (x_2, y_2) are the coordinates of the endpoints of a segment, then the coordinates of the midpoint are

$$\left(\frac{x_1 + x_2}{2}, \frac{y_1 + y_2}{2} \right)$$

EXAMPLE | Segment AB has endpoints $(-8, 5)$ and $(3, -6)$. Find the coordinates of the midpoint of $\overline{AB}$.

Solution | The midpoint is not on a grid intersection point, so we can use the coordinate midpoint property.

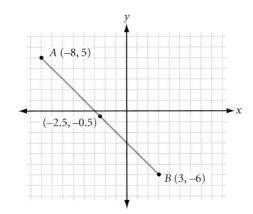

$x = \dfrac{x_1 + x_2}{2} = \dfrac{-8 + 3}{2} = -2.5$

$y = \dfrac{y_1 + y_2}{2} = \dfrac{5 + (-6)}{2} = -0.5$

The midpoint of $\overline{AB}$ is $(-2.5, -0.5)$.

History
CONNECTION

Surveyors and mapmakers of ancient Egypt, China, Greece, and Rome used various coordinate systems to locate points. Egyptians made extensive use of square grids and used the first known rectangular coordinates at Saqqara around 2650 B.C.E. By the 17th century, the age of European exploration, the need for accurate maps and the development of easy-to-use algebraic symbols gave rise to modern coordinate geometry. Notice the lines of latitude and longitude in this 17th-century map.

Exercises

For Exercises 1–3, find the coordinates of the midpoint of the segment with each pair of endpoints.

1. $(12, -7)$ and $(-6, 15)$ **2.** $(-17, -8)$ and $(-1, 11)$ **3.** $(14, -7)$ and $(-3, 18)$

4. One endpoint of a segment is $(12, -8)$. The midpoint is $(3, 18)$. Find the coordinates of the other endpoint.

5. A classmate tells you, "Finding the coordinates of a midpoint is easy. You just find the averages." Is there any truth to it? Explain what you think your classmate means.

6. Find the two points on $\overline{AB}$ that divide the segment into three congruent parts. Point A has coordinates $(0, 0)$ and point B has coordinates $(9, 6)$. Explain your method.

7. Describe a way to find points that divide a segment into fourths.

8. In each figure below, imagine drawing the diagonals $\overline{AC}$ and $\overline{BD}$.

   a. Find the midpoint of $\overline{AC}$ and the midpoint of $\overline{BD}$ in each figure.

   b. What do you notice about the midpoints?

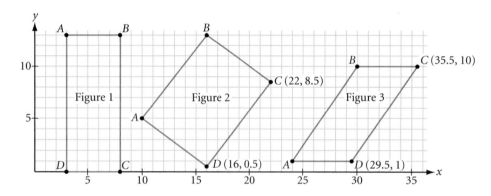

DEVELOPING MATHEMATICAL REASONING

Pentominoes I

In Polyominoes, you learned about shapes called polyominoes. Polyominoes with five squares are called pentominoes. Find all possible pentominoes. One is shown at right. Use graph paper or square dot paper to sketch them.

Finding Angles

People use angles every day. Plumbers measure the angle between connecting pipes to make a good fitting. Woodworkers adjust their saw blades to cut wood at just the correct angle. Air traffic controllers use angles to direct planes. And good pool players must know their angles to plan their shots.

"Inspiration is needed in geometry, just as much as in poetry."

ALEKSANDR PUSHKIN

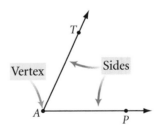

Is the angle between the two hands of the wristwatch smaller than the angle between the hands of Big Ben at the Houses of Parliament in London, England?

You can use the terms that you defined in Lesson 1.1 to write a precise definition of angle. An **angle** is formed by two rays that share a common endpoint, provided that the two rays are noncollinear. In other words, the rays cannot lie on the same line. The common endpoint of the two rays is the **vertex** of the angle. The two rays are the **sides** of the angle.

You can name the angle in the figure below angle *TAP* or angle *PAT*, or use the angle symbol and write $\angle TAP$ or $\angle PAT$. Notice that the vertex must be the middle letter, and the first and last letters each name a point on a different ray. Since there are no other angles with vertex A, you can also simply call this $\angle A$.

Vertex   Sides

EXAMPLE A | Name all the angles in these drawings.

Solution | The angles are $\angle T$, $\angle V$, $\angle TUV$, $\angle 1$, $\angle TUR$, $\angle XAY$, $\angle YAZ$, and $\angle XAZ$. (Did you get them all?) Notice that $\angle 1$ is a shorter way to name $\angle RUV$.

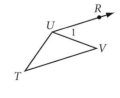

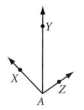

Which angles in Example A seem big to you? Which seem small?

The **measure of an angle** is the smallest amount of rotation about the vertex from one ray to the other, measured in **degrees**. According to this definition, the measure of an angle can be any value between 0° and 180°. The largest amount of rotation less than 360° between the two rays is called the **reflex measure of an angle**.

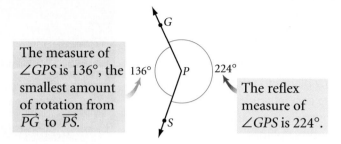

The measure of ∠*GPS* is 136°, the smallest amount of rotation from $\overrightarrow{PG}$ to $\overrightarrow{PS}$.

136°

224°

The reflex measure of ∠*GPS* is 224°.

For a visual tutorial on how to use a protractor, see the **Dynamic Geometry Exploration Protractor** in your ebook.

The geometry tool you use to measure an angle is a **protractor**. Here's how you use it.

Step 1: Place the center mark of the protractor on the vertex.

Step 2: Line up the 0-mark with one side of the angle.

Step 3: Read the measure on the protractor scale.

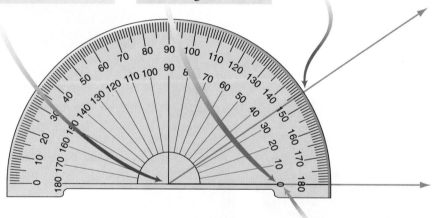

> **Career**
> # CONNECTION

In sports medicine, specialists may examine the healing rate of an injured joint by its angle of recovery. For example, a physician may assess how much physical therapy a patient needs by measuring the degree to which a patient can bend his or her ankle from the floor.

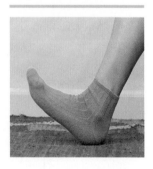

Step 4: Be sure you read the scale that has the 0-mark you are using! The angle in the diagram measures 34° and not 146°.

To show the measure of an angle, use an *m* before the angle symbol. For example, $m\angle ZAP = 34°$ means the measure of ∠*ZAP* is 34 degrees.

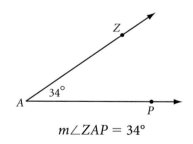

34°

$m\angle ZAP = 34°$

EXAMPLE B

Use your protractor to measure these angles as accurately as you can. Which ones measure more than 90°?

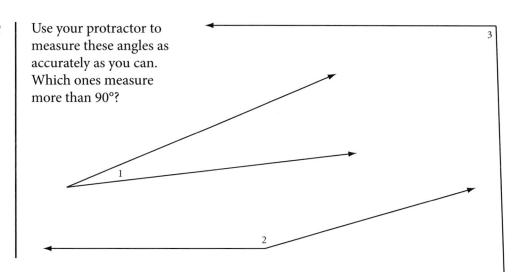

Solution

Measuring to the nearest degree, you should get these approximate answers. (The symbol ≈ means "is approximately equal to.")

$m\angle 1 \approx 16°$ $m\angle 2 \approx 164°$ $m\angle 3 \approx 92°$

$\angle 2$ and $\angle 3$ measure more than 90°.

If it is possible to move one angle to fit over another angle then the two angles are congruent. What is true of congruent angles if we do not wish to copy one and see if it fits exactly on top of the other? Two angles are **congruent** if and only if they have equal measures, the same number of degrees.

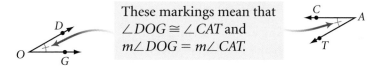

These markings mean that $\angle DOG \cong \angle CAT$ and $m\angle DOG = m\angle CAT$.

A ray is the **angle bisector** if it contains the vertex and divides the angle into two congruent angles. In the figure at right, $\overrightarrow{CD}$ bisects $\angle ACB$ so that $\angle ACD \cong \angle BCD$.

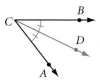

EXAMPLE C

Look for angle bisectors and congruent angles in the figures below.

a. Name each angle bisector and the angle it bisects.

b. Name all the congruent angles in the figure. Use the congruence symbol and name the angles so there is no confusion about which angle you mean.

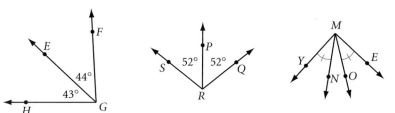

Solution

a. Use the angle bisector definition. $\angle SRP \cong \angle PRQ$, so $\overrightarrow{RP}$ bisects $\angle SRQ$.

b. $\angle SRP \cong \angle PRQ$, $\angle YMN \cong \angle OME$, and $\angle YMO \cong \angle EMN$.

If point D is in the interior of $\angle CAB$, then $m\angle CAD + m\angle DAB = m\angle CAB$. This is called **angle addition**. The following example shows how angle addition is used.

EXAMPLE D | You have a slice of pizza with a central angle that measures 140° that you want to share with your friend. She cuts it through the vertex into two slices. You choose one slice that measures 60°. How many degrees are in the other slice?

Solution | Since the two slices do not overlap, by the angle addition property $x + 60° = 140°$ or $x = 80°$.

 # INVESTIGATION

Virtual Pool

YOU WILL NEED
- the worksheet Poolroom Math
- a protractor

Pocket billiards, or pool, is a game of angles. When a ball bounces off the pool table's cushion, its path forms two angles with the edge of the cushion. The **incoming angle** is formed by the cushion and the path of the ball approaching the cushion.

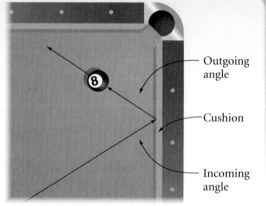

The **outgoing angle** is formed by the cushion and the path of the ball leaving the cushion. As it turns out, the measure of the outgoing angle equals the measure of the incoming angle.

Use your protractor to study these shots.

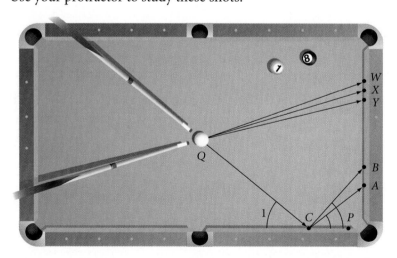

Step 1 Use your protractor to find the measure of $\angle 1$. Which is the correct outgoing angle? Which point—A or B—will the ball hit?

Step 2 Which point on the cushion—W, X, or Y—should the white ball hit so that the ray of the outgoing angle passes through the center of the 8-ball?

Step 3 Compare your results with your group members' results. Does everyone agree?

Step 4 How would you hit the white ball against the cushion so that the ball passes over the same spot on the way back?

Step 5 How would you hit the ball so that it bounces off three different points on the cushions without ever touching cushion $\overleftrightarrow{CP}$?

1.2 Exercises

1. Name each angle in three different ways.

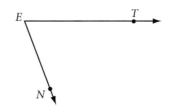
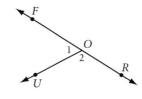

For Exercises 2–4, draw and label each angle.

2. $\angle TAN$ **3.** $\angle BIG$ **4.** $\angle SML$

5. For each figure at right, list the angles that you can name using only the vertex letter.

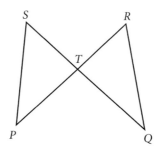
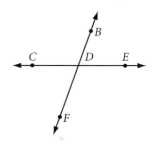

For Exercises 6–13, find the measure of each angle to the nearest degree.

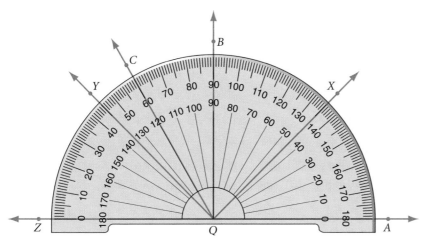

6. $m\angle AQB \approx \underline{\ ?\ }$ **7.** $m\angle AQC \approx \underline{\ ?\ }$ **8.** $m\angle XQA \approx \underline{\ ?\ }$ **9.** $m\angle AQY \approx \underline{\ ?\ }$

10. $m\angle ZQY \approx \underline{\ ?\ }$ **11.** $m\angle ZQX \approx \underline{\ ?\ }$ **12.** $m\angle CQB \approx \underline{\ ?\ }$ ⓗ   **13.** $m\angle XQY \approx \underline{\ ?\ }$

14. Adjacent angles $\angle XQA$ and $\angle XQY$ share a vertex and a side. Taken together they form the larger angle $\angle AQY$. Compare their measures. Does $m\angle XQA + m\angle XQY = m\angle AQY$? Explain why or why not.

15. Draw a figure that contains at least three angles and requires three letters to name each angle.

For Exercises 16–20, use your protractor to find the measure of the angle to the nearest degree.

16. $m\angle MAC \approx$?

17. $m\angle IBM \approx$?

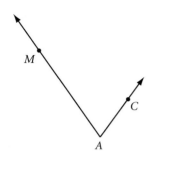

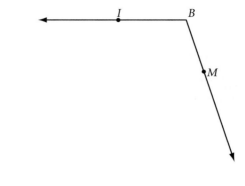

18. $m\angle S \approx$?

19. $m\angle SON \approx$?

20. $m\angle NOR \approx$?

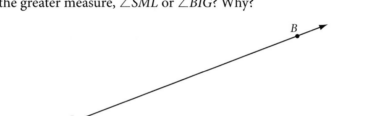

21. Which angle below has the greater measure, $\angle SML$ or $\angle BIG$? Why?

For Exercises 22–24, use your protractor to draw angles with these measures. Label them.

22. $m\angle A = 44°$

23. $m\angle B = 90°$

24. $m\angle CDE = 135°$

25. Use your protractor to draw the angle bisector of $\angle A$ in Exercise 22 and the angle bisector of $\angle D$ in Exercise 24. Use markings to show that the two halves are congruent.

26. Copy triangle CAN shown at right. Use your protractor to find the angle bisector of $\angle A$. Label the point where it crosses $\overline{CN}$ point Y. Use your ruler to find the midpoint of $\overline{CN}$ and label it D. Are D and Y the same point?

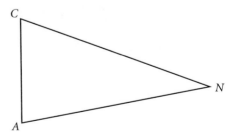

For Exercises 27–29, draw a clock face with hands to show these times.

27. 3:30 Ⓗ

28. 3:40

29. 3:15

30. Give an example of a time when the angle made by the hands of the clock will be greater than 90°.

For Exercises 31–34, copy each figure and mark it with all the given information.

31. $TH = 6$
$m\angle THO = 90°$
$OH = 8$

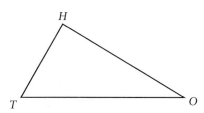

32. $RA = SA$
$m\angle T = m\angle H$
$RT = SH$

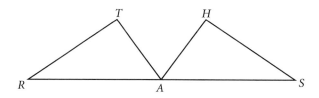

33. $AT = AG$ $\angle AGT \cong \angle ATG$
$AI = AN$ $GI = TN$

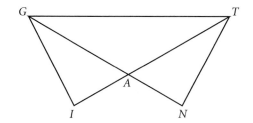

34. $\overline{BW} \cong \overline{TI}$ $\angle WBT \cong \angle ITB$
$\overline{WO} \cong \overline{IO}$ $\angle BWO \cong \angle TIO$

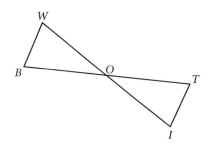

For Exercises 35 and 36, write down what you know from the markings. Do not use your protractor or your ruler.

35. $MI = \underline{\ ?\ }$
$IC = \underline{\ ?\ }$
$m\angle M = \underline{\ ?\ }$

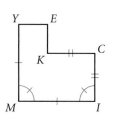

36. $\angle MEO \cong \underline{\ ?\ }$
$\angle SUE \cong \underline{\ ?\ }$
$OU = \underline{\ ?\ }$

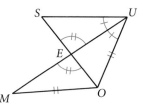

For Exercises 37–39, do not use a protractor. Recall from Chapter 0 that a complete rotation around a point is 360°. Find the angle measures represented by each letter.

37. ⓗ

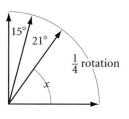

38.

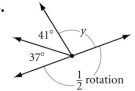

39.

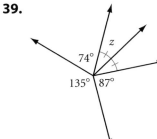

40. Use your protractor to determine the reflex measure of ∠*ACU*.

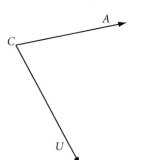

41. Use your protractor to determine the reflex measure of ∠*QUA*.

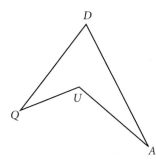

42. What is the relationship between the measure of an angle and the reflex measure of the angle?

43. **Will the ball make it to the pocket?** If the 4-ball is hit as shown, will it go into the corner pocket? Find the path of the ball using only your protractor and straightedge. Will the ball make it to the pocket?

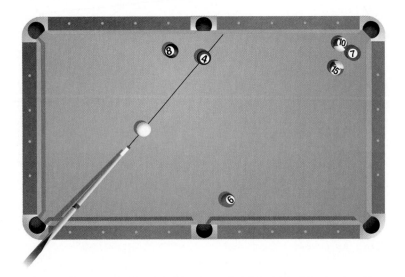

44. The principle you just learned for billiard balls is also true for sound or radio waves bouncing off a surface or for a ray of light reflecting from a mirror. If you hold a laser light angled at the mirror as shown, will the light from the laser hit the target object? Explain.

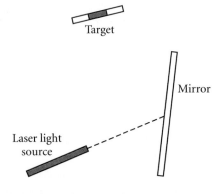

45. Use your ruler and protractor to draw a triangle with angle measures 40° and 70°. Explain your method. Can you draw a second triangle with these two angle measures that looks different from the first? Explain.

Review

46. Use your ruler to draw a segment with length 12 cm. Then use your ruler to locate the midpoint. Label and mark the figure.

47. Explain the difference between $MS = DG$ and $\overline{MS} \cong \overline{DG}$.

48. The balancing point of an object is called its *center of gravity*. Where is the center of gravity of a thin, rodlike piece of wire or tubing? Copy the thin wire shown below onto your paper. Mark the balance point or center of gravity.

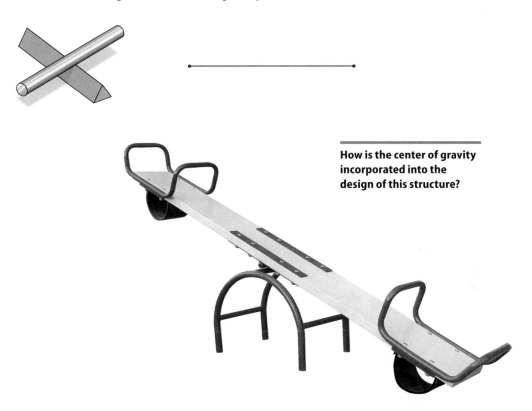

How is the center of gravity incorporated into the design of this structure?

DEVELOPING MATHEMATICAL REASONING

Hexominoes

Polyominoes with six squares are called hexominoes. There are more than 25 but less than 45 hexominoes. There is 1 with a longest string of six squares; there are 3 with a longest string of five squares, and 1 with a longest string of two squares. The rest have a longest string of either four squares or three squares. Use graph paper to sketch the hexominoes. Which ones are nets for cubes? Here is one hexomino that does fold into a cube.

Creating Definitions

Good definitions are very important in geometry. In this lesson you will write your own geometry definitions.

Which creatures in the last group are Widgets?

 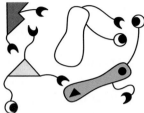 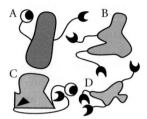

Widgets   Not Widgets   Which are Widgets?

You might have asked yourself, "What things do all the Widgets have in common, and what things do Widgets have that others do not have?" In other words, what characteristics make a Widget a Widget? They all have colorful bodies with nothing else inside; two tails—one like a crescent moon, the other like an eyeball.

By observing what a Widget is and what a Widget isn't, you identified the characteristics that distinguish a Widget from a non-Widget. Based on these characteristics, you should have selected A as the only Widget in the last group. This same process can help you write good definitions of geometric figures.

This statement defines a protractor: "A protractor is a geometry tool used to measure angles." First, you classify what it is (a geometry tool), then you say how it differs from other geometry tools (it is the one you use to measure angles). What should go in the blanks to define a square?

A square is a ⬚⬚⬚⬚⬚ that ⬚⬚⬚⬚⬚ .

       ↑   ↑

Classify it. What is it?   How does it differ from others?

Once you've written a definition, you should test it. To do this, you look for a **counterexample**. That is, try to create a figure that fits your definition but *isn't* what you're trying to define. If you can come up with a counterexample for your definition, you don't have a good definition.

EXAMPLE A

Everyone knows, "A square is a figure with four equal sides." What's wrong with this definition?

a. Sketch a counterexample. (You can probably find more than one!)

b. Write a better definition for a square.

Solution

A restaurant counter example

You probably noticed that "figure" is not specific enough to classify a square, and that "four equal sides" does not specify how it differs from the first counterexample shown below.

a. Three counterexamples are shown here, and you may have found others too.

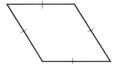

b. One better definition is "A square is a 4-sided figure that has all sides congruent and all angles measuring 90 degrees."

> **Beginning Steps to Creating a Good Definition**
>
> 1. **Classify** your term. What is it? ("*A square is a 4-sided figure . . .*")
> 2. **Differentiate** your term. How does it differ from others in that class? ("*. . . that has four congruent sides and four right angles.*")
> 3. **Test** your definition by looking for a counterexample.

Ready to write a couple of definitions? First, here are two more types of markings that are very important in geometry.

The same number of arrow marks indicates that lines are parallel. The symbol $\parallel$ means "is parallel to." A small square in the corner of an angle indicates that it measures 90°. The symbol $\perp$ means "is perpendicular to."

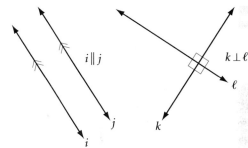

EXAMPLE B

Define these terms:

a. Parallel lines

b. Perpendicular lines

Solution

Following these steps, classify and differentiate each term.

Classify.   Differentiate.

a. Parallel lines are lines in the same plane that never meet.

b. Perpendicular lines are lines that meet at 90° angles.

Why do you need to say "in the same plane" for parallel lines, but not for perpendicular lines? Sketch or demonstrate a counterexample to show the following definition is incomplete: "Parallel lines are lines that never meet." (Two lines that do not intersect and are noncoplanar are **skew** lines.)

INVESTIGATION 1

Defining Angles

Here are some examples and non-examples of special types of angles.

Step 1 Write a definition for each boldfaced term. Make sure your definitions highlight important differences.

Step 2 Trade definitions and test each other's definitions by looking for counterexamples.

Step 3 If another group member finds a counterexample to one of your definitions, write a better definition. As a group, decide on the best definition for each term.

Step 4 As a class, agree on common definitions. Add these to your notebook. Draw and label a picture to illustrate each definition.

Notice the many congruent angles in this Navajo traditional blanket. Are they right, acute, or obtuse angles?

Explore more about Types of Angles using the **Dynamic Geometry Exploration** in your ebook.

Right Angle

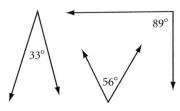

Right angles

Not right angles

Acute Angle

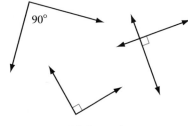

Acute angles

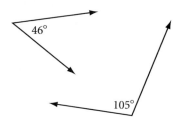

Not acute angles

Obtuse Angle

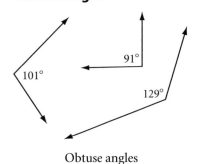

Obtuse angles

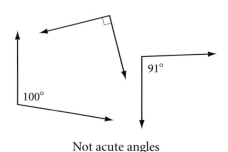

Not obtuse angles

Complementary Angles

$m\angle 1 + m\angle 2 = 90°$

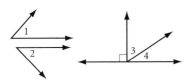

Pairs of complementary angles:
∠1 and ∠2
∠3 and ∠4

$m\angle 1 + m\angle 2 \neq 90°$

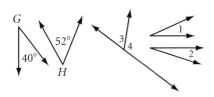

Not pairs of complementary angles:
∠G and ∠H   ∠1 and ∠2
∠3 and ∠4

Supplementary Angles

$m\angle 3 + m\angle 4 = 180°$

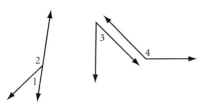

Pairs of supplementary angles:
∠1 and ∠2   ∠3 and ∠4

$m\angle 4 + m\angle 5 > 180°$

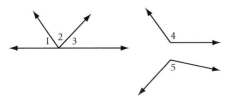

Not pairs of supplementary angles:
∠1, ∠2, and ∠3   ∠4 and ∠5

Vertical Angles

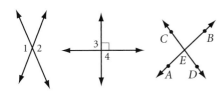

Pairs of vertical angles:
∠1 and ∠2
∠3 and ∠4
∠AED and ∠BEC
∠AEC and ∠DEB

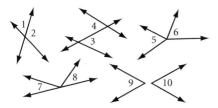

Not pairs of vertical angles:
∠1 and ∠2
∠3 and ∠4
∠5 and ∠6
∠7 and ∠8
∠9 and ∠10

Linear Pair of Angles

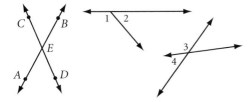

Linear pairs of angles:
∠1 and ∠2
∠3 and ∠4
∠AED and ∠AEC
∠BED and ∠DEA

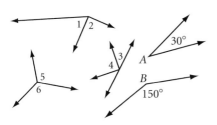

Not linear pairs of angles:
∠1 and ∠2
∠3 and ∠4
∠5 and ∠6
∠A and ∠B

What types of angles or angle pairs do you see in this magnified view of a computer chip?

INVESTIGATION 2

Creating Angles with Patty Paper

Step 1 Fold and crease a random line through your patty paper.

Step 2 Open your patty paper and fold another random line.

Step 3 Show the other members of your group
- a.) an acute angle
- b.) an obtuse angle
- c.) a pair of vertical angles
- d.) a linear pair of angles
- e.) a pair of supplementary angles.

Step 4 On a second patty paper, fold and crease a random line.

Step 5 Fold your first crease on top of itself. What kind of angle does this appear to be? Test your conjecture by placing the corner of another patty paper into the angle formed by the intersection of the two creases. Explain why the angle turned out to have that angle measure. Place a dot at the vertex of the angle.

Step 6 Fold a third crease passing through the point where the two lines intersect (the vertex of your special angle).

Step 7 Show the other members of your group
- a.) two acute angles
- b.) two obtuse angles
- b.) two right angles
- d.) two different pairs of vertical angles
- e.) a linear pair of angles
- f.) two different pairs of supplementary angles
- g.) two different pairs of complementary angles.

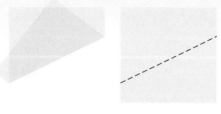

Step 1

Step 2

Step 4

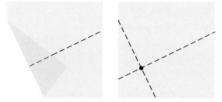

Step 5

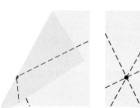

Step 6

Often geometric definitions are easier to write if you refer to labeled figures. For example, you can define the midpoint of a line segment by saying: "Point M is the midpoint of segment AB if M is a point on segment AB, and AM is equal to MB."

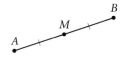
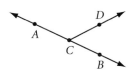

EXAMPLE C | Use a labeled figure to define a linear pair of angles.

Solution | $\angle ACD$ and $\angle BCD$ form a linear pair of angles if point C is on $\overleftrightarrow{AB}$ and lies between points A and B.

Compare this definition with the one you wrote in the investigation. Can there be more than one correct definition?

The design of this Mexican rug contains examples of parallel and perpendicular lines, obtuse and acute angles, and complementary and supplementary angle pairs.

1.3 Exercises

For Exercises 1–8, draw and carefully label the figures. Use the appropriate marks to indicate right angles, parallel lines, congruent segments, and congruent angles. Use a protractor and a ruler when you need to.

1. Acute angle DOG with a measure of $45°$

2. Right angle RTE

3. Obtuse angle BIG with angle bisector $\overrightarrow{IE}$

4. $\overline{DG} \parallel \overleftrightarrow{MS}$

5. $\overline{PE} \perp \overrightarrow{AR}$

6. Vertical angles ABC and DBE

7. Complementary angles $\angle A$ and $\angle B$ with $m\angle A = 40°$

8. Supplementary angles $\angle C$ and $\angle D$ with $m\angle D = 40°$

9. Which creatures in the last group below are Zoids? What makes a Zoid a Zoid?

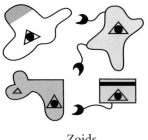

Zoids

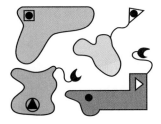

Not Zoids

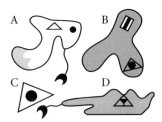

Which are Zoids?

10. What are the characteristics of a good definition?

11. What is the difference between complementary and supplementary angles?

12. If $\angle X$ and $\angle Y$ are supplementary angles, are they necessarily a linear pair? Why or why not?

13. Write these definitions using the classify and differentiate method to fill in the blanks:

   a. An acute angle is _____ that _____.

   b. Complementary angles are _____ that _____.

   c. A midpoint is _____ that _____.

   d. A protractor is _____ that _____.

14. There is something wrong with this definition for a pair of vertical angles: "If $\overleftrightarrow{AB}$ and $\overleftrightarrow{CD}$ intersect at point P, then $\angle APC$ and $\angle BPD$ are a pair of vertical angles." Sketch a counterexample to show why it is not correct. Add a phrase to correct the definition.

For Exercises 15–24, five of the statements are true. Make a sketch or demonstrate each true statement. For each false statement, draw a counterexample and explain why it is false.

15. For every line segment there is exactly one midpoint.

16. For every angle there is exactly one angle bisector.

17. If two different lines intersect, then they intersect at one and only one point.

18. Through a given point on a line, there is one and only one line perpendicular to the given line. ⓗ

19. If two different planes intersect, then they intersect at one and only one line.

20. In every triangle there is exactly one right angle.

21. Through a point not on a line, one and only one line can be constructed parallel to the given line.

22. If $CA = AT$, then A is the midpoint of $\overline{CT}$.

23. If $m\angle D = 40°$ and $m\angle C = 140°$, then angles C and D are a linear pair.

24. If point A is not the midpoint of $\overline{CT}$, then $CA \neq AT$.

Review

For Exercises 25 and 26, refer to the graph at right.

25. Find possible coordinates of a point P so that points P, T, and S are collinear.

26. Find possible coordinates of a point Q so that $\overleftrightarrow{QR} \parallel \overleftrightarrow{TS}$.

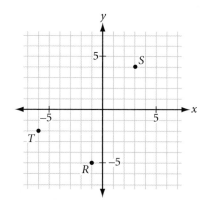

27. A *partial mirror* reflects some light and lets the rest of the light pass through. In the figure at right, half the light from point A passes through the partial mirror to point B. Copy the figure, then draw the outgoing angle for the light reflected from the mirror. What do you notice about the ray of reflected light and the ray of light that passes through? ⓗ

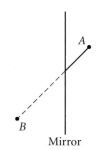

Mirror

28. Find possible coordinates of points *A, B,* and *C* on the graph at right so that ∠*BAC* is a right angle, ∠*BAT* is an acute angle, ∠*ABS* is an obtuse angle, and the points *C, T,* and *R* are collinear. ⓗ

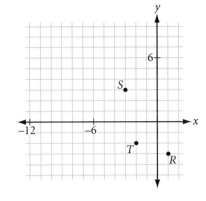

29. If *D* is the midpoint of $\overline{AC}$ and *C* is the midpoint of $\overline{AB}$, and *AD* = 3 cm, what is the length of $\overline{AB}$?

30. If $\overrightarrow{BD}$ is the angle bisector of ∠*ABC,* $\overrightarrow{BE}$ is the angle bisector of ∠*ABD,* and *m*∠*DBC* = 24°, what is *m*∠*EBC*?

31. Draw and label a figure that has two congruent segments and three congruent angles. Mark the congruent angles and congruent segments.

32. Show how three lines in a plane can have zero, exactly one, exactly two, or exactly three points of intersection.

33. Show how it is possible for two triangles to intersect in one point, two points, three points, four points, five points, or six points. Show how they can intersect in infinitely many points. Explain why it is not possible for two triangles to intersect in exactly seven points.

34. Each pizza is cut into slices from the center.

a. What fraction of the pizza is left?

b. What fraction of the pizza is missing?

c. If the pizza is cut into nine equal slices, how many degrees is each angle at the center of the pizza?

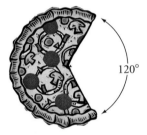

120°

60°

DEVELOPING MATHEMATICAL REASONING

Pentominoes II

In Pentominoes I, you found the 12 pentominoes. Which of the 12 pentominoes can you cut along the edges and fold into a box without a lid? Here is an example.

Polygons

A **polygon** is a closed figure in a plane, formed by connecting line segments endpoint to endpoint with each segment intersecting exactly two others. Each line segment is called a **side** of the polygon. Each endpoint where the sides meet is called a **vertex** of the polygon.

Polygons   Not Polygons

You classify a polygon by the number of sides it has. Familiar polygons have specific names, listed in this table. The ones without specific names are called *n*-sided polygons, or *n*-gons. For instance, you call a 25-sided polygon a 25-gon.

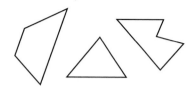

Consecutive angles

Consecutive vertices

Consecutive sides

Sides	Name
3	Triangle
4	Quadrilateral
5	Pentagon
6	Hexagon
7	Heptagon
8	Octagon
9	Nonagon
10	Decagon
11	Undecagon
12	Dodecagon
n	*n*-gon

To name a polygon, list the vertices in consecutive order. You can name the pentagon above pentagon *ABCDE*. You can also call it *DCBAE*, but not *BCAED*. When the polygon is a triangle, you use the triangle symbol. For example, △*ABC* means triangle *ABC*.

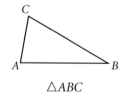

Pentagon *ABCDE*   △*ABC*

A **diagonal** of a polygon is a line segment that connects two nonconsecutive vertices.

A polygon is **convex** if no diagonal is outside the polygon. A polygon is **concave** if at least one diagonal is outside the polygon.

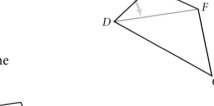

Diagonal

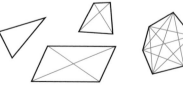

Convex polygons: All diagonals are inside

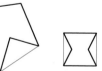

Concave polygons: One or more diagonals are outside

How does the shape of the framework of this Marc Chagall (1887–1985) stained glass window support the various shapes of the design?

If it is possible to move one polygon to be superimposed over another polygon then the two polygons are congruent. What is true of congruent polygons if we do not wish to copy one and see if it fits exactly on top of the other? Two polygons are congruent if and only if they are the same size and shape. This means all the corresponding sides are congruent and all the corresponding angles are congruent.

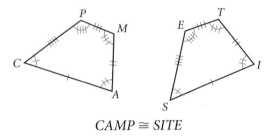

For example, if quadrilateral *CAMP* is congruent to quadrilateral *SITE*, then their four pairs of corresponding angles and four pairs of corresponding sides are also congruent. When you write a statement of congruence, always write the letters of the corresponding vertices in an order that shows the correspondences.

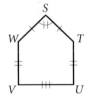

$$CAMP \cong SITE$$

EXAMPLE

Which polygon is congruent to *ABCDE*?

$ABCDE \cong \underline{\ ?\ }$

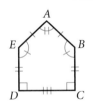 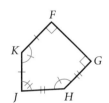 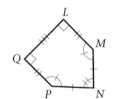

Solution

Polygons *JKFGH* and *ABCDE* have all corresponding angles congruent, but not all corresponding sides. Polygons *STUVW* and *ABCDE* have all corresponding sides congruent, but not all corresponding angles.

All corresponding sides and angles must be congruent, so *ABCDE* ≅ *NPQLM*.

You could also say *ABCDE* ≅ *NMLQP* because all the congruent parts would still match.

The **perimeter** of a polygon equals the sum of the lengths of its sides. Perimeter measures the length of the boundary of a two-dimensional figure.

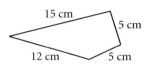

The quadrilateral at right has perimeter 37 cm.

INVESTIGATION

Special Polygons

Write a good definition of each boldfaced term. Discuss your definitions with others in your group. Agree on a common set of definitions for your class and add them to your definitions list. In your notebook, draw and label a figure to illustrate each definition.

Equilateral Polygon

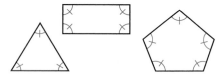

Equilateral polygons

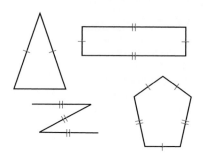

Not equilateral polygons

Equiangular Polygon

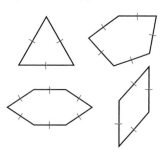

Equiangular polygons

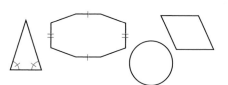

Not equiangular polygons

Regular Polygon

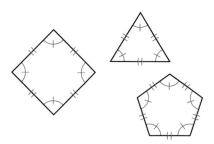

Regular polygons

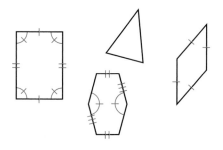

Not regular polygons

1.4 Exercises

For Exercises 1–3, draw an example of each polygon.

1. Quadrilateral   **2.** Dodecagon   **3.** Octagon

YOU WILL NEED

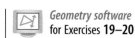

Geometry software for Exercises **19–20**

For Exercises 4–7, classify each polygon. Assume that all sides are straight.

4.

5.

6.

7.

For Exercises 8–10, give one possible name for each polygon.

8.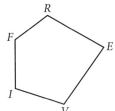

9.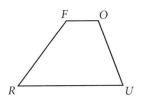

10.

11. Write these definitions using the classify and differentiate method to fill in the blanks:

   a. An octagon is _____ that _____.

   b. A concave polygon is _____ that _____.

   c. A 20-gon, also called an icosagon, is _____ that _____.

   d. An equilateral polygon is _____ that _____.

12. Name a pair of consecutive angles and a pair of consecutive sides in the figure at right.

13. Draw a concave hexagon. How many diagonals does it have?

14. Name the diagonals of pentagon *ABCDE*.

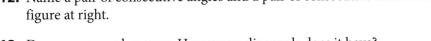

For Exercises 15 and 16, use the information given to name the triangle that is congruent to the first one.

15. △*EAR* ≅ △ _?_ ⓗ

16. △*OLD* ≅ △ _?_

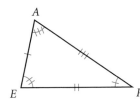
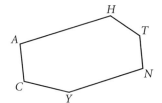

17. In the figure at right, *THINK* ≅ *POWER*.

   a. Find the measures *a*, *b*, and *c*.

   b. If $m\angle P = 87°$ and $m\angle W = 165°$, which angles in *THINK* do you know? Write their measures.

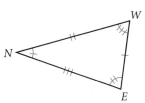
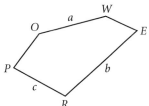
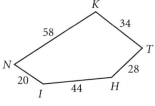

18. If pentagon *FIVER* is congruent to pentagon *PANCH*, then which side in pentagon *FIVER* is congruent to side $\overline{PA}$? Which angle in pentagon *PANCH* is congruent to ∠*IVE*?

19. Use your geometry tools to draw a convex hexagon with two consecutive sides measuring 5 cm and three consecutive angles measuring 130°.

20. Draw an equilateral concave pentagon. Then draw an equiangular convex pentagon. ⓗ

21. Each side of a regular dodecagon measures 7 in. Find the perimeter.

22. The perimeter of an equilateral octagon is 42 cm. Find the length of each side.

23. The perimeter of *ABCDE* is 94 m. Find the lengths of segments *AB* and *CD*.

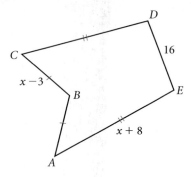

Review

24. Name a pair of complementary angles and a pair of vertical angles in the figure at right.

25. Draw $\overleftrightarrow{AB}$, $\overleftrightarrow{CD}$, and $\overleftrightarrow{EF}$ with $\overleftrightarrow{AB} \parallel \overleftrightarrow{CD}$ and $\overleftrightarrow{CD} \perp \overleftrightarrow{EF}$.

26. Draw a counterexample to show that this statement is false: "If a rectangle has perimeter 50 meters, then a pair of consecutive sides measures 10 meters and 15 meters."

27. Is it possible for four lines in a plane to have exactly zero points of intersection? One point? Two points? Three points? Four points? Five points? Six points? Draw a figure to support each of your answers. ⓗ

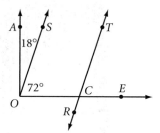

PERFORMANCE TASK

Make a set of sketches to demonstrate how two quadrilaterals can intersect in exactly 1 point, 2 points, 3 points, and so on. What is the maximum number of intersections of two quadrilaterals? Explain how you know.

Triangles

You have learned to be careful with geometry definitions. It turns out that you also have to be careful with diagrams.

When you look at a diagram, be careful not to assume too much from it. To **assume** something is to accept it as true without facts or proof.

Lightning

Not lightning

"The difference between the right word and the almost right word is the difference between lightning and the lightning bug."

MARK TWAIN

Things you may assume:

You may assume that lines are straight, and if two lines intersect, they intersect at one point.

You may assume that points on a line are collinear and that all points shown in a diagram are coplanar unless planes are drawn to show that they are noncoplanar.

Things you may not assume:

You may not assume that just because two lines or segments *look* parallel that they *are* parallel—they must be *marked* parallel!

You may not assume that two lines *are* perpendicular just because they *look* perpendicular—they must be *marked* perpendicular!

Pairs of angles, segments, or polygons are not necessarily congruent unless they are *marked* with information that tells you they must be congruent!

EXAMPLE

In the diagrams below, which pairs of lines are perpendicular? Which pairs of lines are parallel? Which pair of triangles is congruent?

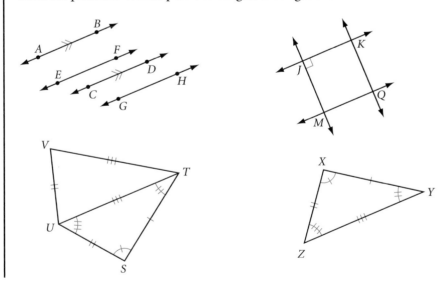

Solution

By studying the markings, you can tell that $\overleftrightarrow{AB} \parallel \overleftrightarrow{CD}$, $\overleftrightarrow{JK} \perp \overleftrightarrow{JM}$, and $\triangle STU \cong \triangle XYZ$.

In this lesson you will write definitions that classify different kinds of triangles based on relationships among their sides and angles.

INVESTIGATION 1

Triangles

Write a good definition of each boldfaced term. Discuss your definitions with others in your group. Agree on a common set of definitions for your class and add them to your definition list. In your notebook, draw and label a figure to illustrate each definition.

Right Triangle

What shape is the basis for the design on this polyhedron?

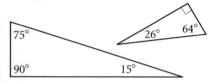

Right triangles

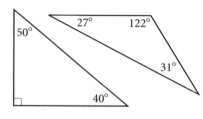

Not right triangles

Acute Triangle

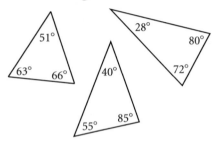

Acute triangles

Not acute triangles

Obtuse Triangle

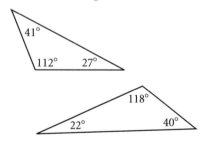

Obtuse triangles

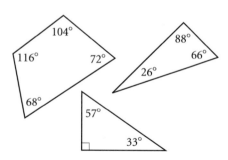

Not obtuse triangles

Scalene Triangle

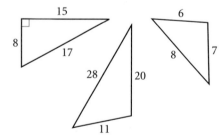

Scalene triangles

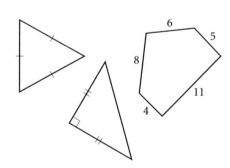

Not scalene triangles

Equilateral Triangle

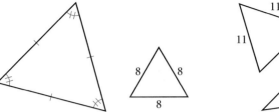
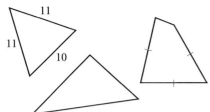

Equilateral triangles   Not equilateral triangles

Isosceles Triangle

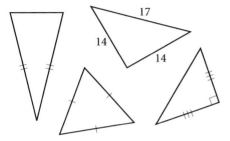
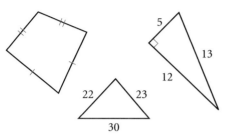

Isosceles triangles   Not isosceles triangles

In an isosceles triangle, the angle between the two sides of equal length is called the **vertex angle**. The side opposite the vertex angle is called the **base** of the isosceles triangle. The two angles opposite the two sides of equal length are called the **base angles** of the isosceles triangle.

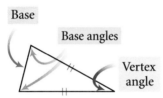

Base

Base angles

Vertex angle

INVESTIGATION 2

Creating Triangles with Patty Paper

Step 1 Fold and crease a random line through your patty paper.

Step 2 Open your patty paper and fold another random line.

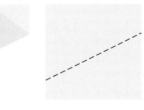

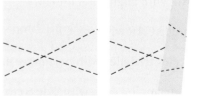

Step 1   Step 2   Step 3

Step 3 Fold another random line to create a triangle. Show the other members of your group your triangle.

a. Is it an acute triangle, obtuse triangle or right triangle? How do you convince the others in your group?

b. Is it a scalene triangle, isosceles triangle or equilateral triangle? How do you convince the others in your group?

Step 4 On a second patty paper, fold and crease a random line.

Step 5 Fold your first crease on top of itself to create a right angle.

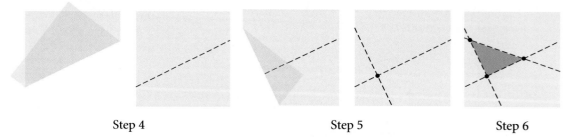

Step 4   Step 5   Step 6

Step 6 Fold a third crease to create an isosceles right triangle. Explain to others in your group what you did so that you knew the triangle must be isosceles ("because it looks it" is not a good enough reason!).

1.5 Exercises

For Exercises 1–4, match the term on the left with its figure on the right.

A. 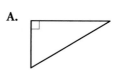 **B.**  **C.**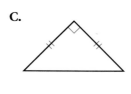

1. Equilateral triangle

2. Scalene right triangle

3. Isosceles right triangle

4. Isosceles obtuse triangle

D. **E.**

For Exercises 5–9, sketch and label the figure. Mark the figures.

5. Isosceles acute triangle ACT with $AC = CT$

6. Scalene triangle SCL with angle bisector $\overline{CM}$

7. Isosceles right triangle CAR with $m\angle CRA = 90°$

8. Two different isosceles triangles with perimeter $4a + b$

9. Two noncongruent triangles, each with side 6 cm and an angle measuring 40°

10. Use your ruler and protractor to draw an isosceles acute triangle with base AC and vertex angle B.

11. Use your ruler and protractor to draw an isosceles obtuse triangle ZAP with base angles A and Z.

For Exercises 12–14, use the graphs below. Can you find more than one answer? Explain.

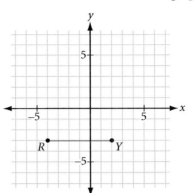
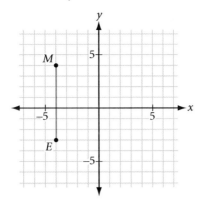
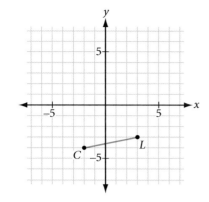

12. Locate a point L so that $\triangle LRY$ is an isosceles triangle.

13. Locate a point O so that $\triangle MOE$ is an isosceles right triangle.

14. Locate a point R so that $\triangle CRL$ is an isosceles right triangle. ⓗ

15. Use your ruler and protractor to draw a triangle with one side 9 cm long and an adjacent angle measuring 45°. Explain your method. Can you draw a second triangle with the given measures that is not congruent to the first? Sketch your results.

16. Use your ruler and protractor to draw a triangle with one angle measuring 40° and an opposite side 10 cm long. Explain your method. Can you draw a second triangle with the given measures that is not congruent to the first? Sketch your results.

Review

For Exercises 17–21, tell whether the statement is true or false. For each false statement, sketch a counterexample and explain why the statement is false.

17. An acute angle is an angle whose measure is less than 90°.

18. If two lines intersect to form a right angle, then the lines are perpendicular.

19. A diagonal is a line segment that connects any two vertices of a polygon.

20. A ray that divides the angle into two angles is the angle bisector.

21. An obtuse triangle has exactly one angle whose measure is greater than 90°.

22. Suppose a set of thin rods is glued together into a triangle as shown. How would you place the triangular arrangement of rods onto the edge of a ruler so that they balance? Explain why. ⓗ

For Exercises 23–24, sketch and carefully label the figure. Mark the congruent parts.

23. Pentagon $PENTA$ with $PE = EN$

24. Hexagon $NGAXEH$ with $\angle HEX \cong \angle EXA$

Special Quadrilaterals

If you attach two congruent triangles, you create many different quadrilaterals that have special properties. For example, the quadrilaterals in the photo at right can be formed by reflecting an isosceles triangle across its base, resulting in a quadrilateral with four equal sides. In this lesson you will define different types of special quadrilaterals based on relationships of their sides and angles.

How many shapes make up the overall triangular shapes of these pyramids at the Louvre in Paris?

INVESTIGATION 1

Special Quadrilaterals

Write a good definition of each boldfaced term. Discuss your definitions with others in your group. Agree on a common set of definitions for your class and add them to your definitions list. In your notebook, draw and label a figure to illustrate each definition.

Trapezoid

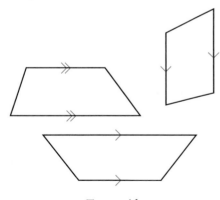

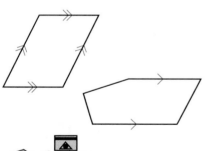

Trapezoids — Not trapezoids

Kite

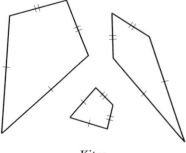

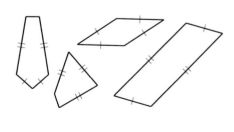

Kites — Not kites

Parallelogram

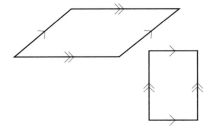

Parallelograms

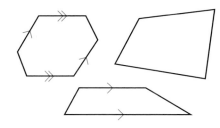

Not parallelograms

Rhombus

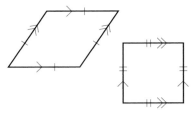

Rhombuses

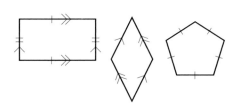

Not rhombuses

Rectangle

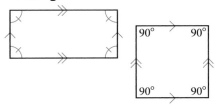

Rectangles

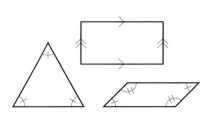

Not rectangles

Square

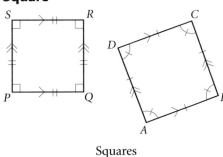

Squares

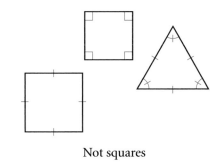

Not squares

As you learned in the investigation, a figure that looks like a square is not a square unless it has the proper markings. Keep this in mind as you work on the exercises.

INVESTIGATION 2

Creating Special Quadrilaterals

Step 1 Draw and cut out two congruent acute scalene triangles on heavy stock paper.

Step 2 Can you arrange them into a parallelogram? Sketch your results, marking all the congruent sides and angles. How do you convince the others in your group that your shape is a parallelogram ("because it looks it" is not a good enough reason!)?

Step 3 Can you arrange them into a kite? Sketch your results, marking all the congruent sides and angles. How do you convince the others in your group that your shape is a kite?

Step 4 Draw and cut out two congruent obtuse isosceles triangles on heavy stock paper.

Step 5 Which special quadrilaterals can you create with these two congruent triangles? Sketch your results, marking all the congruent sides and angles. How do you convince the others in your group that your shape is what you claim it to be?

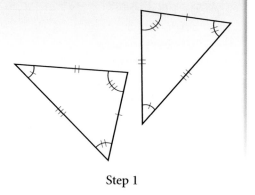

Step 1

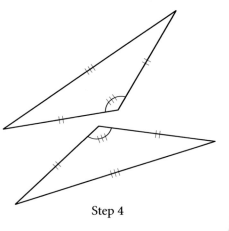

Step 4

YOU WILL NEED

Construction tools
for Exercises **20–23**

1.6 Exercises

1. Based on the marks, what can you assume to be true in each figure?

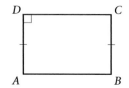
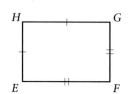
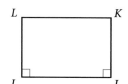
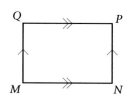

For Exercises 2–6, match the term on the left with its figure on the right.

2. Trapezoid

3. Rhombus

4. Rectangle

5. Kite

6. Parallelogram

A.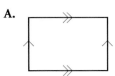

B.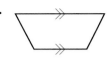

C.

D.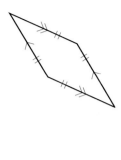

E.

F.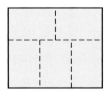

For Exercises 7–10, sketch and label the figure. Mark the figures.

7. Trapezoid *ZOID* with $\overline{ZO} \parallel \overline{ID}$

8. Kite *BENF* with $BE = EN$

9. Rhombus *EQUL* with diagonals $\overline{EU}$ and $\overline{QL}$ intersecting at *A*

10. Rectangle *RGHT* with diagonals $\overline{RH}$ and $\overline{GT}$ intersecting at *I*

11. Draw a hexagon with exactly two outside diagonals.

12. Draw a regular quadrilateral. What is another name for this shape?

13. Find the other two vertices of a square with one vertex (0, 0) and another vertex (4, 2). Can you find another answer? Explain.

14. What is the perimeter of one of the five congruent rectangles shown to the right? The larger rectangle with perimeter 198 cm is divided into five congruent rectangles.

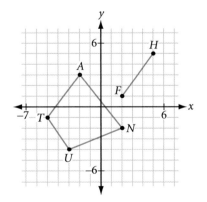

→ Architecture
CONNECTION

Quadrilaterals are used in the architecture of many cultures for both practical purposes and aesthetic appeal. The Taos Pueblo in New Mexico and the Chichén Itzá pyramid in Mexico both use quadrilateral-based designs for constructing climbing structures and enhancing overall attractiveness.

For Exercises 15–18, copy the given polygon and segment onto graph paper. Give the coordinates of the missing points.

15. $\triangle CAR \cong \triangle PET$

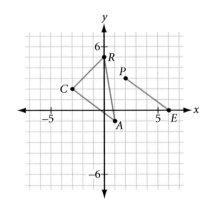

16. $TUNA \cong FISH$

17. *BLUE ≅ FISH*

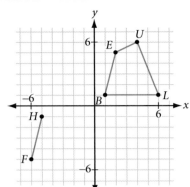

18. *RECT ≅ ANGL*

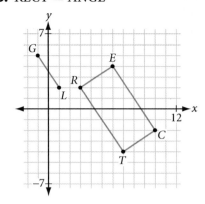

19. Imagine using two congruent triangles to create a special quadrilateral, as you did in the investigation.

    a. What type of triangles do you need to form a rectangle? Explain.

    b. What type of triangles do you need to form a square? Explain.

Review

For Exercises 20–23, sketch and carefully label the figure. Mark the congruent parts.

20. A hexagon with exactly one line of reflectional symmetry. ⓗ

21. Two different equilateral pentagons with perimeter 25 cm.

22. Use your compass, protractor, and straightedge to draw a regular pentagon.

23. Draw an equilateral octagon *ABCDEFGH* with *A*(5, 0), *B*(4, 4), and *C*(0, 5) as three of its vertices. Is it regular?

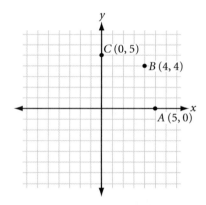

DEVELOPING MATHEMATICAL REASONING

Tetromino Puzzle 1

The 4×4 grid of squares shown to the right can be divided into four congruent regions in such a way that there will be an equal number of stars in reach region. Copy the grid with stars and divide it into four congruent regions with an equal number of stars in each region.

Circles

Unless you walked to school this morning, you arrived on a vehicle with circular wheels.

A **circle** is the set of all points in a plane at a given distance from a given point. The given distance is called the **radius** and the given point is called the **center**. You name a circle by its center. The circle on the bicycle wheel, with center O, is called circle O. When you see a dot at the center of a circle, you can assume that it represents the center point.

Science
CONNECTION

A pebble dropped in a pond sends out circular ripples. These waves radiate from the point where the pebble hits the water in all directions at the same speed, so every point is equally distant from the center. This unique property of circles appears in many other real-world contexts, such as radio waves sent from an antenna, seismic waves moving from the center of an earthquake, or sand draining out of a hole.

A segment from the center to a point on the edge of the circle is called a radius. Its length is also called the radius. A bicycle wheel is a physical model of a circle, and one spoke is a close physical model of a radius.

radius

 ## INVESTIGATION

Defining Circle Terms

Step 1 Write a good definition of each boldfaced term. Discuss your definitions with others in your group. Agree on a common set of definitions as a class and add them to your definition list. In your notebook, draw and label a figure to illustrate each definition.

Chord

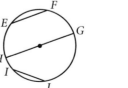

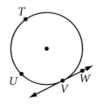

Chords:
$\overline{AB}$, $\overline{CD}$, $\overline{EF}$, $\overline{GH}$, and $\overline{IJ}$

Not chords:
$\overline{PQ}$, $\overleftrightarrow{RS}$, $\overarc{TU}$, and $\overrightarrow{VW}$

Diameter

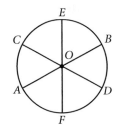

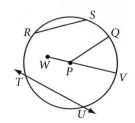

Diameters:
$\overline{AB}$, $\overline{CD}$, and $\overline{EF}$

Not diameters:
$\overline{PQ}$, $\overline{RS}$, $\overleftrightarrow{TU}$, and $\overline{VW}$

Tangent

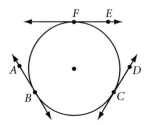

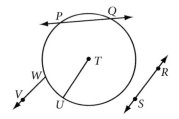

Tangents:
$\overleftrightarrow{AB}$, $\overleftrightarrow{CD}$, and $\overleftrightarrow{EF}$

Not tangents:
$\overrightarrow{PQ}$, $\overleftrightarrow{RS}$, $\overleftrightarrow{TU}$, and $\overrightarrow{WV}$

Note: You can say $\overleftrightarrow{AB}$ is a tangent, or you can say $\overleftrightarrow{AB}$ is tangent to circle O. The point where the tangent touches the circle is called the **point of tangency**.

Step 2 Can a chord of a circle also be a diameter of the circle? Can it be a tangent? Explain why or why not.

Step 3 Can two circles be tangent to the same line at the same point? Draw a sketch and explain.

If two or more circles have the same radius, they are **congruent circles**. If two or more coplanar circles share the same center, they are **concentric circles**. All the CDs represent congruent circles, but if you look closely at each CD, you can also see concentric circles.

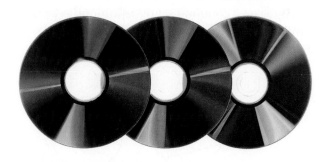

Concentric circles

The **circumference** of a circle is its perimeter which is the distance around that circle. Using the radius, the circumference can be calculated using $C = 2\pi r$. The circle at right has circumference 8π cm.

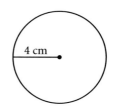

A circle is **circumscribed** about a polygon if and only if it passes through each vertex of the polygon. (The polygon is **inscribed** in the circle.)

Circumscribed circle
(Inscribed triangle)

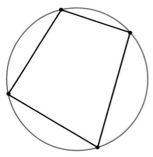

Circumscribed circle
(Inscribed quadrilateral)

A circle is **inscribed** in a polygon if and only if it touches each side of the polygon at exactly one point. (The polygon is **circumscribed** about the circle.)

Inscribed circle
(Circumscribed pentagon)

Inscribed circle
(Circumscribed quadrilateral)

An **arc** of a circle is two points on the circle and a continuous (unbroken) part of the circle between the two points. The two points are called the **endpoints** of the arc.

You write arc AB as $\overarc{AB}$ or $\overarc{BA}$. You classify arcs into three types: semicircles, minor arcs, and major arcs. A **semicircle** is an arc of a circle whose endpoints are the endpoints of a diameter. A **minor arc** is an arc of a circle that is smaller than a semicircle. A **major arc** is an arc of a circle that is larger than a semicircle. You can name minor arcs with the letters of the two endpoints. For semicircles and major arcs, you need three points to make clear which arc you mean—the first and last letters are the endpoints and the middle letter is any other point on the arc.

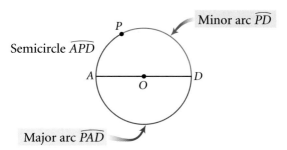

Semicircle $\overarc{APD}$

Minor arc $\overarc{PD}$

Major arc $\overarc{PAD}$

Try to name another minor arc and another major arc in this diagram. Why are three letters needed to name a major arc?

Arcs have a degree measure, just as angles do. A full circle has an arc measure of 360°, a semicircle has an arc measure of 180°, and so on. The **arc measure** of a minor arc is the same as the measure of the **central angle**, the angle with its vertex at the center of the circle, and sides passing through the endpoints of the arc. The measure of a major arc is the same as the reflex measure of the central angle.

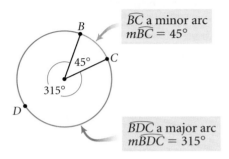

$\widehat{BC}$ a minor arc
$m\widehat{BC} = 45°$

$\widehat{BDC}$ a major arc
$m\widehat{BDC} = 315°$

1.7 Exercises

YOU WILL NEED

Construction tools
for Exercises **12, 17, 18, 22, 23**

1. In the photos below, identify the physical models that represent a circle, a radius, a chord, a tangent, and an arc of a circle.

Circular irrigation on a farm

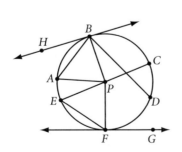

Japanese wood bridge

For Exercises 2–9, use the diagram at right. Points E, P, and C are collinear, and P is the center of the circle.

2. Name three chords.

3. Name one diameter.

4. Name five radii.

5. Name five minor arcs.

6. Name two semicircles.

7. Name two major arcs.

8. Name two tangents.

9. Name a point of tangency.

10. Name two types of vehicles that use wheels, two household appliances that use wheels, and two uses of the wheel in the world of entertainment.

11. In the figure at right, what is $m\overset{\frown}{PQ}$? $m\overset{\frown}{PRQ}$?

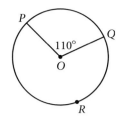

12. Use your compass and protractor to make an arc with measure 65°. Now make an arc with measure 215°. Label each arc with its measure.

13. Name two places or objects where concentric circles appear. Bring an example of a set of concentric circles to class tomorrow. You might look in a magazine for a photo or make a copy of a photo from a book (but not this book!).

14. Sketch two circles that appear to be concentric. Then use your compass to construct a pair of concentric circles.

15. Sketch triangle *ABC*. Sketch an inscribed circle in △*ABC*. Sketch a circle that circumscribes △*ABC*. Do you think every triangle can have an inscribed and circumscribed circle?

16. Sketch circle *P*. Sketch a circumscribed rectangle about circle *P*. Sketch a rectangle inscribed in circle *P*. What do you notice? Do you think this true for all rectangles?

17. Use your compass to construct two circles with the same radius intersecting at two points. Label the centers *P* and *Q*. Label the points of intersection of the two circles *A* and *B*. Construct quadrilateral *PAQB*. What type of quadrilateral is it?

18. Do you remember the daisy construction from Chapter 0? Construct a circle with radius *s*. With the same compass setting, divide the circle into six congruent arcs. Construct the chords to form a regular hexagon inscribed in the circle. Construct radii to each of the six vertices. What type of triangle is formed? What is the ratio of the perimeter of the hexagon to the diameter of the circle?

19. Sketch the path made by the midpoint of a radius of a circle if the radius is rotated about the center.

20. Earth takes 365.25 days to travel one full revolution around the Sun. By approximately how many degrees does the Earth travel each day in its orbit around the Sun?

21. Earth completes one full rotation each day, making the Sun appear to rise and set. If the Sun passes directly overhead, by how many degrees does its position in the sky change every hour?

Review

For Exercises 22–23, draw each kind of triangle or write "not possible" and explain why. Use your geometry tools to make your drawings as accurate as possible.

22. Isosceles right triangle

23. Scalene isosceles triangle

For Exercises 24–32, sketch, label, and mark the figure or write "not possible" and explain why.

24. Obtuse scalene triangle *FAT* with $m\angle FAT = 100°$

25. Trapezoid *TRAP* with $\overline{TR} \parallel \overline{AP}$ and $\angle TRA$ a right angle

26. Two different (noncongruent) quadrilaterals with angles of 60°, 60°, 120°, and 120°

27. Equilateral right triangle

28. Right isosceles triangle RGT with $RT = GT$ and $m\angle RTG = 90°$

29. An equilateral triangle with perimeter $12a + 6b$

30. Two triangles that are not congruent, each with angles measuring 50° and 70°

31. Rhombus $EQUI$ with perimeter $8p$ and $m\angle IEQ = 55°$

32. Kite $KITE$ with $TE = 2EK$ and $m\angle TEK = 120°$

DEVELOPING MATHEMATICAL REASONING

Sudoku

Copy these two sudoku onto another paper. Fill in every empty square (called a *cell*) with digits from 1 through 9 so that every row, column, and every 3 × 3 region contains each digit exactly once. Solve these puzzles logically. Do not guess!

		4			2			
1	9						5	8
		3	9		1	4		
	2			7			6	
		5	2		8	7		
	4			5			8	
		6	1		3	9		
2	7						3	1
		8			6			

4		6	8					
7				1	4	3	6	2
		3		9				
								4
		4	2		9	8		
9								
			4		7			
2	3	8	6	7				1
					3	6		5

Space Geometry

Lesson 1.1 introduced you to point, line, and plane. Throughout this chapter you have used these terms to define a wide range of other geometric figures, from rays to polygons. You did most of your work on a single flat surface, a single plane. Some problems, however, required you to step out of a single plane to visualize geometry in space. In this lesson you will learn more about space geometry, or solid geometry.

Space is the set of all points. Unlike one-dimensional lines and two-dimensional planes, space cannot be contained in a flat surface. Space is three-dimensional, or "3-D."

In an "edge view," you see the front edge of a building as a vertical line, and the other edges as diagonal lines. Isometric dot paper helps you draw these lines, as you can see in the steps below.

Let's practice the visual thinking skill of presenting three-dimensional (3-D) objects in two-dimensional (2-D) drawings.

The geometric solid you are probably most familiar with is a box, or rectangular prism. Below are steps for making a two-dimensional drawing of a rectangular prism. This type of drawing is called an **isometric drawing**. It shows three sides of an object in one view (an edge view). This method works best with isometric dot paper. After practicing, you will be able to draw the box without the aid of the dot grid.

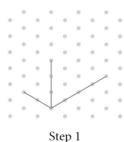

Step 1

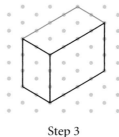

Step 2

Step 3

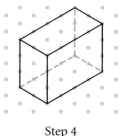

Step 4

Use dashed lines for edges that you couldn't see if the object were solid.

The three-dimensional objects you will study include the six types of geometric solids shown below.

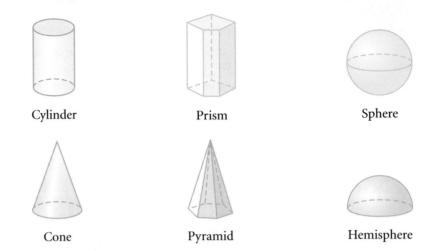

Cylinder   Prism   Sphere

Cone   Pyramid   Hemisphere

The shapes of these solids are probably already familiar to you even if you are not familiar with their proper names. The ability to draw these geometric solids is an important visual thinking skill. Here are some drawing tips. Remember to use dashes for the hidden lines.

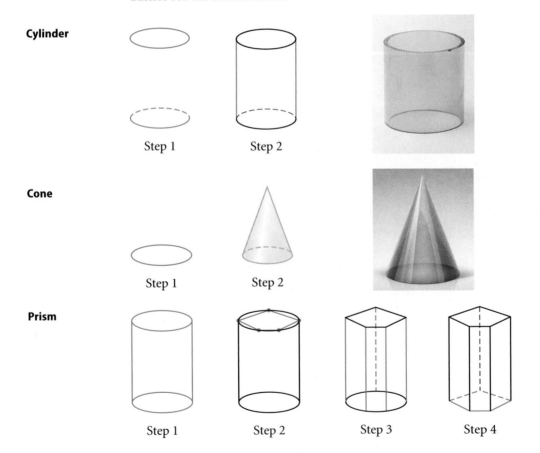

Cylinder

Step 1   Step 2

Cone

Step 1   Step 2

Prism

Step 1   Step 2   Step 3   Step 4

Pyramid

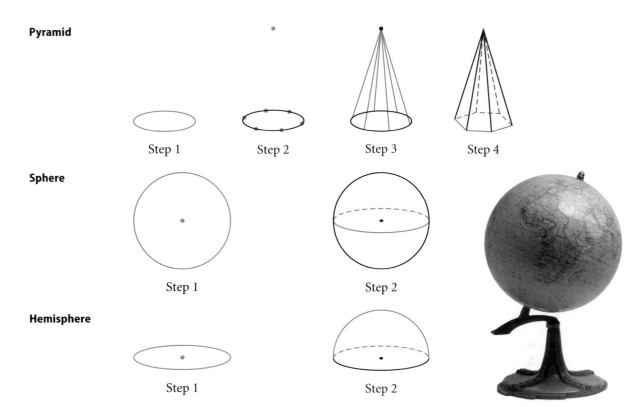

Sphere

Hemisphere

Solid geometry also involves visualizing points and lines in space. In the following investigation, you will have to visualize relationships between geometric figures in a plane and in space.

 INVESTIGATION

Space Geometry

Step 1 Make a sketch or use physical objects to demonstrate each statement in the list below.

Step 2 Work with your group to determine whether each statement is true or false. If the statement is false, draw a picture and explain why it is false.

1. For any two points, there is exactly one line that can be drawn through them.

2. For any line and a point not on the line, there is exactly one plane that can contain them.

3. For any two lines, there is exactly one plane that contains them.

4. If two coplanar lines are both perpendicular to a third line in the same plane, then the two lines are parallel.

5. If two planes do not intersect, then they are parallel.

6. If two lines do not intersect, then they are parallel.

7. If a line is perpendicular to two lines in a plane, and the line is not contained in the plane, then the line is perpendicular to the plane.

1.8 Exercises

For Exercises 1–6, draw each figure. Study the drawing tips provided on the previous page before you start.

1. Cylinder

2. Cone

3. Prism with a hexagonal base

4. Sphere

5. Pyramid with a heptagonal base

6. Hemisphere

7. The photo at right shows a prism-shaped building with a cone roof. Draw a cylindrical building with a pyramid roof.

For Exercises 8 and 9, make a drawing to scale of each figure. Use isometric dot paper. Label each figure. (For example, in Exercise 8, draw the solid so that the dimensions measure 2 units by 3 units by 4 units, then label the figure with meters.)

Trulli houses with conical roofs in Italy.

8. A rectangular solid 2 m by 3 m by 4 m, sitting on its biggest face. ⓗ

9. A rectangular solid 3 inches by 4 inches by 5 inches, resting on its smallest face. Draw lines on the three visible surfaces showing how you can divide the solid into cubic-inch boxes. How many such boxes will fit in the solid? ⓗ

For Exercises 10–12, use isometric dot paper to draw the figure shown.

10.

11.

12.

A **net** is a two-dimensional pattern that you can cut and fold to form a three-dimensional figure. Another visual thinking skill you will need is the ability to visualize nets being folded into solid objects and geometric solids being unfolded into nets. The net below left can be folded into a cube and the net below right can be folded into a pyramid.

Net for a cube   Net for a square-based pyramid

13. Which net(s) will fold to make a cube?

A.

B.

C.

D.

For Exercises 14–17, match the net with its geometric solid.

14.

15.

16.

17.

A.

B.

C.

D.

When a solid is cut by a plane, the resulting two-dimensional figure is called a **cross-section**. For Exercises 18 and 19, sketch the cross-section formed when each solid is sliced by the plane, as shown.

18.

19.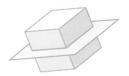

Slicing a block of clay reveals a section of the solid. Here, the cross-section is a rectangle.

Physical models can help you visualize the intersections of lines and planes in space. Can you see examples of intersecting lines in this photo? Parallel lines? Planes? Points?

20. If this net is folded into a cube, what is the color of the cube face opposite the purple face?

21. What is the shortest distance from *A* to *B* traveling on the surface of the cube? On the edges of the cube?

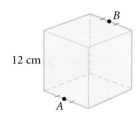

12 cm

All of the statements in Exercises 22–29 are true except for two. Make a sketch to demonstrate each true statement. For each false statement, draw a sketch and explain why it is false.

22. If a line intersects a plane that does not contain the line, then the intersection is exactly one point.

23. If two lines are perpendicular to the same line, then they are parallel. ⓗ

24. If two different planes intersect, then their intersection is a line.

25. If a line and a plane have no points in common, then they are parallel.

26. If a plane intersects two parallel planes, then the lines of intersection are parallel.

27. If three planes intersect, then they divide space into six parts.

28. If two lines are perpendicular to the same plane, then they are parallel to each other.

29. Only one plane can pass through three noncollinear points.

Review

30. If the kite *DIAN* were rotated 90° clockwise about the origin, to what location would point *A* be relocated?

31. Use your ruler to measure the perimeter of △*WIM* (in centimeters) and your protractor to measure the largest angle.

32. Use your geometry tools to draw a triangle with two sides of length 8 cm and length 13 cm and the angle between them measuring 120°.

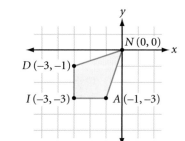

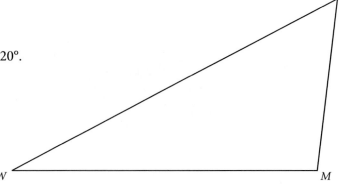

DEVELOPING MATHEMATICAL REASONING

Pentomino Sudoku Puzzle

To the right is a pentomino sudoku. Every row, column, and pentomino region contains the numerals 1–5. Complete the pentomino sudoku below.

1				4
5	4			
			2	
		5		

EXPLORATION

Orthographic Drawing

If you have ever put together a toy from detailed instructions, or built a birdhouse from a kit, or seen blueprints for a building under construction, you have seen isometric drawings.

Isometric means "having equal measure," so the edges of a cube drawn isometrically all have the same length. In contrast, recall that when you drew a cube in two-point perspective, you needed to use edges of different lengths to get a natural look.

When you buy a product from a catalog or off the Internet, you want to see it from several angles. The top, front, and right side views are given in an **orthographic drawing**. Ortho means "straight," and the views of an orthographic drawing show the faces of a solid as though you are looking at them "head-on."

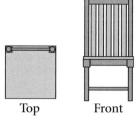

Top   Front

An isometric drawing

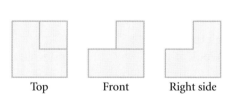

Top   Front   Right side

An orthographic drawing

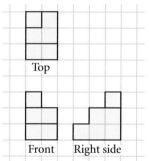

Side   Isometric

EXAMPLE A	Make an orthographic drawing of the solid shown in the isometric drawing at right.

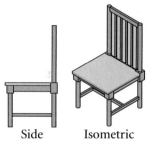

Solution	Visualize how the solid would look from the top, the front, and the right side. Draw an edge wherever there is a change of depth. The top and front views must have the same width, and the front and right side views must have the same height.

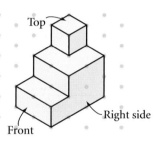

EXAMPLE B	Draw the isometric view of the object shown here as an orthographic drawing. The dashed lines mean that there is an invisible edge.

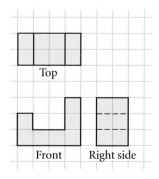

Solution

Find the vertices of the front face and make the shape. Use the width of the side and top views to extend parallel lines. Complete the back edges. You can shade parallel planes to show depth.

YOU WILL NEED
- isometric dot paper
- graph paper
- 12 cubes

Activity

Isometric and Orthographic Drawings

In this investigation you'll build block models and draw their isometric and orthographic views.

Step 1 Practice drawing a cube on isometric dot paper. What is the shape of each visible face? Are they congruent? What should the orthographic views of a cube look like?

Step 2 Stack three cubes to make a two-step "staircase." Turn the structure so that you look at it the way you would walk up stairs. Call that view the front. Next, identify the top and right sides. How many planes are visible from each view? Make an isometric drawing of the staircase on dot paper and the three orthographic views on graph paper.

Step 3 Build solids A–D from their orthographic views, then draw their isometric views.

A   B   C   D

Step 4 Make your own original 8- to 12-cube structure and agree on the orthographic views that represent it. Then trade places with another group and draw the orthographic views of their structure.

Step 5 Make orthographic views for solids E and F, and sketch the isometric views of solids G and H.

E   F   G   H

Transformations

By moving all the points of a geometric figure according to certain rules, you can create an **image** of the original figure. This process is called **transformation**. Each point on the original figure corresponds to a unique point on its image. The image of point A after a transformation of any type is called point A' (read "A prime"), as shown in the transformation of $\triangle ABC$ to $\triangle A'B'C'$ on the next page.

If the image is congruent to the original figure, the process is called **rigid transformation**, or **isometry**. A transformation that does not preserve the size and shape is called **nonrigid transformation**. For example, if an image is reduced or enlarged, or if the shape changes, its transformation is nonrigid.

Three types of rigid transformation are translation, rotation, and reflection.

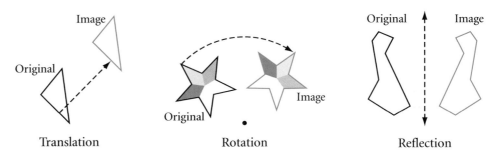

Translation   Rotation   Reflection

Translation is the simplest type of transformation. You can model a translation by tracing a figure onto patty paper, then sliding it along a straight path without turning it. Notice that when you slide the figure, all points move the same distance along parallel paths to form its image. That is, each point in the image is equidistant from the point that corresponds to it in the original figure. This distance, because it is the same for all points, is called the distance of the translation. A translation also has a particular direction. So you can use a **translation vector** to describe the translation.

Translation vector

Translating with patty paper

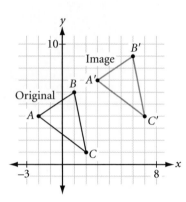

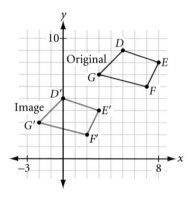

Translations on a coordinate grid

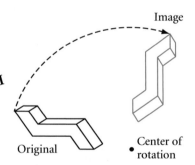

Rotation is another type of transformation. In a rotation, all the points in the original figure rotate, or turn, an identical number of degrees about a fixed center point. You can define a rotation by its center point, the number of degrees it's turned, and whether it's turned clockwise or counterclockwise. If no direction is given, assume the direction of rotation is counterclockwise.

Original

Image

Center of rotation

You can model a rotation by tracing over a figure, then putting your pencil point on a point on the patty paper and rotating the patty paper about the point.

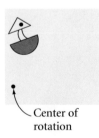

Center of rotation

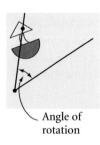

Angle of rotation

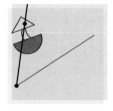

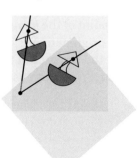

Rotating with patty paper

Reflection is a type of transformation that produces a figure's "mirror image." If you draw a figure onto a piece of paper, place the edge of a mirror perpendicular to your paper, and look at the figure in the mirror, you will see the reflected image of the figure. The line where the mirror is placed is called the **line of reflection**.

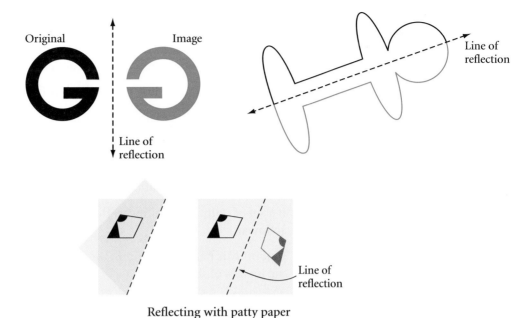

Reflecting with patty paper

INVESTIGATION 1

The Basic Properties of a Reflection

In this investigation you'll model reflection with patty paper and discover important properties of this transformation.

Step 1 Place a line of reflection on a piece of patty paper. Draw a polygon next to it with one of the vertices on the line of reflection.

Step 2 Fold your patty paper along the line of reflection and create the reflected image of your polygon by tracing it. Open up the patty paper.

Step 3 Draw segments connecting each vertex with its image point.

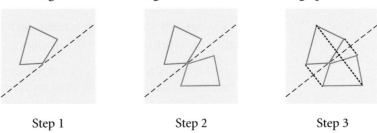

Step 1   Step 2   Step 3

Step 4 Use your patty paper investigation to explain to other members of your group what things are the same in both the original figure and its image. Lengths? Angles? Orientation? What is true about the segments connecting points and their images?

Step 5 In your group discuss which of the following statements are true. If true, demonstrate an example to the other group members. If false, sketch a counterexample. Explain to other group members why your counterexample demonstrates that the statement is false.

a. If $\overline{AB}$ is reflected over line m creating the image $\overline{A'B'}$ then $\overline{AB} \cong \overline{A'B'}$.

b. If $\angle A$ is reflected over line m creating the image $\angle A'$ then $\angle A \cong \angle A'$.

c. If polygon P is reflected over line m creating the image polygon P' then $P \cong P'$.

d. A reflection transformation is a rigid transformation or isometry.

e. If a set of points are collinear, then their reflected images are also collinear.

f. If point N is between A and B, then the reflected image of N is between the images of A and B.

g. If the image of a point A reflected over line m is B, then the image of B reflected over line m is A. (If A is on m, then the image of A coincides with A.)

h. If the clockwise order of the vertices of a quadrilateral $ABCD$ are A, then B, then C, then D, and back to A, then the clockwise order of points of the reflected image $A'B'C'D'$ is the same: A', then B', then C', then D', and back to A'.

i. Every point and its reflected image are always the same distance from the line of reflection. In other words, the line of reflection always bisects any segment connecting a point to its reflected image point.

j. The segment connecting a point to its reflected image is always perpendicular to the line of reflection.

k. The line of reflection bisects every segment connecting a point and its image point.

 INVESTIGATION 2

The Basic Properties of a Translation

In this investigation you'll model translation with patty paper and discover important properties of this transformation.

Step 1 Draw a quadrilateral in one corner of your patty paper. From one of your vertices (label it A), draw a ray to the edge of your patty paper. This will be the direction of the translation. Place a point B on that ray. The distance from A to B is the translation distance. This distance, together with its direction is called the translation vector $\overline{AB}$.

Step 2 Place a second patty paper on top of the first and make a copy of the quadrilateral, the ray, and the translation vector. Place your copy beneath the original and, using the translation vector as a guide, translate the second copy, keeping the rays aligned until the point *A* of the quadrilateral copy is over the point *B* on the original ray. Copy the image of the bottom quadrilateral onto the top patty paper.

Step 3 Draw segments connecting each vertex with its image point.

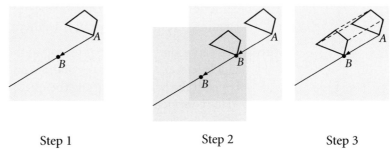

Step 1   Step 2   Step 3

Step 4 Use your patty paper investigation to explain to other members of your group what things are the same in both the original figure and its image. Lengths? Angles? Orientation?

Step 5 In your group discuss which of the following statements are true. If true, demonstrate an example to the other group members. If false, sketch a counterexample. Explain to other group members why your counterexample demonstrates that the statement is false.

a. If $\overline{PQ}$ is translated creating the image $\overline{P'Q'}$ then $\overline{PQ} \cong \overline{P'Q'}$.

b. If $\angle R$ is translated creating the image $\angle R'$ then $\angle R \cong \angle R'$.

c. If polygon *S* is translated creating the image polygon *S'* then polygon $S \cong$ polygon S'.

d. A translation transformation is a rigid transformation or isometry.

e. If a set of points are collinear, then their translated images are also collinear.

f. If point *N* is between *A* and *B*, then the translated image of *N* is between the images of *A* and *B*.

g. If point *A* is translated by the translation vector $\overline{PQ}$ creating image *B*, then the image of *B* translated by the translation vector $\overline{QP}$ is *A*.

h. If the clockwise order of the vertices of a quadrilateral *ABCD* are *A*, then *B*, then *C*, then *D*, and back to *A*, then the clockwise order of points of the translated image *A'B'C'D'* is the same: *A'*, then *B'*, then *C'*, then *D'*, and back to *A'*.

i. Any point and its translated image point are the same distance apart as any other pair of points and corresponding image points.

j. All the segments connecting a point to its translated image point are parallel.

INVESTIGATION 3

The Basic Properties of a Rotation

In this third investigation you'll model rotation with patty paper and discover important properties of this transformation.

Step 1 Draw a quadrilateral in one corner of your patty paper. Place a dot near the center of your patty paper and label it point *P*. This will be your center of rotation. From point *P* draw a segment to one of your vertices (label it *A*).

Step 2 Place a second patty paper on top of the first and make a copy of the quadrilateral, the center of rotation, and the segment *PA*. Place your copy beneath the original aligning the quadrilaterals and the centers of rotation. Place your pen or pencil on top of the centers of rotation. Rotate the copy until the two quadrilaterals are no longer overlapping. Copy the image of the bottom quadrilateral onto the top patty paper.

Step 3 Draw segments connecting each vertex to the center of rotation *P*.

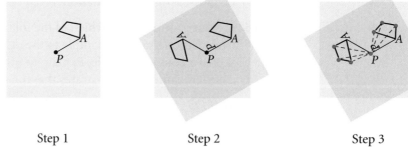

Step 1   Step 2   Step 3

Step 4 Use your patty paper investigation to explain to other members of your group what things are the same in both the original figure and its image. Lengths? Angles? Orientation?

Step 5 In your group discuss which of the following statements are true. If true, demonstrate an example to the other group members. If false, sketch a counterexample. Explain to other group members why your counterexample demonstrates that the statement is false.

a. If $\overline{PQ}$ is rotated creating the image $\overline{P'Q'}$ then $\overline{PQ} \cong \overline{P'Q'}$.

b. If $\angle R$ is rotated creating the image $\angle R'$ then $\angle R \cong \angle R'$.

c. If polygon *S* is rotated creating the image polygon *S'* then polygon $S \cong$ polygon *S'*.

d. A rotation transformation is a rigid transformation or isometry.

e. If three or more points are collinear, then their rotated images are also collinear.

f. If point *N* is between *A* and *B*, then the rotated image of *N* is between the rotated images of *A* and *B*.

g. If point *A* is rotated clockwise creating image *B*, then the image of *B* rotated clockwise is *A*.

h. If the clockwise order of the vertices of a quadrilateral *ABCD* are *A*, then *B*, then *C*, then *D*, and back to *A*, then the clockwise order of points of the rotated image *A′B′C′D′* is the same: *A′*, then *B′*, then *C′*, then *D′*, and back to *A′*.

i. Any point and its rotated image point are the same distance apart as any other pair of points and corresponding image points.

j. All the segments connecting a point to its rotated image point are parallel.

1.9 Exercises

In Exercises 1–3, say whether the transformations are rigid or nonrigid. Explain how you know.

YOU WILL NEED

Construction tools
for Exercises **15–19**, **29–30**

1.

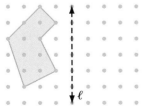

2.

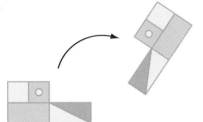

3.

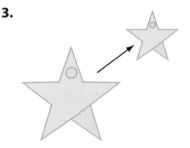

4. An ice skater gliding in one direction creates several translation transformations. Give another real-world example of translation.

5. An ice skater twirling about a point creates several rotation transformations. Give another real-world example of rotation.

In Exercises 6–8, copy the figure onto graph or square dot paper and perform each transformation.

6. Reflect the figure across the line of reflection, line ℓ.

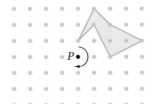

7. Rotate the figure 180° about the center of rotation, point *P*.

8. Translate the figure by the translation vector.

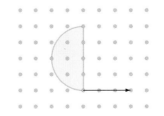

For Exercises 9–14 transform each △PQR on the coordinate plane by the given rule.

9. Translate 3 units left, 2 units up.

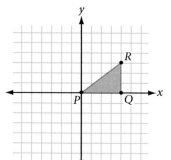

10. Translate 1 unit left, 4 units down.

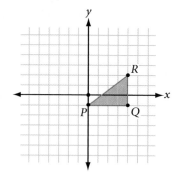

11. Reflect across *x*-axis

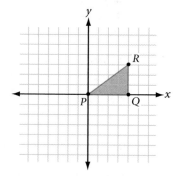

12. Reflect across the *y*-axis

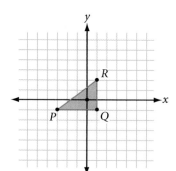

13. Rotate 90° clockwise about the origin.

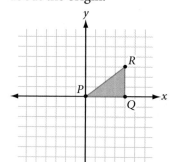

14. Rotate 90° counterclockwise about the origin.

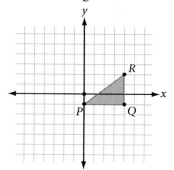

In Exercises 15–17, copy the figure onto patty paper. Fold to locate a line of reflection so that the reflected image coincides with the original. Explain your reasoning.

15.

16.

17.

In Exercises 18–20, perform each transformation. Attach your patty paper to your homework.

18. Copy the figure and the line of reflection onto a piece of patty paper. Fold the paper and trace the figure to construct the reflected image.

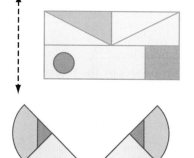

19. Copy the figure and its reflected image onto a piece of patty paper. Locate the line of reflection. Explain your method.

20. Trace the circular figure and the center of rotation, *P*. Rotate the design 90° clockwise about point *P*. Draw the image of the figure, as well as the dotted line.

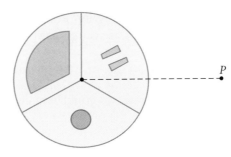

21. △*RSE* with *O*, a random point on $\overline{RS}$, are reflected across line *p* to create △*R'S'E'*. Which of the following statements are true? Explain how you know.

   a. $\overline{RE} \cong \overline{R'E'}$

   b. $\angle S \cong \angle S'$

   c. Points *R'*, *O'*, and *S'* are collinear

   d. The distance from *S* to line *p* is equal to the distance from *S'* to line *p*.

22. △*ABC* with *M*, the midpoint of $\overline{AC}$, are translated to create △*A'B'C'*. Which of the following statements are true? Explain how you know.

   a. $\overline{AB} \cong \overline{A'B'}$

   b. $\angle C \cong \angle C'$

   c. *M'* is the midpoint of *A'C'*

   d. $\overline{BB'} \cong \overline{MM'}$

23. △*DEF* with $\overline{EG}$ the bisector of $\angle E$ are rotated to create △*D'E'F'*. Which of the following statements are true? Explain how you know.

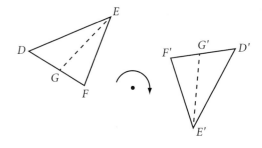

   a. $\overline{DF} \cong \overline{D'F'}$

   b. $\angle F \cong \angle F'$

   c. $\angle DEG \cong \angle D'E'G'$

   d. $\overline{DD'} \cong \overline{GG'}$

Review

In Exercises 24 and 25, sketch the next two figures.

24. , , , , , __?__, __?__

25.

						?	?		?	?

26. Sketch and carefully label equiangular quadrilateral *QUAD* with *QU* ≠ *QD*.

For Exercises 27–28, draw each kind of triangle or write "not possible" and explain why. Use your geometry tools to make your drawings as accurate as possible.

27. Scalene obtuse triangle

28. Isosceles obtuse triangle

29. Use your compass and straightedge to draw two congruent circles intersecting in exactly one point. How does the distance between the two centers compare with the radius?

30. Use your compass and straightedge to construct two congruent circles so that each circle passes through the center of the other circle. Label the centers P and Q. Construct $\overline{PQ}$ connecting the centers. Label the points of intersection of the two circles A and B. Construct chord $\overline{AB}$. What is the relationship between $\overline{AB}$ and $\overline{PQ}$? Explain how you know.

PERFORMANCE TASK

Folding Rectangles

Step 1 A square piece of paper is folded in half as shown in Figure 1 and then cut into two rectangles along the fold. The perimeter of each of the two rectangles is 18 inches. What is the perimeter of the original square? Explain.

Step 2 A square piece of paper is folded into three congruent rectangles as shown in Figure 2. Each of the three rectangles has a perimeter of 16 centimeters. How many centimeters are in the perimeter of the square? Explain.

Step 3 The square piece of paper (Figure 3) is folded into four congruent rectangles. The perimeter of each of the four congruent rectangles is 25 cm. What is the perimeter of the square? Explain.

Step 4 The square piece of paper (Figure 4) is folded into n congruent rectangles. The perimeter of each of the n congruent rectangles is 88 cm ($10 < n < 40$). If the perimeter of the original square is 168, what is n? Explain.

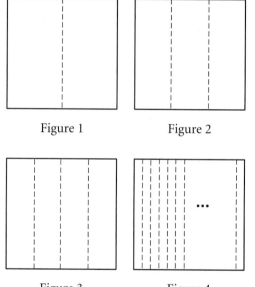

Figure 1   Figure 2

Figure 3   Figure 4

It may seem that there's a lot to memorize in this chapter. But having defined terms yourself, you're more likely to remember and understand them. The key is to practice using these new terms and to be organized.

Whether you've been keeping a good list or not, go back now through each lesson in the chapter and double-check that you've completed each definition and that you understand it. For example, if someone mentions a geometry term to you, can you sketch it? If you are shown a transformation, can you identify what kind it is? If you are shown a geometric figure, can you name it? Can you describe the difference between rigid and nonrigid transformations? Compare your list of geometry terms with the lists of your group members.

Exercises

YOU WILL NEED

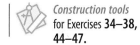

Construction tools for Exercises **34–38, 44–47.**

Answers to all exercises in every Chapter Review are provided in the back of the book.

For Exercises 1–16, identify the statement as true or false. For each false statement, explain why it is false and sketch a counterexample.

1. The three basic building blocks of geometry are point, line, and plane.

2. "The ray through point *P* from point *Q*" is written in symbolic form as $\overrightarrow{PQ}$.

3. "The length of segment *PQ*" can be written as *PQ*.

4. The vertex of angle *PDQ* is point *P*.

5. The symbol for *perpendicular* is ⊥.

6. A scalene triangle is a triangle with no two sides the same length.

7. An acute angle is an angle whose measure is more than 90°.

8. If $\overleftrightarrow{AB}$ intersects $\overleftrightarrow{CD}$ at point *P*, then ∠*APD* and ∠*APC* are a pair of vertical angles.

9. A diagonal is a line segment in a polygon connecting any two nonconsecutive vertices.

10. If two lines lie in the same plane and are perpendicular to the same line, then they are parallel.

11. If the sum of the measures of two angles is 180°, then the two angles are complementary.

12. A trapezoid is a quadrilateral having exactly one pair of parallel sides.

13. A polygon with ten sides is a decagon.

14. A square is a rectangle with all the sides equal in length.

A knowledge of parallel lines, planes, arcs, circles, and symmetry is necessary to build durable guitars that sound pleasing.

15. A pentagon has five sides and six diagonals.

16. The largest chord of a circle is a diameter of the circle.

For Exercises 17–25, match each term with its figure below, or write "no match."

17. Octagon

18. Isosceles right triangle

19. Rhombus

20. Trapezoid

21. Pyramid

22. Cylinder

23. Concave polygon

24. Chord

25. Minor arc

A.
B.
C.
D.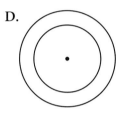

E.
F.
G.
H.

I.
J.
K.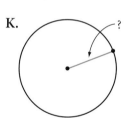
L.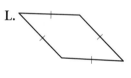

M.
N.
O.

For Exercises 26–33, sketch, label, and mark each figure.

26. Kite *KYTE* with $\overline{KY} \cong \overline{YT}$

27. Scalene triangle *PTS* with *PS* = 3, *ST* = 5, *PT* = 7, and angle bisector $\overline{SO}$

28. Hexagon *REGINA* with diagonal $\overline{AG}$ parallel to sides $\overline{RE}$ and $\overline{NI}$

29. Trapezoid *TRAP* with $\overline{AR}$ and $\overline{PT}$ the nonparallel sides. Let *E* be the midpoint of $\overline{PT}$ and let *Y* be the midpoint of $\overline{AR}$. Draw $\overline{EY}$.

30. A triangle with exactly one line of reflectional symmetry

31. A circle with center at *P*, radii $\overline{PA}$ and $\overline{PT}$, and chord $\overline{TA}$ creating a minor arc $\overset{\frown}{TA}$

32. A pair of concentric circles with the diameter $\overline{AB}$ of the inner circle perpendicular at *B* to a chord $\overline{CD}$ of the larger circle

33. A pyramid with a pentagonal base

34. Draw a rectangular prism 2 inches by 3 inches by 5 inches, resting on its largest face. Draw lines on the three visible faces, showing how the solid can be divided into 30 smaller cubes.

35. Use your protractor to draw a 125° angle.

36. Use your protractor, ruler, and compass to draw an isosceles triangle with a vertex angle having a measure of 40°.

37. Use your geometry tools to draw a regular octagon.

38. What is the measure of ∠A? Use your protractor.

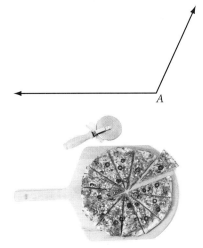

39. If D is the midpoint of $\overline{AC}$, C is the midpoint of $\overline{AB}$, and BD = 12 cm, what is the length of $\overline{AB}$?

40. If $\overrightarrow{BD}$ is the angle bisector of ∠ABC and $\overrightarrow{BE}$ is the angle bisector of ∠DBC, find m∠EBA if m∠DBE = 32°.

41. If the pizza is cut into 12 congruent pieces, how many degrees are in each central angle?

42. If the right triangle BAR were rotated 90° clockwise about point B, to what location would point A be relocated?

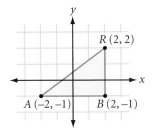

43. Sketch the three-dimensional figure formed by folding the net below into a solid.

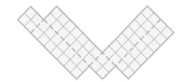

In Exercises 44–47, perform each transformation. Attach your patty paper to your homework.

44. Copy the figure and the line of reflection onto a piece of patty paper. Fold to construct the reflected image. Explain your method. Is the image congruent to the original? How do you know?

45. Copy the figure and its translation vector onto a piece of patty paper. Draw the original and its image after the translation on your patty paper. Explain your method. Is the image congruent to the original? Explain.

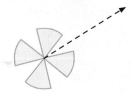

46. Copy the figure and the center of rotation, *P*. Rotate the design 180° clockwise about point *P*. Draw the image of the figure, as well as the dotted line. Explain your method. Is the image congruent to the original? How do you know?

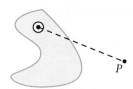

47. Copy the figure onto two pieces of patty paper. Locate the line of reflection so that when one of the copies is reflected the image coincides with the original. Is there more than one line of reflection for this figure that results in the image coinciding with the original? Explain.

CHAPTER 2

Reasoning in Geometry

"That which an artist makes is a mirror image of what he sees around him."

M. C. ESCHER

M. C. Escher's *Hand with Reflecting Sphere (Self Portrait in Spherical Mirror)*, ©2014 The M. C. Escher Company—The Netherlands. All rights reserved. www.mcescher.com

OBJECTIVES

In this chapter you will

- perform geometry investigations and make many discoveries by observing common features or patterns
- use your discoveries to solve problems through a process called inductive reasoning
- use inductive reasoning to discover patterns
- learn to use deductive reasoning
- make conjectures about vertical angles and linear pairs
- apply properties of transformations to coordinate geometry
- learn about composition of transformations on a coordinate plane

Visual Reasoning

A picture is worth a thousand words! That expression certainly applies to geometry. A drawing of an object often conveys information more quickly than a long written description. People in many occupations use drawings and sketches to communicate ideas. Architects create blueprints. Composers create musical scores. Choreographers visualize and map out sequences of dance steps. Basketball coaches design plays. Interior designers—well, you get the picture.

Visualization skills are extremely important in geometry. So far, you have visualized geometric situations in every lesson. To visualize a plane, you pictured a flat surface extending infinitely. In another lesson you visualized the number of different ways that four lines can intersect. Can you picture what the hands of a clock look like when it is 3:30?

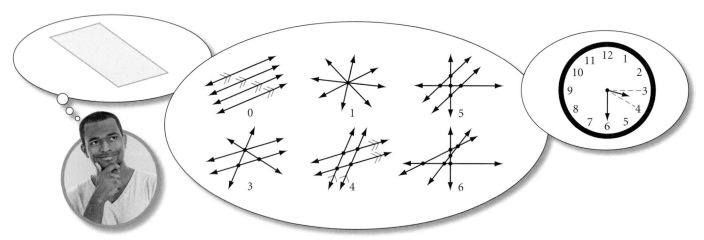

By drawing diagrams, you apply visual thinking to problem solving. Let's look at some examples that show how to use visual thinking to solve word problems.

EXAMPLE A

Volumes 1 and 2 of a two-volume set of math books sit next to each other on a shelf. They sit in their proper order: Volume 1 on the left and Volume 2 on the right. Each front and back cover is $\frac{1}{8}$-inch thick, and the pages portion of each book is 1-inch thick. If a bookworm starts at the first page of Volume 1 and burrows all the way through to the last page of Volume 2, how far will it travel?

Solution

Did you get $2\frac{1}{4}$ inches? It seems reasonable, doesn't it?

However, that's not the answer. Let's reread the problem to identify what information is given and what we are asked to find.

We are given the thickness of each cover, the thickness of the pages portion, and the position of the books on the shelf. We are trying to find how far it is from the first page of Volume 1 to the last page of Volume 2. Draw a picture and locate the position of the pages referred to in the problem.

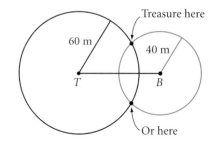

First page of Volume 1

Last page of Volume 2

Now "look" how easy it is to solve the problem. The bookworm traveled only $\frac{1}{4}$ inch through the two covers!

EXAMPLE B

Harold, Dina, and Linda are standing on a flat, dry field reading their treasure map. Harold is standing at one of the features marked on the map, a gnarled tree stump, and Dina is standing atop a large black boulder. The map shows that the treasure is buried 60 meters from the tree stump and 40 meters from the large black boulder. Harold and Dina are standing 80 meters apart. What is the locus of points where the treasure might be buried?

Solution

Start by drawing a diagram based on the information given in the first two sentences, then add to the diagram as new information is added. Can you visualize all the points that are 60 meters from the tree stump? Mark them on your diagram. They should lie on a circle. The treasure is also 40 meters from the boulder. All the possible points lie in a circle around the boulder. The two possible spots where the treasure might be buried are the points where the two circles intersect.

Explore different types of solutions for Example B using the **Dynamic Geometry Exploration** in your ebook.

Tree stump   Boulder

T 80 m B

Initial diagram

60 m

T B

Improved diagram

Treasure here

60 m   40 m

T B

Or here

Final diagram

As in the previous example, when there is more than one point or even many points that satisfy a set of conditions, the set of points is called a **locus** (derived from the Latin word for location). The plural of locus is loci (pronounced "low-sigh").

A diagram can also help organize information to help make sense of difficult concepts. A **Venn diagram** represents larger groups that contain smaller groups as circles within circles, or ovals within ovals. For example, a larger circle for "high school students" would contain a smaller circle for "sophomores." Overlapping circles show that it is possible to belong to two different groups at the same time, such as "sophomores" and "geometry students."

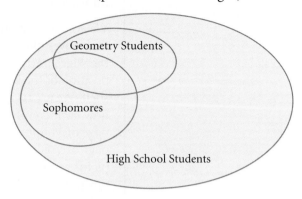

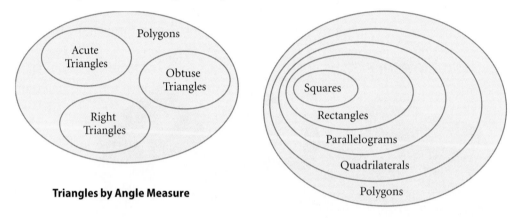

Triangles by Angle Measure

Squares as Special Polygons

Sometimes there is no overlap of groups as seen in the Venn diagram above left. Sometimes a group can be nested within a group that is nested within another group as seen in the Venn diagram above right.

2.1 Exercises

1. Surgeons, engineers, carpenters, plumbers, electricians, and furniture movers all rely on trained experience with visual thinking. Describe how one of these tradespeople or someone in another occupation uses visual thinking in his or her work.

Read each problem, determine what you are trying to find, draw a diagram, and solve the problem.

2. In the city of Rectangulus, all the streets running east–west are numbered and those streets running north–south are lettered. The even-numbered streets are one-way east and the odd-numbered streets are one-way west. All the vowel-lettered avenues are one-way north and the rest are two-way. Can a car traveling south on S Street make a legal left turn onto 14th Street? Explain.

3. Midway through a 2000-meter race, a photo is taken of five runners. It shows Meg 20 meters behind Edith. Edith is 50 meters ahead of Wanda, who is 20 meters behind Olivia. Olivia is 40 meters behind Nadine. Who is ahead? In your diagram, use *M* for Meg, *E* for Edith, and so on.

4. Mary Ann is building a fence around the outer edge of a rectangular garden plot that measures 25 feet by 45 feet. She will set the posts 5 feet apart. How many posts will she need?

5. Freddie the Frog is at the bottom of a 30-foot well. Each day he jumps up 3 feet, but then, during the night, he slides back down 2 feet. How many days will it take Freddie to get to the top and out? ⓗ

6. This is a good example of a difficult-sounding problem becoming clear once a diagram has been made. Try it. ⓗ

A 30-foot electric line is suspended between the tops of two 20-foot electric poles on level ground. The lowest point of the line is 5 feet above the ground. What is the distance between the two electric poles?

7. Points *A* and *B* lie in a plane. Sketch the locus of points in *the plane* that are equally distant from points *A* and *B*. Sketch the locus of points in *space* that are equally distant from points *A* and *B*. ⓗ

8. Draw an angle. Label it ∠*A*. Sketch the locus of points in the plane of angle *A* that are the same distance from the two sides of angle *A*.

9. Line *AB* lies in plane $\mathcal{P}$. Sketch the locus of points in plane $\mathcal{P}$ that are 3 cm from $\overleftrightarrow{AB}$. Sketch the locus of points in space that are 3 cm from $\overleftrightarrow{AB}$.

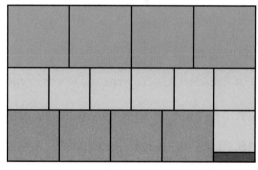

10. The rectangle shown to the right is divided into four green squares, seven gold squares, four orange squares and one blue rectangle. If the perimeter of the blue rectangle is 20 cm, what is the perimeter of the larger rectangle? Explain your reasoning.

11. Create a Venn diagram showing the relationships among scalene, isosceles, and equilateral triangles.

12. Create a Venn diagram showing the relationships among squares, rhombuses, rectangles, and parallelograms.

13. Create a Venn diagram showing the relationships among trapezoids, isosceles trapezoids, polygons, quadrilaterals, triangles, and isosceles triangles.

14. Beth Mack and her dog Trouble are exploring in the woods east of Birnam Woods Road, which runs north-south. They begin walking in a zigzag pattern: 1 km south, 1 km west, 1 km south, 2 km west, 1 km south, 3 km west, and so on. They walk at the rate of 4 km/h. If they started 15 km east of Birnam Woods Road at 3:00 p.m., and the sun sets at 7:30 p.m., will they reach Birnam Woods Road before sunset? Explain.

In geometry you will use visual thinking all the time. In Exercises 15 and 16 you will be asked to locate and recognize congruent geometric figures even if they are in different positions due to translations (slides), rotations (turns), or reflections (flips).

15. If trapezoid *ABCD* were rotated 90° counterclockwise about (0, 0), to what (*x, y*) location would points *A, B, C,* and *D* be relocated? Ⓗ

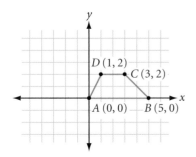

16. If △*CYN* were reflected across the *y*-axis, to what location would points *C, N,* and *Y* be relocated?

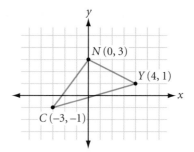

Review

For Exercises 17–26, write the words or the symbols that make the statement true.

17. The three undefined terms of geometry are ?, ?, and ?.

18. "Line *AB*" may be written using a symbol as ?.

19. "Arc *AB*" may be written using a symbol as ?.

20. The point where the two sides of an angle meet is the ? of the angle.

21. "Ray *AB*" may be written using a symbol as ?.

22. "Line *AB* is parallel to segment *CD*" is written in symbolic form as ?.

23. The geometry tool you use to measure an angle is a ?.

24. "Angle *ABC*" is written in symbolic form as ?.

25. The sentence "Segment *AB* is perpendicular to line *CD*" is written in symbolic form as ?.

26. The angle formed by a light ray coming into a mirror is ? the angle formed by a light ray leaving the mirror.

27. Sketch the next two figures in the pattern below. If this pattern were to continue, what would be the perimeter of the eighth figure in the pattern? (Assume the length of each segment is 1 cm.) ⓗ

28. A tabletop represents a plane. Examine the combination of points and lines that hold each tabletop in place. Removing one point or line would cause the tabletop to wobble or fall. In geometry, we say that these combinations of points and lines **determine** a plane. For each photo, use geometric terms to describe what determines the plane represented by the tabletop.

DEVELOPING MATHEMATICAL REASONING

Puzzling Patterns

These patterns are "different." Your task is to find the next term.

1. 18, 46, 94, 63, 52, 61, ?
2. O, T, T, F, F, S, S, E, N, ?
3. 1, 4, 3, 16, 5, 36, 7, ?
4. 4, 8, 61, 221, 244, 884, ?
5. 6, 8, 5, 10, 3, 14, 1, ?
6. B, 0, C, 2, D, 0, E, 3, F, 3, G, ?
7. 2, 3, 6, 1, 8, 6, 8, 4, 8, 4, 8, 3, 2, 3, 2, 3, ?
8. A E F H I K L M N T V W
    B C D G J O P Q R S U
    Where do the X, Y, and Z go?

Inductive Reasoning

As a child, you learned by experimenting with the natural world around you. You learned how to walk, to talk, and to ride your first bicycle, all by trial and error. From experience you learned to turn a water faucet on with a counterclockwise motion and to turn it off with a clockwise motion. You achieved most of your learning by a process called **inductive reasoning**. It is the process of observing data, recognizing patterns, and making generalizations about those patterns.

Geometry is rooted in inductive reasoning. In ancient Egypt and Babylonia, geometry began when people developed procedures for measurement after much experience and observation. Assessors and surveyors used these procedures to calculate land areas and to reestablish the boundaries of agricultural fields after floods. Engineers used the procedures

> **Language**
> **CONNECTION**
>
> The word "geometry" means "measure of the earth" and was originally inspired by the ancient Egyptians. The ancient Egyptians devised a complex system of land surveying in order to reestablish land boundaries that were erased each spring by the annual flooding of the Nile River.

to build canals, reservoirs, and the Great Pyramids. Throughout this course you will use inductive reasoning. You will perform investigations, observe similarities and patterns, and make many discoveries that you can use to solve problems.

Inductive reasoning guides scientists, investors, and business managers. All of these professionals use past experience to assess what is likely to happen in the future.

When you use inductive reasoning to make a generalization, the generalization is called a **conjecture**. Consider the following example from science.

EXAMPLE A

A scientist dips a platinum wire into a solution containing salt (sodium chloride), passes the wire over a flame, and observes that it produces an orange-yellow flame.

She does this with many other solutions that contain salt, finding that they all produce an orange-yellow flame. Make a conjecture based on her findings.

Solution

The scientist tested many other solutions containing salt and found no counterexamples. You should conjecture: "If a solution contains sodium chloride, then in a flame test it produces an orange-yellow flame."

Like scientists, mathematicians often use inductive reasoning to make discoveries. For example, a mathematician might use inductive reasoning to find patterns in a number sequence. Once she knows the pattern, she can find the next term.

EXAMPLE B

Consider the sequence

2, 4, 7, 11, . . .

Make a conjecture about the rule for generating the sequence. Then find the next three terms.

Solution

Look at the numbers you add to get each term. The 1st term in the sequence is 2. You add 2 to find the 2nd term. Then you add 3 to find the 3rd term, and so on.

$$\begin{array}{cccc} & +2 & +3 & +4 \\ 2, & 4, & 7, & 11 \end{array}$$

You can conjecture that if the pattern continues, you always add the next counting number to get the next term. The next three terms in the sequence will be 16, 22, and 29.

$$\begin{array}{cccc} & +5 & +6 & +7 \\ 11, & 16, & 22, & 29 \end{array}$$

In the following investigation you will use inductive reasoning to recognize a pattern in a series of drawings and use it to find a term much farther out in a sequence.

 INVESTIGATION

Shape Shifters

Look at the sequence of shapes below. Pay close attention to the patterns that occur in every other shape.

Step 1 What patterns do you notice in the 1st, 3rd, and 5th shapes?

Step 2 What patterns do you notice in the 2nd, 4th, and 6th shapes?

Step 3 Draw the next two shapes in the sequence.

Step 4 Use the patterns you discovered to draw the 25th shape.

Step 5 Describe the 30th shape in the sequence. You do not have to draw it!

Sometimes a conjecture is difficult to find because the data collected are unorganized or the observer is mistaking coincidence with cause and effect. Good use of inductive reasoning depends on the quantity and quality of data. Sometimes not enough information or data have been collected to make a proper conjecture. For example, if you are asked to find the next term in the pattern 3, 5, 7, you might conjecture that the next term is 9—the next odd number. Someone else might notice that the pattern is the consecutive odd primes and say that the next term is 11. If the pattern were 3, 5, 7, 11, 13, what would you be more likely to conjecture?

2.2 Exercises

1. On his way to the local Hunting and Gathering Convention, caveperson Stony Grok picks up a rock, drops it into a lake, and notices that it sinks. He picks up a second rock, drops it into the lake, and notices that it also sinks. He does this five more times. Each time, the rock sinks straight to the bottom of the lake. Stony conjectures: "Ura nok seblu," which translates to ?. What counterexample would Stony Grok need to find to disprove, or at least to refine, his conjecture? ⓗ

2. Sean draws these geometric figures on paper. His sister Courtney measures each angle with a protractor. They add the measures of each pair of angles to form a conjecture. Write their conjecture.

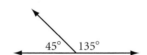

For Exercises 3–10, use inductive reasoning to find the next two terms in each sequence.

3. 1, 10, 100, 1000, ?, ?

4. $\frac{1}{6}, \frac{1}{3}, \frac{1}{2}, \frac{2}{3}$, ?, ? ⓗ

5. 7, 3, −1, −5, −9, −13, ?, ?

6. 1, 3, 6, 10, 15, 21, ?, ?

7. 1, 1, 2, 3, 5, 8, 13, ?, ? ⓗ

8. 1, 4, 9, 16, 25, 36, ?, ? ⓗ

9. 32, 30, 26, 20, 12, 2, ?, ?

10. 1, 2, 4, 8, 16, 32, ?, ?

For Exercises 11–16, use inductive reasoning to draw the next shape in each picture pattern.

11.

12.

13.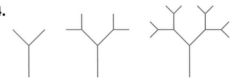

14.

15.

16.

Use the rule provided to generate the first five terms of the sequence in Exercise 17 and the next five terms of the sequence in Exercise 18.

17. $3n - 2$ ⓗ

18. $1, 3, 6, 10, \ldots, \dfrac{n(n+1)}{2}, \ldots$

19. Now it's your turn. Generate the first five terms of a sequence. Give the sequence to a member of your family or to a friend and ask him or her to find the next two terms in the sequence. Can he or she find your pattern?

20. Write the first five terms of two different sequences in which 12 is the 3rd term.

21. Think of a situation in which you have used inductive reasoning. Write a paragraph describing what happened and explaining why you think you used inductive reasoning. ⓗ

22. The sequence 2, 6, 12, 20, 30, 42, . . . is called a rectangular number pattern because the terms can be visualized as rectangular arrangements of dots. What would be the 7th term in this sequence? What would be the 10th term? The 25th term? ⓗ

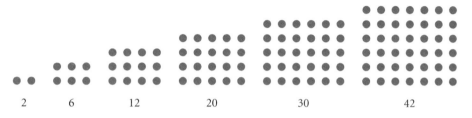

23. Look at the pattern in these pairs of equations. Decide if the conjecture is true. If it is true, explain why. If it is not true, find a counterexample and explain why it is not true.

$12^2 = 144$ and $21^2 = 441$
$13^2 = 169$ and $31^2 = 961$
$103^2 = 10609$ and $301^2 = 90601$
$112^2 = 12544$ and $211^2 = 44521$

Conjecture: If two numbers have the same digits in reverse order, then the squares of those numbers will have identical digits, but in reverse order.

24. Study the pattern and make a conjecture by completing the fifth line. What would be the conjecture for the sixth line? What about for the tenth line? ⓗ

$1 \cdot 1 = 1$
$11 \cdot 11 = 121$
$111 \cdot 111 = 12{,}321$
$1{,}111 \cdot 1{,}111 = 1{,}234{,}321$
$11{,}111 \cdot 11{,}111 = \underline{\ ?\ }$

Review

For Exercises 25–27, sketch the cross-section formed when the cone is sliced by the plane, as shown.

25.

26.

27.

28. Sketch the three-dimensional figure formed by folding the net below into a solid. ⓗ

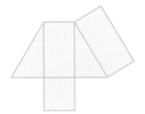

29. Sketch the figure shown below, but with the red edge vertical and facing you. ⓗ

30. Sketch the solid of rotation formed when the two-dimensional figure is rotated about the line.

For Exercises 31–40, write the word that makes the statement true.

31. Points are ? if they lie on the same line.

32. A triangle with two congruent sides is ?.

33. A polygon with 12 sides is called a(n) ?.

34. A trapezoid has exactly one pair of ? sides.

35. The geometry tool used to measure the size of an angle in degrees is called a(n) ?.

36. A(n) ? of a circle connects its center to a point on the circle.

37. A segment connecting any two non-adjacent vertices in a polygon is called a(n) ?.

38. A(n) ? polygon is both equiangular and equilateral.

39. If angles are complementary, then their measures add to ?.

40. If two lines intersect to form a right angle, then they are ?.

41. Use your ruler and protractor to draw a triangle with angles measuring 40° and 60° and a side between them with length 9 cm. Explain your method. Can you draw a second triangle using the same instructions that is not congruent to the first? Sketch your result.

42. Reflect isosceles right $\triangle ABC$ across the y-axis to create $\triangle A'B'C'$. What are the coordinates of A', B', and C'? Is $\triangle A'B'C'$ a right isosceles triangle? Explain why or why not.

43. Reflect right $\triangle DEF$ across the line $y = 3$ to create $\triangle D'E'F'$. What are the coordinates of D', E', and F'? Is $\triangle D'E'F'$ a right triangle? Explain why or why not.

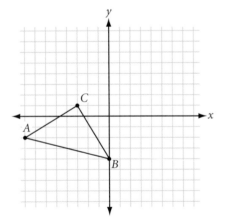

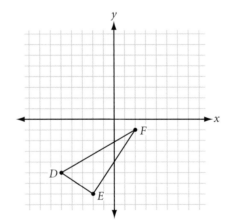

For Exercises 44–47, sketch and label the figure.

44. Pentagon *GIANT* with diagonal $\overline{AG}$ parallel to side $\overline{NT}$

45. A quadrilateral that has reflectional symmetry, but not rotational symmetry

46. A prism with a hexagonal base

47. A counterexample to show that the following statement is false: The diagonals of a kite bisect the angles. ⓗ

Mathematical Modeling

"It's amazing what one can do when one doesn't know what one can't do."

GARFIELD THE CAT

Physical models have many of the same features as the original object or activity they represent, but are often more convenient to study. For example, building a new airplane and testing it is difficult and expensive. But you can analyze a new airplane design by building a model and testing it in a wind tunnel.

In Chapter 1 you learned that geometry ideas such as points, lines, planes, triangles, polygons, and diagonals are **mathematical models** of physical objects.

3D computer image of a prototype car.

When you draw graphs or pictures of situations or when you write equations that describe a problem, you are creating mathematical models. A physical model of a complicated telecommunications network, for example, might not be practical, but you can draw a mathematical model of the network using points and lines.

Computer aided design software can be used to create 3D models on this 3D printer.

In this investigation you will attempt to solve a problem first by acting it out, then by creating a mathematical model.

 INVESTIGATION

Party Handshakes

Each of the 30 people at a party shook hands with everyone else. How many handshakes were there altogether?

Step 1 Act out this problem with members of your group. Collect data for "parties" of one, two, three, and four people, and record your results in a table.

People	1	2	3	4	…	30
Handshakes	0	1			…	

Step 2 Look for a pattern. Generalize from your pattern to find the 30th term.

Acting out a problem is a powerful problem-solving strategy that can give you important insight into a solution. Were you able to make a generalization from just four terms? If so, how confident are you of your generalization? To collect more data, you can ask more classmates to join your group. You can see, however, that acting out a problem sometimes has its practical limitations. That's when you can use mathematical models.

Step 3 Model the problem by using points to represent people and line segments connecting the points to represent handshakes.

Record your results in a table like this one:

Number of points (people)	1	2	3	4	5	6	...	n	...	30
Number of segments (handshakes)	0	1						...	...	

Notice that the pattern does not have a constant difference. That is, the rule is not a linear function. So we need to look for a different kind of rule.

3 points
2 segments per
vertex

4 points
3 segments per
vertex

5 points
_?_ segments per
vertex

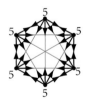

6 points
_?_ segments per
vertex

Step 4 Refer to the table you made for Step 3. The pattern of differences is increasing by one: 1, 2, 3, 4, 5, 6, 7. Read the dialogue between Erin and Stephanie as they attempt to use logical reasoning to find the rule.

In the diagram with 3 vertices, there are 2 segments from each vertex.

If there are 2 segments from each of the 3 vertices, why isn't the rule 2 · 3, or 6 segments?

Because you are counting each segment twice, the answer is really $\frac{3 \cdot 2}{2}$, or 3 segments.

So in the diagram with 4 vertices, there are 3 segments from each vertex …

Right, but each segment got counted twice. So divide by 2.

… so there are $\frac{4 \cdot 3}{2}$, or 6 segments.

3

3 · 2

$\frac{3 \cdot 2}{2}$

4

4 · 3

$\frac{4 \cdot 3}{2}$

Let's continue with Stephanie and Erin's line of reasoning.

Step 5 In the diagram with 5 vertices, how many segments are there from each vertex? So the total number of segments written in factored form is $\frac{5 \cdot ?}{2}$.

Step 6 Complete the table below by expressing the total number of segments in factored form.

Number of points (people)	1	2	3	4	5	6	...	n
Number of segments (handshakes)	$\frac{(1)(0)}{2}$	$\frac{(2)(1)}{2}$	$\frac{(3)(2)}{2}$	$\frac{(4)(3)}{2}$	$\frac{(5)(?)}{2}$	$\frac{(6)(?)}{2}$	...	$\frac{(?)(?)}{2}$

Step 7 The larger of the two factors in the numerator represents the number of points. What does the smaller of the two numbers in the numerator represent? Why do we divide by 2?

Step 8 How many handshakes were there at the party with 30 people? How many handshakes are there for n people?

Fifteen pool balls can be arranged in a triangle, so 15 is a triangular number.

The numbers in the pattern in the previous investigation are called the **triangular numbers** because you can arrange them into a triangular pattern of dots.

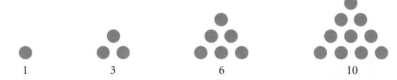

The triangular numbers appear in many geometric situations, as you will see in the exercises. They are related to this sequence of **rectangular numbers**:

2, 6, 12, 20, 30, 42, . . .

Rectangular numbers can be visualized as rectangular arrangements of objects, in which the length and width are factors of the numbers.

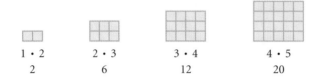

In this sequence, the width is equal to the term number and the length is one more than the term number. The rectangle representing the 3rd term, for instance, has width 3 and length $3 + 1$, or 4, so the total number of squares is equal to $3 \cdot 4$, or 12. You can apply this pattern to find any term in the sequence. The 25th rectangle, for example, would have width 25, length 26, and a total number of squares equal to $25 \cdot 26$, or 650.

In general, the nth rectangle in this sequence has a width equal to the term number, n, and a length equal to one more than the term number, or $n + 1$. So the nth rectangular number is $n(n + 1)$.

Here is a visual approach to arrive at the rule for the party handshakes problem. If we arrange the triangular numbers in stacks,

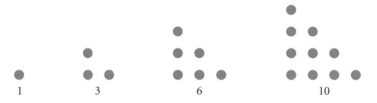

you can see below that each is half of a rectangular number, $n(n + 1)$.

So the triangular array has $\dfrac{n(n + 1)}{2}$ dots.

2.3 Exercises

For Exercises 1–6, draw the next figure. Complete a table and find the *n*th term. Then find the 35th term.

1. Lines passing through the same point are **concurrent**. Into how many regions do 35 concurrent lines divide the plane?

Lines	1	2	3	4	5	...	*n*	...	35
Regions	2					...		...	

2. Into how many regions do 35 parallel lines in a plane divide that plane?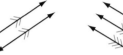

3. How many diagonals can you draw from one vertex in a polygon with 35 sides?

  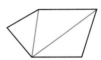

4. What's the total number of diagonals in a 35-sided polygon? *(h)*

5. If you place 35 points on a piece of paper so that no three points are in a line, how many line segments are necessary to connect each point to all the others? *(h)*

6. If you draw 35 lines on a piece of paper so that no two lines are parallel to each other and no three lines are concurrent, how many times will they intersect? *(h)*

  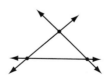

7. Look at the formulas you found in Exercises 4–6. Describe how the formulas are related. Then explain how the three problems are related geometrically.

For Exercises 8–9, draw a diagram, find the appropriate geometric model, and solve.

8. If each team in a ten-team league plays each of the other teams four times in a season, how many league games are played during one season? What geometric figures can you use to model teams and games played? *(h)*

9. Each person at a party shook hands with everyone else exactly once. There were 66 handshakes. How many people were at the party?

Review

For Exercises 10–18, identify the statement as true or false. For each false statement, explain why it is false and sketch a counterexample.

10. The largest chord of a circle is a diameter of the circle.

11. The vertex of ∠*TOP* is point *O*.

12. An isosceles right triangle is a triangle with an angle measuring 90° and no two sides congruent.

13. If $\overleftrightarrow{AB}$ intersects $\overleftrightarrow{CD}$ in point *E*, then ∠*AED* and ∠*BED* form a linear pair of angles. ⓗ

14. If two lines lie in the same plane and are perpendicular to the same line, they are perpendicular.

15. The opposite sides of a kite are never parallel.

16. A rectangle is a parallelogram with all sides congruent.

17. A line segment that connects any two vertices in a polygon is called a diagonal.

18. To show that two lines are parallel, you mark them with the same number of arrowheads.

19. The sequence 2, 9, 20, 35, . . . is another example of a rectangular number pattern, as illustrated in the art below. What is the 50th term of this sequence? ⓗ

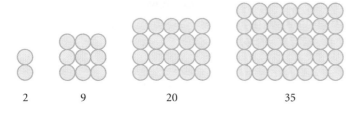

2   9   20   35

For Exercises 20 and 21, find the lengths *x* and *y*. (Every angle on each block is a right angle.)

20.

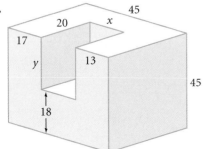

21.

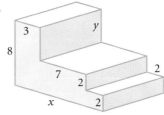

110 CHAPTER 2 Reasoning in Geometry

In Exercises 22 and 23, each figure represents a two-dimensional figure with a wire attached. The three-dimensional solid formed by spinning the figure on the wire between your fingers is called a **solid of revolution**. Sketch the solid of revolution formed by each two-dimensional figure.

22. ⓗ

23.

A real-life example of a "solid of revolution" is a clay pot on a potter's wheel.

DEVELOPING MATHEMATICAL REASONING

Knight's Tour Puzzle 1

The Knight in chess moves on the diagonal of a 2 × 3 rectangle. The knight's move is shown in the photo below left. The original Knight's Tour Puzzle asks, *"Is it possible to move the chess knight so it visits each square of an empty 8 × 8 chessboard exactly once?"* The answer is yes, not only is it possible, but it is possible to start anywhere on the board and complete the tour so that the knight ends one knight's move away from the starting square! This is called a **closed knight's tour**. One of the trillions of closed knight's tours is shown below right. If the knight visits every square exactly once but does not end one knight's move away from the starting point, the tour is an **open knight's tour**.

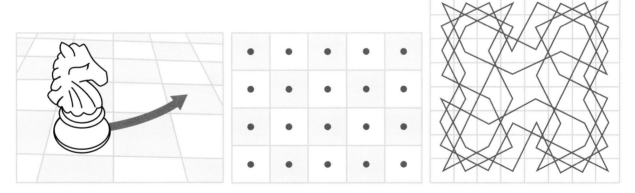

Your task in this puzzle is to create an open knight's tour on the 4 × 5 grid of squares above center.

Coordinate Properties
of Transformations

In earlier lessons, you reflected, translated, and rotated polygons with the aid of patty paper. In this lesson you will learn to do this on a coordinate plane. To create a transformation in the coordinate plane we create an ordered pair rule that describes how the points are to be transformed. Let's look at an example.

EXAMPLE A | Transform the polygon at right using the ordered pair rule $(x, y) \rightarrow (x + 2, y - 3)$. Describe the type of transformation.

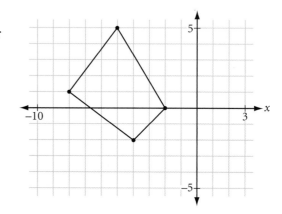

Solution | Apply the rule to each ordered pair. Every point of the polygon moves right 2 units and down 3 units. The transformation is a translation.

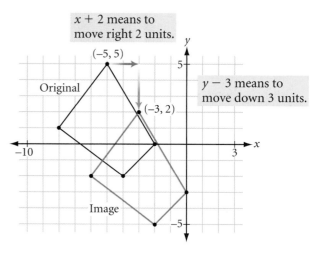

$x + 2$ means to move right 2 units.

$y - 3$ means to move down 3 units.

In general, for any point on a figure, the ordered pair rule $(x, y) \rightarrow (x + h, y + k)$ results in a horizontal move of h units and a vertical move of k units for any numbers h and k. That is, if (x, y) is a point on the original figure, $(x + h, y + k)$ is its corresponding point on the image.

An ordered pair rule can also be written as a **vector**. As shown at right, a vector is named by its horizontal and vertical components. The **translation vector** for the example above is $\langle 2, -3 \rangle$.

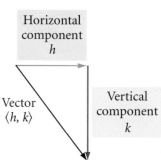

Horizontal component h

Vector $\langle h, k \rangle$

Vertical component k

Let's look at another example to see how an ordered pair rule can create a reflection transformation.

EXAMPLE B

Transform the polygon at right using the ordered pair rule $(x, y) \rightarrow (x, -y)$. Describe the type of transformation.

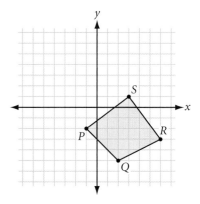

Solution

Apply the rule to the ordered pair for each vertex. The rule says "Every x-coordinate stays the same and every y-coordinate changes sign." Therefore $P(-1, -2)$ becomes $P'(-1, 2)$, $Q(2, -5)$ becomes $Q'(2, 5)$, $R(6, -3)$ becomes $R'(6, 3)$, and $S(3, 1)$ becomes $S'(3, -1)$. A transformation by the ordered pair rule $(x, y) \rightarrow (x, -y)$ is a reflection across the x-axis.

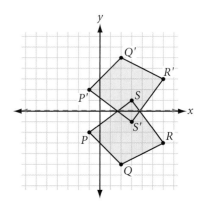

Let's look at another example to see how an ordered pair rule can create a rotation transformation.

EXAMPLE C

Transform the polygon at right using the ordered pair rule $(x, y) \rightarrow (y, -x)$. Describe the type of transformation.

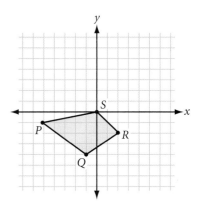

Solution

Apply the rule to the ordered pair for each vertex. The rule says "Take every x-coordinate, change its sign and it becomes the y-coordinate and every y-coordinate becomes the x-coordinate after the transformation rule has been applied." Therefore $P(-5, -1)$ becomes $P'(-1, 5)$, $Q(-1, -4)$ becomes $Q'(-4, 1)$, $R(2, -2)$ becomes $R'(-2, -2)$, and $S(0, 0)$ becomes $S'(0, 0)$. A transformation by the ordered pair rule $(x, y) \rightarrow (y, -x)$ is a 90° rotation about the origin. If we compare any side to its image, for example $\overline{SR}$ to $\overline{S'R'}$, we see that the side has been rotated by 90° about the origin.

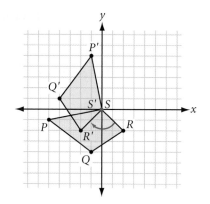

 # INVESTIGATION

Ordered Pair Rules

So far you have seen in the previous examples that:

- The ordered pair rule $(x, y) \rightarrow (x + h, y + k)$ is a translation transformation by the vector $<h, k>$.
- The ordered pair rule $(x, y) \rightarrow (x, -y)$ is a reflection transformation across the x-axis.
- The ordered pair rule $(x, y) \rightarrow (y, -x)$ is a 90° clockwise rotation transformation about the origin.

In this investigation you will discover the transformations created by the following ordered pair rules:

- The ordered pair rule $(x, y) \rightarrow (-x, y)$.
- The ordered pair rule $(x, y) \rightarrow (-x, -y)$.
- The ordered pair rule $(x, y) \rightarrow (y, x)$.
- The ordered pair rule $(x, y) \rightarrow (-y, x)$.
- The ordered pair rule $(x, y) \rightarrow (-y, -x)$.

Step 1 On graph paper, create and label five sets of coordinate axes. Draw the same polygon in the same position in the same quadrant of each of the five graphs and write one of the above ordered pair rules below each graph.

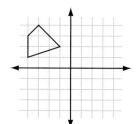

Step 2 Use the ordered pair rule you assigned to each graph to relocate the vertices of your polygon and create its image.

Step 3 Use patty paper to see if your transformation is a reflection, translation, or rotation. Compare your results with those of your group members and share your reasoning.

Step 4 Complete the conjectures below. Be as specific as possible (not just *reflection* or *rotation*). If, for example, it is a reflection, identify the line of reflection. If it is a rotation, identify the center of rotation and the number of degrees in the clockwise rotation.

> **Coordinate Transformations Conjecture**
>
> The ordered pair rule $(x, y) \rightarrow (-x, y)$ is a __?__.
>
> The ordered pair rule $(x, y) \rightarrow (-x, -y)$ is a __?__.
>
> The ordered pair rule $(x, y) \rightarrow (y, x)$ is a __?__.
>
> The ordered pair rule $(x, y) \rightarrow (-y, x)$ is a __?__.
>
> The ordered pair rule $(x, y) \rightarrow (-y, -x)$ is a __?__.

Exercises

For Exercises 1–3, translate each quadrilateral by the given vector.

1. $<-4, 3>$

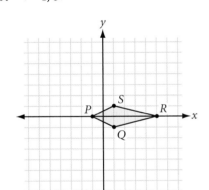

2. $<0, 4>$

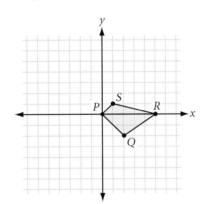

3. $<-3, 0>$

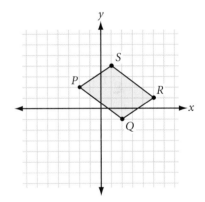

For Exercises 4–6, reflect each quadrilateral by the given ordered pair rule. Identify the line of reflection.

4. $(x, y) \rightarrow (x, -y)$ ⓗ

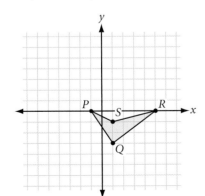

5. $(x, y) \rightarrow (-x, y)$

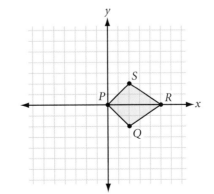

6. $(x, y) \rightarrow (y, x)$

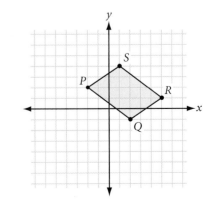

For Exercises 7–9, transform each quadrilateral by the given ordered pair rule. Identify either the line of reflection or the center of rotation.

7. $(x, y) \rightarrow (y, -x)$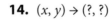

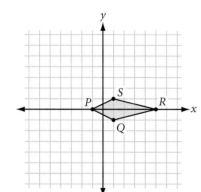

8. $(x, y) \rightarrow (-y, x)$

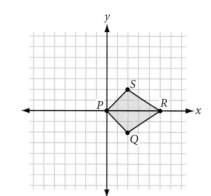

9. $(x, y) \rightarrow (-y, -x)$

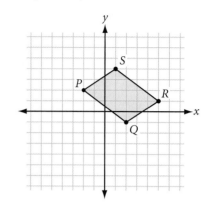

For Exercises 10–12, transform each quadrilateral by the given ordered pair rule. Explain how these transformations are different than the previous transformations.

10. $(x, y) \rightarrow (x, 3y)$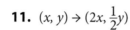

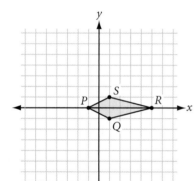

11. $(x, y) \rightarrow (2x, \frac{1}{2}y)$

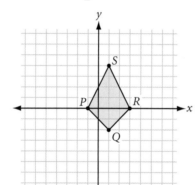

12. $(x, y) \rightarrow (3x, 3y)$

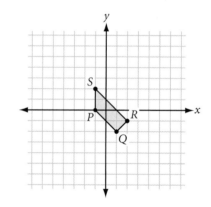

For Exercises 13–24 describe the type of transformation. Then find the ordered pair rule that transformed the blue/green triangle $\triangle PQR$ to the blue/green triangle $\triangle P'Q'R'$.

13. $(x, y) \rightarrow (?, ?)$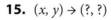

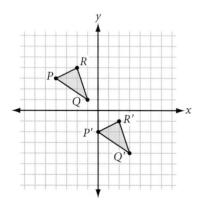

14. $(x, y) \rightarrow (?, ?)$

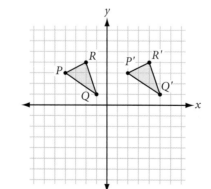

15. $(x, y) \rightarrow (?, ?)$

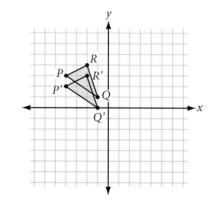

16. $(x, y) \rightarrow (?, ?)$ ⓗ

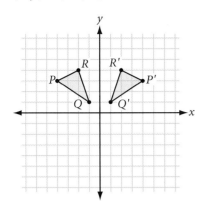

17. $(x, y) \rightarrow (?, ?)$

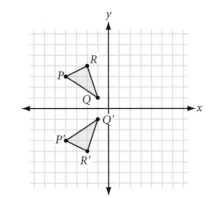

18. $(x, y) \rightarrow (?, ?)$

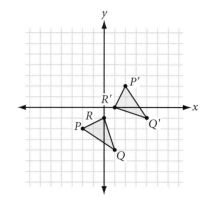

19. $(x, y) \rightarrow (?, ?)$ ⓗ

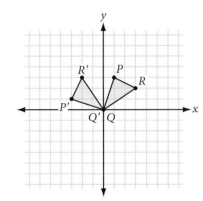

20. $(x, y) \rightarrow (?, ?)$

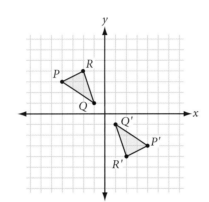

21. $(x, y) \rightarrow (?, ?)$

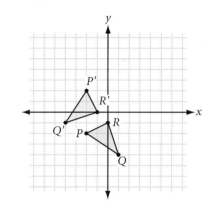

22. $(x, y) \rightarrow (?, ?)$ ⓗ

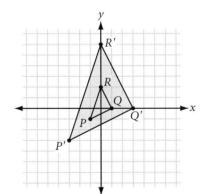

23. $(x, y) \rightarrow (?, ?)$

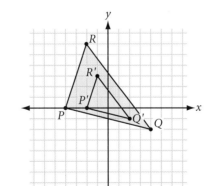

24. $(x, y) \rightarrow (?, ?)$

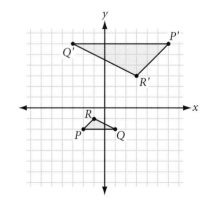

25. Given $\triangle ABC$ with vertices: $A(2, -2)$, $B(7, -4)$, $C(5, 1)$. Transform $\triangle ABC$ by the ordered pair rule $(x, y) \rightarrow (-x, y)$ to create $\triangle A'B'C'$. What are the coordinates of the vertices of $\triangle A'B'C'$? What type of transformation is that? What is the ordered pair rule that transforms $\triangle A'B'C'$ to $\triangle ABC$?

26. Given quadrilateral $PQRS$ with vertices: $P(-5, -3)$, $Q(-4, -6)$, $R(0, -2)$ and $S(-4, -1)$. Transform quadrilateral $PQRS$ by $(x, y) \rightarrow (-x, -y)$ to create quadrilateral $P'Q'R'S'$. What are the coordinates of the vertices of quadrilateral $P'Q'R'S'$? What type of transformation is that? What is the ordered pair rule that transforms $P'Q'R'S'$ to $PQRS$?

27. Given $\triangle ABC$ with vertices: $A(-5, -5)$, $B(-1, -6)$, $C(-3, -1)$.

    a. Reflect $\triangle ABC$ across the y-axis to create $\triangle A'B'C'$.

    b. What are the coordinates of the vertices of $\triangle A'B'C'$?

    c. What is the transformation rule, $(x, y) \to (?, ?)$, that transforms $\triangle ABC$ to $\triangle A'B'C'$?

    d. What is the transformation rule, $(x, y) \to (?, ?)$, that transforms $\triangle A'B'C'$ to $\triangle ABC$?

28. Given $\triangle ABC$ with vertices: $A(-6, 5)$, $B(-3, 1)$, $C(-2, 7)$ and $\triangle DEF$ with vertices: $D(3, 1)$, $E(4, 7)$, $F(0, 5)$.

    a. Do the two triangles appear to be congruent?

    b. If they are congruent, what is the statement of congruence, $(\triangle ABC \cong \triangle ???)$?

    c. If congruent, what is the single transformation rule that takes $\triangle ABC$ onto $\triangle DEF$?

    d. If they are not congruent, explain why not.

For Exercises 29–36 match the composition of transformations with the ordered pair rule.

29. $(x, y) \to (x + h, y + k)$ **a.** 90° clockwise rotation about the origin.

30. $(x, y) \to (x, -y)$ **b.** reflection across the x-axis.

31. $(x, y) \to (y, -x)$ **c.** 90° counterclockwise rotation about the origin.

32. $(x, y) \to (-x, y)$ **d.** reflection across the y-axis.

33. $(x, y) \to (-x, -y)$ **e.** translation by the vector $<h, k>$.

34. $(x, y) \to (y, x)$ **f.** reflection across the line $y = x$.

35. $(x, y) \to (-y, x)$ **g.** reflection across the line $y = -x$.

36. $(x, y) \to (-y, -x)$ **h.** 180° rotation about the origin.

DEVELOPING MATHEMATICAL REASONING

Logical Translation Puzzle

Upon arriving in the land of Ogor, the explorer Jenny Nomo learns "lo-er-moi" means "chase blue rabbit," "wab-er" means "blue dog," and "lo-gibby" means "crazy Rabbit." How do you say "chase crazy dog" in the land of Ogor?

Deductive Reasoning

Have you ever noticed that the days are longer in the summer? Or that mosquitoes appear after a summer rain? Over the years you have made conjectures, using inductive reasoning, based on patterns you have observed. When you make a conjecture, the process of discovery may not always help explain *why* the conjecture works. You need another kind of reasoning to help answer this question.

Deductive reasoning is the process of showing that certain statements follow logically from agreed-upon assumptions and proven facts. When you use deductive reasoning, you try to reason in an orderly way to convince yourself or someone else that your conclusion is valid. If your initial statements are true and you give a logical argument, then you have shown that your conclusion is true. For example, in a trial, lawyers use deductive arguments to show how the evidence that they present proves their case. A lawyer might make a very good argument. But first, the court must believe the evidence and accept it as true.

The success of an attorney's case depends on the jury accepting the evidence as true and following the steps in his deductive reasoning.

You use deductive reasoning in algebra. When you provide a reason for each step in the process of solving an equation, you are using deductive reasoning. Here is an example.

EXAMPLE A

Solve the equation for x. Give a reason for each step in the process.

$$3(2x + 1) + 2(2x + 1) + 7 = 42 - 5x$$

Solution

$3(2x + 1) + 2(2x + 1) + 7 = 42 - 5x$	The original equation.
$6x + 3 + 4x + 2 + 7 = 42 - 5x$	Distribute.
$10x + 12 = 42 - 5x$	Combine like terms.
$10x = 30 - 5x$	Subtract 12 from both sides.
$15x = 30$	Add $5x$ to both sides.
$x = 2$	Divide both sides by 15.

The next example shows how to use both kinds of reasoning: inductive reasoning to discover the property and deductive reasoning to explain why it works.

EXAMPLE B

In each diagram, $\overrightarrow{AC}$ bisects $\angle BAD$. Classify $\angle BAD$, $\angle DAC$, and $\angle CAB$ as acute, right, or obtuse. Then complete the conjecture.

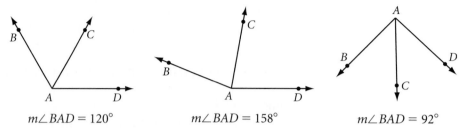

$m\angle BAD = 120°$ $m\angle BAD = 158°$ $m\angle BAD = 92°$

Conjecture: If an obtuse angle is bisected, then the two newly formed congruent angles are ? .

Justify your conjecture with a deductive argument.

Solution

In each diagram, $\angle BAD$ is obtuse because $m\angle BAD$ is greater than 90°. In each diagram, the angles formed by the bisector are acute because their measures—60°, 79°, and 46°—are less than 90°. So one possible conjecture is

Conjecture: If an obtuse angle is bisected, then the two newly formed congruent angles are acute.

To explain why this is true, a useful reasoning strategy is to represent the situation algebraically. Let's use m to represent any angle measure.

Deductive Argument

By our definition, an angle measure is less than 180°.

$m < 180°$

When you bisect an angle, the newly formed angles each measure half the original angle.

$\frac{1}{2}m < \frac{1}{2}(180°)$

$\frac{1}{2}m < 90°$

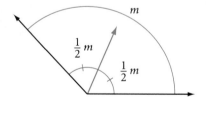

The new angles measure less than 90°, so they are acute.

Inductive reasoning allows you to discover new ideas based on observed patterns. Deductive reasoning can help explain why your conjectures are true.

Good use of deductive reasoning depends on the quality of the argument. Just like the saying "A chain is only as strong as its weakest link," a deductive argument is only as good (or as true) as the statements used in the argument. A conclusion in a deductive argument is true only if *all* the statements in the argument are true and the statements in your argument clearly follow from each other.

Inductive and deductive reasoning work very well together. In this investigation you will use inductive reasoning to form a conjecture. Then in your groups, you will use deductive reasoning to explain why it's true.

INVESTIGATION

Overlapping Segments

In each segment, $\overline{AB} \cong \overline{CD}$.

25 cm   75 cm   25 cm   36 cm   80 cm   36 cm
●—┼—●————————●—┼—●   ●—╫—●——————————●—╫—●
A   B   C   D   A   B   C   D

Step 1 From the markings on each diagram, determine the lengths of $\overline{AC}$ and $\overline{BD}$. What do you discover about these segments?

Step 2 Draw a new segment. Label it $\overline{AD}$. Place your own points B and C on $\overline{AD}$ so that $\overline{AB} \cong \overline{CD}$.

●—╫╫—●●—╫╫—●
A   B C   D

Step 3 Measure $\overline{AC}$ and $\overline{BD}$. How do these lengths compare?

Step 4 Complete the conclusion of this conjecture:

If $\overline{AD}$ has points A, B, C, and D in that order with $\overline{AB} \cong \overline{CD}$, then ? . (Overlapping Segments Conjecture)

DEVELOPING PROOF

In your groups, discuss how you can use logical reasoning to show that your conjecture from Step 4 will always be true. Remember, a useful reasoning strategy is to represent the situation algebraically. Then write down your ideas as a deductive argument.

In the investigation you used inductive reasoning to discover the Overlapping Segments Conjecture. In your group discussion you then used deductive reasoning to explain why this conjecture is always true. You will use a similar process to discover and prove the Overlapping Angles Conjecture in Exercises 10 and 11.

2.4 Exercises

1. When you use ? reasoning, you are generalizing (making a conjecture) from careful observation that something is probably true. When you use ? reasoning, you are establishing that if a set of properties is accepted as true, something else must be true.

2. $\angle A$ and $\angle B$ are complementary. $m\angle A = 25°$. What is $m\angle B$? What type of reasoning do you use, inductive or deductive, when solving this problem?

3. If the pattern continues, what are the next two terms? What type of reasoning do you use, inductive or deductive, when solving this problem?

 1   4   9   16

4. $\triangle DGT$ is isosceles with $TD = DG$. If the perimeter of $\triangle DGT$ is 756 cm and $GT = 240$ cm, then $DG = $? . What type of reasoning do you use, inductive or deductive, when solving this problem?

5. The sum of the measures of the five marked angles in stars A through C is shown below each star. Use your protractor to carefully measure the five marked angles in star D.

  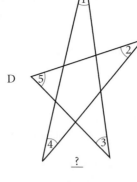 

A   B   C   D   E

180°   180°   180°   ?   ?

If this pattern continues, without measuring, make a conjecture. What would be the sum of the measures of the marked angles in star E? What type of reasoning do you use, inductive or deductive, when solving this problem?

6. The definition of a parallelogram says, "If both pairs of opposite sides of a quadrilateral are parallel, then the quadrilateral is a parallelogram." Quadrilateral *LNDA* has both pairs of opposite sides parallel. What conclusion can you make? What type of reasoning did you use?

7. **DEVELOPING PROOF** Using the ideas and algebra you discussed with your group, write a deductive argument for the Overlapping Segments Conjecture.

8. Use the Overlapping Segments Conjecture to complete each statement.

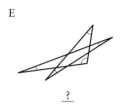

A *B*   *C* *D*

a. If *AB* = 3, then *CD* = _?_.

b. If *AC* = 10, then *BD* = _?_.

c. If *BC* = 4 and *CD* = 3, then *AC* = _?_.

9. **DEVELOPING PROOF** In Example B of this lesson you conjectured through inductive reasoning that if an obtuse angle is bisected, then the two newly formed congruent angles are acute. You then used deductive reasoning to explain why they were acute. Go back to the example and look at the sizes of the acute angles formed. What is the smallest possible size for the two congruent acute angles formed by the bisector of an obtuse angle? Use deductive reasoning to explain why. *(h)*

10. Do the geometry investigation and make a conjecture.

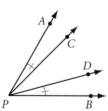

Given ∠*APB* with points *C* and *D* in its interior and *m*∠*APC* = *m*∠*DPB*,

If *m*∠*APD* = 48°, then *m*∠*CPB* = _?_
If *m*∠*CPB* = 17°, then *m*∠*APD* = _?_
If *m*∠*APD* = 62°, then *m*∠*CPB* = _?_

Conjecture: If points *C* and *D* lie in the interior of ∠*APB*, and *m*∠*APC* = *m*∠*DPB*, then *m*∠*APD* = _?_. (Overlapping Angles Conjecture)

11. **DEVELOPING PROOF** Using reasoning similar to that in Exercise 7, write a deductive argument to explain why the Overlapping Angles Conjecture is true.

Here is an example of inductive reasoning, supported by deductive reasoning. El Niño is the warming of water in the tropical Pacific Ocean, which produces unusual weather conditions and storms worldwide. For centuries, farmers living in the Andes Mountains of South America observed that if the stars in the Pleiades constellation look dim in June, an El Niño year was coming. What is the connection? Scientists recently found that in an El Niño year, increased evaporation from the ocean produces high-altitude clouds that are invisible to the eye but create a haze that makes stars more difficult to see. The pattern that Andean farmers knew about for centuries is now supported by a scientific explanation.

12. Think of a situation you observed outside of school in which deductive reasoning was used correctly. Write a paragraph or two describing what happened and explaining why you think it called for deductive reasoning.

Review

13. Mark Twain once observed that the lower Mississippi River is very crooked and that over the years, as the bends and the turns straighten out, the river gets shorter and shorter. Using numerical data about the length of the lower part of the river, he noticed that in the year 1700, the river was more than 1200 miles long, yet by the year 1875, it was only 973 miles long. Twain concluded that any person "can see that 742 years from now the lower Mississippi will be only a mile and three-quarters long." What is wrong with this inductive reasoning?

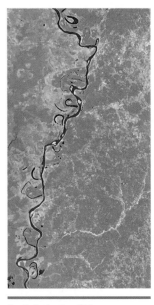

Aerial photo of the Mississippi River

14. What was the ordered pair rule used to relocate the four vertices of *ABCD* to *A′B′C′D′*?

15. What was the ordered pair rule to relocate the four vertices of *EFGH* to *E′F′G′H′*? What type of transformations?

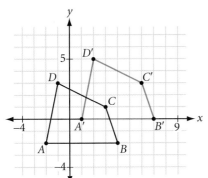

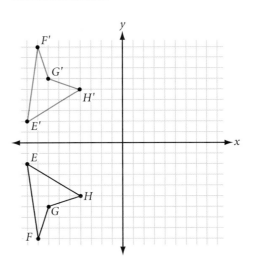

For Exercises 16–18, use inductive reasoning to find the next two terms of the sequence.

16. 180, 360, 540, 720, _?_, _?_

17. 0, 10, 21, 33, 46, 60, _?_, _?_

18. $\frac{1}{2}$, 9, $\frac{2}{3}$, 10, $\frac{3}{4}$, 11, _?_, _?_

For Exercises 19–22, draw the next shape in each picture pattern.

19.

20.

21. ⓗ

22.

23. Think of a situation you have observed in which inductive reasoning was used incorrectly. Write a paragraph or two describing what happened and explaining why you think it was an incorrect use of inductive reasoning.

Match each term in Exercises 24–33 with one of the figures A–O.

24. Kite

25. Consecutive angles in a polygon

26. Trapezoid

27. Diagonal in a polygon

28. Pair of complementary angles

29. Radius

30. Pair of vertical angles

31. Chord

32. Acute angle

33. Angle bisector in a triangle

A.   B.   C.   D.   E.

F.   G.   H.   I.   J.

K.   L.   M.   N. (124°) O.

For Exercises 34–37, sketch and carefully label the figure.

34. Pentagon *WILDE* with $\angle ILD \cong \angle LDE$ and $\overline{LD} \cong \overline{DE}$

35. Isosceles obtuse triangle *OBG* with $m\angle BGO = 140°$

36. Circle *O* with a chord $\overline{CD}$ perpendicular to radius $\overline{OT}$

37. Circle *K* with acute angle *DKN* where *D* and *N* are points on circle *K*

DEVELOPING MATHEMATICAL REASONING

Rotating Gears

In what direction will gear E rotate if gear A rotates in a counterclockwise direction?

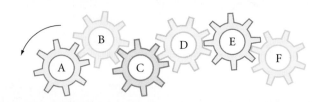

EXPLORATION

The Seven Bridges of Königsberg

Leonhard Euler

The River Pregel (now Pregolya) runs through the university town of Königsberg (now Kaliningrad in Russia). In the middle of the river are two islands connected to each other and to the rest of the city by seven bridges. Many years ago, a tradition developed among the townspeople of Königsberg. They challenged one another to make a round trip over all seven bridges, walking over each bridge once and only once before returning to the starting point.

For a long time no one was able to do it, and yet no one was able to show that it couldn't be done. In 1735, they finally wrote to Leonhard Euler (1707–1783), a Swiss mathematician, asking for his help on the problem. Euler (pronounced "oyler") reduced the problem to a network of paths connecting the two sides of the rivers C and B, and the two islands A and D, as shown in the network above. Then Euler demonstrated that the task is impossible.

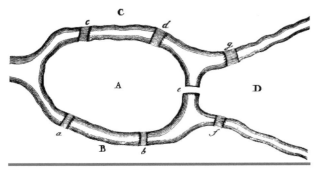

The seven bridges of Königsberg

In this activity you will work with a variety of networks to see if you can come up with a rule to find out whether a network can or cannot be "traveled."

Activity

Traveling Networks

A collection of points connected by paths is called a **network**. When we say a network can be traveled, we mean that the network can be drawn with a pencil without lifting the pencil off the paper and without retracing any paths. (Points can be passed over more than once.)

Step 1 Try these networks and see which ones can be traveled and which are impossible to travel.

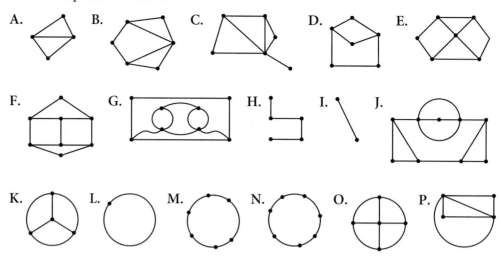

Which networks were impossible to travel? Are they impossible or just difficult? How can you be sure? As you do the next few steps, see whether you can find the reason why some networks are impossible to travel.

Step 2 Draw the River Pregel and the two islands shown on the first page of this exploration. Draw an eighth bridge so that you can travel over all the bridges exactly once if you start at point *C* and end at point *B*.

Step 3 Draw the River Pregel and the two islands. Can you draw an eighth bridge so that you can travel over all the bridges exactly once, starting and finishing at the same point? How many solutions can you find?

Step 4 Euler realized that it is the points of intersection that determine whether a network can be traveled. Each point of intersection is either "odd" or "even."

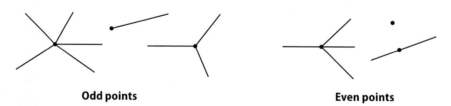

Odd points   **Even points**

Did you find any networks that have only one odd point? Can you draw one? Try it. How about three odd points? Or five odd points? Can you create a network that has an odd number of odd points? Explain why or why not.

Step 5 How does the number of even points and odd points affect whether a network can be traveled?

> **Networks Conjecture**
>
> A network can be traveled if _?_ .

Composition of Transformations on the Coordinate Plane

In earlier lessons, you reflected, translated, and rotated polygons using ordered pair rules on the coordinate grid. In this lesson you will learn to transform a figure and then transform the image of that figure. When you apply one transformation to a figure and then apply another transformation to its image, the resulting transformation is called a **composition** of transformations. Let's look at an example of a composition of two translations.

EXAMPLE A

Triangle ABC with vertices $A(-1, 0)$, $B(4, 0)$, and $C(2, 6)$ is first translated by the rule $(x, y) \rightarrow (x - 6, y - 5)$, and then its image, $\triangle A'B'C'$, is translated by the rule $(x, y) \rightarrow (x + 14, y + 3)$ to get $\triangle A''B''C''$.

a. What single translation is equivalent to the composition of these two translations?

b. What single translation brings the second image, $\triangle A''B''C''$, back to the position of the original triangle, $\triangle ABC$?

Solution

Draw $\triangle ABC$ on a set of axes and relocate its vertices using the first rule to get $\triangle A'B'C'$. Then relocate the vertices of $\triangle A'B'C'$ using the second rule to get $\triangle A''B''C''$.

The translation $(x, y) \rightarrow (x - 6, y - 5)$ moves $C(2, 6)$ to $C'(-4, 1)$.

The single translation $(x, y) \rightarrow (x + 8, y - 2)$ moves $C(2, 6)$ directly to $C''(10, 4)$.

The translation $(x, y) \rightarrow (x + 14, y + 3)$ moves $C'(-4, 1)$ to $C''(10, 4)$.

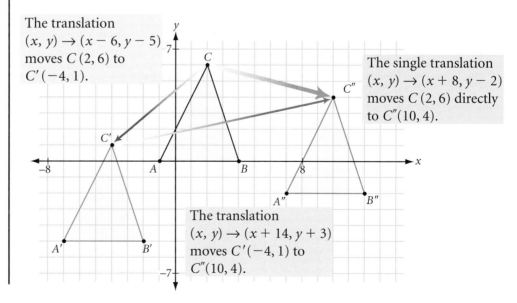

a. Each vertex is moved left 6 then right 14, and down 5 then up 3. So the equivalent single translation would be $(x, y) \rightarrow (x - 6 + 14, y - 5 + 3)$ or $(x, y) \rightarrow (x + 8, y - 2)$. You can also write this as a translation by the translation vector $<8, -2>$.

b. Reversing the steps, the translation by the vector $<-8, 2>$ brings the second image, $\triangle A''B''C''$, back to $\triangle ABC$.

Next, let's look at a composition of two reflection transformations.

EXAMPLE B

Given $\triangle PQR$ with vertices: $P(-5, 3)$, $Q(-3, 6)$, $R(-6, 5)$. Reflect $\triangle PQR$ across the y-axis to create $\triangle P'Q'R'$. Reflect $\triangle P'Q'R'$ across the line $y = 1$ to create $\triangle P''Q''R''$.

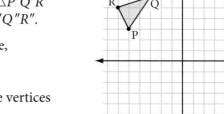

a. What is the transformation rule, $(x, y) \rightarrow (?, ?)$, that transforms $\triangle PQR$ to $\triangle P'Q'R'$?

b. What are the coordinates of the vertices of $\triangle P'Q'R'$?

c. What are the coordinates of the vertices of $\triangle P''Q''R''$?

d. What is the transformation rule, $(x, y) \rightarrow (?, ?)$, that transforms $\triangle P'Q'R'$ onto $\triangle P''Q''R''$?

e. What is the single transformation rule, $(x, y) \rightarrow (?, ?)$, that takes $\triangle PQR$ onto $\triangle P''Q''R''$?

Solution

Step 1 Draw $\triangle PQR$ on a set of axes and relocate its vertices by reflecting $\triangle PQR$ across the y-axis to get $\triangle P'Q'R'$. Earlier you discovered that a reflection across the y-axis keeps the y-values of the ordered pairs the same but reverses the sign of each x-value. Thus it is equivalent to the ordered pair rule $(x, y) \rightarrow (-x, y)$. Therefore $P(-5, 3)$, $Q(-3, 6)$, and $R(-6, 5)$ become $P'(5, 3)$, $Q'(3, 6)$, and $R'(6, 5)$.

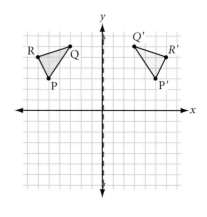

Step 2 Reflecting the vertices $P'(5, 3)$, $Q'(3, 6)$, and $R'(6, 5)$ across the line $y = 1$ results in $P''(5, -1)$, $Q''(3, -4)$, and $R''(6, -3)$. This is because when you reflect vertically, the x-coordinate values are all the same between points P' and P'', Q' and Q'', and R' and R''. In addition, every pair of (point, image point) are always the same distance from the line of reflection.

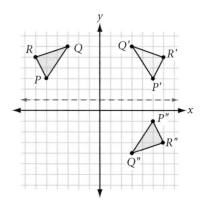

Step 3 Earlier you discovered that a reflection across the x-axis is equivalent to the ordered pair rule $(x, y) \rightarrow (x, -y)$. You might notice that reflecting across the line $y = 1$ is similar to reflecting across the x-axis because the x-values between points and image points remain the same and the y-values change. What rule would describe how the y-values change? If you change the sign of each y-value in points P', Q', and R' and then add 2 you get the y-values for points P'', Q'', and R''. Thus the ordered pair rule is $(x, y) \rightarrow (x, -y + 2)$.

P'	$(5, 3)$	P''	$(5, -1)$
Q'	$(3, 6)$	Q''	$(3, -4)$
R'	$(6, 5)$	R''	$(6, -3)$

Next, let's look at a composition of rotation and reflection transformations.

EXAMPLE C

Given $\triangle DEF$ with vertices: $D(-4, 2)$, $E(-1, 0)$, $F(0, 6)$. Reflect $\triangle DEF$ across the line $y = x$ to create $\triangle D'E'F'$. Rotate $\triangle DEF$ 90° clockwise about the origin to create $\triangle D''E''F''$. Reflect $\triangle D''E''F''$ across the x-axis to create $\triangle D'''E'''F'''$.

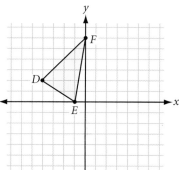

a. What is the transformation rule, $(x, y) \rightarrow (?, ?)$, that transforms $\triangle DEF$ to $\triangle D'E'F'$?

b. What are the coordinates of the vertices of $\triangle D'E'F'$?

c. What are the coordinates of the vertices of $\triangle D''E''F''$?

d. What is the transformation rule, $(x, y) \rightarrow (?, ?)$, that transforms $\triangle DEF$ to $\triangle D''E''F''$?

e. What are the coordinates of the vertices of $\triangle D'''E'''F'''$?

f. What is the single transformation rule that takes $\triangle D''E''F''$ onto $\triangle D'''E'''F'''$?

g. What is the single transformation rule that takes $\triangle DEF$ onto $\triangle D'''E'''F'''$?

$$(x, y) \rightarrow (y, x)$$

Solution

Step 1 Draw $\triangle DEF$ on a set of axes and relocate its vertices by reflecting $\triangle DEF$ across the line $y = x$ to get $\triangle D'E'F'$. Earlier you discovered that a reflection across the line $y = x$ switches the x- and y-values of each ordered pair thus it is equivalent to the ordered pair rule $(x, y) \rightarrow (y, x)$. Therefore $D(-4, 2)$, $E(-1, 0)$, $F(0, 6)$ become $D'(2, -4)$, $E'(0, -1)$, $F'(6, 0)$.

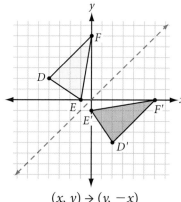

$$(x, y) \rightarrow (y, -x)$$

Step 2 Earlier you discovered that a rotation of 90° clockwise is equivalent to the ordered pair rule $(x, y) \rightarrow (y, -x)$. Relocating the vertices of $\triangle DEF$ using the ordered pair rule gives us vertices $D''(2, 4)$, $E''(0, 1)$ and $F''(6, 0)$.

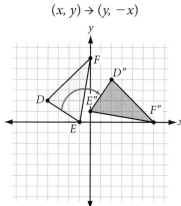

Step 3 Earlier you discovered that a reflection across the x-axis is equivalent to the ordered pair rule $(x, y) \rightarrow (x, -y)$. Relocating the vertices of $\triangle D''E''F''$ using the ordered pair rule gives us vertices $D'''(2, 4)$, $E'''(0, 1)$, and $F'''(6, 0)$.

$(x, y) \rightarrow (x, -y)$

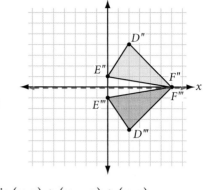

Step 4 The ordered pair rule that takes $\triangle DEF$ onto $\triangle D''E''F''$ is $(x, y) \rightarrow (y, -x)$. The ordered pair rule that takes $\triangle D''E''F''$ onto $\triangle D'''E'''F'''$ is $(x, y) \rightarrow (x, -y)$. Thus the ordered pair rule that takes $\triangle DEF$ onto $\triangle D'''E'''F'''$ is $(x, y) \rightarrow (y, -x) \rightarrow (y, x)$, or simply $(x, y) \rightarrow (y, x)$. Notice, this is the same as the ordered pair rule $(x, y) \rightarrow (y, x)$ that reflected $\triangle DEF$ onto $\triangle D'E'F'$.

Exercises

1. Given $\triangle ABC$ with vertices: $A(-6, -2)$, $B(1, 1)$, $C(-5, 2)$
   a. Translate $\triangle ABC$ by the translation rule $(x, y) \rightarrow (x, y + 4)$ to create $\triangle A'B'C'$.
   b. What are the coordinates of the vertices of $\triangle A'B'C'$?
   c. Translate $\triangle A'B'C'$ by the translation rule $(x, y) \rightarrow (x + 6, y - 7)$ to create $\triangle A''B''C''$.
   d. What are the coordinates of the vertices of $\triangle A''B''C''$?
   e. What is the single transformation rule that takes $\triangle ABC$ onto $\triangle A''B''C''$?
   f. What is the single transformation rule that takes $\triangle A''B''C''$ back onto $\triangle ABC$?
   g. Suppose $\triangle ABC$ is translated by an ordered pair rule $(x, y) \rightarrow (x + a, y + b)$ to create $\triangle A'B'C'$ and then $\triangle A'B'C'$ is translated by the rule $(x, y) \rightarrow (x + c, y + d)$ to create $\triangle A''B''C''$. What is the single ordered pair rule that takes $\triangle ABC$ to create $\triangle A''B''C''$?

2. Given $\triangle ABC$ with vertices: $A(-6, -1)$, $B(-4, -3)$, $C(-3, 0)$
   a. Reflect $\triangle ABC$ across the x-axis to create $\triangle A'B'C'$.
   b. What are the coordinates of the vertices of $\triangle A'B'C'$?
   c. What is the transformation rule, $(x, y) \rightarrow (?, ?)$, that transforms $\triangle ABC$ to $\triangle A'B'C'$?
   d. Reflect $\triangle A'B'C'$ across the line $x = -2$ to create the image $\triangle A''B''C''$.
   e. What are the coordinates of the vertices of $\triangle A''B''C''$?
   f. What is the single transformation rule that takes $\triangle ABC$ onto $\triangle A''B''C''$?

3. Given $\triangle ABC$ with vertices: $A(-2, 3)$, $B(2, 2)$, $C(4, 7)$
   a. Reflect $\triangle ABC$ across the line $y = 3$ to create $\triangle A'B'C'$.
   b. What are the coordinates of the vertices of $\triangle A'B'C'$?
   c. What is the transformation rule, $(x, y) \rightarrow (?, ?)$, that transforms $\triangle ABC$ to $\triangle A'B'C'$?
   d. Reflect $\triangle A'B'C'$ across the line $y = -1$ to create $\triangle A''B''C''$.
   e. What are the coordinates of the vertices of $\triangle A''B''C''$?
   f. What is the single transformation rule that takes $\triangle ABC$ onto $\triangle A''B''C''$?

4. Given $\triangle ABC$ with vertices: $A(-1, 3)$, $B(3, 2)$, $C(5, 6)$

   a. Reflect $\triangle ABC$ across the x-axis to create $\triangle A'B'C'$.

   b. What are the coordinates of the vertices of $\triangle A'B'C'$?

   c. What is the transformation rule, $(x, y) \rightarrow (?, ?)$, that transforms $\triangle ABC$ to $\triangle A'B'C'$?

   d. Translate $\triangle A'B'C'$ by the transformation rule, $(x, y) \rightarrow (x - 5, y + 5)$ to create $\triangle A''B''C''$.

   e. What are the coordinates of the vertices of $\triangle A''B''C''$?

   f. What is the single transformation rule that takes $\triangle ABC$ onto $\triangle A''B''C''$?

5. Given $\triangle ABC$ with vertices: $A(-8, 2)$, $B(-4, -2)$, $C(-3, 3)$

   a. Reflect $\triangle ABC$ across the y-axis to create $\triangle A'B'C'$.

   b. What are the coordinates of the vertices of $\triangle A'B'C'$?

   c. What is the transformation rule, $(x, y) \rightarrow (?, ?)$, that transforms $\triangle ABC$ to $\triangle A'B'C'$?

   d. Rotate $\triangle A'B'C'$ 90° clockwise about the origin to create $\triangle A''B''C''$.

   e. What are the coordinates of the vertices of $\triangle A''B''C''$?

   f. What is the transformation rule, $(x, y) \rightarrow (?, ?)$, that transforms $\triangle A'B'C'$ to $\triangle A''B''C''$?

   g. What is the single transformation rule that takes $\triangle ABC$ onto $\triangle A''B''C''$?

DEVELOPING MATHEMATICAL REASONING

Hexomino Sudoku Puzzle

The hexomino sudoku shown has six different hexominoes filling the 6×6 grid. Every row, column, and hexomino region contains the numerals 1–6. Copy and complete the hexomino sudoku.

Angle Relationships

Now that you've had experience with inductive reasoning, let's use it to start discovering geometric relationships. This investigation is the first of many investigations you will do using your geometry tools.

"Discovery consists of looking at the same thing as everyone else and thinking something different."

ALBERT SZENT-GYÖRGYI

> Create an investigation section in your notebook. Include a title and illustration for each investigation and write a statement summarizing the results of each one.

 ## INVESTIGATION 1

YOU WILL NEED
- a protractor
- a straightedge

The Linear Pair Conjecture

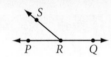

Step 1 On a sheet of paper, draw $\overleftrightarrow{PQ}$ and place a point R between P and Q. Choose another point S not on $\overleftrightarrow{PQ}$ and draw $\overrightarrow{RS}$. You have just created a linear pair of angles. Place the "zero edge" of your protractor along $\overleftrightarrow{PQ}$. What do you notice about the sum of the measures of the linear pair of angles?

Step 2 Compare your results with those of your group. Does everyone make the same observation? Complete the statement.

Linear Pair Conjecture	C-1
If two angles form a linear pair, then ? .	

> The important conjectures have been given a name and a number. Start a list of them in your notebook. The Linear Pair Conjecture (C-1) and the Vertical Angles Conjecture (C-2) should be the first entries on your list. Make a sketch for each conjecture.

In the previous investigation you discovered the relationship between a linear pair of angles, such as ∠1 and ∠2 in the diagram at right. You will discover the relationship between vertical angles, such as ∠1 and ∠3, in the next investigation.

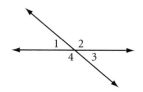

INVESTIGATION 2

Vertical Angles Conjecture

● a straightedge
● patty paper

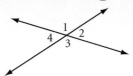

Step 1 Draw two intersecting lines onto patty paper or tracing paper. Label the angles as shown. Which angles are vertical angles?

Step 2 Fold the paper so that the vertical angles lie over each other. What do you notice about their measures?

Step 3 Fold the paper so that the other pair of vertical angles lie over each other. What do you notice about their measures?

Step 4 Compare your results with the results of others. Complete the statement.

Vertical Angles Conjecture	C-2
If two angles are vertical angles, then ? .	

DEVELOPING PROOF

You used inductive reasoning to discover both the Linear Pair Conjecture and the Vertical Angles Conjecture. Are they related? If you accept the Linear Pair Conjecture as true, can you use deductive reasoning to show that the Vertical Angles Conjecture must be true?

Read the example below. Without turning the page, write a deductive argument with your group. Remember the reasoning strategy of representing a situation algebraically. Another strategy is to apply previous conjectures and definitions to a new situation. Then compare your solution to the one on the next page.

EXAMPLE

Use the Linear Pair Conjecture and the diagram at right to write a deductive argument explaining why ∠1 must be congruent to ∠3.

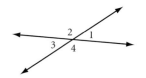

z

c

f

o

r

Solution | You can see from the diagram that the sum of the measures of angles 1 and 2 is equal to the sum of the measures of angles 2 and 3 because they are both linear pairs. Because angle 2 is the same in both sums, angle 1 must equal angle 3. To write a deductive argument, go through this logic one step at a time.

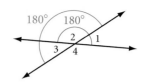

Deductive Argument

For any linear pair of angles, their measures add up to 180°.

$$m\angle 1 + m\angle 2 = 180°$$

$$m\angle 2 + m\angle 3 = 180°$$

Since both expressions on the left equal 180°, they equal each other.

$$m\angle 1 + m\angle 2 = m\angle 2 + m\angle 3$$

Subtract $m\angle 2$ from both sides of the equation.

$$m\angle 1 = m\angle 3$$

Vertical angles 1 and 3 have equal measures, so they are congruent.

You discovered the Vertical Angles Conjecture: If two angles are vertical angles, then they are congruent. Does that also mean that all congruent angles are vertical angles? The **converse** of an "if-then" statement switches the "if" and "then" parts. The converse of the Vertical Angles Conjecture may be stated: If two angles are congruent, then they are vertical angles. Is this converse statement true? Remember that if you can find even one counterexample, like the diagram below, then the statement is false.

Therefore, the converse of the Vertical Angles Conjecture is false.

2.5 Exercises

YOU WILL NEED

Geometry software
for Exercise 12

Without using a protractor, but with the aid of your two new conjectures, find the measure of each lettered angle in Exercises 1–5. Copy the diagrams so that you can write on them. List your answers in alphabetical order.

1.

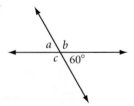

2.

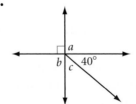

3.

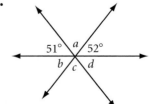

4. (ⓗ)

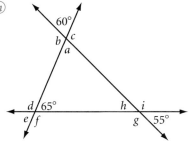

5.

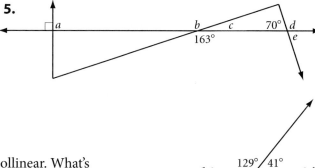

6. **DEVELOPING PROOF** Points A, B, and C at right are collinear. What's wrong with this picture?

7. Yoshi is building a cold frame for his plants. He wants to cut two wood strips so that they'll fit together to make a right-angled corner. At what angle should he cut ends of the strips?

8. A tree on a 30° slope grows straight up. What are the measures of the greatest and smallest angles the tree makes with the hill? Explain.

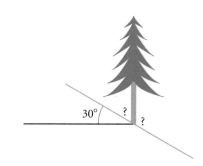

9. You discovered that if a pair of angles is a linear pair, then the angles are supplementary. Is the converse true? If so, explain why. If not, sketch a counterexample and explain why not.

10. If two congruent angles are supplementary, what must be true of the two angles? Make a sketch, then complete the following conjecture: If two angles are both congruent and supplementary, then ? .

11. **DEVELOPING PROOF** Using algebra, write a deductive argument that explains why the conjecture from Exercise 10 is true.

12. Use geometry software to construct two intersecting lines. Measure a pair of vertical angles. Use the software to calculate the ratio of their measures. What is the ratio? Drag one of the lines. Does the ratio ever change? Does this demonstration convince you that the Vertical Angles Conjecture is true? Does it explain why it is true?

Review

For Exercises 13–17, sketch, label, and mark the figure.

13. Scalene obtuse triangle PAT with $PA = 3$ cm, $AT = 5$ cm, and $\angle A$ an obtuse angle

14. A quadrilateral that has rotational symmetry, but not reflectional symmetry

15. A circle with center at O and radii $\overline{OA}$ and $\overline{OT}$ creating a minor arc $\overparen{AT}$

16. A pyramid with an octagonal base

17. A 3-by-4-by-6-inch rectangular solid rests on its smallest face. Draw lines on the three visible faces to show how you can divide it into 72 identical smaller cubes.

18. Miriam the Magnificent placed four cards face up (the first four cards shown below). Blindfolded, she asked someone from her audience to come up to the stage and turn one card 180°.

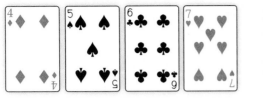

Before turn

After turn

Miriam removed her blindfold and claimed she was able to determine which card was turned 180°. What is her trick? Can you figure out which card was turned? Explain.

19. If a pizza is cut into 16 congruent pieces, how many degrees are in each angle at the center of the pizza?

20. Paulus Gerdes, a mathematician from Mozambique, uses traditional *sona* patterns from Angola to practice inductive thinking. Shown below are three *lusona* designs. Sketch the fourth *lusona* design, assuming the pattern continues.

  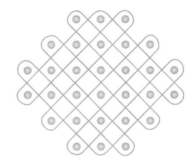

21. Hydrocarbon molecules in which all the bonds between the carbon atoms are single bonds except one double bond are called *alkenes*. The first three alkenes are modeled below.

$$
\begin{array}{ccc}
\text{H} & & \\
| & & \\
\text{H}-\text{C}=\text{C} & & \\
| \quad | & & \\
\text{H} \quad \text{H} & &
\end{array}
$$

Ethene
$$\left(\text{C}_2\text{H}_4\right)$$

$$
\begin{array}{ccc}
\text{H} & \text{H} & \\
| & | & \\
\text{H}-\text{C}-\text{C}=\text{C} & & \\
| \quad | \quad | & & \\
\text{H} \quad \text{H} \quad \text{H} & &
\end{array}
$$

Propene
$$\left(\text{C}_3\text{H}_6\right)$$

$$
\begin{array}{ccc}
\text{H} & \text{H} & \text{H} \\
| & | & | \\
\text{H}-\text{C}-\text{C}-\text{C}=\text{C} & & \\
| \quad | \quad | \quad | & & \\
\text{H} \quad \text{H} \quad \text{H} \quad \text{H} & &
\end{array}
$$

Butene
$$\left(\text{C}_4\text{H}_8\right)$$

Sketch the alkene with eight carbons in the chain. What is the general rule for alkenes ($\text{C}_n\text{H}_?$)? In other words, if there are n carbon atoms (C), how many hydrogen atoms (H) are in the alkene?

> **Science**
> **CONNECTION**
>
> Organic chemistry is the study of carbon compounds and their reactions. Drugs, vitamins, synthetic fibers, and food all contain organic molecules.

22. If the pattern of rectangles continues, what is the rule for the perimeter of the *n*th rectangle, and what is the perimeter of the 200th rectangle? What is the rule for the number of 1-by-1 squares in the *n*th rectangle, and how many 1-by-1 squares are in the 200th rectangle?

Rectangle	1	2	3	4	5	6	...	*n*	...	200
Perimeter of rectangle	10	14	18				...		...	
Number of squares	6	12	20				...		...	

For Exercises 23–25, use the ordered pair rule shown to relocate the four points on the given circle. Can the four new points be connected to create a new circle? Does the new figure appear congruent to the original circle?

23. $(x, y) \rightarrow (x - 1, y + 2)$ **24.** $(x, y) \rightarrow (2x, 2y)$ **25.** $(x, y) \rightarrow (2x, y)$

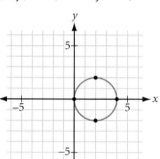 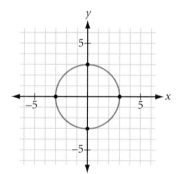 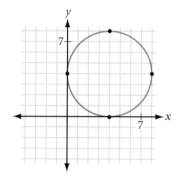

26. If there are 20 couples at a party, how many different handshakes can there be between pairs of people? Assume that the two people in each couple do not shake hands with each other. *(h)*

27. If a polygon has 24 sides, how many diagonals are there from each vertex? How many diagonals are there in all?

28. If a polygon has a total of 560 diagonals, how many vertices does it have? *(h)*

29. A midpoint divides a segment into two congruent segments. Point *M* divides segment $\overline{AY}$ into two congruent segments $\overline{AM}$ and $\overline{MY}$. What conclusion can you make? What type of reasoning did you use?

DEVELOPING MATHEMATICAL REASONING

Color Network Puzzle

In this Color Network Puzzle, color each circle with Red (R), Yellow (Y), Blue (B), or Green (G), without coloring two vertices of a non-overlapping quadrilateral the same color. Which color goes in the circle with a question mark?

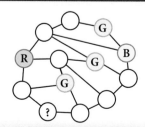

Special Angles on Parallel Lines

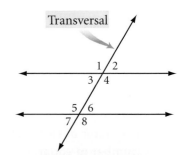

Transversal

A line intersecting two or more other lines in the plane is called a transversal. A transversal creates different types of angle pairs. Three types are listed below.

One pair of **corresponding angles** is ∠1 and ∠5. Can you find three more pairs of corresponding angles?

One pair of **alternate interior angles** is ∠3 and ∠6. Do you see another pair of alternate interior angles?

One pair of **alternate exterior angles** is ∠2 and ∠7. Do you see the other pair of alternate exterior angles?

When parallel lines are cut by a transversal, there is a special relationship among the angles. Let's investigate.

INVESTIGATION 1

Which Angles Are Congruent?

YOU WILL NEED

- lined paper
- a straightedge
- patty paper
- a protractor *(optional)*

Using the lines on your paper as a guide, draw a pair of parallel lines. Or use both edges of your ruler or straightedge to create parallel lines. Label them *k* and ℓ. Now draw a transversal that intersects the parallel lines. Label the transversal *m*, and label the angles with numbers, as shown at right.

Step 1 Place a piece of patty paper over the set of angles 1, 2, 3, and 4. Copy the two intersecting lines *m* and ℓ and the four angles onto the patty paper.

Step 2 Translate the patty paper down to the intersection of lines *m* and *k* (the translation vector is the segment on the transversal between the parallel lines). Compare angles 1 through 4 with each of the corresponding angles 5 through 8. What is the relationship between corresponding angles? Alternate interior angles? Alternate exterior angles?

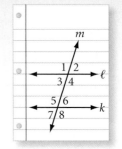

Compare your results with the results of others in your group and complete the three conjectures below.

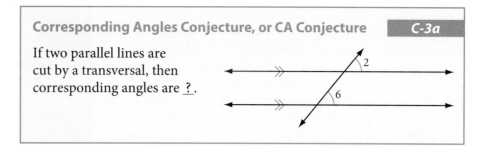

Corresponding Angles Conjecture, or CA Conjecture — C-3a

If two parallel lines are cut by a transversal, then corresponding angles are ? .

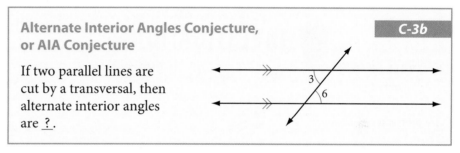

Alternate Interior Angles Conjecture, or AIA Conjecture — C-3b

If two parallel lines are cut by a transversal, then alternate interior angles are ? .

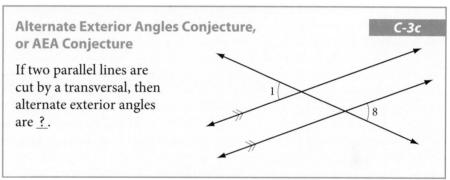

Alternate Exterior Angles Conjecture, or AEA Conjecture — C-3c

If two parallel lines are cut by a transversal, then alternate exterior angles are ? .

The three conjectures you wrote can all be combined to create a Parallel Lines Conjecture, which is really three conjectures in one.

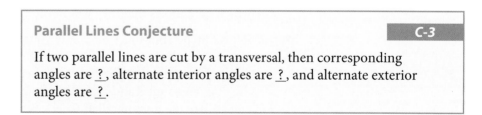

Parallel Lines Conjecture — C-3

If two parallel lines are cut by a transversal, then corresponding angles are ? , alternate interior angles are ? , and alternate exterior angles are ? .

Step 3 What happens if the lines you start with are not parallel? Check whether your conjectures will work with nonparallel lines.

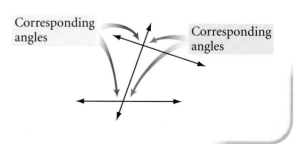

Corresponding angles

Corresponding angles

What about the converse of each of your conjectures? Suppose you know that a pair of corresponding angles, or alternate interior angles, is congruent. Will the lines be parallel? Is it possible for the angles to be congruent but for the lines not to be parallel?

 ## INVESTIGATION 2

Is the Converse True?

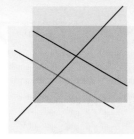 

Step 1 Draw two intersecting lines on your paper. Copy these lines onto a piece of patty paper. Because you copied the angles, the two sets of angles are congruent.

Slide the top copy so that the transversal stays lined up.

Trace the lines and the angles from the bottom original onto the patty paper again. When you do this, you are constructing sets of congruent corresponding angles. Mark the congruent angles.

Are the two lines parallel? You can test to see if the distance between the two lines remains the same, which guarantees that they will never meet.

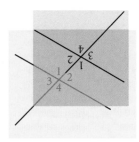

Step 2 Repeat Step 1, but this time rotate your patty paper 180° so that the transversal lines up again. What kinds of congruent angles have you created? Trace the lines and angles and mark the congruent angles. Are the lines parallel? Check them.

Step 3 Compare your results with those of your group. If your results do not agree, discuss them until you have convinced each other. Complete the conjecture below and add it to your conjecture list.

Explore both investigations using the **Dynamic Geometry Exploration** in your ebook.

Converse of the Parallel Lines Conjecture	C-4

If two lines are cut by a transversal to form pairs of congruent corresponding angles, congruent alternate interior angles, or congruent alternate exterior angles, then the lines are __?__.

DEVELOPING PROOF

You used inductive reasoning to discover all three parts of the Parallel Lines Conjecture. However, if you accept any one of them as true, you can use deductive reasoning to show that the others are true.

Read the example below. Before you read the solution, write a deductive argument with your group. Remember the reasoning strategy of applying previous conjectures and definitions. Then compare your solution to the one presented.

Write a deductive argument explaining why the Alternate Interior Angles Conjecture is true. Assume that the Vertical Angles Conjecture and Corresponding Angles Conjecture are both true.

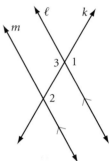

Deductive Argument

In the diagram, lines ℓ and m are parallel and intersected by transversal k. If the Corresponding Angles Conjecture is true, the corresponding angles are congruent.

$$\angle 1 \cong \angle 2$$

If the Vertical Angles Conjecture is true, the vertical angles are congruent.

$$\angle 1 \cong \angle 3$$

Because both $\angle 2$ and $\angle 3$ are congruent to $\angle 1$, they're congruent to each other.

$$\angle 2 \cong \angle 3$$

Alternate interior angles 2 and 3 are congruent. Therefore, if the corresponding angles are congruent, then the alternate interior angles are congruent.

> It helps to visualize each statement and to mark all congruences you know on your paper.

2.6 Exercises

1. $w = \underline{\ ?\ }$

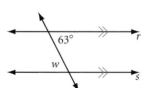

2. $x = \underline{\ ?\ }$

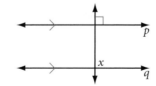

3. Is line k parallel to line ℓ? Explain.

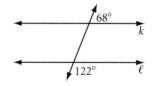

4. Quadrilateral *TUNA* is
a parallelogram.
$y =$ _?_ ⓗ

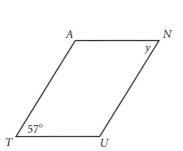

5. Is quadrilateral *FISH*
a parallelogram?

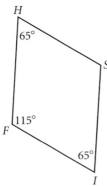

6. $m \parallel n$
$z =$ _?_ ⓗ

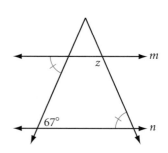

7. DEVELOPING PROOF Trace the diagram below. Calculate each lettered angle measure. Explain how you determined measures *n*, *p*, and *q*. ⓗ

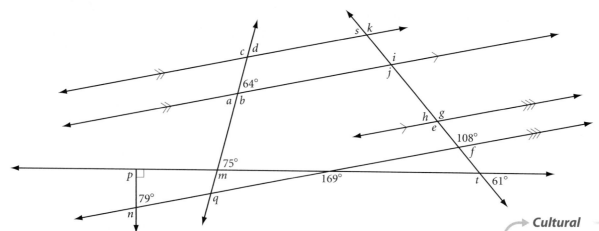

8. DEVELOPING PROOF Write a deductive argument explaining why the Alternate Exterior Angles Conjecture is true. Assume that the Vertical Angles Conjecture and Corresponding Angles Conjecture are both true.

Cultural CONNECTION

Sculptor Maya Lin designed the Vietnam Veterans Memorial Wall in Washington, D.C. Engraved in the granite wall are the names of United States armed forces service members who died in the Vietnam War or remain missing in action. Do the top and bottom of the wall meet in the distance, or are they parallel? How could you know from angle measures a and b in the diagram below? Learn more about the Memorial Wall and Lin's other projects in your ebook.

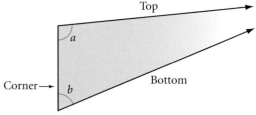

9. DEVELOPING PROOF What's wrong with this picture?

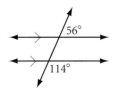
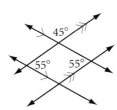

10. DEVELOPING PROOF What's wrong with this picture?

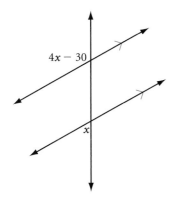

11. Draw a line on your paper and label it line *AB*. Place a point *P* about one to two inches from the line. Draw another line (a transversal) that passes through point *P* and line *AB*. Use your straightedge and protractor to draw line *PQ* that is parallel to line *AB*. Explain your method and why you know the lines are parallel.

12. Is the following statement true? "If yesterday was part of the weekend, then tomorrow is a school day." Write the converse of the statement. Is the converse true?

13. Find *x*.   **14.** If $r \parallel s$, find *y*.   **15.** If $x = 12°$, is $p \parallel q$?

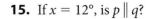

$4x - 30$

x

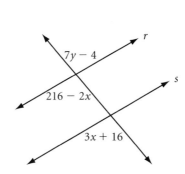

$7y - 4$

r

$216 - 2x$

s

$3x + 16$

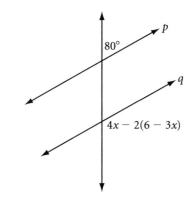

$80°$

p

q

$4x - 2(6 - 3x)$

Review

16. What type (or types) of triangle has one or more lines of symmetry?

17. What type (or types) of quadrilateral has only rotational symmetry? ⓗ

18. If *D* is the midpoint of $\overline{AC}$ and *C* is the midpoint of $\overline{BD}$, what is the length of $\overline{AB}$ if *BD* = 12 cm?

19. If $\overrightarrow{AI}$ is the angle bisector of $\angle KAN$ and $\overrightarrow{AR}$ is the angle bisector of $\angle KAI$, what is $m\angle RAN$ if $m\angle RAK = 13°$?

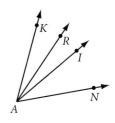

20. **How many blue squares and yellow squares are in the 35th figure of this pattern?**
Assume the pattern of blue and yellow shaded *T*'s continues. Copy and complete the table for blue and yellow squares and for the total number of squares. ⓗ

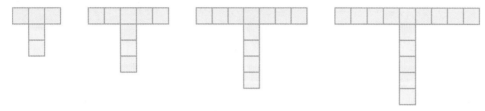

Figure number	1	2	3	4	5	6	...	n	...	35
Number of yellow squares	2						...		...	
Number of blue squares	3						...		...	
Total number of squares	5						...		...	

For Exercises 21–23, draw each polygon on graph paper. Relocate the vertices according to the rule. Connect the new points to form a new polygon. Describe what happened to the figure. Is the new polygon congruent to the original?

21. Rule: Subtract 1 from each *x*-coordinate. ⓗ

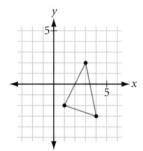

22. Rule: Reverse the sign of each *x*- and *y*-coordinate.

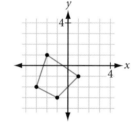

23. Rule: Double the *x*- and *y*-coordinates.

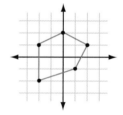

PERFORMANCE TASK

A periscope permits a sailor on a submarine to see above the surface of the ocean. This periscope is designed so that the line of sight *a* is parallel to the light ray *b*. The middle tube is perpendicular to the top and bottom tubes. What are the measures of the incoming and outgoing angles formed by the light rays and the mirrors in this periscope? Are the surfaces of the mirrors parallel? How do you know? Explain your reasoning. Draw an accurate diagram showing each angle measure. Compare your diagram with your group members. Are all your diagrams the same? Explain why or why not.

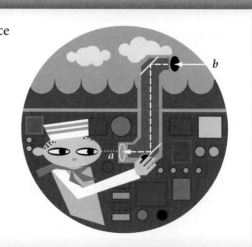

This chapter introduced you to inductive and deductive reasoning. You used inductive reasoning to observe patterns and make conjectures. You learned how to predict number sequences with rules and how to use these rules to model application problems. You learned to disprove a conjecture with a counterexample and to explain why a conjecture is true with deductive reasoning. You applied your knowledge of transformations to the coordinate plane and learned how a composition of transformations may also result in a single transformation. Then you discovered special relationships about angle pairs and made your first geometry conjectures. Finally you explored the properties of angles formed by a transversal across parallel lines. As you review the chapter, be sure you understand all the important terms. Go back to the lesson to review any terms you're unsure of.

Exercises

1. True-False

   __ **a.** Every net of a cube has either reflectional or rotational symmetry.

   __ **b.** If AB = 12 cm and BC = 13 cm, then AC = 25 cm.

   __ **c.** The bisector of a segment is unique.

   __ **d.** If a pentagon is equiangular and the perimeter is 50 cm then each side is 10 cm.

   __ **e.** There are no true statements in *a* through *e*.

2. "My dad is in the navy, and he says that food is great on submarines," said Diana. "My mom is a pilot," added Jill, "and she says that airline food is notoriously bad." "My mom is an astronaut trainee," said Julio, "and she says that astronauts' food is the worst imaginable." Diana concludes "I bet no life exists beyond Earth! As you move farther from the surface of Earth, food tastes worse. At extreme altitudes, food must taste so bad that no creature could stand to eat. Therefore, no life exists out there." What do you think of Diana's reasoning? Is it inductive or deductive?

3. Think of a situation you observed outside of school in which inductive reasoning was used incorrectly. Write a paragraph or two describing what happened and explaining why you think inductive reasoning was used poorly.

4. Think of a situation you observed outside of school in which deductive reasoning was used incorrectly. Write a paragraph or two describing what happened and explaining why you think deductive reasoning was used poorly.

For Exercises 5 and 6, find the next two terms in the sequence.

5. 7, 2, 5, −3, 8, −11, ? , ?

6. A, 4, D, 9, H, 16, M, 25, ? , ?

7. Tanya's favorite lunch is peanut butter and jelly on wheat bread with a glass of milk. Lately, she has been getting an allergic reaction after eating this lunch. She is wondering if she might be developing an allergy to peanut butter, wheat, or milk. What experiment could she do to find out which food it might be? What type of reasoning would she be using?

For Exercises 8 and 9, draw the next shape in the pattern.

8.

9.

For Exercises 10 and 11, look for a pattern and complete the conjecture.

10. Conjecture: The sum of the first 30 odd whole numbers is _?_ .

11. Conjecture: The sum of the first 30 even whole numbers is _?_ .

For Exercises 12 and 13, find the nth term and the 20th term in the sequence.

12.

n	1	2	3	4	5	6	...	n	...	20
$f(n)$	2	-1	-4	-7	-10	-13	...		...	

13.

n	1	2	3	4	5	6	...	n	...	20
$f(n)$	1	3	6	10	15	21	...		...	

14. How many blocks will Victoria need? Victoria is a store window designer for Savant Toys. She plans to build a stack of blocks similar to the ones shown below, but 30 blocks high. Make a conjecture for the value of the nth term and for the value of the 30th term. Explain your reasoning.

   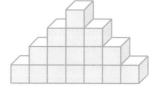

15. The stack of bricks at right is four bricks high. Find the total number of bricks for a stack that is 100 bricks high.

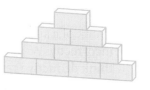

16. If at a party there are a total of 741 handshakes and each person shakes hands with everyone else at the party exactly once, how many people are at the party?

17. If a whole bunch of lines (no two parallel, no three concurrent) intersect in a plane 2926 times, how many lines are in the bunch?

18. If in a 54-sided polygon all possible diagonals are drawn from one vertex, they divide the interior of the polygon into how many regions?

19. In the diagram at right, $\overleftrightarrow{AC} \parallel \overleftrightarrow{BD}$.

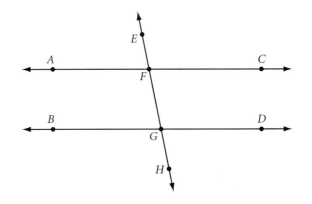

    a. Name a pair of vertical angles.

    b. Name a linear pair of angles.

    c. Name a pair of corresponding angles.

    d. Name a pair of alternate interior angles.

20. DEVELOPING PROOF In Exercise 19, name three angles congruent to $\angle AFE$ and the conjectures that support your answers.

21. Consider this statement: "If two polygons are congruent, then they have the same number of sides." Is this statement true? Now write the converse of the statement. Is the converse true? If it is true, explain why; if it is not true, draw a counterexample and explain why not.

22. Using a ruler and a protractor, draw a parallelogram with one interior angle measuring 56° and sides with lengths 4.5 cm and 7 cm.

23. DEVELOPING PROOF Which pairs of lines are parallel? Explain how you know.

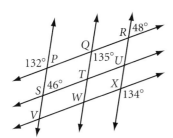

24. DEVELOPING PROOF What's wrong with this picture?

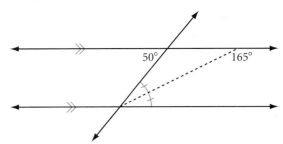

25. DEVELOPING PROOF Trace the diagram below. Calculate each lettered angle measure. Explain how you determined the measures *e, f,* and *g.*

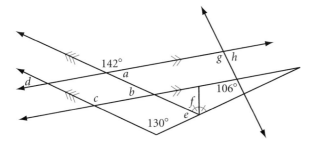

26. Given quadrilateral $ABCD$ with vertices $A(-6, -1)$, $B(-2, 3)$, $C(-5, 6)$, $D(-7, 2)$ and quadrilateral $EFGH$ with vertices $E(1, -4)$, $F(5, 0)$, $G(2, 3)$, $H(0, -1)$.

a. Translate quadrilateral $ABCD$ by the ordered pair rule $(x, y) \rightarrow (x + 7, y - 3)$ to create quadrilateral $A'B'C'D'$.

b. What happened? Does quadrilateral $A'B'C'D'$ appear to coincide with quadrilateral $EFGH$?

c. If they are congruent, what is the statement of congruence, quadrilateral $A'B'C'D' \cong$ quadrilateral (????)?

d. If they are not congruent, explain why not.

27. Given $\triangle ABC$ with vertices $A(-6, 5)$, $B(-3, 1)$, $C(-2, 7)$ and $\triangle DEF$ with vertices $D(6, 5)$, $E(3, 1)$, $F(2, 7)$.

a. Reflect $\triangle ABC$ by the ordered pair rule $(x, y) \rightarrow (-x, y)$ to create $\triangle A'B'C'$.

b. What happened? Does $\triangle A'B'C'$ appear to coincide with $\triangle DEF$?

c. If they are congruent, what is the statement of congruence, $\triangle A'B'C' \cong \triangle$(???)?

d. If they are not congruent, explain why not.

28. Given $\triangle ABC$ with vertices $A(3, 1)$, $B(-1, -2)$, $C(2, -2)$

a. Reflect $\triangle ABC$ across the line $y = 2$ to create $\triangle A'B'C'$.

b. What are the coordinates of the vertices of $\triangle A'B'C'$?

c. What is the transformation rule, $(x, y) \rightarrow (?, ?)$, that transforms $\triangle ABC$ to $\triangle A'B'C'$?

d. Reflect $\triangle A'B'C'$ across the x-axis to create $\triangle A''B''C''$.

e. What are the coordinates of the vertices of $\triangle A''B''C''$?

f. What is the single transformation rule that takes $\triangle ABC$ onto $\triangle A''B''C''$?

CHAPTER

3

Using Tools of Geometry

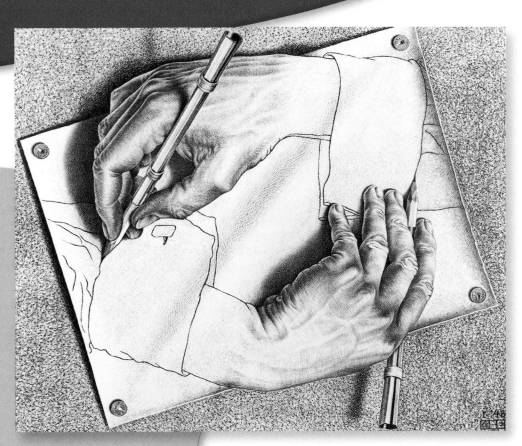

M. C. Escher's Bookplate for Albert Ernst Bosman ©2014 The M. C. Escher Company—The Netherlands. All rights reserved. www.mcescher.com

"There is indeed great satisfaction in acquiring skill, in coming to thoroughly understand the qualities of the material at hand and in learning to use the instruments we have— in the first place, our hands!—in an effective and controlled way."

M. C. ESCHER

OBJECTIVES

In this chapter you will

- learn about the history of geometric constructions
- develop skills using a compass, a straightedge, patty paper, and geometry software
- see how to create complex figures using only a compass, a straightedge, and patty paper
- explore points of concurrency in triangles

Duplicating Segments and Angles

Mathematics CONNECTION

Euclidean geometry is the study of geometry based on the assumptions of Euclid (325–265 B.C.E.). Euclid established the basic rules for constructions using only a compass and a straightedge. In his work *Elements,* Euclid proposed definitions and constructions about points, lines, angles, surfaces, and solids. He also explained why the constructions were correct with deductive reasoning.

The compass, like the straightedge, has been a useful geometry tool for thousands of years. The ancient Egyptians used the compass to mark off distances. During the Golden Age of Greece, Greek mathematicians made a game of geometric constructions. In his work *Elements*, Euclid (325–265 B.C.E.) established the basic rules for constructions using only a compass and a straightedge. In this course you will learn how to construct geometric figures using these tools as well as patty paper.

FUCLIDES

Constructions with patty paper are a variation on the ancient Greek game of geometric constructions. Almost all the figures that can be constructed with a compass and a straightedge can also be constructed using a straightedge and patty paper, waxed paper, or tracing paper. If you have access to geometry software, you can do constructions electronically.

In the previous chapters, you drew and sketched many figures. In this chapter, however, you'll *construct* geometric figures. The words *sketch, draw,* and *construct* have specific meanings in geometry.

When you *sketch* an equilateral triangle, you may make a freehand sketch of a triangle that looks equilateral. You don't need to use any geometry tools.

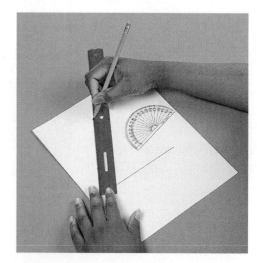

When you *draw* an equilateral triangle, you should draw it carefully and accurately, using your geometry tools. You may use a protractor to measure angles and a ruler to measure the sides to make sure they are equal in measure.

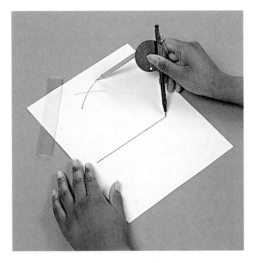
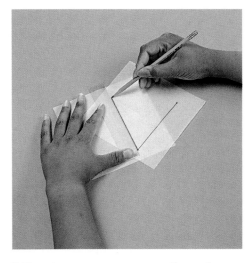

When you *construct* an equilateral triangle with a compass and straightedge, you don't rely on measurements from a protractor or ruler. You must use only a compass and a straightedge. This method of construction guarantees that your triangle is equilateral.

When you *construct* an equilateral triangle with patty paper and straightedge, you fold the paper and trace equal segments. You may use a straightedge to draw a segment, but you may not use a compass or any measuring tools.

When you sketch or draw, use the special marks that indicate right angles, parallel segments, and congruent segments and angles.

By tradition, neither a ruler nor a protractor is ever used to perform geometric constructions, because no matter how precise we try to be, measurement always involves some amount of inaccuracy. Rulers and protractors are measuring tools, not construction tools. You may use a ruler as a straightedge in constructions, provided you do not use its marks for measuring. In the next two investigations you will discover how to duplicate a line segment and an angle using only your compass and straightedge, or using only patty paper and a straightedge. By *duplicate*, we mean to copy using construction tools.

 INVESTIGATION 1

YOU WILL NEED

- a compass
- a straightedge
- a ruler
- patty paper

Duplicating a Segment

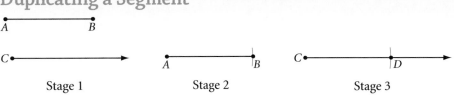

Stage 1   Stage 2   Stage 3

Step 1 The complete construction for copying a segment, $\overline{AB}$, is shown above. Describe each stage of the process.

Step 2 Use a ruler to measure $\overline{AB}$ and $\overline{CD}$. How do the two segments compare?

Step 3 Describe how to duplicate a segment using patty paper instead of a compass.

Using only a compass and a straightedge, how would you duplicate an angle? In other words, how would you construct an angle that is congruent to a given angle? You may not use your protractor, because a protractor is a measuring tool, not a construction tool.

 INVESTIGATION 2

Duplicating an Angle

YOU WILL NEED

- a compass
- a straightedge
- a protractor

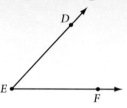

Step 1 The first two stages for copying ∠*DEF* are shown below. Describe each stage of the process.

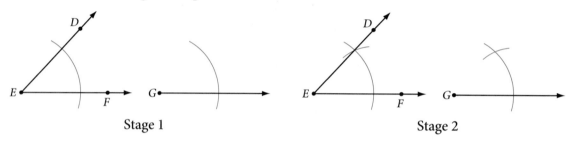

Stage 1   Stage 2

Step 2 What will be the final stage of the construction?

Step 3 Use a protractor to measure ∠*DEF* and ∠*G*. What can you state about these angles?

Step 4 Describe how to duplicate an angle using patty paper instead of a compass.

You've just discovered how to duplicate segments and angles using a straightedge and compass or patty paper. These are the basic constructions. You will use combinations of these to do many other constructions. You may be surprised that you can construct figures more precisely *without* using a ruler or protractor!

3.1 Exercises

Now that you can duplicate line segments and angles using construction tools, do the constructions in Exercises 1–10. You will duplicate polygons in Exercises 7 and 11.

YOU WILL NEED

Construction tools
for Exercises **1–9, 11**

Geometry software
for Exercise **10**

1. Using only a compass and a straightedge, duplicate the three line segments shown below. Label them as they're labeled in the figures.

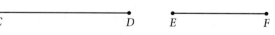

2. Use the segments from Exercise 1 to construct a line segment with length *AB* + *CD*. ⓗ

3. Use the segments from Exercise 1 to construct a line segment with length $AB + 2EF - CD$.

4. Use a compass and a straightedge to duplicate each angle. There's an arc in each angle to help you.

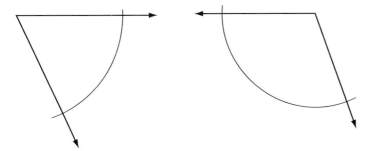

5. Draw an obtuse angle. Label it *LGE*, then duplicate it.

6. Draw two acute angles on your paper. Construct a third angle with a measure equal to the sum of the measures of the first two angles. Remember, you cannot use a protractor—use a compass and a straightedge only.

7. Draw a large acute triangle on the top half of your paper. Duplicate it on the bottom half, using your compass and straightedge. Do not erase your construction marks so others can see your method.

8. Construct an equilateral triangle using your compass and straightedge. Each side should be the length of this segment.

9. Repeat Exercises 7 and 8 using constructions with patty paper.

10. Use geometry software to construct an equilateral triangle. Drag each vertex to make sure it remains equilateral.

11. Draw quadrilateral *QUAD*. Duplicate it, using your compass and straightedge. Label the construction *COPY* so that $QUAD \cong COPY$. ⓗ

Review

12. Copy the diagram at right. Use the Vertical Angles Conjecture and the Parallel Lines Conjecture to calculate the measure of each angle.

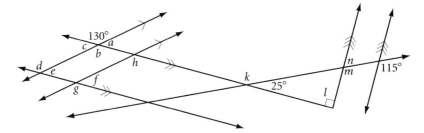

13. Hyacinth is standing on the curb waiting to cross 24th Street. A half block to her left is Avenue J, and Avenue K is a half block to her right. Numbered streets run parallel to one another and are all perpendicular to lettered avenues. If Avenue P is the northernmost avenue, which direction (north, south, east, or west) is she facing?

14. Write a new definition for an isosceles triangle, based on the triangle's reflectional symmetry. Does your definition apply to equilateral triangles? Explain. ⓗ

15. Sketch the three-dimensional figure formed by folding this net into a solid.

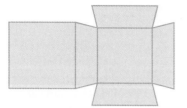

16. △*TRY* has been reflected twice to create △*T"R"Y"*. Sketch in two lines of reflection.

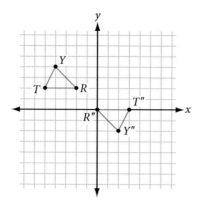

17. Use your ruler to draw a triangle with side lengths 8 cm, 10 cm, and 11 cm. Explain your method. Can you draw a second triangle with the same three side lengths that is not congruent to the first? ⓗ

DEVELOPING MATHEMATICAL REASONING

Pyramid Puzzle

Place four different numbers in the bubbles at the vertices of each pyramid so that the two numbers at the ends of each edge add to the number on that edge.

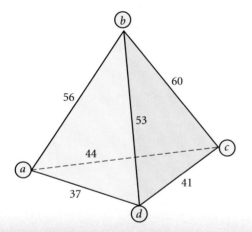

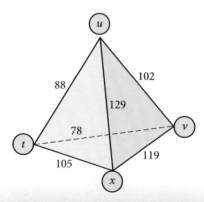

Constructing Perpendicular Bisectors

Each segment has exactly one midpoint. A **segment bisector** is a line, ray, or segment that passes through the midpoint of a segment.

A segment has many perpendiculars and many bisectors, but in a plane each segment has only one bisector that is also perpendicular to the segment. This line is its **perpendicular bisector**.

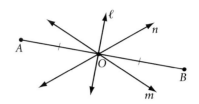

Lines ℓ, *m*, and *n* bisect $\overline{AB}$.

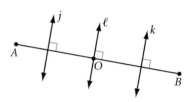

Lines *j*, *k*, and ℓ are perpendicular to $\overline{AB}$.

The construction of the perpendicular bisector of a segment creates a line of symmetry. You use this property when you hang a television. If you want to center the TV above the entertainment unit, you need to place a nail in the wall somewhere along the perpendicular bisector of the segment that forms the top edge of the unit closest to the wall.

Line ℓ is the perpendicular bisector of $\overline{AB}$.

In an earlier lesson you discovered that the line of reflection bisects the segments connecting each point and its image point. In addition, the line of reflection is perpendicular to each of the segments. This can now be combined. The line of reflection is the perpendicular bisector of any segment connecting a point and its image point after a reflection.

INVESTIGATION 1

Finding the Right Bisector

In this investigation you will discover how to construct the perpendicular bisector of a segment.

Step 1 Draw a segment on patty paper. Label it $\overline{PQ}$.

Step 1

Step 2 Fold your patty paper so that endpoints *P* and *Q* land exactly on top of each other, that is, they **coincide.** Crease your paper along the fold.

Step 2

Step 3 Unfold your paper. Draw a line in the crease. What is the relationship of this line to $\overline{PQ}$? Check with others in your group. Use your ruler and protractor to verify your observations.

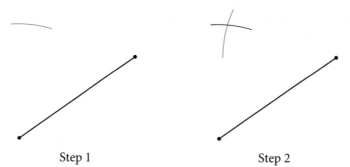

Step 3

How would you describe the relationship of the points on the perpendicular bisector to the endpoints of the bisected segment?

Step 4 Place three points on your perpendicular bisector. Label them *A*, *B*, and *C*. With your compass, compare the distances *PA* and *QA*. Compare the distances *PB* and *QB*. Compare the distances *PC* and *QC*. What do you notice about the two distances from each point on the perpendicular bisector to the endpoints of the segment? Compare your results with the results of others. Then copy and complete the conjecture.

Step 4

Remember to add each conjecture to your conjecture list and draw a figure for it.

Perpendicular Bisector Conjecture   C-5

If a point is on the perpendicular bisector of a segment, then it is ? from the endpoints.

You've just completed the Perpendicular Bisector Conjecture. What about the converse of this statement?

INVESTIGATION 2

Constructing the Perpendicular Bisector

YOU WILL NEED
- a compass
- a straightedge

If a point is **equidistant**, or the same distance, from two endpoints of a line segment in a plane, will it be on the segment's perpendicular bisector? If so, then locating two such points can help you construct the perpendicular bisector.

Step 1   Step 2

Step 1 Draw a line segment. Set your compass to more than half the distance between the endpoints. Using one endpoint as center, swing an arc on one side of the segment.

Step 2 Using the same compass setting, but using the other endpoint as center, swing a second arc intersecting the first.

Step 3 The point where the two arcs intersect is equidistant from the endpoints of your segment. Just as you did on one side of the segment, use your compass to find another such point. Use these points to construct a line. Is this line the perpendicular bisector of the segment? Explain. Use the paper-folding technique of Investigation 1 to check.

Step 4 Complete the conjecture below, and write a summary of what you did in this investigation.

> **Converse of the Perpendicular Bisector Conjecture**   **C-6**
>
> If a point is equidistant from the endpoints of a segment, then it is on the ? of the segment.

Notice that constructing the perpendicular bisector also locates the midpoint of a segment. Now that you know how to construct the perpendicular bisector and the midpoint, you can construct rectangles, squares, and right triangles. You can also construct two special segments in any triangle: medians and midsegments.

The segment connecting the vertex of a triangle to the midpoint of its opposite side is a **median**. There are three midpoints and three vertices in every triangle, so every triangle has three medians.

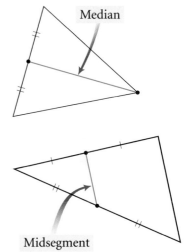
Median

The segment that connects the midpoints of two sides of a triangle is a **midsegment**. A triangle has three sides, each with its own midpoint, so there are three midsegments in every triangle.

Midsegment

3.2 Exercises

YOU WILL NEED

For Exercises 1–5, construct the figures using only a compass and a straightedge.

Construction tools for Exercises **1–6, 8–11, 13, 15–17, 24**

1. Draw and label $\overline{AB}$. Construct the perpendicular bisector of $\overline{AB}$.

2. Draw and label $\overline{QD}$. Construct perpendicular bisectors to divide $\overline{QD}$ into four congruent segments. *(h)*

Geometry software for Exercise **14**

3. Draw a line segment so close to the edge of your paper that you can swing arcs on only one side of the segment. Then construct the perpendicular bisector of the segment. *(h)*

4. Using $\overline{AB}$ and $\overline{CD}$, construct a segment with length $2AB - \frac{1}{2}CD$. *(h)*

A •————————————————————• B   C •————————————————————• D

5. Construct $\overline{MN}$ with length equal to the average length of $\overline{AB}$ and $\overline{CD}$ above. *(h)*

6. Do Exercises 1–5 using patty paper.

7. Complete each statement as fully as possible.

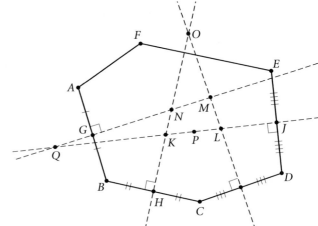

   a. *P* is equidistant from _____ .

   b. *Q* is equidistant from _____ .

   c. *K* is equidistant from _____ .

   d. *L* is equidistant from _____ .

   e. *M* is equidistant from _____ .

   f. *O* is equidistant from _____ .

For Exercises 8–11, you have your choice of construction tools. Use either a compass and a straightedge, or patty paper and a straightedge. Do *not* use patty paper and compass together.

8. Construct $\triangle ALI$. Construct the perpendicular bisector of each side. What do you notice about the three bisectors?

9. Construct $\triangle ABC$. Construct medians $\overline{AM}$, $\overline{BN}$, and $\overline{CL}$. Notice anything special? *(h)*

10. Construct $\triangle DEF$. Construct midsegment $\overline{GH}$ where G is the midpoint of $\overline{DF}$ and H is the midpoint of $\overline{DE}$. What do you notice about the relationship between $\overline{EF}$ and $\overline{GH}$?

11. Copy rectangle *DSOE* onto your paper. Construct the midpoint of each side. Label the midpoint of $\overline{DS}$ point *I*, the midpoint of $\overline{SO}$ point *C*, the midpoint of $\overline{OE}$ point *V*, and the midpoint of $\overline{ED}$ point *R*. Construct quadrilateral *RICV*. Describe *RICV*.

12. The island shown at right has two post offices. The postal service wants to divide the island into two zones so that anyone within each zone is always closer to their own post office than to the other one. Copy the island and the locations of the post offices and locate the dividing line between the two zones. Explain how you know this dividing line solves the problem. Or pick several points in each zone and make sure they are closer to that zone's post office than they are to the other one.

13. Copy parallelogram *FLAT* onto your paper. Construct the perpendicular bisector of each side. What do you notice about the quadrilateral formed by the four lines? How do you know?

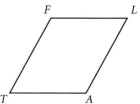

14. Use geometry software to construct a triangle. Construct a median. Are the two triangles created by the median congruent? Use an area measuring tool in your software program to find the areas of the two triangles. How do they compare? If you made the original triangle from heavy cardboard, and you wanted to balance that cardboard triangle on the edge of a ruler, what would you do? Explain your reasoning.

15. Construct a very large triangle on a piece of cardboard or mat board and construct a median. Cut out the triangle and see if you can balance it on the edge of a ruler. Where should you try placing the ruler? Hint: If you were to cut the triangle into two pieces along the median and weigh the two pieces how would they compare?

16. Copy the figure and its reflected image onto a sheet of paper. Locate the line of reflection using a compass and straightedge. Explain your method.

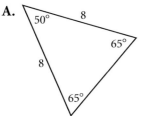 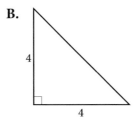

17. Copy the figure and the line of reflection onto a sheet of paper. Use a compass and straightedge to construct the reflected image. Explain your method. ⓗ

Review

In Exercises 18–23, match the term with its figure below.

18. Scalene acute triangle

19. Isosceles obtuse triangle

20. Isosceles right triangle

21. Isosceles acute triangle

22. Scalene obtuse triangle

23. Scalene right triangle

A.

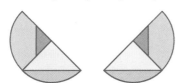

B.

C.

D.

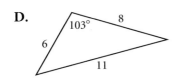

E.

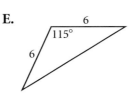

F.

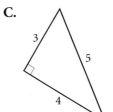

24. Use your ruler and protractor to draw a triangle with angle measures 40° and 70° and a side opposite the 70° angle with length 10 cm. Explain your method. Can you draw a second triangle using the same instructions that is not congruent to the first? ⓗ

Constructing Perpendiculars to a Line

If you are in a room, look over at one of the walls. What is the distance from where you are to that wall? How would you measure that distance? There are a lot of distances from where you are to the wall, but in geometry when we speak of a distance from a point to a line we mean the perpendicular distance.

The construction of a perpendicular from a point to a line (with the point not on the line) is another of Euclid's constructions, and it has practical applications in many fields, including agriculture and engineering. For example, think of a high-speed Internet cable as a line and a building as a point not on the line. Suppose you wanted to connect the building to the Internet cable using the shortest possible length of connecting wire. How can you find out how much wire you need, so you don't buy too much?

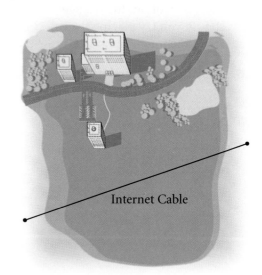

Internet Cable

 ## INVESTIGATION 1

Finding the Right Line

You already know how to construct perpendicular bisectors of segments. You can use that knowledge to construct a perpendicular from a point to a line.

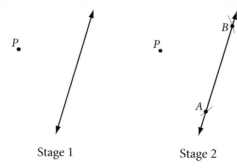

Stage 1   Stage 2

Step 1 Draw a line and a point labeled *P* not on the line, as shown above.

Step 2 Describe the construction steps you take at Stage 2.

Step 3 How is *PA* related to *PB*? What does this answer tell you about where point *P* lies? Hint: See the Converse of the Perpendicular Bisector Conjecture.

Step 4 Construct the perpendicular bisector of $\overline{AB}$. Label the midpoint *M*.

You have now constructed a perpendicular through a point not on the line. This is useful for finding the distance to a line.

Step 5 Label three randomly placed points on $\overleftrightarrow{AB}$ as Q, R, and S. Measure PQ, PR, PS, and PM. Which distance is shortest? Compare results with those of others in your group.

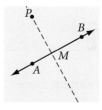

You are now ready to state your observations by completing the conjecture.

> **Shortest Distance Conjecture** C-7
>
> The shortest distance from a point to a line is measured along the ? from the point to the line.

Let's take another look. How could you use patty paper to do this construction?

INVESTIGATION 2

Patty Paper Perpendiculars

YOU WILL NEED
- patty paper
- a straightedge

In Investigation 1, you constructed a perpendicular from a point to a line. Now let's do the same construction using patty paper.

On a piece of patty paper, perform the steps below.

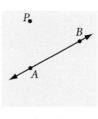      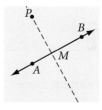

Step 1   Step 2   Step 3

Step 1 Draw and label $\overleftrightarrow{AB}$ and a point P not on $\overleftrightarrow{AB}$.

Step 2 Fold the line onto itself, and slide the layers of paper so that point P appears to be on the crease. Is the crease perpendicular to the line? Check it with the corner of a piece of patty paper.

Step 3 Label the point of intersection M. Are $\angle AMP$ and $\angle BMP$ congruent? Supplementary? Why or why not?

In Investigation 2, is M the midpoint of $\overline{AB}$? Do you think it needs to be? Think about the techniques used in the two investigations. How do the techniques differ?

The construction of a perpendicular from a point to a line lets you find the shortest distance from a point to a line. The geometry definition of distance from a point to a line is based on this construction, and it reads, "The **distance from a point to a line** is the length of the perpendicular segment from the point to the line."

You can also use this construction to find an altitude of a triangle. An **altitude** of a triangle is a perpendicular segment from a vertex to the opposite side or to a line containing the opposite side.

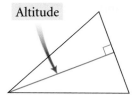

Altitude

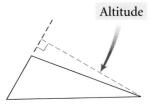

Altitude

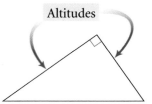

Altitudes

An altitude can be inside the triangle.

An altitude can be outside the triangle.

An altitude can be one of the sides of the triangle.

The length of the altitude is the height of the triangle. A triangle has three different altitudes, so it has three different heights.

3.3 Exercises

YOU WILL NEED

Construction tools
for Exercises **3–14,
16, 17, 22, 23**

1. Why do we define an altitude of a triangle as a perpendicular segment from a vertex to the opposite side or to a line containing the opposite side?

2. Use the diagrams to complete the following statements:

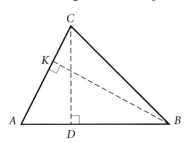

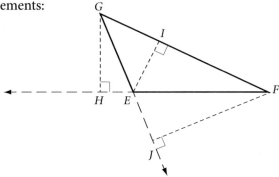

   a. $\overline{CD}$ is the altitude from C to _____.

   b. _____ is the altitude from B to $\overline{AC}$.

   c. $\overline{EI}$ is the _____ from E to $\overline{GF}$.

   d. $\overline{GH}$ is the altitude from _____ to $\overrightarrow{FH}$.

   e. _____ is the altitude from F to $\overrightarrow{GE}$.

Use your compass and straightedge and the definition of distance to do Exercises 3–7.

3. Draw an obtuse angle *BIG*. Place a point *P* inside the angle. Now construct perpendiculars from the point to both sides of the angle. Which side is closer to point *P*?

4. Draw an acute triangle. Label it *ABC*. Construct altitude $\overline{CD}$ with point *D* on $\overleftrightarrow{AB}$. (We didn't forget about point *D*. It's at the foot of the perpendicular. Your job is to locate it.)

In this sketch, the architect has constructed a set of converging lines and vertical lines to produce an illusion of distance.

5. Draw obtuse triangle *OBT* with obtuse angle *O*. Construct altitude $\overline{BU}$. In an obtuse triangle, an altitude can fall outside the triangle. To construct an altitude from point B of your triangle, extend side $\overline{OT}$. In an obtuse triangle, how many altitudes fall outside the triangle and how many fall inside the triangle? ⓗ

6. How can you construct a perpendicular to a line through a point that is on the line? Draw a line. Mark a point on your line. Now experiment. Devise a method to construct a perpendicular to your line at the point. ⓗ

7. Draw a line. Mark two points on the line and label them *Q* and *R*. Now construct a square *SQRE* with $\overline{QR}$ as a side. ⓗ

For Exercises 8–11, use patty paper and a straightedge. (Attach your patty paper work to your problems.)

8. Draw a line across your patty paper with a straightedge. Place a point *P* not on the line, and fold the perpendicular to the line through the point *P*. How would you fold to construct a perpendicular through a point on a line? Place a point *Q* on the line. Fold a perpendicular to the line through point *Q*. What do you notice about the two folds?

9. Draw a very large acute triangle on your patty paper. Place a point inside the triangle. Now construct perpendiculars from the point to all three sides of the triangle by folding. Mark your figure. How can you use your construction to decide which side of the triangle your point is closest to?

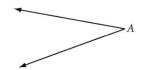

10. Construct an isosceles right triangle. Label its vertices *A*, *B*, and *C*, with point *C* the right angle. Fold to construct the altitude $\overline{CD}$. What do you notice about this line?

11. Draw obtuse triangle *OBT* with angle *O* obtuse. Fold to construct the altitude $\overline{BU}$. (Don't forget, you must extend the side $\overline{OT}$.)

For Exercises 12–14, you may use either patty paper or a compass and a straightedge.

12. Construct a square *ABLE* such that the length of *PR* is half the perimeter. ⓗ

13. Construct a rectangle whose width is half its length.

14. Construct the complement of ∠*A*. ⓗ

15. Jerilyn is helping her dad Jerry set the corners for the rectangular concrete pad that they are pouring for their new backyard patio. Jerry is using an old technique he learned from his dad. He lays out two stakes about fifty feet apart and draws a chalk line between them. Next Jerry attaches the two ends of a long rope to the two stakes. He then instructs Jerilyn to grab hold of the rope and pull it tight on one side of the chalk line and asks her to pound another stake in the ground at that location. Jerry then asked Jerilyn, "All right, what do I do next to get a stake on the other side of the chalk line so that the line connecting the two stakes is perpendicular to the chalk line?"

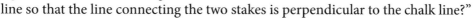

Jerilyn of course knew her geometry so she was able to answer him. What does she need to do to complete the construction of the perpendicular? Draw a diagram and explain the geometry Jerilyn needed to complete the task.

16. Place two congruent segments, say $\overline{AB} \cong \overline{CD}$, randomly on your paper. Recall that the line of reflection is the perpendicular bisector of any segment connecting a point and its image point. Use that property of reflections with your compass and straightedge to construct the reflection of $\overline{AB}$ onto $\overline{CD}$. ⓗ

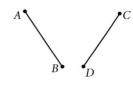

17. Place two congruent angles, say $\angle B \cong \angle E$, randomly on your paper. Recall that the line of reflection is the perpendicular bisector of any segment connecting a point and its image point. Use that property of reflections with your compass and straightedge to construct the reflection of $\angle ABC$ onto $\angle DEF$. Explain how you know. ⓗ

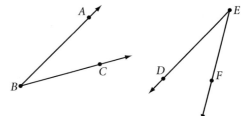

Review

18. Copy and complete the table. Make a conjecture for the value of the *n*th term and for the value of the 35th term. ⓗ

Rectangular pattern with triangles

Rectangle	1	2	3	4	5	6	...	*n*	...	35
Number of shaded triangles	2	9					...		...	

  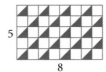 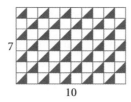

19. Sketch the solid of revolution formed when the two-dimensional figure at right is revolved about the line.

For Exercises 20–23, label the vertices with the appropriate letters. When you sketch or draw, use the special marks that indicate right angles, parallel segments, and congruent segments and angles.

20. Sketch obtuse triangle *FIT* with $m\angle I > 90°$ and median $\overline{IY}$.

21. Sketch $\overline{AB} \perp \overline{CD}$ and $\overline{EF} \perp \overline{CD}$.

22. Use your protractor to draw a regular pentagon. Draw all the diagonals. Use your compass to construct a regular hexagon. Draw three diagonals connecting alternating vertices. Do the same for the other three vertices. ⓗ

23. Draw a triangle with a 6 cm side and an 8 cm side and the angle between them measuring 40°. Draw a second triangle with a 6 cm side and an 8 cm side and exactly one 40° angle that is not between the two given sides. Are the two triangles congruent?

Constructing Angle Bisectors

A stained glass artist is designing her latest piece of glass art. She plans to position a number of colorful rondels into the different angles in his design. Because the glass artist knows the properties of an angle bisector, she knows she needs to construct an angle bisector in each arm of the star to help her locate the centers of the circles. As with a perpendicular bisector of a segment, an angle bisector forms a line of symmetry. While the definition in Chapter 1 defined an angle bisector as a ray, you may also refer to a segment as an angle bisector if it lies on the ray and passes through the vertex.

INVESTIGATION 1

YOU WILL NEED

- patty paper
- a straightedge

▶ **Art**
CONNECTION

The designer of stained glass arranges pieces of painted glass to form the elaborate mosaics that you might see in Gothic cathedrals or on Tiffany lampshades. He first organizes the glass pieces by shape and color according to the design. He mounts these pieces into a metal framework that will hold the design. With precision, the designer cuts every glass piece so that it fits against the next one with a strip of cast lead. The result is a pleasing combination of colors and shapes that form a luminous design when viewed against light.

Angle Bisecting by Folding

Each person should draw his or her own acute angle for this investigation.

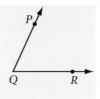

Step 1

Step 2

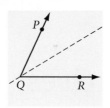

Step 3

Step 1 On patty paper, draw a large-scale angle. Label it ∠*PQR*.

Step 2 Fold your patty paper so that $\overrightarrow{QP}$ and $\overrightarrow{QR}$ coincide. Crease the fold. You have reflected $\overrightarrow{QP}$ onto $\overrightarrow{QR}$ and the crease is the line of reflection and thus the line of symmetry for the angle.

Step 3 Unfold your patty paper. Draw a ray with endpoint *Q* along the crease. Does the ray bisect ∠*PQR*? How can you tell?

Step 4 Place a point on your angle bisector. Label it *A*. Compare the distances from *A* to each of the two sides. Remember that "distance" means *shortest* distance! Try it with other points on the angle bisector. Compare your results with those of others. Copy and complete the conjecture.

Angle Bisector Conjecture   C-8

If a point is on the bisector of an angle, then it is ⟶?⟵ from the sides of the angle.

You've found the bisector of an angle by folding patty paper. Now let's see how you can construct the angle bisector with a compass and a straightedge.

 INVESTIGATION 2

YOU WILL NEED

• a compass
• a straightedge

Angle Bisecting with Compass

In this investigation, you will find a method for bisecting an angle using a compass and straightedge. Each person in your group should investigate a different angle.

Step 1 Draw an angle.

Step 2 Find a method for constructing the bisector of the angle. Experiment!

Hint: Start by drawing an arc centered at the vertex.

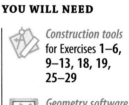

Step 3 Once you think you have constructed the angle bisector, fold your paper to see if the ray you constructed is actually the bisector. Share your method with other students in your group. Agree on a best method.

Step 4 Write a summary of what you did in this investigation.

In earlier lessons, you learned to construct a 90° angle. Now you know how to bisect an angle. What angles can you construct by combining these two skills?

3.4 Exercises

YOU WILL NEED

Construction tools
for Exercises 1–6, 9–13, 18, 19, 25–29

Geometry software
for Exercise 30

1. With your protractor carefully draw an 80° angle. Use your compass and straightedge to construct the bisector of the angle.

2. With your protractor carefully draw a 140° angle on a sheet of patty paper. Fold to construct the bisector of the angle. What is the measure of the two angles created?

3. Construct an obtuse angle and bisect it. Pick a point on the angle bisector, label it *O* and construct a perpendicular to each of the two rays of the angle. Construct a circle with *O* the center of the circle and the radius of the circle is the length of the perpendicular to the two sides of the angle. You have just constructed a circle tangent to the two sides of the angle.

4. Construct an equilateral triangle. Bisect one angle. What do you notice about the two smaller triangles just created?

5. Construct an angle with each given measure and label it. Remember, you may use only your compass and straightedge. No protractor!
   a. 90°   b. 45°   c. 135°

6. Repeat Exercise 5 with patty paper. Which set of construction tools do you prefer? Why?

7. Which ray is the angle bisector? Explain your reasoning.

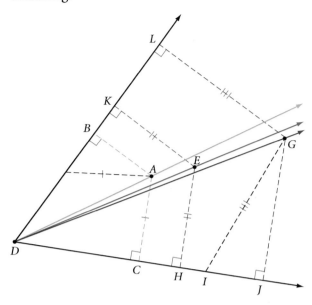

8. If points *D* and *E* lie on the bisector of angle *ABC* then what are the measures *x* and *y*?

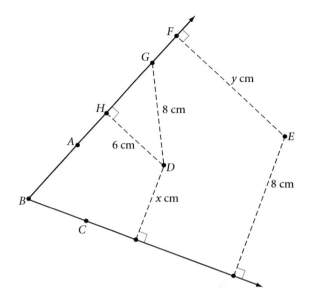

For Exercises 9–11, construct a figure with the given specifications.

9. Given:

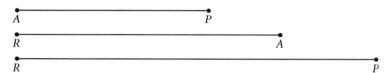

Construct: An isosceles right triangle with *z* as the length of each of the two congruent sides. Bisect each acute angle.

10. Given:

Construct: △*RAP* with median $\overline{PM}$ and angle bisector $\overline{RB}$

11. Given:

Construct: △*MSE* angle bisector $\overline{EU}$ and *O* the midpoint of $\overline{MS}$.

12. Draw a large acute triangle. Bisect the angle at one vertex with a compass and a straightedge. Construct an altitude from the second vertex and a median from the third vertex.

13. Use your straightedge to construct a linear pair of angles. Use your compass to bisect each angle of the linear pair. What do you notice about the two angle bisectors? Can you make a conjecture? Can you explain why it is true?

14. In this lesson you discovered the Angle Bisector Conjecture. Write the converse of the Angle Bisector Conjecture. Do you think it's true? Why or why not?

15. Solve for y.

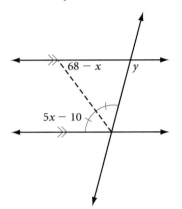

16. If $\overrightarrow{AE}$ bisects $\angle CAR$ and $m\angle CAR = 84°$, find $m\angle R$.

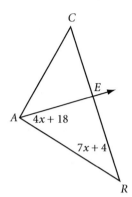

17. Which angle is largest, $\angle A$, $\angle B$, or $\angle C$? Explain.

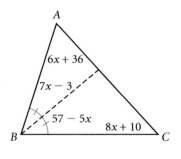

18. Place two congruent segments that share a vertex, say $\overline{AB} \cong \overline{BC}$, on your paper. Construct the line of reflection that would reflect $\overline{AB}$ onto $\overline{BC}$. Explain how you know that your line is the line of reflection.

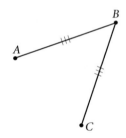

19. Place two congruent angles that share a vertex, say $\angle ABC \cong \angle DBE$, on your paper. Construct the line of reflection that would reflect $\angle ABC$ onto $\angle DBE$. Explain how you know that your line is the line of reflection. ⓗ

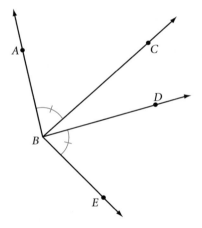

Review

For Exercises 20–24, match each geometric construction with its diagram.

20. Construction of an angle bisector

21. Construction of a median

22. Construction of a midsegment

23. Construction of a perpendicular bisector

24. Construction of an altitude

A.

B.

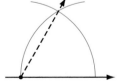

C.

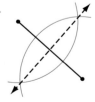

D.

E.

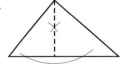

F.

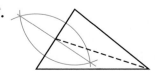

Draw or construct each figure in Exercises 25–30. Label the vertices with the appropriate letters. If you're unclear on the difference between "draw" and "construct," refer back to pages 156 and 157.

25. Draw a regular octagon. What traffic sign comes to mind? ⓗ

26. Construct regular octagon *ALTOSIGN*. ⓗ

27. Draw △*ABC* so that *AC* = 3.5 cm, *AB* = 5.6 cm, and *m*∠*BAC* = 130°.

28. Draw isosceles right △*ABC* so that *BC* = 6.5 cm and *m*∠*B* = 90°.

29. Draw a triangle with a 40° angle, a 60° angle, and a side between the given angles measuring 8 cm. Draw a second triangle with a 40° angle and a 60° angle but with a side measuring 8 cm *opposite* the 60° angle. Are the triangles congruent? ⓗ

30. Use geometry software to construct $\overline{AB}$ and $\overline{CD}$, with point *C* on $\overline{AB}$ and point *D* not on $\overleftrightarrow{AB}$. Construct the perpendicular bisector of $\overline{CD}$.

    a. Trace this perpendicular bisector as you drag point *C* along $\overline{AB}$. Describe the shape formed by this locus of lines.

    b. Erase the tracings from part a. Now trace the midpoint of $\overline{CD}$ as you drag *C*. Describe the locus of points.

31. Given △*ABC* with vertices: *A*(−6, 2), *B*(−3, 0), *C*(−2, 4) and △*DEF* with vertices: *D*(2, 6), *E*(0, 3), *F*(4, 2).

    a. Rotate △*ABC* by the transformation rule (*x*, *y*) → (*y*, −*x*) to create △*A′B′C′*.

    b. What happened? Does triangle *A′B′C′* appear to coincide with triangle *DEF*?

    c. If they are congruent, what is the statement of congruence, △*A′B′C′* ≅ △(???)?

    d. If they are not congruent explain why not.

DEVELOPING MATHEMATICAL REASONING

Coin Swap Puzzles

In each of the three coin swap puzzles below, your task is to switch the positions of the dimes and pennies in the exact number of moves required. A coin can slide into an empty square next to it, or it can jump over one coin into an empty space. Use symbols like those shown to the right to explain your solutions.

Penny Jumps Right   Dime Slides Left

Coin Swap Puzzle 1: Reverse the position of the two dimes and two pennies on the grid of five squares in exactly eight moves.

Coin Coin Swap Puzzle 2: Reverse the position of the three dimes and three pennies on the grid of seven squares in exactly 15 moves.

Coin Swap Puzzle 3: Reverse the position of the four dimes and four pennies on the grid of nine squares in exactly 24 moves.

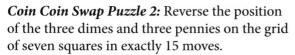 

Constructing Parallel Lines

Parallel lines are lines that lie in the same plane and do not intersect.

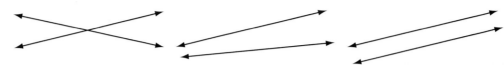

Parallel lines appear everywhere in our man-made world. Some parallel lines may only be decorative but many have important uses. Railroad tracks are parallel, the edges of steps are parallel; lanes on a highway are parallel; parallel streets are used in city planning; planting your vegetables in parallel rows in a garden is common; and the parallel mirrors on opposite walls in hair salons are all examples of important uses of parallel lines. What would happen in these examples if the items were no longer parallel? A train could derail; unparallel steps could cause falls; and highways would be more costly and dangerous. What is good about using parallels in these other examples? You will get a chance to answer that in the exercise set.

INVESTIGATION

YOU WILL NEED
- patty paper
- a straightedge

Constructing Parallel Lines by Folding

How would you check whether two lines are parallel? One way is to draw a transversal and compare corresponding angles. You can also use this idea to *construct* a pair of parallel lines.

Step 1 Draw a line and a point on patty paper as shown.

Step 1

Step 2 Fold the paper to construct a perpendicular so that the crease runs through the point as shown. Describe the four newly formed angles.

Step 2

Step 3 Through the point, make another fold that is perpendicular to the first crease.

Step 3

Step 4 Compare the pairs of corresponding angles created by the folds. Are they all congruent? Why? What conclusion can you make about the lines?

Step 4

There are many ways to construct parallel lines. You can construct parallel lines much more quickly with patty paper than with compass and straightedge. You can also use properties you discovered in the Parallel Lines Conjecture to construct parallel lines by duplicating corresponding angles, alternate interior angles, or alternate exterior angles. Or you can construct two perpendiculars to the same line. In the exercises you will practice all of these methods.

3.5 Exercises

YOU WILL NEED

Construction tools for Exercises 2–8, 10–12

In this exercise set, use the specified construction tools to do each construction. If no tools are specified, you may choose either patty paper or compass and straightedge.

1. How do parallel lines improve the following situations?
   a. Planting crops in parallel rows. ⓗ
   b. Parallel mirrors in hair salons.
   c. Parallel and perpendicular grid of city streets

2. Use a compass and straightedge. Draw a line and a point not on the line. Construct a second line through the point that is parallel to the first line, by duplicating alternate interior angles.

3. Use a compass and straightedge. Draw a line and a point not on the line. Construct a second line through the point that is parallel to the first line, by duplicating corresponding angles.

4. Construct a parallelogram with two consecutive sides *y* and *z* and *∠A* as one of the acute angles of the parallelogram.

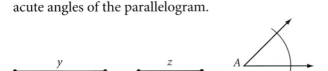

5. Construct a rhombus with *x* as the length of each side and *∠A* as one of the acute angles.

6. Construct trapezoid *TRAP* with $\overline{TR}$ and $\overline{AP}$ as the two parallel sides and with *AP* as the distance between them. (There are many solutions!)

7. Using patty paper and straightedge, or a compass and straightedge, construct parallelogram *GRAM* with $\overline{RG}$ and $\overline{RA}$ as two consecutive sides and *ML* as the distance between $\overline{RG}$ and $\overline{AM}$. (How many solutions can you find?)

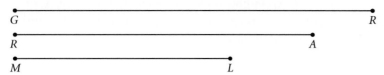

You may choose to do Exercises 8, 10, and 12 using geometry software.

8. Draw a large scalene acute triangle and label it △*SUM*. Through vertex *M* construct a line parallel to side $\overleftrightarrow{SU}$ as shown in the diagram. Use your protractor or a piece of patty paper to compare ∠1 and ∠2 with the other two angles of the triangle (∠*S* and ∠*U*). Notice anything special? Write down what you observe.

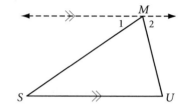

9. DEVELOPING PROOF Use deductive reasoning to explain why your observation in Exercise 8 is true for any triangle.

10. Draw a large scalene acute triangle and label it △*PAR*. Place point *E* anywhere on side *PR*, and construct a line $\overleftrightarrow{EL}$ parallel to side $\overline{PA}$ as shown in the diagram. Use your ruler to measure the lengths of the four segments, $\overline{AL}$, $\overline{LR}$, $\overline{RE}$, and $\overline{EP}$, and compare ratios $\frac{RL}{LA}$ and $\frac{RE}{EP}$. Notice anything special? Write down what you observe.

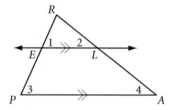

11. DEVELOPING PROOF Measure the four labeled angles in Exercise 10. Notice anything special? Use deductive reasoning to explain why your observation is true for any triangle.

12. Draw a pair of parallel lines by tracing along both edges of your ruler. Draw a transversal. Use your compass to bisect each angle of a pair of alternate interior angles. What shape is formed?

13. DEVELOPING PROOF Use deductive reasoning to explain why the resulting shape is formed in Exercise 12.

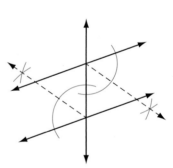

Review

14. Sketch trapezoid *ZOID* with $\overline{ZO} \parallel \overline{ID}$, point *T* the midpoint of $\overline{OI}$, and *R* the midpoint of $\overline{ZD}$. Sketch $\overline{TR}$.

15. Draw rhombus *ROMB* with *m*∠*R* = 60° and diagonal $\overline{OB}$.

16. Draw rectangle *RECK* with diagonals $\overline{RC}$ and $\overline{EK}$ both 8 cm long and intersecting at point *W*.

17. DEVELOPING PROOF Copy the diagram below. Use your conjectures to calculate the measure of each lettered angle. Explain how you determined measures *m, p,* and *r.*

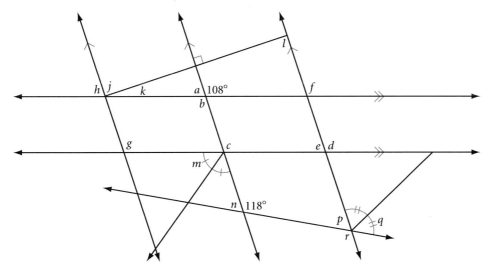

18. Given quadrilateral *ABCD* with vertices: $A(3, -2)$, $B(6, 3)$, $C(4, 7)$, $D(1, 3)$ and quadrilateral *EFGH* with vertices: $E(-8, 3)$, $F(-6, -2)$, $G(-3, 3)$, $H(-6, 7)$.

a. Reflect quadrilateral *ABCD* by the transformation rule $(x, y) \rightarrow ? (-x - 2, y)$ to create quadrilateral *A′B′C′D′*.

b. What happened? Does quadrilateral *A′B′C′D′* appear to coincide with quadrilateral *EFGH*?

c. If they are congruent, what is the statement of congruence, quadrilateral *A′B′C′D′* ≅ quadrilateral (????)?

d. If they are not congruent explain why not.

DEVELOPING MATHEMATICAL REASONING

Folding Cubes I

In the problems below, the figure at the left represents the net for a cube. When the net is folded, which cube at the right will it become?

1. 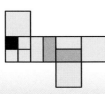   **A.**   **B.**   **C.**

2. 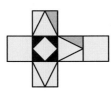   **A.**   **B.**   **C.**

3. 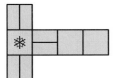   **A.**   **B.**   **C.**

Construction Problems

Islamic art is perhaps the ultimate success story of geometric constructions. As you saw in Lesson 0.6, Islamic designs are a rich source of intricate abstract geometric art. The builders of the cathedrals of Europe during the Gothic period were the master geometers of their time and the compass and straightedge were the tools of their trade. Those artisans that knew the geometric constructions were prized for their special knowledge.

Once you know the basic constructions, you too can solve intricate geometric design problems. For example, how would you construct the circle tangent to the three gothic arches shown in the diagram below left or create a design similar to the Islamic design below right? You will get your chance in the exercises in this lesson.

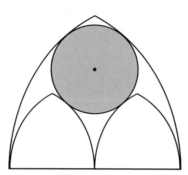

With your knowledge of compass and straightedge constructions you can also discover more of the properties of Euclidean geometry. You know how to duplicate segments and angles with compass and straightedge. Given a triangle, you can use these two constructions to duplicate the triangle by copying each segment and angle. Can you construct a triangle if you are given the parts separately? Would you need all six parts—three segments and three angles—to construct a triangle?

Let's first consider a case in which only three segments are given.

EXAMPLE A

Construct $\triangle ABC$ using the three segments $\overline{AB}$, $\overline{BC}$, and $\overline{CA}$ shown below. How many different-size triangles can be drawn?

Solution

You can begin by duplicating one segment, for example $\overline{AC}$. Then adjust your compass to match the length of another segment. Using this length as a radius, draw an arc centered at one endpoint of the first segment. Now use the third segment length as the radius for another arc, this one centered at the other endpoint. Where the arcs intersect is the location of the third vertex of the triangle.

In the construction on the previous page, the segment lengths determine where the arcs intersect. Once the triangle "closes" at the intersection of the arcs, the angles are determined too. So the lengths of the segments affect the size of the angles.

There are other ways to construct △ABC. For example, you could draw the arcs below $\overline{AC}$, and point B would be below $\overline{AC}$. Or you could start by duplicating $\overline{BC}$ instead of $\overline{AC}$. But if you try these constructions, you will find that they all produce congruent triangles. There is only one size of triangle that can be drawn with the segments given, so the segments **determine** the triangle. Does having three angles also determine a triangle?

EXAMPLE B | Construct △ABC with patty paper by duplicating the three angles ∠A, ∠B, and ∠C shown at right. How many different size triangles can be drawn?

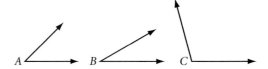

Solution | In this patty paper construction the angles do not determine the segment length. You can locate the endpoint of a segment anywhere along an angle's side without affecting the angle measures. As shown in the illustration below, the patty paper with ∠A can slide horizontally over the patty paper with ∠B to create triangles of different sizes. (The third angle in both cases is equal to ∠C.) By sliding ∠A, infinitely many different triangles can be drawn with the angles given. Therefore, three angles do not determine a triangle.

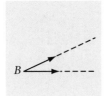
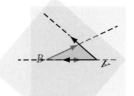
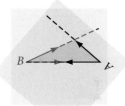

Because a triangle has a total of six parts, there are several combinations of segments and angles that may or may not determine a triangle. Having one or two parts given is not enough to determine a triangle. Is having three parts enough? That answer depends on the combination. In the exercises you will construct triangles and quadrilaterals with various combinations of parts given.

3.6 Exercises

In Exercises 1–8, first sketch and label the figure you are going to construct. Second, construct the figure, using either a compass and straightedge, or patty paper and straightedge. Third, describe the steps in your construction in a few sentences.

YOU WILL NEED

Construction tools
for Exercises **1–8,
10, 16**

Geometry software
for Exercises **9, 11**

1. Given:

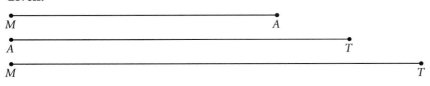

Construct: △MAT

2. Given:

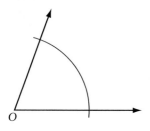

Construct: $\triangle DOT$

3. Given:

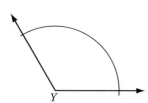
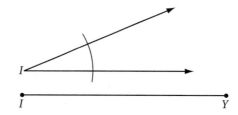

Construct: $\triangle IGY$

4. Given the triangle shown at right, construct another triangle with angles congruent to the given angles but with sides *not* congruent to the given sides. Is there more than one noncongruent triangle with the same three angles?

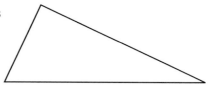

5. The two segments and the angle below do not determine a triangle.

Given:

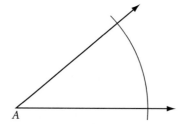

Construct: Two different (noncongruent) triangles named $\triangle ABC$ that have the three given parts ⓗ

6. Given:

Construct: Isosceles triangle *CAT* with perimeter y and length of the base equal to x ⓗ

7. Construct a kite.

8. Construct a quadrilateral with two pairs of opposite sides of equal length.

9. Using geometry software, draw a large scalene obtuse triangle ABC with $\angle B$ the obtuse angle. Construct the angle bisector $\overline{BR}$, the median $\overline{BM}$, and the altitude $\overline{BS}$. What is the order of the points on $\overline{AC}$? Drag B. Is the order of points always the same? Write a conjecture.

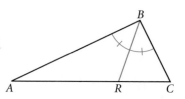

10. An equilateral Gothic arch is an arch made by constructing an equilateral triangle (see diagram to the right). In the diagram at the beginning of this lesson two smaller equilateral Gothic arches have been constructed on the base of a larger equilateral Gothic arch. The radii of the smaller arcs are half the size of the larger arcs. Construct a Gothic arch with two smaller Gothic arches as shown and then construct a circle tangent to both small Gothic arches and tangent to the larger one. ⓗ

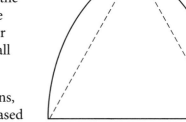

11. Many Islamic designs are based on regular hexagons, octagons, decagons, or dodecagon. Use dynamic geometry software to construct a design based on the regular decagon or dodecagon. ⓗ

Review

12. Draw the new position of △*TEA* if it is reflected over the dotted line. Label the coordinates of the vertices.

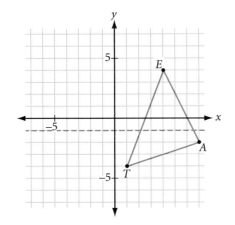

13. Draw each figure and decide how many reflectional and rotational symmetries it has. Copy and complete the table below.

Figure	Reflectional symmetries	Rotational symmetries
Trapezoid		
Kite		
Parallelogram		
Rhombus		
Rectangle		

14. Sketch the three-dimensional figure formed by folding the net at right into a solid.

15. If a polygon has 500 diagonals from each vertex, how many sides does it have?

16. Use your geometry tools to draw parallelogram *CARE* so that $CA = 5.5$ cm, $CE = 3.2$ cm, and $m\angle A = 110°$. ⓗ

DEVELOPING MATHEMATICAL REASONING

Rook's Tour Puzzle

For a 6×6 rook's tour puzzle, the objective is to fill the remaining empty squares with integers from 1 to 36 so that when completed there is a continuous path of numbers from 1 through 36. The path may move horizontally or vertically from square to adjacent square, but not diagonally, just like a rook. The empty circles mark the locations of the starting and ending squares (1 and 36). Fill in the remaining empty squares in the rook's tour puzzle.

30					
					6
	27	○	○		
				12	
23					14

Transformations Using Constructions

"It's amazing what one can do when one doesn't know what one can't do."

GARFIELD THE CAT

In the movie, Transformers, the Autobot Bumblebee transforms into a Camero. Is this a geometric transformation? Why or why not?

In Chapter 1 you discovered a number of properties of the three rigid transformations: reflections, rotations, and translations. You discovered they are all isometries and thus:

- If $\overline{AB}$ is reflected, translated, or rotated creating the image $\overline{A'B'}$ then $\overline{AB} \cong \overline{A'B'}$.

- If $\angle R$ is reflected, translated, or rotated creating the image $\angle R'$ then $\angle R \cong \angle R'$.

- If polygon P is reflected, translated, or rotated creating the image polygon P' then polygon $P \cong$ polygon P'.

You also discovered that every point and its reflected image are always the same distance from the line of reflection. In other words, the line of reflection is the perpendicular bisector of any segment connecting a point to its reflected image point (providing, of course, the point is not on the reflection line).

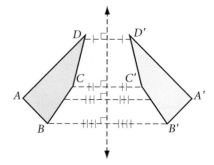

In this lesson you will be asked to explore whether the converse of the first two properties are also true. Namely:

- If two segments are congruent, there is a sequence of transformations that transforms an image of one segment onto the other. (In other words, if $\overline{TV} \cong \overline{XY}$, there is a sequence of transformations that transforms $\overline{TV}$ so that $\overline{T''V''}$ coincides with $\overline{XY}$.)

- If two angles are congruent, there is a sequence of transformations that transforms one angle onto the other. (In other words, if $\angle R \cong \angle S$, there is a sequence of transformations that transforms an image of $\angle R$ so that $\angle R''$ coincides with $\angle S$.)

INVESTIGATION 1

Transforming One Segment onto a Congruent Segment

Step 1 Construct two congruent segments ($\overline{AB} \cong \overline{CD}$) randomly on your paper.

Step 2 Construct the perpendicular bisector m of the segment connecting points A and C. If A is reflected across a line of reflection m, the image of A, point A', coincides with which point? Why?

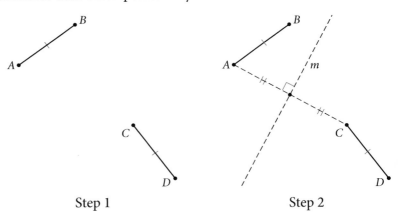

Step 1   Step 2

Step 3 To find the image of B, point B', construct a perpendicular line from B through m. Label the point of intersection of the perpendicular and m, point P. The location of B' on the perpendicular is found because $\overline{BP} \cong \overline{PB'}$. Why? You have constructed $\overline{A'B'}$, the image of $\overline{AB}$, reflected over line m.

Step 4 To construct the transformation of $\overline{A'B'}$ onto $\overline{CD}$, construct the perpendicular bisector n of the segment connecting points B' and D. If B' is reflected across a line of reflection n, the image of B', point B'', must coincide with point D. Why? The image of A' must coincide with C. Why?

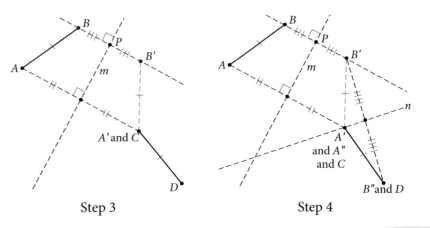

Step 3   Step 4

You just created two congruent segments randomly placed on your paper and you were able to transform an image of one onto the other by construction. Therefore, if two segments are congruent, there is a sequence of transformations that transforms an image of one segment onto the other. (If $\overline{AB} \cong \overline{CD}$, there is a sequence of transformations that transforms $\overline{AB}$ so that $\overline{A''B''}$ coincides with $\overline{CD}$.)

Let's look at the other converse. If two angles are congruent, is there a sequence of transformations that transforms an image of one angle onto the other?

INVESTIGATION 2

Transforming One Angle onto a Congruent Angle

Step 1 Construct two congruent angles ($\angle TRY \cong \angle ANG$) randomly placed on your paper.

Step 2 Construct the perpendicular bisector *m* of the segment connecting points *R* and *N*. If *N* is reflected across a line of reflection *m*, the image of *N*, point *N'*, must coincide with point *R*. Why?

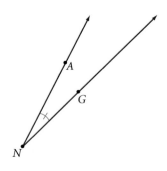

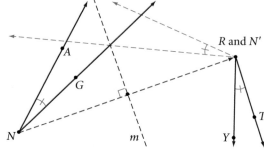

Step 1   Step 2

Step 3 To construct *A'*, the image of *A*, construct a perpendicular from *A* through the perpendicular bisector *m*, and label the point of intersection *L*. Then locate *A'* on the perpendicular so that $\overline{AL} \cong \overline{A'L}$. Repeat to locate *G'*, the image of *G*. Construct a perpendicular from *G* through the perpendicular bisector *m*, and label the point of intersection *E*. Then *G'* is located so that $\overline{GE} \cong \overline{G'E}$. Thus you have constructed $\angle A'N'G'$, the reflection of $\angle ANG$.

Step 4 Next you need to construct the transformation of $\angle A'N'G'$ onto $\angle TRY$. In an earlier exercise you discovered that if two congruent angles share a common vertex then the bisector of the angle between them is the line of reflection for one angle to be reflected onto the other. Reflect $\angle A'N'G'$ over the angle bisector to complete the sequence of transformations.

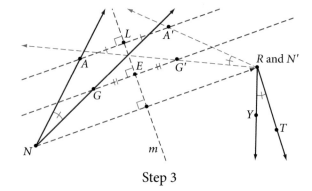

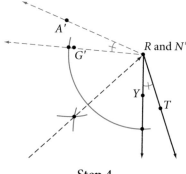

Step 3   Step 4

You just created two congruent angles randomly placed on your paper and you were able to transform one onto the other by a series of constructions. Therefore, if two angles are congruent, there is a sequence of transformations that transforms one angle onto the other. (If $\angle R \cong \angle N$, there is a sequence of transformations that transforms $\angle R$ so that $\angle R''$ coincides with $\angle N$.)

And finally, let's look at the third converse. If two triangles are congruent, is there a sequence of transformations that transforms an image of one triangle onto the other?

INVESTIGATION 3

Transforming One Triangle onto a Congruent Triangle

Step 1 Construct two congruent triangles ($\triangle ABC \cong \triangle DEF$) randomly on your paper.

Step 2 Construct the perpendicular bisector m of the segment connecting points A and D. Why did we pick A and D as the points? Construct a perpendicular from C through the perpendicular bisector m, and label the point of intersection L. Then locate C' on the perpendicular so that $\overline{CL} \cong \overline{C'L}$. Repeat to locate B', the image of B. Thus you have constructed $\triangle A'B'C'$, the reflection of $\triangle ABC$.

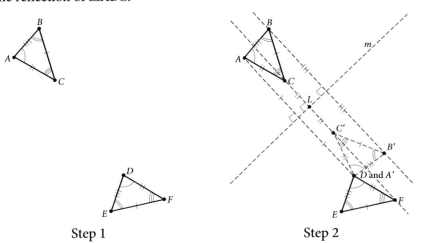

Step 1   Step 2

Step 3 Next, using the same technique as you did in Step 2, construct the perpendicular bisector of $\overline{B'E}$. and reflect $\triangle A'B'C'$ so that B' coincides with E and C' is reflected across the reflection line to create C''.

Step 4 Finally, reflect $\triangle A''B''C''$ across the perpendicular bisector of $\overline{C''F}$ (or across the bisector of $\angle C''A''F$) to create the image $\triangle A'''B'''C'''$. You have thus successfully transformed $\triangle ABC$ onto $\triangle DEF$ after three reflections.

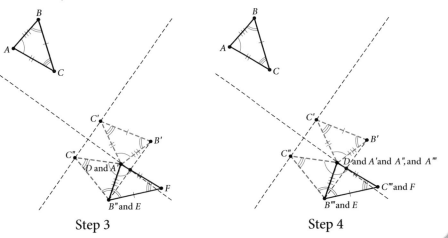

Step 3   Step 4

You just created two congruent triangles randomly placed on your paper and were able to transform one onto the other by construction. Therefore, if two triangles are congruent, there is a sequence of transformations that transforms one triangle onto the other. (If $\triangle ABC \cong \triangle DEF$, there is a sequence of transformations that transforms $\triangle ABC$ so that $\triangle A'''B'''C'''$ coincides with $\triangle DEF$.)

3.7 Exercises

1. Copy the two congruent segments onto your paper and then construct the line of reflection so that you can reflect one onto the other.

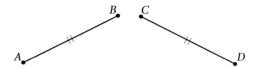

2. Copy the two congruent angles onto your paper and then construct the line of reflection so that you can reflect one onto the other.

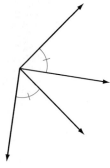

3. Copy the two congruent triangles onto your paper and then construct the line of reflection so that you can reflect one onto the other.

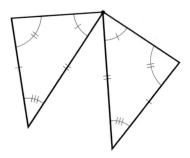

4. Copy the two congruent segments onto your paper and then construct the two lines of reflection so that after the composition of the two reflections one segment is reflected onto the other.

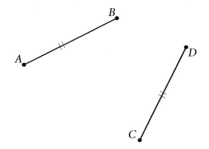

5. Copy the two congruent angles onto your paper and then construct the two lines of reflection so that after the composition of the two reflections one angle is reflected onto the other.

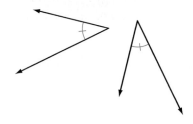

6. Copy the two congruent triangles onto your paper and then construct the two lines of reflection so that after the composition of the two reflections one triangle is reflected onto the other. What is the statement of congruence ($\triangle PRS \cong \triangle$???)?

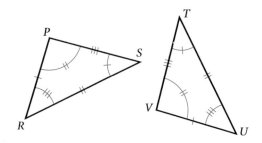

Review

7. List the letters from the alphabet below that have a horizontal line of symmetry.

A B C D E F G H I J K L M N O P Q R S T U V W X Y Z

8. Sketch and label a polygon that has exactly three sides of equal length and exactly two angles of equal measure.

9. Sketch two triangles. Each should have one side measuring 5 cm and one side measuring 9 cm, but they should not be congruent.

10. Construct a quadrilateral with exactly three sides of equal length.

11. Construct a quadrilateral with all four sides of equal length.

12. Given $\triangle ABC$ with vertices: $A(-6, -5)$, $B(6, -3)$, $C(3, 8)$

   a. Transform $\triangle ABC$ by the ordered pair rule $(x, y) \rightarrow (2x, 2y)$ to create $\triangle A'B'C'$.

   b. What are the coordinates of the vertices of $\triangle A'B'C'$?

   c. Are the two triangles congruent?

   d. How do the measures of the corresponding angles compare? Use patty paper to compare.

   e. How do the measures of the corresponding sides compare? Use patty paper to compare.

   f. What do you notice about the origin, A, and A' and the origin, B, and B'?

For Exercises 13–17, complete each geometric construction and name it.

13.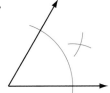

14.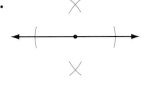

15.

16.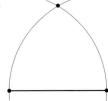

17.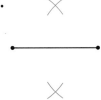

DEVELOPING MATHEMATICAL REASONING

Card Trick Puzzle

This card trick uses one complete suit (hearts, clubs, spades, or diamonds) from a deck of playing cards. How must you arrange the cards so that you can successfully complete the trick? Here is what your audience should see and hear as you perform.

   1. As you take the top card off the pile and place it back underneath of the pile, say "A."

   2. Then take the second card, place it at the bottom of the pile, and say "C."

   3. Take the third card, place it at the bottom, and say "E."

   4. You've just spelled *ace*. Now take the fourth card and turn it faceup on the table, not back in the pile. The card should be an ace.

   5. Continue in this fashion, saying "T," "W," and "O" for the next three cards. Then turn the next card faceup. It should be a 2.

   6. Continue spelling *three, four, . . . , jack, queen, king*. Each time you spell a card, the next card turned faceup should be that card.

Constructing Points of Concurrency

You now can perform a number of constructions in triangles, including angle bisectors, perpendicular bisectors of the sides, medians, and altitudes. In this lesson and the next lesson you will discover special properties of these lines and segments. When a set of lines has a point in common, they are **concurrent**. Segments, rays, and even planes are concurrent if they intersect in a single point.

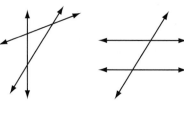

Not concurrent   Point of concurrency

Concurrent

The point of intersection is the **point of concurrency**.

INVESTIGATION 1

Concurrence

YOU WILL NEED

- patty paper
- construction tools
- geometry software (optional)

In this investigation you will discover that some special lines in a triangle have points of concurrency.

As a group, you should investigate each set of lines on an acute triangle, an obtuse triangle, and a right triangle to be sure that your conjectures apply to all triangles.

Step 1 Draw a large triangle on patty paper. Make sure you have at least one acute triangle, one obtuse triangle, and one right triangle in your group.

Step 2 Construct the three angle bisectors for each triangle. Are they concurrent?

Compare your results with the results of others. State your observations as a conjecture.

Angle Bisector Concurrency Conjecture	C-9
The three angle bisectors of a triangle _?_ .	

Step 3 Draw a large triangle on a new piece of patty paper. Make sure you have at least one acute triangle, one obtuse triangle, and one right triangle in your group.

Step 4 Construct the perpendicular bisector for each side of the triangle and complete the conjecture.

Step 5 Draw a large triangle on a new piece of patty paper. Make sure you have at least one acute triangle, one obtuse triangle, and one right triangle in your group.

Step 6 Construct the lines containing the altitudes of your triangle and complete the conjecture.

> **Altitude Concurrency Conjecture**   `C-11`
>
> The three altitudes (or the lines containing the altitudes) of a triangle ? .

Step 7 For what kind of triangle will all the points of concurrency be the same point?

The point of concurrency for the three angle bisectors is the **incenter**. The point of concurrency for the perpendicular bisectors is the **circumcenter**. The point of concurrency for the three altitudes is called the **orthocenter**. Use these definitions to label each patty paper from the previous investigation with the correct name for each point of concurrency. You will investigate a triangle's medians in the next lesson.

INVESTIGATION 2

Circumcenter

In this investigation you will discover special properties of the circumcenter.

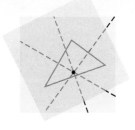

Step 1 Using your patty paper from Steps 3 and 4 of the previous investigation, measure and compare the distances from the circumcenter to each of the three vertices. Are they the same? Compare the distances from the circumcenter to each of the three sides. Are they the same?

Step 2 Tape or glue your patty paper firmly on a piece of regular paper. Use a compass to construct a circle with the circumcenter as the center and that passes through any one of the triangle's vertices. What do you notice?

Step 3 Use your observations to state your next conjecture.

> **Circumcenter Conjecture**   `C-12`
>
> The circumcenter of a triangle ? .

INVESTIGATION 3

YOU WILL NEED

- patty paper
- construction tools
- geometry software (optional)

Incenter

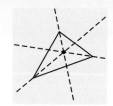

In this investigation you will discover special properties of the incenter.

Step 1 Using the patty paper from the first two steps of Investigation 1, measure and compare the distances from the incenter to each of the three sides. (Remember to use the perpendicular distance.) Are they the same?

Step 2 Construct the perpendicular from the incenter to any one of the sides of the triangle. Mark the point of intersection between the perpendicular line and the side of the triangle.

Step 3 Tape or glue your patty paper firmly on a piece of regular paper. Use a compass to construct a circle with the incenter as the center and that passes through the point of intersection in Step 2. What do you notice?

Step 4 Use your observations to state your next conjecture.

Incenter Conjecture	*C-13*

The incenter of a triangle __?__ .

You just discovered a very useful property of the circumcenter and a very useful property of the incenter. You will see some applications of these properties in the exercises. With earlier conjectures and logical reasoning, you can explain why your conjectures are true.

DEVELOPING PROOF

Circumcenter

In your group, read and discuss the deductive argument below that explains why the circumcenter is equally distant to the three vertices. You will then be asked to create a similar argument for the incenter.

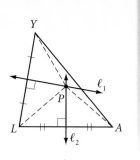

Because the circumcenter is constructed from perpendicular bisectors, the diagram of $\triangle LYA$ at right shows two (of the three) perpendicular bisectors, ℓ_1 and ℓ_2. We want to show that the circumcenter, point P, is equidistant from all three vertices. In other words, we want to show that

$$\overline{PL} \cong \overline{PA} \cong \overline{PY}$$

A useful reasoning strategy is to break the problem into parts. In this case, we might first think about explaining why $\overline{PL} \cong \overline{PA}$. To do that, let's simplify the diagram by looking at just the bottom triangle formed by points P, L, and A.

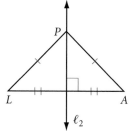

If a point is on the perpendicular bisector of a segment, it is equidistant from the endpoints.

Point P lies on the perpendicular bisector of $\overline{LA}$, therefore

$PA = PL$

As part of the strategy of concentrating on just part of the problem, think about explaining why $\overline{PA} \cong \overline{PY}$.

Point P also lies on the perpendicular bisector of $\overline{LY}$, therefore

$PL = PY$

Therefore P is equidistant from all three vertices.

$PA = PL = PY$

Incenter

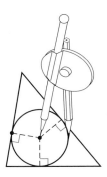

Now it is your turn. In your group discuss, plan, and create a logical argument that explains why the incenter is equally distant from the three sides of the triangle. In triangle $\triangle ABC$, $\overline{BD}$ and $\overline{CE}$ are angle bisectors and thus I is the incenter. Here are two questions to begin your discussion:

• Why is $IH = IG$?

• Why is $IG = IF$?

In your groups discuss the following two questions and then write down your answers.

1. Why does the circumcenter construction guarantee that it is the center of the circle that circumscribes the triangle?

2. Why does the incenter construction guarantee that it is the center of the circle that is inscribed in the triangle?

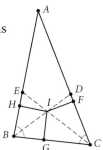

3.8 Exercises

For Exercises 1–4, make a sketch and explain how to find the answer.

1. An artist wishes to circumscribe a circle about a triangle in his latest abstract design. Which point of concurrency does he need to locate?

2. Rosita wants to install a circular sink in her new triangular countertop. She wants to choose the largest sink that will fit. Which point of concurrency must she locate? Explain.

3. Julian Chive wishes to center a butcher-block table at a location equidistant from the refrigerator, stove, and sink. Which point of concurrency does Julian need to locate?

YOU WILL NEED

Construction tools
for Exercises **5, 6, 9–11, 15–18, 20, 23, 24**

Geometry software
for Exercise **12–14, 21**

4. One event at this year's Battle of the Classes will be a pie-eating contest between the sophomores, juniors, and seniors. Five members of each class will be positioned on the football field at the points indicated at right. At the whistle, one student from each class will run to the pie table, eat exactly one pie, and run back to his or her group. The next student will then repeat the process. The first class to eat five pies and return to home base will be the winner of the pie-eating contest. Where should the pie table be located so that it will be a fair contest? Describe how the contest planners should find that point.

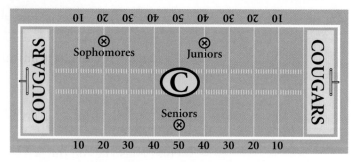

5. Draw a large triangle. Construct a circle inscribed in the triangle. *ⓗ*

6. Draw a triangle. Construct a circle circumscribed about the triangle. *ⓗ*

7. Is the inscribed circle the greatest circle to fit within a given triangle? Explain. If you think not, give a counterexample and explain why it is not true. *ⓗ*

8. Does the circumscribed circle create the smallest circular region that contains a given triangle? Explain. If you think not, give a counterexample and explain why it is not true. *ⓗ*

9. Construct a circle. Construct an equilateral triangle inscribed in the circle.

10. Construct a circle. Construct a square inscribed in the circle.

11. Construct a circle. Construct a regular hexagon inscribed in the circle.

12. Use geometry software to construct the circumcenter of a triangle. Hide the perpendicular bisectors. Drag a vertex to observe how the location of the circumcenter changes as the triangle changes from acute to obtuse. What do you notice? Where is the circumcenter located for a right triangle?

> For Exercises 12–14, you might also use the **Dynamic Geometry Exploration** Triangle Centers in your ebook.

13. Use geometry software to construct the orthocenter of a triangle. Hide the altitudes. Drag a vertex to observe how the location of the orthocenter changes as the triangle changes from acute to obtuse. What do you notice? Where is the orthocenter located for a right triangle?

14. Use geometry software to construct the orthocenter of a triangle. Hide the altitudes. Draw segments from each vertex to the orthocenter shown. Now find the orthocenter of each of the three new triangles formed. What happens?

Review

Use the segments and angle at right to construct each figure in Exercises 15–18.

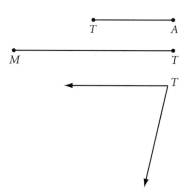

15. Construct △*MAT*. Construct *H* the midpoint of $\overline{MT}$ and *S* the midpoint of $\overline{AT}$. Construct the midsegment $\overline{HS}$. Compare the lengths of $\overline{HS}$ and $\overline{MA}$. Notice anything special?

16. An **isosceles trapezoid** is a trapezoid with the nonparallel sides congruent. Construct isosceles trapezoid *MOAT* with $\overline{MT} \parallel \overline{OA}$ and *AT* = *MO*. Use patty paper to compare ∠*T* and ∠*M*. Notice anything special?

17. Construct a circle with diameter $\overline{MT}$. Construct chord $\overline{TA}$. Construct chord $\overline{MA}$ to form $\triangle MTA$. What is the measure of $\angle A$? Notice anything special?

18. Construct a rhombus with *TA* as the length of a side and $\angle T$ as one of the acute angles. Construct the two diagonals. Notice anything special?

19. Sketch the locus of points on the coordinate plane in which the sum of the *x*-coordinate and the *y*-coordinate is 9. ⓗ

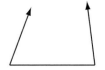

20. How can you construct the bisector of an angle of a triangle without using the vertex in the construction? Bisect the missing angle of this triangle. ⓗ

21. Is it possible for the midpoints of the three altitudes of a triangle to be collinear? Investigate by using geometry software. Write a paragraph describing your findings.

22. Sketch the cross-section formed when the plane slices the cube as shown.

23. Use your geometry tools to draw rhombus *RHOM* so that $HO = 6.0$ cm and $m\angle R = 120°$.

24. Use your geometry tools to draw kite *KYTE* so that $KY = YT = 4.8$ cm, diagonal $YE = 6.4$ cm, and $m\angle Y = 80°$. ⓗ

PERFORMANCE TASK

Fire Station Boundaries

There are three fire stations in the small county of Dry Lake. County planners need to divide the county into three zones so that fire alarms alert the closest station. Trace the county and the three fire stations onto patty paper, and locate the boundaries of the three zones. Explain how these boundaries solve the problem.

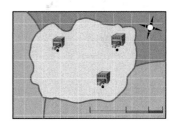

First-aid Center

The first-aid center of Mt. Thermopolis State Park needs to be at a point that is equidistant from three bike paths that intersect to form a triangle. Locate this point so that in an emergency, medical personnel will be able to get to any one of the paths by the shortest route possible. Which point of concurrency is it?

The Centroid

"*The universe may be as great as they say, but it wouldn't be missed if it didn't exist.*"

PIET HEIN

In the previous lesson you discovered that the three angle bisectors are concurrent, the three perpendicular bisectors of the sides are concurrent, and the three altitudes in a triangle are concurrent. You also discovered the properties of the incenter and the circumcenter. In this lesson you will investigate the medians of a triangle.

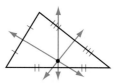

Three angle bisectors
(incenter)

Three perpendicular bisectors
(circumcenter)

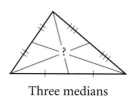

Three altitudes
(orthocenter)

Three medians
_?_

INVESTIGATION 1

YOU WILL NEED

- patty paper
- construction tools
- geometry software (optional)

Are Medians Concurrent?

Each person in your group should draw a different triangle for this investigation. Make sure you have at least one acute triangle, one obtuse triangle, and one right triangle in your group.

Step 1 On a sheet of patty paper, draw as large a scalene triangle as possible and label it *CNR*, as shown at right. Locate the midpoints of the three sides. Construct the medians and complete the conjecture.

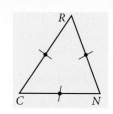

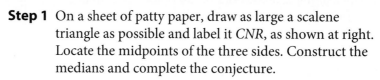

Median Concurrency Conjecture ▕ C-14

The three medians of a triangle _?_ .

The point of concurrency of the three medians is the centroid.

Step 2 Label the three medians $\overline{CT}$, $\overline{NO}$, and $\overline{RE}$. Label the centroid *D*.

Step 3 Use your compass or another sheet of patty paper to investigate whether there is anything special about the centroid. Is the centroid equidistant from the three vertices? From the three sides? Is the centroid the midpoint of each median?

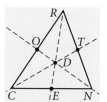

Step 4 The centroid divides a median into two segments. Focus on one median. Use your patty paper or compass to compare the length of the longer segment to the length of the shorter segment and find the ratio.

Step 5 Find the ratios of the lengths of the segment parts for the other two medians. Do you get the same ratio for each median?

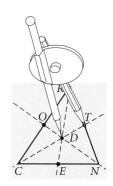

Compare your results with the results of others. State your discovery as a conjecture, and add it to your conjecture list.

> ### Centroid Conjecture   C-15
>
> The centroid of a triangle divides each median into two parts so that the distance from the centroid to the vertex is _?_ the distance from the centroid to the midpoint of the opposite side.

Explore the first investigation using the **Dynamic Geometry Exploration** The Centroid in your ebook.

In earlier lessons you discovered that the midpoint of a segment is the balance point or center of gravity. You also saw that when a set of segments is arranged into a triangle, the line through each midpoint of a side and the opposite vertex can act as a line of balance for the triangle. Can you then balance a triangle on a median? Let's take a look.

INVESTIGATION 2

Balancing Act

YOU WILL NEED
- patty paper
- construction tools
- geometry software (optional)
- cardboard

Use your patty paper from Investigation 1 for this investigation. If you used geometry software, print out your triangle with medians.

Step 1 Place your patty paper or printout from the previous investigation on a piece of mat board or cardboard. With a sharp pencil tip or compass tip, mark the three vertices, the three midpoints, and the centroid on the board.

Step 2 Draw the triangle and medians on the cardboard. Cut out the cardboard triangle.

Step 3 Try balancing the triangle on one of the three medians by placing the median on the edge of a ruler. If you are successful, what does that imply about the areas of the two triangles formed by one median? Try balancing the triangle on another median. Will it balance on each of the three medians?

Step 4 Is there a single point where you can balance the triangle?

If you have found the balancing point for the triangle, you have found its **center of gravity**. State your discovery as a conjecture, and add it to your conjecture list.

Center of Gravity Conjecture	C-16
The ? of a triangle is the center of gravity of the triangular region.	

The triangle balances on each median and the centroid is on each median, so the triangle balances on the centroid. As long as the weight of the cardboard is distributed evenly throughout the triangle, you can balance any triangle at its centroid. For this reason, the centroid is a very useful point of concurrency, especially in physics.

You have discovered special properties of three of the four points of concurrency—the incenter, the circumcenter, and the centroid. The incenter is the center of an inscribed circle, the circumcenter is the center of a circumscribed circle, and the centroid is the center of gravity.

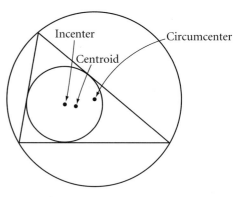

3.9 Exercises

YOU WILL NEED

 Construction tools for Exercises **1, 5,** and **10**

 Geometry software for Exercise **7**

1. On patty paper, draw a large isosceles triangle with an acute vertex angle that measures less than 40°. Copy it onto three other pieces of patty paper. Construct the centroid on one patty paper, the incenter on a second, the circumcenter on a third, and the orthocenter on a fourth. Record the results of all four pieces of patty paper on one piece of patty paper. What do you notice about the four points of concurrency? What is the order of the four points of concurrency from the vertex to the opposite side in an acute isosceles triangle?

In Exercises 2–4, use your new conjectures to find each length.

2. Point M is the centroid.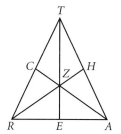

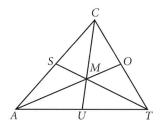

$CM = 16$
$MO = 10$
$TS = 21$
$AM = \underline{\ ?\ }$
$SM = \underline{\ ?\ }$
$TM = \underline{\ ?\ }$
$UM = \underline{\ ?\ }$

3. Point G is the centroid.

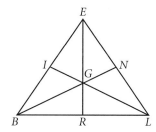

$GI = GR = GN$
$ER = 36$
$BG = \underline{\ ?\ }$
$IG = \underline{\ ?\ }$

4. Point Z is the centroid.

$CZ = 14$
$TZ = 30$
$RZ = AZ$
$RH = \underline{\ ?\ }$
$TE = \underline{\ ?\ }$

5. Construct an equilateral triangle, then construct angle bisectors from two vertices, medians from two vertices, and altitudes from two vertices. What can you conclude?

6. Birdy McFly is designing a large triangular hang glider. She needs to locate the center of gravity for her glider. Which point does she need to locate? Birdy wishes to decorate her glider with the largest possible circle within her large triangular hang glider. Which point of concurrency does she need to locate?

7. Use geometry software to construct a large isosceles acute triangle. Construct the four points of concurrency. Hide all constructions except for the points of concurrency. Label them. Drag until it has an obtuse vertex angle. Now what is the order of the four points of concurrency from the vertex angle to the opposite side? When did the order change? Do the four points ever become one?

8. Where do you think the center of gravity is located on a square? A rectangle? A rhombus? In each case the center of gravity is not that difficult to find, but what about an ordinary quadrilateral? Experiment to discover a method for finding the center of gravity for a quadrilateral by geometric construction. Test your method on a large cardboard quadrilateral. ⓗ

Review

9. Sally Solar is the director of Lunar Planning for Galileo Station on the moon. She has been asked to locate the new food production facility so that it is equidistant from the three main lunar housing developments. Which point of concurrency does she need to locate?

10. Construct circle O. Place an arbitrary point P within the circle. Construct the longest chord passing through P. Construct the shortest chord passing through P. How are they related?

11. A billiard ball is hit so that it travels a distance equal to *AB* but bounces off the cushion at point *C*. Copy the figure, and sketch where the ball will rest.

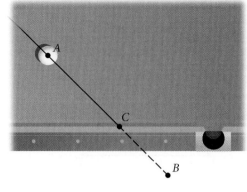

12. In alkyne molecules all the bonds are single bonds except one triple bond between two carbon atoms. The first three alkynes are modeled below. The dash (−) between letters represents single bonds. The triple dash (≡) between letters represents a triple bond.

H − C ≡ C − H	H − C ≡ C − C − H	H − C − C ≡ C − C − H
Ethyne (C_2H_2)	Propyne (C_3H_4)	Butyne (C_4H_6)

Sketch the alkyne with eight carbons in the chain, octyne. What is the general rule for alkynes $(C_nH_?)$? In other words, if there are *n* carbon atoms (C), how many hydrogen atoms (H) are in the alkyne?

13. When plane figure A is rotated about the line, it produces the solid figure B. What is the plane figure that produces the solid figure D?

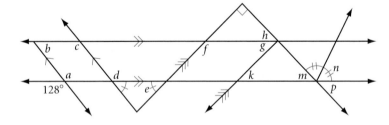

A   B   C   D

14. Copy the diagram below. Use your Vertical Angles Conjecture and Parallel Lines Conjecture to calculate each lettered angle measure.

b c a d e f h g k m n p
128°

15. A brother and a sister have inherited a large triangular plot of land. The will states that the property is to be divided along the altitude from the northernmost point of the property. However, the property is covered with quicksand at the northern vertex. The will states that the heir who figures out how to draw the altitude without using the northern vertex point gets to choose his or her parcel first. How can the heirs construct the altitude? Is this a fair way to divide the land? Why or why not? *(h)*

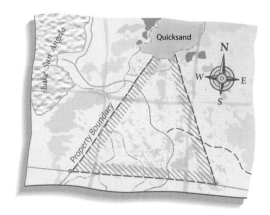

EXPLORATION

The Euler Line

In the previous lessons you discovered the four points of concurrency: circumcenter, incenter, orthocenter, and centroid. In this activity you will discover how these points relate to a special line, the **Euler line**.

Activity

Three Out of Four

You are going to look for a relationship among the points of concurrency.

Step 1 Draw a scalene triangle and have each person in your group trace the same triangle on a separate piece of patty paper.

Step 2 Have each group member construct with patty paper a different point of the four points of concurrency for the triangle.

Step 3 Record the group's results by tracing and labeling all four points of concurrency, one at a time, on one of the four pieces of patty paper. What do you notice? Compare your group results with the results of other groups near you. State your discovery as a conjecture.

> **Euler Line Conjecture**
>
> The _?_, _?_, and _?_ are the three points of concurrency that always lie on a line.

The three special points that lie on the Euler line determine a segment called the **Euler segment**. The point of concurrency between the two endpoints of the Euler segment divides the segment into two smaller segments whose lengths have an exact ratio.

Step 4 With a compass or patty paper, compare the lengths of the two parts of the Euler segment. What is the ratio? Compare your group's results with the results of other groups and state your conjecture.

> **Euler Segment Conjecture**
>
> The _?_ divides the Euler segment into two parts so that the smaller part is _?_ the larger part.

Step 5 Use your conjectures to solve this problem.

$\overline{AC}$ is an Euler segment containing three points of concurrency, A, B, C, so that $AB > BC$. $AC = 24$ m. $AB = $ _?_. $BC = $ _?_.

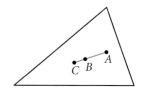

Explore this activity using the **Dynamic Geometry Exploration** The Euler Line in your ebook.

→ *History*
CONNECTION

The Euler line is named after the Swiss mathematician Leonhard Euler (1707–1783), who proved that three points of concurrency are collinear.

In Chapter 1, you defined many terms that help establish the building blocks of geometry. In Chapter 2, you learned and practiced inductive reasoning skills. With the construction skills you learned in this chapter, you performed investigations that lay the foundation for geometry.

The investigation section of your notebook should be a detailed report of the mathematics you've already done. Beginning in Chapter 1 and continuing in this chapter, you summarized your work in the definition list and the conjecture list. Before you begin the review exercises, make sure your conjecture list is complete. Do you understand each conjecture? Can you draw a clear diagram that demonstrates your understanding of each definition and conjecture? Can you explain them to others? Can you use them to solve geometry problems?

Exercises

For Exercises 1–10, identify the statement as true or false. For each false statement, explain why it is false and sketch a counterexample.

YOU WILL NEED

Construction tools
for Exercises **19–24,**
and **27–32**

1. In a geometric construction, you use a protractor and a ruler.

2. A diagonal is a line segment in a polygon that connects any two vertices.

3. A trapezoid is a quadrilateral with exactly one pair of parallel sides.

4. A square is a rhombus with all angles congruent.

5. If a point is equidistant from the endpoints of a segment, then it must be the midpoint of the segment.

6. The set of all the points in the plane that are a given distance from a line segment is a pair of lines parallel to the given segment.

7. It is not possible for a trapezoid to have three congruent sides.

8. The incenter of a triangle is the point of intersection of the three angle bisectors.

9. The orthocenter of a triangle is the point of intersection of the three altitudes.

10. The incenter, the centroid, and the orthocenter are always inside the triangle.

For Exercises 11–18, match each geometric construction with one of the figures below.

11. Construction of a midsegment

12. Construction of an altitude

13. Construction of a centroid in a triangle

14. Construction of an incenter

15. Construction of an orthocenter in a triangle

16. Construction of a circumcenter

17. Construction of an equilateral triangle

18. Construction of an angle bisector

A.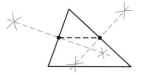

B.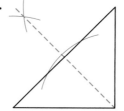

C.

D.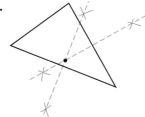

E.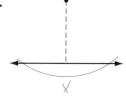

F.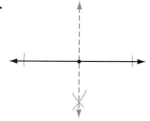

G.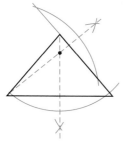

H.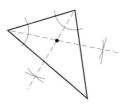

I.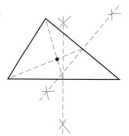

J.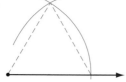

K.

L.

For Exercises 19–24, perform a construction with compass and straightedge or with patty paper. Choose the method for each problem, but do not mix the tools in any one problem. In other words, play each construction game fairly.

19. Draw an angle and construct a duplicate of it.

20. Draw a line segment and construct its perpendicular bisector.

21. Draw a line and a point not on the line. Construct a perpendicular to the line through the point.

22. Draw an angle and bisect it.

23. Construct an angle that measures 22.5°.

24. Draw a line and a point not on the line. Construct a second line so that it passes through the point and is parallel to the first line.

25. Brad and Janet are building a home for their pet hamsters, Riff and Raff, in the shape of a triangular prism. Which point of concurrency in the triangular base do they need to locate in order to construct the largest possible circular entrance?

26. Adventurer Dakota Davis has a map that once showed the location of a large bag of gold. Unfortunately, the part of the map that showed the precise location of the gold has burned away. Dakota visits the area shown on the map anyway, hoping to find clues. To his surprise, he finds three headstones with geometric symbols on them.

The clues lead him to think that the treasure is buried at a point equidistant from the three stones. If Dakota's theory is correct, how should he go about locating the point where the bag of gold might be buried?

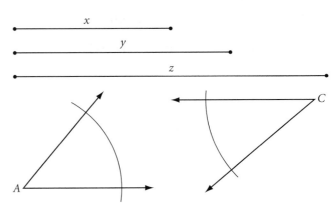

For Exercises 27–31, use the given segments and angles to construct each figure. The lowercase letter above each segment represents the length of the segment.

27. △ABC given ∠A, ∠C, and AC = z

28. A segment with length $2y + x - \frac{1}{2}z$

29. △PQR with PQ = 3x, QR = 4x, and PR = 5x

30. Isosceles triangle ABD given ∠A, and AB = BD = 2y

31. Right triangle TRI with hypotenuse $\overline{TI}$, TR = x, and RI = y, and a square on $\overline{TI}$, with $\overline{TI}$ as one side

32. Copy the two congruent triangles onto your paper and then construct the necessary lines of reflection so that after the composition of the reflections one triangle is reflected onto the other. How can you tell ahead of time how many reflections you will need?

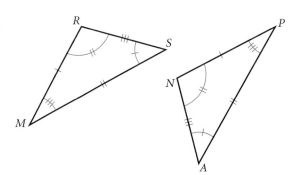

Mixed Review

For Exercises 33–36, match the term with its construction.

33. Centroid   **34.** Circumcenter   **35.** Incenter   **36.** Orthocenter

     A.   B.   C.   D.

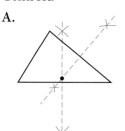
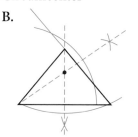
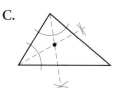
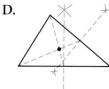

For Exercises 37–50, identify the statement as true or false. For each false statement, explain why it is false and sketch a counterexample.

37. An isosceles right triangle is a triangle with an angle measuring 90° and no two sides congruent.

38. If two parallel lines are cut by a transversal, then the alternate interior angles are congruent.

39. An altitude of a triangle must be inside the triangle.

40. The orthocenter of a triangle is the point of intersection of the three perpendicular bisectors of the sides.

41. If two lines are parallel to the same line, then they are parallel to each other.

42. If the sum of the measure of two angles is 180°, then the two angles are vertical angles.

43. Any two consecutive sides of a kite are congruent.

44. If a polygon has two pairs of parallel sides, then it is a parallelogram.

45. The measure of an arc is equal to one half the measure of its central angle.

46. If $\overline{TR}$ is a median of $\triangle TIE$ and point D is the centroid, then $TD = 3DR$.

47. The shortest chord of a circle is the radius of a circle.

48. An obtuse triangle is a triangle that has one angle with measure greater than 90°.

49. Inductive reasoning is the process of showing that certain statements follow logically from accepted truths.

50. There are exactly three true statements in Exercises 37–50.

51. In the diagram, $p \parallel q$.

    a. Name a pair of corresponding angles.

    b. Name a pair of alternate exterior angles.

    c. If $m\angle 3 = 42°$, what is $m\angle 6$?

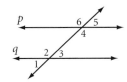

In Exercises 52 and 53, use inductive reasoning to find the next number or shape in the pattern.

52. 100, 97, 91, 82, 70

53.

54. Consider the statement "If the month is October, then the month has 31 days."

    a. Is the statement true?

    b. Write the converse of this statement.

    c. Is the converse true?

55. Find the point on the cushion at which a pool player should aim so that the white ball will hit the cushion and pass over point Q.

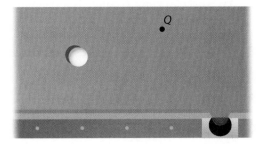

56. The sequence 3, 8, 15, 24, . . . is another rectangular number pattern. How many squares are there in the 50th rectangular array? Ⓗ

    3   8   15   24

For Exercises 57–59, sketch the three-dimensional figure formed by folding each net into a solid. Name the solid.

57.

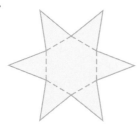

58.

59.

60. DEVELOPING PROOF Calculate each lettered angle measure. Explain how you determined the measures *c* and *f*.

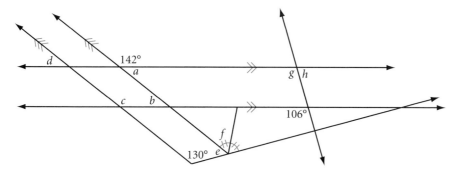

61. Draw a scalene triangle *ABC*. Use a straightedge and compass to construct the incenter of △*ABC*.

62. DEVELOPING PROOF What's wrong with this picture?

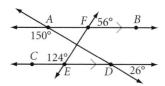

63. What is the minimum number of regions that are formed by 100 distinct lines in a plane? What is the maximum number of regions formed by 100 lines in the plane?

64. Circle O with center at $O(3, -2)$ passes through $A(7, 1)$ and circle Q with center at $Q(-3, 8)$ passes through $B(0, 4)$.

  a. Are the two circles congruent? Explain.

  b. If congruent, what is the single transformation rule that takes circle O onto circle Q?

  c. If they are not congruent explain why not.

65. Given parallelogram $ABCD$ with vertices: $A(-3, -6)$, $B(2, -6)$, $C(4, 2)$, $D(-1, 2)$. Transform $ABCD$ by the transformation rule $(x, y) \rightarrow (3x, 0.5y)$ to create quadrilateral $A'B'C'D'$. Is $A'B'C'D'$ a parallelogram? Are any of the corresponding sides or angles congruent? For example, is $\overline{AB} \cong \overline{A'B'}$ or $\angle BCD \cong \angle B'C'D'$? Is the transformation created by the ordered pair rule $(x, y) \rightarrow (3x, 0.5y)$ a rigid transformation? Explain.

66. The three steps below demonstrate Matthew's construction of $\angle FAB$. He says the measure of $\angle FAB$ is 30°. Do you agree? Why or why not?

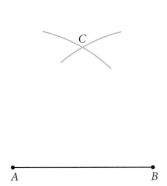

Step 1. Swing congruent arcs from endpoints A and B intersecting at C.

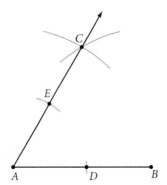

Step 2. Swing an arc with center at A passing through the two rays of $\angle CAB$ at points D and E.

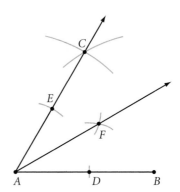

Step 3. Swing congruent arcs from points D and E intersecting at F. Draw $\overrightarrow{AF}$

Discovering and Proving Triangle Properties

"Is it possible to make a representation of recognizable figures that has no background?"

M. C. ESCHER

M. C. Escher's *Symmetry Drawing* ©2014 The M. C. Escher Company—The Netherlands. All rights reserved. www.mcescher.com

OBJECTIVES

In this chapter you will

- learn why triangles are so useful in structures
- discover relationships between the sides and angles of triangles
- learn about the conditions that guarantee that two triangles are congruent

Triangle Sum Conjecture

Triangles have certain properties that make them useful in all kinds of structures, from bridges to high-rise buildings. One such property of triangles is their rigidity. Another application of triangles is a procedure used in surveying called triangulation. This procedure allows surveyors to locate points or positions on a map by measuring angles and distances and creating a network of triangles. Triangulation is based on an important property of plane geometry that you will discover in this lesson.

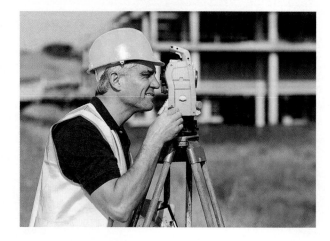

INVESTIGATION

The Triangle Sum

YOU WILL NEED

- a protractor
- a straightedge
- scissors
- patty paper

There is an endless variety of triangles that you can draw with different shapes and angle measures. Do their angle measures have anything in common? Start by drawing different kinds of triangles. Make sure your group has at least one acute and one obtuse triangle.

Step 1 Measure the three angles of each triangle as accurately as possible with your protractor.

Step 2 Find the sum of the measures of the three angles in each triangle. Compare results with others in your group. Does everyone get about the same result? What is it?

Step 3 Check the sum another way. Write the letters *a*, *b*, and *c* in the interiors of the three angles of one of the triangles, and carefully cut out the triangle.

Step 4 Tear off the three angles. Arrange them so that their vertices meet at a point. How does this arrangement show the sum of the angle measures?

Step 5 Compare results with others in your group. State your observations as a conjecture.

Triangle Sum Conjecture   C-17

The sum of the measures of the angles in every triangle is _?_ .

 DEVELOPING PROOF

Triangle Sum Conjecture

The investigation may have convinced you that the Triangle Sum Conjecture is true, but can you explain *why* it is true for every triangle?

One method used to explain why the Triangle Sum Conjecture is true is to use a **paragraph proof,** a deductive argument that uses written sentences to support its claims with reasons.

Look back at the investigation and the new line formed by rearranging the angles in the triangle. There are a number of ways of arranging the three angles. See the examples below.

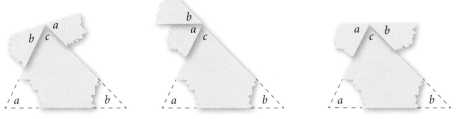

Figure 1   Figure 2   Figure 3

In Figures 1 and 2, copies of ∠*a* and ∠*b* are added to ∠*c* forming a straight line but nothing else interesting resulted. In Figure 3 however, ∠*a* is added to the left of ∠*c* and ∠*b* is added to the right of ∠*c* forming a much more interesting line. What do you notice about the positions of ∠*a* and its copy and the position of ∠*b* and its copy in Figure 3? Does alternate interior angles ring a bell? What is true about the line formed by the sum of the three angles of the triangle in Figure 3? This will help you in planning your proof. In your proof you will need to add this line to your drawing of your triangle. This line is called an **auxiliary line** (or helping line), an extra line that helps with a proof.

The figure at right includes $\overleftrightarrow{EC}$, an auxiliary line parallel to side $\overline{AB}$. Use this diagram to discuss these questions with your group.

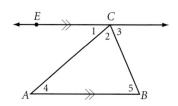

- What are you trying to prove?

- What is the relationship among $\angle 1$, $\angle 2$, and $\angle 3$?

- Why was the auxiliary line drawn to be parallel to one of the sides?

- What other congruencies can you determine from the diagram?

Use your responses to these questions to mark your diagram. Discuss how you can use the information you have to prove that the Triangle Sum Conjecture is true for every triangle. As a group, write a paragraph proof.

So far, you have been writing deductive arguments to explain why conjectures are true. The paragraph proof format puts a little more emphasis on justifying your reasons. You will also learn about another proof format later in this chapter.

If you have two angles of a triangle, you can use the Triangle Sum Conjecture to construct the third angle. This example shows one way to do this.

EXAMPLE

Given $\angle A$ and $\angle N$, construct $\angle D$, the third angle of $\triangle AND$.

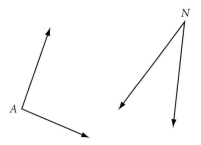

Solution

Label $\angle A$ and $\angle N$ as $\angle 1$ and $\angle 2$ respectively. Draw a line. Duplicate $\angle 1$ opening to the left on this line. Duplicate $\angle 2$ opening to the right at the same vertex on this line. Because the measures of the three angles add to 180°, the measure of $\angle 3$ is equal to that of $\angle D$.

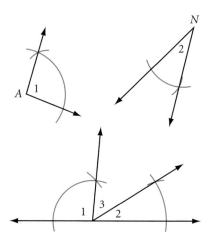

4.1 Exercises

YOU WILL NEED

Geometry software
for Exercise 1

Construction tools
for Exercises **10–13, 15**

1. Using geometry software, construct a triangle. Use the software to measure the three angles and calculate their sum. Drag the vertices and describe your observations.

Use the Triangle Sum Conjecture to determine each lettered angle measure in Exercises 2–5. You might find it helpful to copy the diagrams so you can write on them.

2. $x = \underline{\ ?\ }$

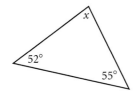

3. $v = \underline{\ ?\ }$

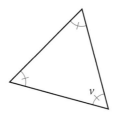

4. $x = \underline{\ ?\ }$
   $y = \underline{\ ?\ }$

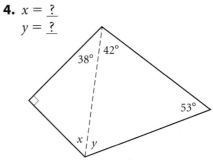

5. $z = \underline{\ ?\ }$

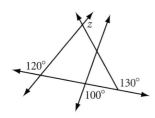

6. Find the sum of the measures of the marked angles. ⓗ

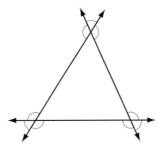

7. Find the sum of the measures of the marked angles. ⓗ

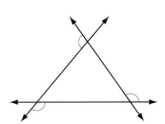

8. $a = \underline{\ ?\ }$ ⓗ
   $b = \underline{\ ?\ }$
   $c = \underline{\ ?\ }$
   $d = \underline{\ ?\ }$
   $e = \underline{\ ?\ }$

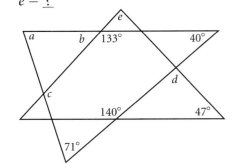

9. $m = \underline{\ ?\ }$
   $n = \underline{\ ?\ }$
   $p = \underline{\ ?\ }$
   $q = \underline{\ ?\ }$
   $r = \underline{\ ?\ }$
   $s = \underline{\ ?\ }$
   $t = \underline{\ ?\ }$
   $u = \underline{\ ?\ }$

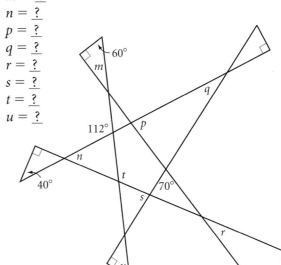

In Exercises 10–12, use what you know to construct each figure. Use only a compass and a straightedge.

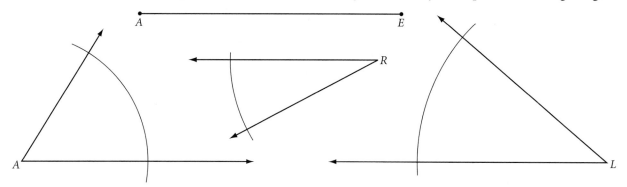

10. Given $\angle A$ and $\angle R$ of $\triangle ARM$, construct $\angle M$.

11. In $\triangle LEG$, $m\angle E = m\angle G$. Given $\angle L$, construct $\angle G$. ⓗ

12. Given $\angle A$, $\angle R$, and side $\overline{AE}$, construct $\triangle EAR$. ⓗ

13. Repeat Exercises 10–12 with patty paper constructions.

14. **DEVELOPING PROOF** In $\triangle MAS$ to the right, $\angle M$ is a right angle. Let's call the two acute angles, $\angle A$ and $\angle S$, "wrong angles." Write a paragraph proof or use algebra to show that "two wrongs make a right," at least for angles in a right triangle.

15. Use your ruler and protractor to draw $\triangle PDQ$ if $m\angle P = 40°$, $m\angle Q = 55°$, and $PD = 7$ cm. How can the Triangle Sum Conjecture make this easier to do?

16. Suppose two angles of one triangle have the same measures as two angles of another triangle. **What can you conclude about the third pair of angles?**

Draw a triangle on your notebook paper. Create a second triangle on patty paper by tracing two of the angles of your original triangle, but make the side between your new angles longer than the corresponding side in the original triangle. How do the third angles in the two triangles compare?

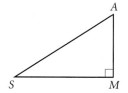

CONJECTURE: If two angles of one triangle are equal in measure to two angles of another triangle, then the third angles of the triangles ?. (Third Angle Conjecture)

17. **DEVELOPING PROOF** Use the Triangle Sum Conjecture and the figures at right to write a paragraph proof explaining why the Third Angle Conjecture is true. ⓗ

18. **DEVELOPING PROOF** Write a paragraph proof, or use algebra, to explain why each angle of an equiangular triangle measures 60°.

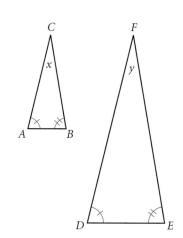

Review

In Exercises 19–23, tell whether the statement is true or false. For each false statement, explain why it is false and sketch a counterexample.

19. If two sides in one triangle are congruent to two sides in another triangle, then the two triangles are congruent.

20. If two angles in one triangle are congruent to two angles in another triangle, then the two triangles are congruent.

21. If a side and an angle in one triangle are congruent to a side and an angle in another triangle, then the two triangles are congruent.

22. If three angles in one triangle are congruent to three angles in another triangle, then the two triangles are congruent.

23. If three sides in one triangle are congruent to three sides in another triangle, then the two triangles are congruent.

24. What is the number of stories in the tallest house you can build with two 52-card decks? How many cards would it take?

One story (2 cards)   Two stories (7 cards)   Three stories (15 cards)

DEVELOPING MATHEMATICAL REASONING

Hundreds Puzzle

Fill in the blanks of each equation below. All nine digits—1 through 9—must be used, in order! You may use any combination of signs for the four basic operations ($+$, $-$, $\cdot$, $\div$), parentheses, decimal points, exponents, factorial signs, and square root symbols, and you may place the digits next to each other to create two-digit or three-digit numbers.

Example: $1 + 2(3 + 4.5) + 67 + 8 + 9 = 100$

   1. $1 + 2 + 3 - 4 + 5 + 6 + \underline{?} + 9 = 100$

   2. $1 + 2 + 3 + 4 + 5 + \underline{?} = 100$

   3. $1 + 2 + 3 \cdot 4 \cdot 5 \div 6 + \underline{?} = 100$

   4. $(-1 - \underline{?}) \div 5 + 6 + 7 + 89 = 100$

   5. $1 + 23 - 4 + \underline{?} + 9 = 100$

Properties of Isosceles Triangles

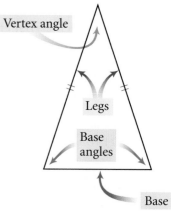

Vertex angle

Legs

Base angles

Base

"Imagination is built upon knowledge."

ELIZABETH STUART PHELPS

Recall from Chapter 1 that an isosceles triangle is a triangle with at least two congruent sides. In an isosceles triangle, the angle between the two congruent sides is called the **vertex angle,** and the other two angles are called the base angles. The side between the two base angles is called the base of the isosceles triangle. The other two sides are called the **legs.**

In this lesson you'll discover some properties of isosceles triangles.

→ *Architecture*
CONNECTION

The Rock and Roll Hall of Fame and Museum in Cleveland, Ohio, is a dynamic structure. Its design reflects the innovative music that it honors. The front part of the museum is a large glass pyramid, divided into small triangular windows. The pyramid structure rests on a rectangular tower and a circular theater that looks like a performance drum. Architect I. M. Pei (b 1917) used geometric shapes to capture the resonance of rock and roll musical chords.

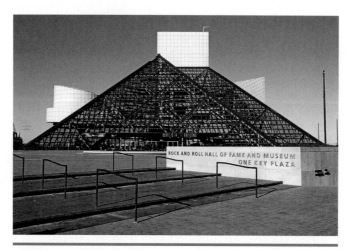

The Rock and Roll Hall of Fame and Museum structure is a pyramid containing many triangles that are isosceles and equilateral.

The famous Transamerica Building in San Francisco contains many isosceles triangles.

INVESTIGATION 1

YOU WILL NEED
- patty paper
- a straightedge
- a protractor

Base Angles in an Isosceles Triangle

Let's examine the angles of an isosceles triangle. Each person in your group should draw a different angle for this investigation. Your group should have at least one acute angle and one obtuse angle.

Step 1 Draw an angle on patty paper. Label it ∠C. This angle will be the vertex angle of your isosceles triangle.

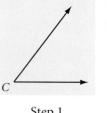

C

Step 1

Step 2 Place a point *A* on one ray. Fold your patty paper so that the two rays match up. Trace point *A* onto the other ray.

Step 2

Step 3 Label the point on the other ray point *B*. Draw $\overline{AB}$. You have constructed an isosceles triangle. Explain how you know it is isosceles. Name the base and the base angles.

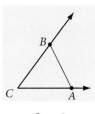

Step 4 Use your protractor to compare the measures of the base angles. What relationship do you notice? How can you fold the paper to confirm your conclusion?

Step 3

Step 5 Compare results in your group. Was the relationship you noticed the same for each isosceles triangle? State your observations as your next conjecture.

Isosceles Triangle Conjecture   C-18

If a triangle is isosceles, then ? .

 INVESTIGATION 2

YOU WILL NEED
• a compass
• a straightedge

Is the Converse True?

Suppose a triangle has two congruent angles. Must the triangle be isosceles?

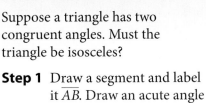

Step 1 Draw a segment and label it $\overline{AB}$. Draw an acute angle at point *A*. This angle will be a base angle. (Why can't you draw an obtuse angle as a base angle?)

Step 1   Step 2

Step 2 Copy $\angle A$ at point *B* on the same side of $\overline{AB}$. Label the intersection of the two rays point *C*.

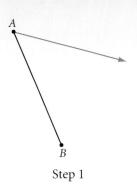

Step 3 Use your compass to compare the lengths of sides $\overline{AC}$ and $\overline{BC}$. What relationship do you notice? How can you use patty paper to confirm your conclusion?

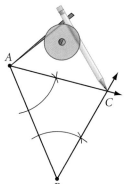

Step 4 Compare results in your group. State your observation as your next conjecture.

Converse of the Isosceles Triangle Conjecture   C-19

If a triangle has two congruent angles, then ? .

Equilateral triangles have at least two congruent sides, so they fit the definition of isosceles triangles. That means any properties you discover for isosceles triangles will also apply to equilateral triangles. How does the Isosceles Triangle Conjecture apply to equilateral triangles?

INVESTIGATION 3

An Equilateral Triangle Thought Experiment

As a group, discuss and answer the following questions then agree on the wording for your next conjecture.

Step 1 If $\triangle ABC$ is equilateral then $\overline{AB} \cong \overline{CA} \cong \overline{CB}$. If $\triangle ABC$ is also isosceles, then $\overline{CA} \cong \overline{CB}$. Then by the Isosceles Triangle Conjecture what can you conclude about $\angle A$ and $\angle B$? If $\triangle ABC$ is isosceles, then $\overline{AB} \cong \overline{AC}$. Then by the Isosceles Triangle Conjecture what can you conclude about $\angle C$ and $\angle B$?

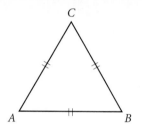

Step 2 If $\angle A \cong \angle B$ and $\angle C \cong \angle B$, then what can you conclude about the three angles? Explain your reasoning. What kind of triangle is this?

Now let's look at the converse. If a triangle is equiangular, what can we say about its three sides?

Step 3 If $\triangle ABC$ is equiangular, then $\angle A \cong \angle B \cong \angle C$. But if $\angle A \cong \angle B$ in $\triangle ABC$, then what can you conclude about the sides $\overline{CA}$ and $\overline{CB}$? Why? If $\angle C \cong \angle B$ in $\triangle ABC$, then what can you conclude about the sides $\overline{BA}$ and $\overline{CA}$? Why?

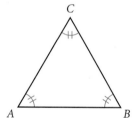

Step 4 If $\overline{AB} \cong \overline{AC}$ and $\overline{AC} \cong \overline{BC}$, then what can you conclude about all three sides? What kind of triangle is this?

You should be ready to complete the next conjecture:

Equilateral/Equiangular Triangle Conjecture	**C-20**
Every equilateral triangle is _?_, and, conversely, every equiangular triangle is _?_.	

If both a statement and its converse are true, they can be combined into one statement and that statement is called a **biconditional**. For example the compound statement, "*if A, then B and if B, then A*," would be written as the biconditional, "*A if and only if B*." You will be asked to write the biconditionals of these conjectures in the exercise set.

Isosceles Triangle Conjectures

The two investigations may have convinced you that the Isosceles Triangle Conjecture and its converse are true, but can you explain why they are true?

Explaining why the Isosceles Triangle Conjecture is true. We'll use the reflection isometry to explain why the Isosceles Triangle Conjecture is true. Let's start with a right triangle $\triangle ADC$ with $\angle D$ the right angle. Reflect $\triangle ADC$ across $\overline{DC}$ and label the reflection of A, point B.

Since $\triangle ADC$ was reflected across $\overline{DC}$, $\triangle ADC \cong \triangle BDC$. Why is $\overline{AC} \cong \overline{BC}$? Why is $\angle A \cong \angle B$? Why are points A, D, and B collinear? Discuss this with your group members. As a group, write a paragraph proof explaining why the Isosceles triangle conjecture is true.

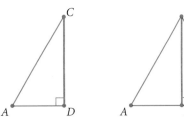

Explaining why the Converse of the Isosceles Triangle Conjecture is true. Let's start with $\angle A$. Select a point on one of the sides of the angle, label it point D. Construct a perpendicular line k through D. Label the intersection of the side of $\angle A$ and line k with point C.

Reflect $\angle A$ over line k and label the image of point A as point B. Why is $\triangle ADC \cong \triangle BDC$? Why is $\angle A \cong \angle B$? Why is $\overline{AC} \cong \overline{BC}$ and thus $\triangle ABC$ is isosceles? Discuss this with your group members. As a group, write a paragraph proof explaining why the Converse of the Isosceles triangle conjecture is true.

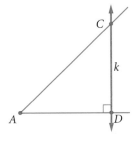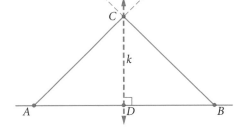

YOU WILL NEED

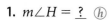

Construction tools
for Exercises **16–18**

For Exercises 1–6, use your new conjectures to find the missing measures.

1. $m\angle H = \underline{\ ?\ }$ ⓗ

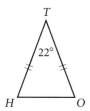

2. $m\angle G = \underline{\ ?\ }$

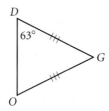

3. $\angle OLE = \underline{\ ?\ }$

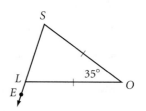

4. $m\angle R = \underline{\ ?\ }$
$RM = \underline{\ ?\ }$

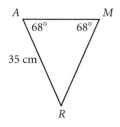

5. $m\angle Y = \underline{\ ?\ }$
$RD = \underline{\ ?\ }$

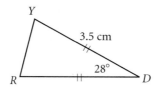

6. The perimeter of $\triangle MUD$
is 36.6 cm.
$m\angle D = \underline{\ ?\ }$
$m\angle U = \underline{\ ?\ }$
$MD = \underline{\ ?\ }$

7. $m\angle T = \underline{\ ?\ }$
perimeter of $\triangle TBS = \underline{\ ?\ }$

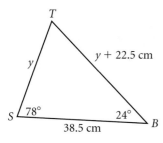

8. The perimeter of $\triangle NBC$
is 555 m.
$NB = \underline{\ ?\ }$
$m\angle N = \underline{\ ?\ }$

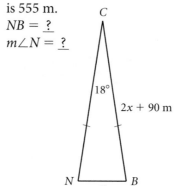

9. The perimeter of $\triangle MTV$
is 605 in.
$MV = \underline{\ ?\ }$
$m\angle M = \underline{\ ?\ }$

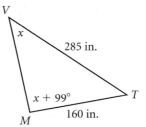

10. **DEVELOPING PROOF** Copy the figure
at right. Calculate the measure of
each lettered angle. Explain how
you determined the measures
d and h. ⓗ

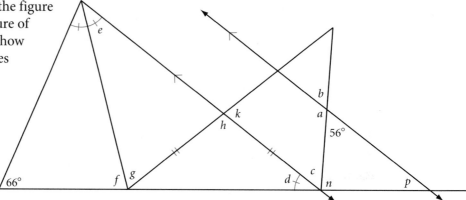

11. The Islamic design below right is based on the star decagon construction shown below left. The ten angles surrounding the center are all congruent. Find the lettered angle measures. How many triangles are not isosceles? ⓗ

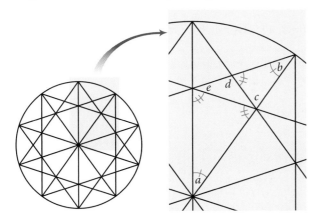

12. Write these two statements as a biconditional: If a triangle is equilateral then it is equiangular and if a triangle is equiangular then it is equilateral.

13. Write these two statements as a biconditional: If a triangle is isosceles then the base angles are congruent and if a triangle has two congruent angles then it is isosceles.

Review

In Exercises 14 and 15, complete the statement of congruence from the information given. Remember to write the statement so that corresponding parts are in order.

14. △*GEA* ≅ △ ?

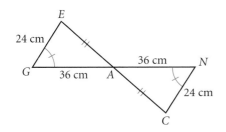

15. △*JAN* ≅ △ ?

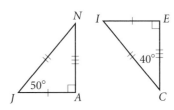

In Exercises 16 and 17, use a compass or patty paper, and a straightedge, to construct a different triangle that is not congruent to the given triangle, but has the given parts congruent. The symbol ≇ means "not congruent to."

16. Construct △*ABC* ≇ △*DEF* with ∠*A* ≅ ∠*D*, ∠*B* ≅ ∠*E*, and ∠*C* ≅ ∠*F*. ⓗ

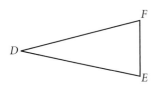

17. Construct △*GHK* ≇ △*MNP* with $\overline{HK}$ ≅ $\overline{NP}$, $\overline{GH}$ ≅ $\overline{MN}$, and ∠*G* ≅ ∠*M*. ⓗ

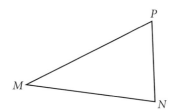

18. With a straightedge and patty paper, construct an angle that measures 105°.

In Exercises 19–22, determine whether each pair of lines through the points below is parallel, perpendicular, or neither.

$A(1, 3)$ $B(6, 0)$ $C(4, 3)$ $D(1, -2)$ $E(-3, 8)$ $F(-4, 1)$ $G(-1, 6)$ $H(4, -4)$

19. $\overleftrightarrow{AB}$ and $\overleftrightarrow{CD}$ ⓗ

20. $\overleftrightarrow{FG}$ and $\overleftrightarrow{CD}$

21. $\overleftrightarrow{AD}$ and $\overleftrightarrow{CH}$

22. $\overleftrightarrow{DE}$ and $\overleftrightarrow{GH}$

23. Using the preceding coordinate points, is *FGCD* a trapezoid, a parallelogram, or neither? Explain.

24. Given Pentagon *ABCDE* with diagonals $\overline{BE}$ and $\overline{CE}$, find the measures *x, y, z*.

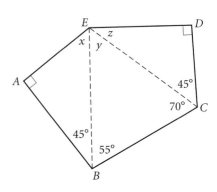

For Exercises 25 and 26, use the ordered pair rule shown to relocate each of the vertices of the given triangle. Connect the three new points to create a new triangle. Is the new triangle congruent to the original one? Describe how the new triangle has changed position from the original.

25. $(x, y) \rightarrow (x + 5, y - 3)$ ⓗ

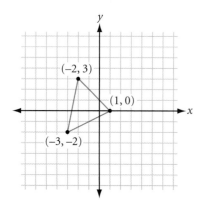

26. $(x, y) \rightarrow (x, -y)$

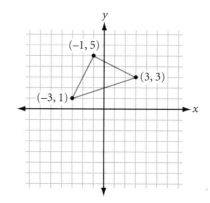

PERFORMANCE TASK

Ross' Constructions

Ross swung an arc with his compass from the vertex of the right angle of △*ABC* with a radius of $\overline{BC}$ creating an isosceles triangle △*BCD*. He then placed the needle of his compass at *D* and swung another arc with the same radius $\overline{DB}$ and found that the arc also passed through vertex *A*! What must be the measures of angles *A* and *C* for this to have happened? Explain how you know to Ross. Once you have solved for *x*, construct a right triangle with one acute angle with a measure of *x* and a longer leg of 8 cm.

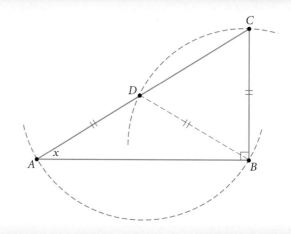

Point of Concurrency: Centroid

In the previous chapter, you saw that you could find the centroid by folding to locate the midpoint of the sides and then constructing the medians. Suppose you know the coordinates of the vertices of a triangle. With these coordinates, you can also find the centroid of a triangle on the coordinate plane by solving a pair of equations of two lines containing two of the medians. Let's look at an example.

Example

Consider $\triangle ABC$ with $A(-5, -3)$, $B(3, -5)$, and $C(-1, 2)$.

a. Find the coordinates of the centroid of $\triangle ABC$ by writing equations for two lines containing medians and finding their point of intersection.

b. Find the mean of the x-coordinates and the mean of the y-coordinates of the triangle's vertices. What do you notice?

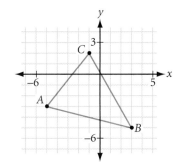

Solution

The centroid is the intersection of two medians of the triangle. A median joins a vertex with the midpoint of the opposite side.

a. The midpoint of $\overline{AB}$ is $\left(\frac{-5 + 3}{2}, \frac{-3 + (-5)}{2}\right)$ or $(-1, -4)$. The coordinates of C are $(-1, 2)$, so the line that goes through both of these points is the vertical line $x = -1$. Next, find the equation of the line containing the median from A to $\overline{BC}$. The midpoint of $\overline{BC}$ is $\left(\frac{3 + (-1)}{2}, \frac{-5 + 2}{2}\right)$, or $\left(1, -\frac{3}{2}\right)$. The slope from A to this midpoint is $\frac{-\frac{3}{2} - (-3)}{1 - (-5)}$, or $\frac{1}{4}$.

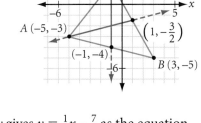

Using the definition of slope, the equation of the dashed line is $\frac{y - (-3)}{x - (-5)} = \frac{1}{4}$. Solving for y gives $y = \frac{1}{4}x - \frac{7}{4}$ as the equation of the line containing the median.

Finally, use substitution to solve this system.

$$\begin{cases} y = \frac{1}{4}x - \frac{7}{4} \\ x = -1 \end{cases}$$

Equation of the line containing the median from A to $\overline{BC}$.

Equation of the line containing the median from C to $\overline{AB}$.

$y = \frac{1}{4}(-1) - \frac{7}{4}$ Substitute -1 for x in the first equation.

$y = -2$ Simplify.

The centroid is $(-1, -2)$. You can verify this result by writing the equation for the third median and making sure $(-1, -2)$ satisfies it.

b. The mean of the x-coordinates is
$$\frac{-5 + 3 + (-1)}{3} = \frac{-3}{3} = -1.$$

The mean of the y-coordinates is
$$\frac{-3 + (-5) + 2}{3} = \frac{-6}{3} = -2.$$

Notice that these means give you the coordinates of the centroid: $(-1, -2)$.

As you have just seen in the example, there is a more efficient method to finding the centroid than finding the intersection of two equations. You can generalize the findings from the Example to all triangles. The easiest way to find the coordinates of the centroid is to find the mean of the vertex coordinates.

Exercises

In Exercises 1 and 2, use $\triangle RES$ with vertices $R(0, 0)$, $E(4, -6)$, and $S(8, 4)$.

1. Find the equation of the line containing the median from R to $\overline{ES}$.

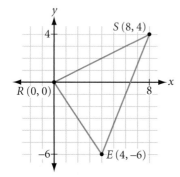

2. Find the equation of the line containing the median from E to $\overline{RS}$.

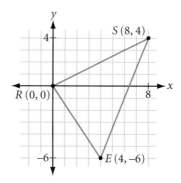

In Exercises 3 and 4, use algebra to find the coordinates of the centroid for each triangle.

3. Right triangle MNO

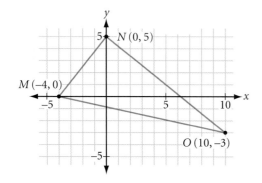

4. Isosceles triangle CDE

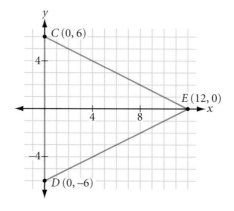

5. Find the coordinates of the centroid of the triangle formed by the x-axis, the y-axis, and the line $12x + 9y = 36$.

6. The three lines $8x + 3y = 12$, $6y - 7x = 24$, and $x + 9y + 33 = 0$ intersect to form a triangle. Find the coordinates of its centroid.

In Chapter 3 you discovered that the three medians of a triangle are concurrent in a point called the centroid. Now you have the skills to prove it using coordinate geometry.

7. DEVELOPING PROOF You prove that the medians of a triangle are concurrent the same way you found the centroid in the example except you use letters instead of numbers. To make the manipulating of symbols easier, place the points on the coordinate grid at "nice" locations (usually on one of the axes). Locate the points of your diagram so that they correspond to the given information, and you are not assuming extra properties. The plan for the coordinate proof is started for you. Complete the proof to show that the medians of a triangle are concurrent.

Given: $\triangle OAB$, without loss of generalitly, vertices $O(0, 0)$, $A(2a, 0)$, $B(2b, 2c)$

Show: The three medians of a triangle are concurrent.

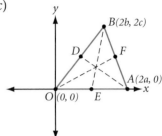

Plan:
- Find the midpoint of $\overline{OA}$, $\overline{OB}$, and $\overline{AB}$ {D, E, F}
- Find the equations of medians $\overline{OF}$, $\overline{AD}$, and $\overline{BE}$.
- Find the point of intersection of medians $\overline{OF}$ and $\overline{AD}$.
- Find the point of intersection of of medians $\overline{OF}$ and $\overline{BE}$.
- If the point of intersection of medians $\overline{OF}$ and $\overline{AD}$ and the point of intersection of medians $\overline{OF}$ and $\overline{BE}$ are the same, then you have proved the three medians are concurrent!

DEVELOPING MATHEMATICAL REASONING

Pick a Card

Nine cards are arranged in a 3-by-3 array. Every jack borders on a king and on a queen. Every king borders on an ace. Every queen borders on a king and on an ace. (The cards border each other edge-to-edge, but not corner-to-corner.) There are at least two aces, two kings, two queens, and two jacks. Which card is in the center position of the 3-by-3 array?

Triangle Inequalities

How long must each side of this drawbridge be so that the bridge spans the river when both sides come down?

Drawbridges over the Chicago River in Chicago, Illinois

The sum of the lengths of the two parts of the drawbridge must be equal to or greater than the distance across the waterway. Triangles have similar requirements.

You can build a triangle using one blue rod, one green rod, and one red rod. Could you still build a triangle if you used a yellow rod instead of the green rod? Why or why not? Could you form a triangle with two yellow rods and one green rod? What if you used two green rods and one yellow rod?

How can you determine which sets of three rods can be arranged into triangles and which can't? How do the measures of the angles in the triangle relate to the lengths of the rods? How is measure of the exterior angle formed by the yellow and blue rods in the triangle above related to the measures of the angles inside the triangle? In this lesson you will investigate these questions.

INVESTIGATION 1

What Is the Shortest Path from *A* to *B*?

Each person in your group should do each construction. Compare results when you finish.

Step 1 Construct a triangle with each set of segments as sides.

Given:

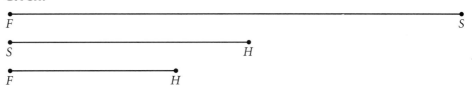

Construct: △*CAT*

Given:

Construct: △*FSH*

Step 2 You should have been able to construct △*CAT*, but not △*FSH*. Why? Discuss your results with others. State your observations as your next conjecture.

> **Triangle Inequality Conjecture**   **C-21**
>
> The sum of the lengths of any two sides of a triangle is _?_ the length of the third side.

Explore more about Triangle Inequality using the **Dynamic Geometry Exploration** in your ebook.

What does the title of this investigation have to do with what you investigated? The Triangle Inequality Conjecture relates the lengths of the three sides of a triangle. You can also think of it in another way: The shortest path between two points is along the segment connecting them. In other words, the path from *A* to *C* to *B* can't be shorter than the path from *A* to *B*.

INVESTIGATION 2

Where Are the Largest and Smallest Angles?

Each person should draw a different scalene triangle for this investigation. Some group members should draw acute triangles, and some should draw obtuse triangles.

Step 1 Measure the angles in your triangle. Label the angle with greatest measure ∠*L*, the angle with second greatest measure ∠*M*, and the smallest angle ∠*S*.

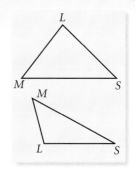

Step 2 Measure the three sides. Label the longest side *l*, the second longest side *m*, and the shortest side *s*.

Step 3 Which side is opposite ∠*L*? ∠*M*? ∠*S*?

Discuss your results with others. Write a conjecture that states where the largest and smallest angles are in a triangle, in relation to the longest and shortest sides.

Side-Angle Inequality Conjecture	C-22

In a triangle, if one side is longer than another side, then the angle opposite the longer side is _?_ .

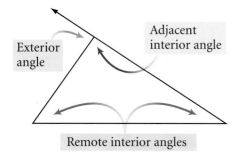

So far in this chapter, you have studied interior angles of triangles. Triangles also have exterior angles. If you extend one side of a triangle beyond its vertex, then you have constructed an **exterior angle** at that vertex.

Each exterior angle of a triangle has an **adjacent interior angle** and a pair of **remote interior angles**. The remote interior angles are the two angles in the triangle that do not share a vertex with the exterior angle.

INVESTIGATION 3

Exterior Angles of a Triangle

YOU WILL NEED
- a straightedge
- patty paper

Each person should draw a different scalene triangle for this investigation. Some group members should draw acute triangles, and some should draw obtuse triangles.

Step 1 On your paper, draw a scalene triangle, △*ABC*. Extend $\overline{AB}$ beyond point *B* and label a point *D* outside the triangle on $\overrightarrow{AB}$. Label the angles as shown.

Step 2 Copy the two remote interior angles, ∠*A* and ∠*C*, onto patty paper to show their sum.

Step 3 How does the sum of *a* and *c* compare with *x*? Use your patty paper from Step 2 to compare.

Step 4 Discuss your results with your group. State your observations as a conjecture.

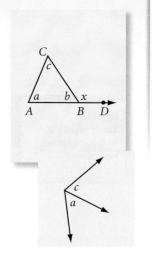

Triangle Exterior Angle Conjecture	C-23

The measure of an exterior angle of a triangle _?_ .

DEVELOPING PROOF

Triangle Exterior Angle Conjecture

The investigation may have convinced you that the Triangle Exterior Angle Conjecture is true, but can you explain why it is true for every triangle?

As a group, discuss how to prove the Triangle Exterior Angle Conjecture. Use reasoning strategies such as draw a labeled diagram, represent a situation algebraically, and apply previous conjectures. Use the diagram on the right and list the relationships you already know among the angles in the diagram, then plan out the logic of your proof.

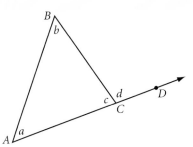

4.3 Exercises

In Exercises 1–4, determine whether it is possible to draw a triangle with sides having the given measures. If possible, write yes. If not possible, write no and make a sketch demonstrating why it is not possible.

1. 3 cm, 4 cm, 5 cm   **2.** 4 m, 5 m, 9 m   **3.** 5 ft, 6 ft, 12 ft   **4.** 3.5 cm, 4.5 cm, 7 cm

In Exercises 5–7, use your new conjectures to arrange the unknown measures in order from greatest to least.

5.
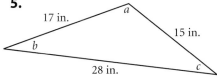

6.
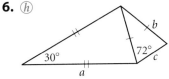

7.
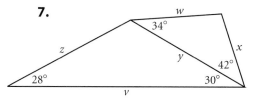

8. DEVELOPING PROOF What's wrong with this picture? Explain.

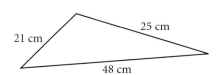

9. DEVELOPING PROOF What's wrong with this picture? Explain.

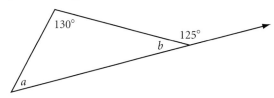

In Exercises 10–11, use one of your new conjectures to find the missing measures.

10. $t + p = \underline{?}$

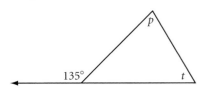

11. $x = \underline{?}$

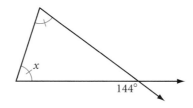

12. If 54 and 48 are the lengths of two sides of a triangle, what is the range of possible values for the length of the third side? ⓗ

13. Two pieces of spaghetti are the same length. You break one piece of spaghetti at a random point. Now you have three pieces of spaghetti. What is the probability that they form a triangle?

14. What is the area of a triangle with sides of 24, 38, and 14?

15. Read the Recreation Connection to the right. If you want to know the perpendicular distance from a landmark to the path of your boat, what should be the measurement of your bow angle when you begin recording?

▸ **Recreation**
CONNECTION

Geometry is used quite often in sailing. For example, to find the distance between the boat and a landmark on shore, sailors use a rule called *doubling the angle on the bow*. The rule says, measure the angle on the bow (the angle formed by your path and your line of sight to the landmark, also called your bearing) at point *A*. Check your bearing until, at point *B*, the bearing is double the reading at point *A*. The distance traveled from *A* to *B* is also the distance from the landmark to your new position.

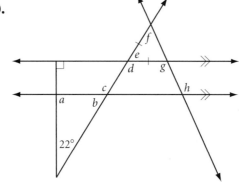

Review

In Exercises 16–18, complete the statement of congruence.

16. $\triangle BAR \cong \triangle \underline{?}$ ⓗ

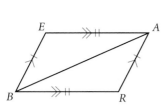

17. $\triangle FAR \cong \triangle \underline{?}$

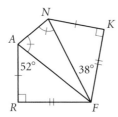

18. $\overline{HG} \cong \overline{HE} \cong \overline{HJ}$
$\overline{JE} \cong \overline{HO}$
$\angle GHO \cong \angle J$
$\triangle HEJ \cong \triangle \underline{?}$

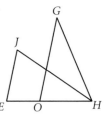

In Exercises 19 and 20, calculate each lettered angle measure.

19.

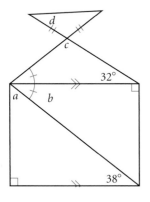

20.

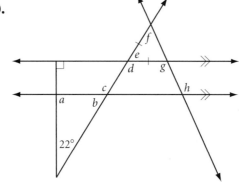

21. What's wrong with this picture of △TRG? Explain. ⓗ

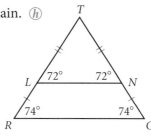

22. From the marked figure, determine the measures of *x, y,* and *z* and if $\overleftrightarrow{AB} \parallel \overleftrightarrow{CD}$. Explain your methods.

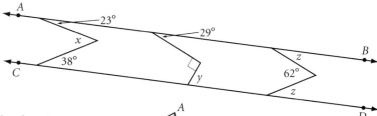

23. Quad *QUAR* is divided into four triangles by drawing segments from an interior point *T* to each of the four vertices. Find the measures *x* and *y*.

24. Ross continued to experiment with his compass on special right triangles. He swung an arc with his compass from the vertex of the right angle of △*ABC* with a radius of $\overline{BC}$ creating an isosceles triangle △*BCD*. He then placed the needle of his compass at *D* and swung another arc with the same radius $\overline{DB}$ creating another isosceles triangle △*BED*. His partner Jeff was watching and said, "Hey, let's try it again." With the compass needle at *E* and a radius of $\overline{ED}$ Jeff swung an arc, and sure enough he found that the arc also passed through vertex *A*! What must be the relationship between *x* and *y* for this to happen? Explain to Jeff and Ross why this worked out this way. Once you have solved for *x* and *y*, construct a right triangle with acute angle measures of *x* and *y* and a longer leg of 8 cm. ⓗ

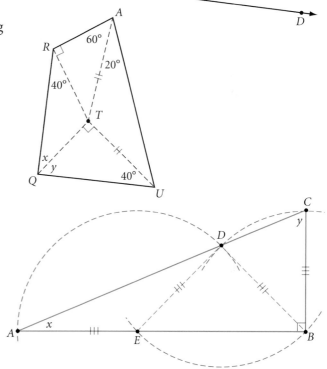

DEVELOPING MATHEMATICAL REASONING

King's Tour Puzzle

For a 6 × 6 king's tour puzzle, the objective is to fill the remaining empty squares with integers from 1 to 36 so when completed there is a continuous path of numbers from 1 through 36. The path may meander horizontally, vertically, or diagonally from square to adjacent square, just like a king. The circles represent the locations of the smallest and the largest numbers on the grid (the starting and stopping points of the tour).

				23	
29	33		2	24	
30		◯	3	20	
	11	◯	19		
	7		18		
8		6			

EXPLORATION

Origamics

You probably have heard of **Origami,** the traditional Japanese art of paper folding, which started in the 17th century A.D. It is now a popular art form the world over. The goal of origami is to fold a square sheet of paper into a finished sculpture representing animals, flowers, or other familiar objects. When you fold paper, mathematically you are creating reflections; thus origami has obvious links to geometry.

Modular origami (also called unit origami), as the name implies, is an origami technique of producing a number of identical origami pieces and assembling them into one finished piece of origami art.

But what is Origamics? **Origamics** (origami + mathematics) is a term coined by Dr. Kazuo Haga, for what he calls "scientific origami." Here are a few warm up origamics-type exercises. If you fold a square piece of paper by bringing a pair of opposite sides together you create a rectangle with the shorter sides half the length of the longer sides and the area half the area of the original square. Is the perimeter half the original square? If you fold a pair of opposite vertices together you get an isosceles right triangle with an area half the area of the original square. Is the perimeter half? Got the idea?

Activity

A four-fold exploration

In this activity you'll see that you can apply properties of transformations and origami folds to solve mathematical problems. To make the diagrams easier to follow the two sides of the square paper are colored differently so you can tell front from back.

Using a sheet of origami paper or patty paper, perform the following five steps, then find the measure of each labeled angle.

Step 1 Fold to locate midpoints E and F.

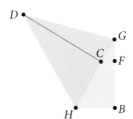

Step 2 Bring C to midline $\overline{EF}$.

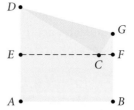

Step 3 Bring $\overline{DA}$ to $\overline{DC}$.

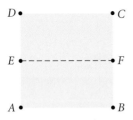

Step 4 Reflect $\triangle GBH$ over $\overline{GH}$.

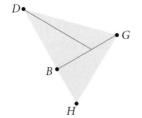

Step 5 Unfold. Find the measure of each labeled angle.

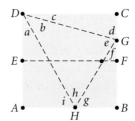

Are There Congruence Shortcuts?

▶ *Career*
CONNECTION

Congruence is very important in design and manufacturing. Modern assembly-line production relies on identical, or congruent, parts that are interchangeable. In the assembly of an automobile, for example, the same part needs to fit into each car coming down the assembly line.

If it is possible to move one triangle to be superimposed over another triangle, then the two triangles are congruent. You can do this informally by tracing one and seeing if it fits onto the second. More formally, it is possible to use some combination of isometries to make one coincide with the other. We also know that two triangles are congruent if and only if all the corresponding sides are congruent and all the corresponding angles are congruent. But do we really need to know that all six corresponding parts are congruent to determine that the two triangles are congruent? Are there any shortcuts?

A building contractor has just assembled massive triangular trusses to support the roof of a recreation hall. Before the roof materials can be added, the contractor needs to verify that the triangular trusses are identical. Must the contractor measure and compare all six parts of both triangles?

You learned from the Third Angle Conjecture that if there is a pair of angles congruent in each of two triangles, then the third angles must be congruent. But will this guarantee that the trusses are the same size? You probably need to also know something about the sides in order to be sure that two triangles are congruent. Recall from earlier exercises that fewer than three parts of one triangle can be congruent to corresponding parts of another triangle, without the triangles being congruent.

So let's begin looking for congruence shortcuts by comparing three parts of each triangle. There are six different ways that the three corresponding parts of two triangles may be congruent. They are diagrammed below. Some of these will be congruence shortcuts, and some will not.

Side-Side-Side (SSS)

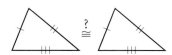

Three pairs of congruent sides

Side-Angle-Side (SAS)

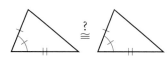

Two pairs of congruent sides and one pair of congruent angles (angles between the pairs of sides)

Angle-Side-Angle (ASA)

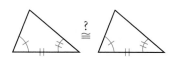

Two pairs of congruent angles and one pair of congruent sides (sides between the pairs of angles)

Side-Angle-Angle (SAA)

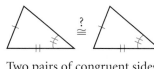

Two pairs of congruent angles and one pair of congruent sides (sides not between the pairs of angles)

Side-Side-Angle (SSA)

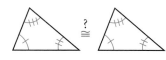

Two pairs of congruent sides and one pair of congruent angles (angles not between the pairs of sides)

Angle-Angle-Angle (AAA)

Three pairs of congruent angles

You will investigate three of these cases in this lesson and the other three in the next lesson to discover which of these six possible cases turn out to be congruence shortcuts and which do not.

INVESTIGATION 1

YOU WILL NEED
- a compass or patty paper
- a straightedge

Is SSS a Congruence Shortcut?

First you will investigate the Side-Side-Side (SSS) case. If the three sides of one triangle are congruent to the three sides of another, must the two triangles be congruent?

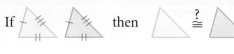

Step 1 Construct a triangle from the three parts shown. Be sure you match up the endpoints labeled with the same letter. If you need help with this construction, see Lesson 3.6, Example A.

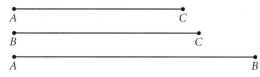

Step 2 Compare your triangle with the triangles made by others in your group. (One way to compare them is to place the triangles on top of each other and see if they coincide.) Is it possible to construct different triangles from the same three parts, or will all the triangles be congruent?

Step 3 You are now ready to complete the conjecture for the SSS case.

> ### SSS Congruence Conjecture　　　　　　　　　C-24
>
> If the three sides of one triangle are congruent to the three sides of another triangle, then _?_.

An angle that is included between two sides of a triangle is called an **included angle**, as shown in the diagram at right. You will investigate this case next.

Included angle

INVESTIGATION 2

YOU WILL NEED
- a compass or patty paper
- a straightedge

Is SAS a Congruence Shortcut?

Next you will consider the Side-Angle-Side (SAS) case. If two sides and the included angle of one triangle are congruent to two sides and the included angle of another, must the triangles be congruent?

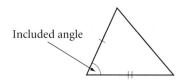

Step 1 Construct a triangle from the three parts shown. Be sure you match up the endpoints labeled with the same letter. If you need help with this construction, see Lesson 3.6, Exercise 2.

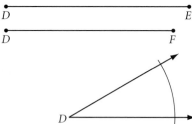

Step 2 Compare your triangle with the triangles made by others in your group. Is it possible to construct different triangles from the same three parts, or will all the triangles be congruent?

Step 3 You are now ready to complete the conjecture for the SAS case.

> ### SAS Congruence Conjecture   `C-25`
>
> If two sides and the included angle of one triangle are congruent to two sides and the included angle of another triangle, then _?_.

INVESTIGATION 3

YOU WILL NEED

- a compass or patty paper
- a straightedge

Is SSA a Congruence Shortcut?

Finally you will consider the Side-Side-Angle (SSA) case. If two sides and a non-included angle of one triangle are congruent to the corresponding two sides and non-included angle of another, must the triangles be congruent?

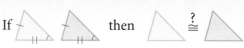

Step 1 Construct a triangle from the three parts shown. Be sure you match up the endpoints labeled with the same letter. If you need help with this construction, see Lesson 3.6, Exercise 5.

Step 2 Compare your triangle with the triangles made by others in your group. Is it possible to construct different triangles from the same three parts, or will all the triangles be congruent?

Step 3 If two sides and a non-included angle of one triangle are congruent to the corresponding two sides and non-included angle of another triangle, do the two triangles have to be congruent? Explain why or show a counterexample.

Step 4 You should now be ready to state a conjecture.

> ### SSA Non-congruence Conjecture
>
> If two sides and a non-included angle of one triangle are congruent to the corresponding two sides and non-included angle of another triangle, the two triangles are _?_ congruent.

In the investigations you discovered a few shortcuts for showing that two triangles are congruent. This is very useful for proving that other segments or angles are congruent. Let's look at an example.

EXAMPLE

Given $\triangle ABC$ and $\triangle DEF$ with $\overline{AC} \cong \overline{DF}$, $\overline{BC} \cong \overline{EF}$, and $\overline{AB} \cong \overline{DE}$. Is $\angle B \cong \angle E$?

Solution | Since the three sides of △ABC are congruent to the three sides of △DEF then the two triangles are congruent by the SSS congruence shortcut. If △ABC ≅ △DEF then by the *definition of congruent triangles* all six parts of one triangle are congruent to the six parts of the other triangle. Thus ∠B ≅ ∠E.

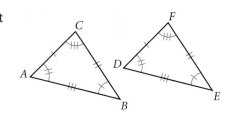

4.4 Exercises

YOU WILL NEED

Construction tools for Exercises **22** and **23**

1. The picture statement below represents the SSS Triangle Congruence Conjecture. Explain what the picture statement means.

If you know this: **then you also know this:**

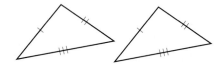   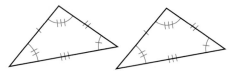

2. Create a picture statement to represent the SAS Triangle Congruence Conjecture. Explain what the picture statement means.

3. In the third investigation you discovered that the SSA case is not a triangle congruence shortcut. Sketch a counterexample and explain why this is not a shortcut.

For Exercises 4–9, decide whether the triangles are congruent and name the congruence shortcut you used. If the triangles cannot be shown to be congruent as labeled, write "cannot be determined."

4. Which conjecture tells you △LUZ ≅ △IDA? ⓗ

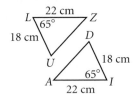

5. Which conjecture tells you △AFD ≅ △EFD? ⓗ

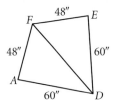

6. Which conjecture tells you △COT ≅ △NPA?

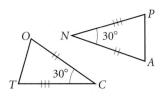

7. Which conjecture tells you △CAV ≅ △CEV?

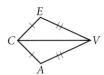

8. Which conjecture tells you △KAP ≅ △AKQ?

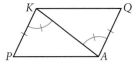

9. Y is a midpoint. Which conjecture tells you △AYB ≅ △RYN?

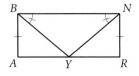

10. The perimeter of △ABC is 180 m. Is △ABC ≅ △ADE? Which conjecture supports your conclusion?

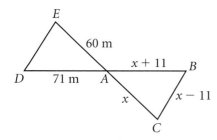

11. Explain why the board secured across the back of the shelves on the right is a better shelving system than the one on the left. ⓗ

DEVELOPING PROOF In Exercises 12–17, if possible, name a triangle congruent to the given triangle and state the congruence conjecture. If you cannot show any triangles to be congruent from the information given, write "cannot be determined" and explain why.

12. △ANT ≅ △ _?_ ⓗ
Is ∠N ≅ ∠L? Explain why.

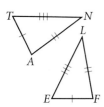

13. △RED ≅ △ _?_

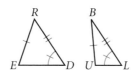

14. △GIT ≅ △ _?_
Is ∠G ≅ ∠A? Explain why.

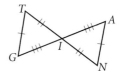

15. △MAN ≅ △ _?_ ⓗ

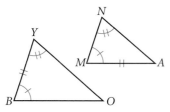

16. △SAT ≅ △ _?_
Is $\overline{AO} ≅ \overline{AT}$? Explain why.

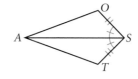

17. △WOM ≅ △ _?_
Is $\overline{WO} ≅ \overline{WT}$? Explain why.

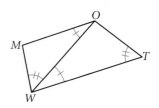

In Exercises 18 and 19, determine whether the segments or triangles in the coordinate plane are congruent and explain your reasoning.

18. △SUN ≅ △ _?_ ⓗ
Is ∠RYA ≅ ∠SNU?

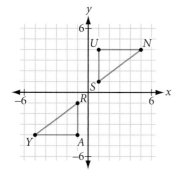

19. △DRO ≅ △ _?_
$\overline{PR}$ and $\overline{DS}$ intersect at the origin.

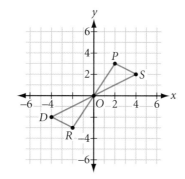

20. Is $\overline{PQ} ≅ \overline{RS}$? Explain how you know. ⓗ

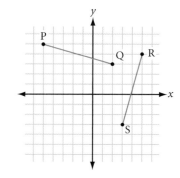

21. How wide is the crater? NASA scientists using a lunar exploration vehicle (LEV) wish to determine the distance across the deep crater shown at right. They have mapped out a path for the LEV as shown. What do the scientists need to measure to find the approximate distance across the crater? Explain why.

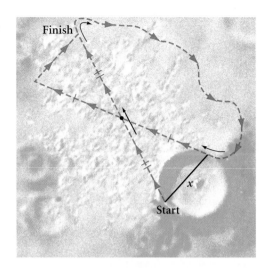

In Exercises 22 and 23, use a compass and straightedge, or patty paper, to perform these constructions.

22. Draw a triangle. Use the SSS Congruence Conjecture to construct a second triangle congruent to the first.

23. Draw a triangle. Use the SAS Congruence Conjecture to construct a second triangle congruent to the first.

Review

24. Given $\triangle ABC$ with vertices $A(-8, 2)$, $B(-7, -4)$, $C(-5, 7)$ and $\triangle DEF$ with vertices $D(1, 7)$, $E(4, 2)$, $F(3, -4)$.

a. Are the two triangles congruent? ⓗ

b. If they are congruent, what is the statement of congruence, ($\triangle ABC \cong \triangle$???)?

c. If congruent, what is the single transformation rule that takes one triangle onto the other?

d. If they are not congruent explain why not.

25. The SSS Congruence Conjecture explains why triangles are rigid structures though other polygons are not. By adding one "strut" (diagonal) to a quadrilateral you create a quadrilateral that consists of two triangles, and that makes it rigid. What is the minimum number of struts needed to make a pentagon rigid? A hexagon? A dodecagon? What is the minimum number of struts needed to make other polygons rigid? Complete the table and make your conjecture.

Number of sides	3	4	5	6	7	...	12	...	n	...	20
Number of struts needed to make polygon rigid						...		...		...	

DEVELOPING MATHEMATICAL REASONING

Moving Coins

Create a triangle of coins similar to the one shown. How can you move exactly three coins so that the triangle is pointing down rather than up? When you have found a solution, use a diagram to explain it.

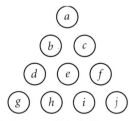

Are There Other Congruence Shortcuts?

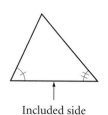

Included side

"There is no more a math mind than there is a history mind."

GLORIA STEINEM quoting
SHEILA TOBIAS

In the last lesson, you discovered that there are six ways that three parts of two triangles can be the same. You found that SSS and SAS both lead to the congruence of the two triangles, but that SSA does not. In this lesson you will investigate the other three cases.

A side that is included between two angles of a triangle is called an **included side**, as shown in the diagram at right. You will investigate this case next.

INVESTIGATION 1

YOU WILL NEED

- a compass or patty paper
- a straightedge

Is ASA a Congruence Shortcut?

First you will consider the Angle-Side-Angle (ASA) case. If two angles and the included side of one triangle are congruent to two angles and the included side of another, must the triangles be congruent?

Step 1 Construct a triangle from the three parts shown. Be sure you match up the angles with the endpoints labeled with the same letter. If you need help with this construction, see Lesson 3.6, Exercise 3.

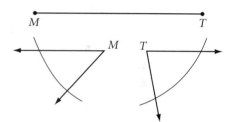

Step 2 Compare your triangle with the triangles made by others in your group. Is it possible to construct different triangles from the same three parts, or will all the triangles be congruent?

Step 3 You are now ready to complete the conjecture for the ASA case.

> **ASA Congruence Conjecture**   C-26
>
> If two angles and the included side of one triangle are congruent to two angles and the included side of another triangle, then _?_ .

In Lesson 4.1, you learned that if you are given two angles of a triangle, you can construct the third angle using the Triangle Sum Conjecture.

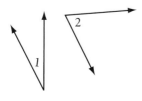 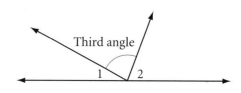

Third angle

INVESTIGATION 2

Is AAA a Congruence Shortcut?

Next you will investigate the Angle-Angle-Angle (AAA) case. If the three angles of one triangle are congruent to the three angles of another, must the triangles be congruent?

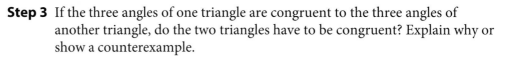

Step 1 Construct a triangle from the three parts shown. If you need help with this construction, see Lesson 3.6, Example B.

Step 2 Compare your triangle with the triangles made by others in your group. Is it possible to construct different triangles from the same three parts, or will all the triangles be congruent?

Step 3 If the three angles of one triangle are congruent to the three angles of another triangle, do the two triangles have to be congruent? Explain why or show a counterexample.

Step 4 You should now be ready to state a conjecture.

> **AAA Non-congruence Conjecture**
>
> If the three angles of one triangle are congruent to the three angles of another triangle, then the two triangles are _?_ necessarily congruent.

INVESTIGATION 3

Is SAA a Congruence Shortcut?

Finally you will consider the Side-Angle-Angle (SAA) case. If two angles and a non-included side of one triangle are congruent to the corresponding two angles and non-included side of another, must the triangles be congruent?

Step 1 Construct a triangle from the three parts shown. Be sure you match up the angles with the endpoints labeled with the same letter. If you need help with this construction, see Lesson 4.1, Exercise 12.

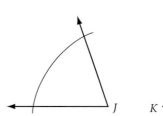
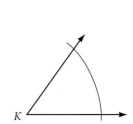

Step 2 Compare your triangle with the triangles made by others in your group. Is it possible to construct different triangles from the same three parts, or will all the triangles be congruent?

Step 3 You are now ready to complete the conjecture for the SAA case.

> **SAA Congruence Conjecture** `C-27`
>
> If two angles and a non-included side of one triangle are congruent to the corresponding two angles and non-included side of another triangle, _?_ .

DEVELOPING PROOF

SAA Congruence Conjecture

In Investigation 3 you found the SAA Congruence Conjecture inductively. You can also derive it deductively from the ASA Congruence Conjecture. As a group, discuss how to prove the SAA Congruence Conjecture. Use reasoning strategies such as apply previous conjectures. Start by studying the diagrams and listing the relationships you already know among the angles in the diagram, then plan out the logic of your proof. If you can explain why $\angle C \cong \angle Z$, then you can explain why $\triangle ABC \cong \triangle XYZ$.

In $\triangle ABC$ and $\triangle XYZ$, $\angle A \cong \angle X$, $\angle B \cong \angle Y$, and $\overline{BC} \cong \overline{YZ}$.

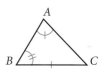

4.5 Exercises

YOU WILL NEED

Construction tools
for Exercises 20–23
and 26

1. The picture statement below represents the ASA Triangle Congruence Conjecture. Explain what the picture statement means.

If you know this: **then you also know this:**

2. Create a picture statement to represent the SAA Triangle Congruence Conjecture. Explain what the picture statement means.

3. In the second investigation you discovered that the AAA case is not a triangle congruence shortcut. Sketch a counterexample and explain why this is not a shortcut.

For Exercises 4–9, determine whether the triangles are congruent, and name the congruence shortcut. If the triangles cannot be shown to be congruent, write "cannot be determined."

4. △AMD ≅ △RMC

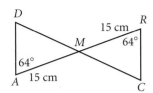

5. △FSH ≅ △FSI

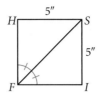

6. △GAS ≅ △IOL ⓗ

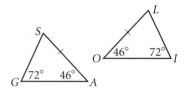

7. △HOW ≅ △FEW

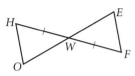

8. △BOX ≅ △CAR

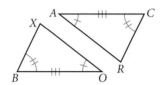

9. △ALT ≅ △INT

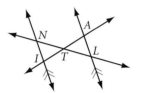

DEVELOPING PROOF In Exercises 10–17, if possible, name a triangle congruent to the triangle given and state the congruence conjecture. If you cannot show any triangles to be congruent from the information given, write "cannot be determined" and explain why.

10. △FAD ≅ △ ?

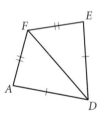

11. $\overline{OH} \parallel \overline{AT}$
△WHO ≅ △ ?

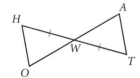

12. $\overline{AT}$ is an angle bisector.
△LAT ≅ △ ?

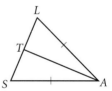

13. PO = PR
∠O ≅ ∠R
∠OPE and ∠NPR are right angles
△POE ≅ △ ?

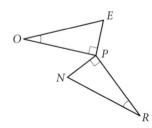

14. △ ? ≅ △ ?

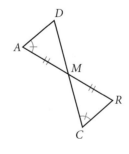

15. △RMF ≅ △ ?

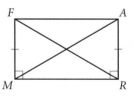

16. △BLA ≅ △ ? ⓗ

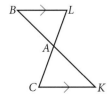

17. △LAW ≅ △ ?

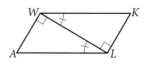

18. The perimeter of △ABC is 138 cm and $\overline{BC} \parallel \overline{DE}$. Is △ABC ≅ △ADE? Which conjecture supports your conclusion?

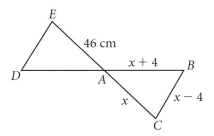

19. Use slope properties to show $\overline{AB} \perp \overline{BC}$, $\overline{CD} \perp \overline{DA}$, and $\overline{BC} \parallel \overline{DA}$. △ABC ≅ △ ? . Why?

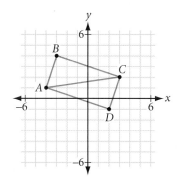

In Exercises 20–22, use a compass or patty paper, and a straightedge, to perform each construction.

20. Draw a triangle. Use the ASA Congruence Conjecture to construct a second triangle congruent to the first. Write a paragraph to justify your steps.

21. Draw a triangle. Use the SAA Congruence Conjecture to construct a second triangle congruent to the first. Write a paragraph to justify your method.

22. Construct two triangles that are not congruent even though the three angles of one triangle are congruent to the three angles of the other. ⓗ

Review

23. Using only a compass and a straightedge, construct an isosceles triangle with a vertex angle that measures 135°.

24. If n concurrent lines divide the plane into 250 parts then $n = $? .

25. "If the two diagonals of a quadrilateral are perpendicular, then the quadrilateral is a rhombus." Explain why this statement is true or sketch a counterexample and explain why it is false.

26. Construct an isosceles right triangle with $\overline{KM}$ as one of the legs. How many noncongruent triangles can you construct? Why?

27. Sketch five lines in a plane that intersect in exactly five points. Now do this in a different way.

28. Scientists use seismograms and triangulation to pinpoint the epicenter of an earthquake.

   a. Data recorded for one quake show that the epicenter is 480 km from Eureka, California, 720 km from Elko, Nevada, and 640 km from Las Vegas, Nevada. Trace the locations of these three towns and use the scale and your construction tools to find the location of the epicenter.

   b. Is it necessary to have seismogram information from three towns? Would two towns suffice? Explain.

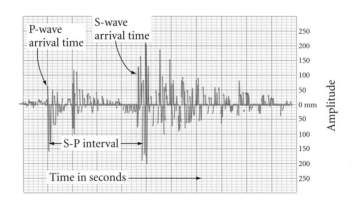

29. Given △*ABC* with vertices *A*(3, 4), *B*(7, 2), *C*(5, 7)

   a. Rotate △*ABC* 90° counterclockwise about the origin to create △*A′B′C′*.

   b. What are the coordinates of the vertices of △*A′B′C′*?

   c. What is the transformation rule, (*x, y*) → (?, ?), that transformed △*ABC* to △*A′B′C′*?

   d. Rotate △*A′B′C′* 90° counterclockwise about the origin to create △*A″B″C″*.

   e. What are the coordinates of the vertices of △*A″B″C″*?

   f. What is the transformation rule, (*x, y*) → (?, ?), that transformed △*A′B′C′* to △*A″B″C″*?

   g. What is the single transformation rule that takes △*ABC* onto △*A″B″C″*?

DEVELOPING MATHEMATICAL REASONING

Geometry Vocabulary Network Puzzle

A geometry term or expression is hidden in each of these two network puzzles. Begin at one of the letters and move to the next, traveling along each path exactly once. You may return to some letters but never travel along the same path more than once.

Puzzle A

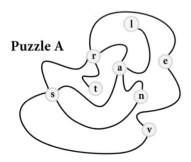

Puzzle B

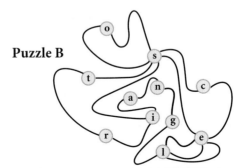

Corresponding Parts of Congruent Triangles

"The job of the younger generation is to find solutions to the solutions found by the older generation."

ANONYMOUS

In Lessons 4.4 and 4.5, you discovered four shortcuts for showing that two triangles are congruent—SSS, SAS, ASA, and SAA. The definition of congruent triangles states that if two triangles are congruent, then the *Corresponding Parts of those Congruent Triangles are Congruent.* We'll use the letters **CPCTC** to refer to the definition. Let's see how you can use congruent triangles and CPCTC.

EXAMPLE | Is $\overline{AD} \cong \overline{BC}$ in the figure to the right? Use a deductive argument to explain why they must be congruent.

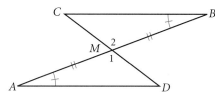

Solution | Here is one possible explanation:
$\angle 1 \cong \angle 2$ because they are vertical angles. And it is given that $\overline{AM} \cong \overline{BM}$ and $\angle A \cong \angle B$. So, by ASA, $\triangle AMD \cong \triangle BMC$. Because the triangles are congruent, $\overline{AD} \cong \overline{BC}$ by CPCTC.

If you use a congruence shortcut to show that two triangles are congruent, then you can use CPCTC to show that any of their corresponding parts are congruent.

When you are trying to prove that triangles are congruent, it can be hard to keep track of what you know. Mark all the information on the figure. If the triangles are hard to see, you can use different colors or redraw them separately.

DEVELOPING PROOF

Proof Techniques–Overlapping Triangles

As a group, discuss how to prove $\overline{AE} \cong \overline{BD}$ in $\triangle ABC$ below on the right.

When you are trying to prove that triangles are congruent, it can be hard to keep track of what you know. Mark all the information on the figure.

If the triangles are hard to see, you can use different colors or redraw them separately. For example the triangles you can use to show congruence are $\triangle ABD$ and $\triangle BAE$. You can separate or color them to see them more clearly.

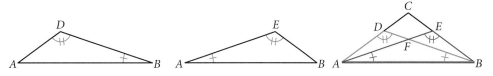

You can see that the two triangles have two pairs of congruent angles and they share a side. Write a paragraph proof to show that $\overline{AE} \cong \overline{BD}$.

4.6 Exercises

YOU WILL NEED

Construction tools
for Exercises **17** and
18

Geometry software
for Exercise **23**

DEVELOPING PROOF For Exercises 1–9, copy the figures onto your paper and
mark them with the given information. Answer the question about segment or
angle congruence. If your answer is yes, write a paragraph proof explaining why.
Remember to use your reasoning strategies, especially apply previous conjectures
and add an auxiliary line. If there is not enough information to prove congruence,
write "cannot be determined;" otherwise state which congruence shortcut you used.

1. $\angle A \cong \angle C$,
$\angle ABD \cong \angle CBD$
Is $\overline{AB} \cong \overline{CB}$? (h)

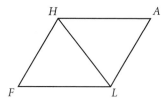

2. $\overline{CN} \cong \overline{WN}$, $\angle C \cong \angle W$
Is $\overline{RN} \cong \overline{ON}$? (h)

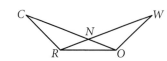

3. $\overline{CS} \cong \overline{HR}$, $\angle 1 \cong \angle 2$
Is $\overline{CR} \cong \overline{HS}$?

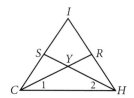

4. $\angle S \cong \angle I$, $\angle G \cong \angle A$
T is the midpoint of $\overline{SI}$.
Is $\overline{SG} \cong \overline{IA}$? (h)

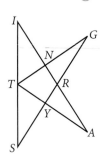

5. $\overline{FI} \cong \overline{FE}$, $\overline{VI} \cong \overline{VE}$
Is $\angle I \cong \angle E$? (h)

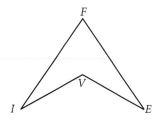

6. $\overline{MN} \cong \overline{MA}$, $\overline{ME} \cong \overline{MR}$
Is $\angle E \cong \angle R$?

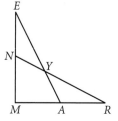

7. $\overline{BT} \cong \overline{EU}$, $\overline{BU} \cong \overline{ET}$
Is $\angle B \cong \angle E$? (h)

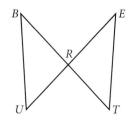

8. $HALF$ is a parallelogram.
Is $\overline{HA} \cong \overline{HF}$?

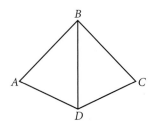

9. $\angle D \cong \angle C$, $\angle O \cong \angle A$,
$\angle G \cong \angle T$. Is $\overline{TA} \cong \overline{GO}$?

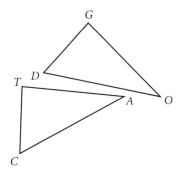

For Exercises 10 and 11, you can use the right angles and the lengths of horizontal and vertical segments shown on the grid. Answer the question about segment or angle congruence. If your answer is yes, explain why.

10. Is $\overline{FR} \cong \overline{GT}$? Why? ⓗ

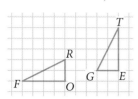

11. Is $\angle OND \cong \angle OCR$? Why?

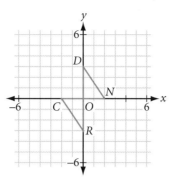

12. Is $\angle P \cong \angle U$? Explain how you know. ⓗ

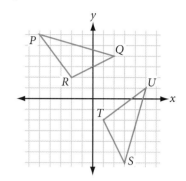

13. **DEVELOPING PROOF** In Chapter 3, you used inductive reasoning to discover how to duplicate an angle using a compass and straightedge. Now you have the skills to explain why the construction works using deductive reasoning. The construction is shown at right. Write a paragraph proof explaining why it works.

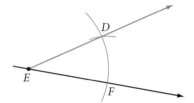

Review

In Exercises 14–16, complete each statement. If the figure does not give you enough information to show that the triangles are congruent, write "cannot be determined."

14. $\overline{AM}$ is a median.
$\triangle CAM \cong \triangle$?

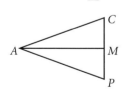

15. $\triangle HEI \cong \triangle$?

16. U is the midpoint of both $\overline{FE}$ and $\overline{LT}$. $\triangle ULF \cong \triangle$?

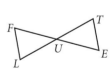

17. Draw a triangle. Use the SAS Congruence Conjecture to construct a second triangle congruent to the first.

18. Construct two triangles that are *not* congruent, even though two sides and a non-included angle of one triangle are congruent to two sides and a corresponding non-included angle of the other triangle. ⓗ

19. **DEVELOPING PROOF** Copy the figure. Calculate the measure of each lettered angle. Explain how you determined the measures *f* and *m*.

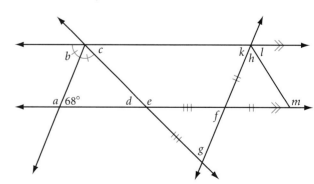

20. According to math legend, the Greek mathematician Thales (ca. 625–547 B.C.E.) could tell how far out to sea a ship was by using congruent triangles. First, he marked off a long segment in the sand. Then, from each endpoint of the segment, he drew the angle to the ship. He then remeasured the two angles on the other side of the segment away from the shore. The point where the rays of these two angles crossed located the ship. What congruence conjecture was Thales using? Explain.

21. Isosceles right triangle ABC has vertices $A(-8, 2)$, $B(-5, -3)$, and $C(0, 0)$. Find the coordinates of the centroid.

22. The 15-by-15 grid to the right was held together by three types of connectors: "elbow," "T," and "cross." It was damaged and needs to be replaced. How many of each type of connector do you need to rebuild a 15-by-15 grid? ⓗ

Elbow   Ⓛ

T   ⊤

Cross   ✚

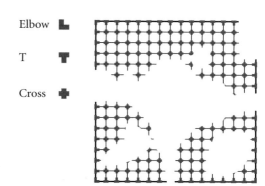

23. GUESS-N-CHECK Line ℓ is parallel to $\overline{AB}$. If P moves to the right along ℓ, which of the following always decreases? First, try this as a "mental experiment." Take a guess, explain how you know, and then create the diagram with your geometry software and see how good you were at visualization.

  A. The distance PC

  B. The distance from C to $\overline{AB}$

  C. The ratio $\frac{AB}{AP}$

  D. The ratio $\frac{BC}{BP}$

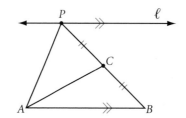

24. Find the lengths x and y. Each angle is a right angle.

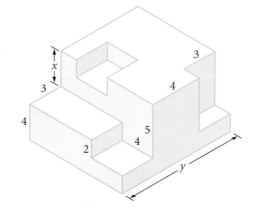

DEVELOPING MATHEMATICAL REASONING

Sliding Block Puzzle

Maneuver the rectangular block marked with an X out of the playing grid through one of the two openings. In order to get the 1×2 block out of the six-by-six grid, you need to move the other 1×2 and 1×3 blocks out of the way. Each block can only move back and forth in a straight line in the direction of its length or longer dimension. For example, block F can move left and right, but not up or down. Block C can move up and down, but not left or right. Use "↑" for up, "↓" for down, "→" for right, and "←" for left in writing your solution.

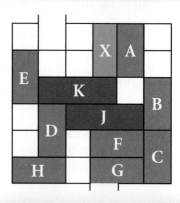

Flowchart Thinking

You have been making many discoveries about triangles. As you try to explain why the new conjectures are true, you build upon definitions and conjectures you made before.

So far, you have written your explanations as deductive arguments or paragraph proofs. First, we'll look at a diagram and explain why two angles must be congruent by writing a paragraph proof in Example A. Then we'll look at a different tool for writing proofs and use that tool to write the same proof in Example B.

EXAMPLE A

In the figure at right, $\overline{EC} \cong \overline{AC}$ and $\overline{ER} \cong \overline{AR}$. Is $\angle A \cong \angle E$? If so, give a logical argument to explain why they are congruent.

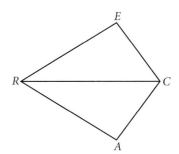

Solution

First, mark the given information on the figure. Then consider whether $\angle A$ is congruent to $\angle E$. It looks as if there are two congruent triangles, so use the reasoning strategy of applying previous conjectures to explain why.

Paragraph Proof: Show that $\angle A \cong \angle E$.

$\overline{EC} \cong \overline{AC}$ and $\overline{ER} \cong \overline{AR}$ because that information is given. $\overline{RC} \cong \overline{RC}$ because it is the same segment, and any segment is congruent to itself. So, $\triangle CRE \cong \triangle CRA$ by the SSS Congruence Conjecture. If $\triangle CRE \cong \triangle CRA$, then $\angle A \cong \angle E$ by CPCTC.

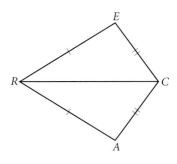

Were you able to follow the logical steps in Example A? Sometimes a logical argument or a proof is long and complex, and a paragraph might not be the clearest way to present all the steps. A **flowchart** is a visual way to organize all the steps in a complicated procedure in proper order. Arrows connect the boxes to show how facts lead to conclusions.

Flowcharts make your logic visible so that others can follow your reasoning. To present your reasoning in flowchart form, create a **flowchart proof.** Place each statement in a box. Write the logical reason for each statement beneath its box. For example, you would write "$\overline{RC} \cong \overline{RC}$, because it is the same segment," as

$$\boxed{\overline{RC} \cong \overline{RC}}$$

Same segment

Here is the same logical argument that you created in Example A in flowchart proof format.

EXAMPLE B

In the figure at right, $\overline{EC} \cong \overline{AC}$ and $\overline{ER} \cong \overline{AR}$. Is $\angle E \cong \angle A$? If so, write a flowchart proof to explain why.

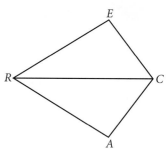

Solution

First, restate the given information clearly. It helps to mark the given information on the figure. Then state what you are trying to show.

Given: $\overline{AR} \cong \overline{ER}$
$\overline{EC} \cong \overline{AC}$

Show: $\angle E \cong \angle A$

Flowchart Proof

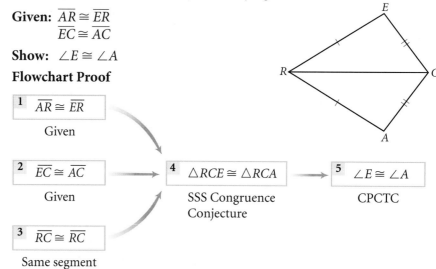

In a flowchart proof, the arrows show how the logical argument flows from the information that is given to the conclusion that you are trying to prove. Drawing an arrow is like saying "therefore." You can draw flowcharts top to bottom or left to right.

Compare the paragraph proof in Example A with the flowchart proof in Example B. What similarities and differences are there? What are the advantages of each format?

 DEVELOPING PROOF

In Chapter 3, you learned how to construct the bisector of an angle using a compass and straightedge. Now you have the skills to explain *why* the construction works using deductive reasoning. As a group, create a flowchart proof that explains why the construction method works.

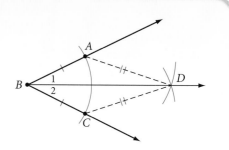

Given: $\angle ABC$ with $\overline{BA} \cong \overline{BC}$ and $\overline{CD} \cong \overline{AD}$

Show: $\overline{BD}$ is the angle bisector of $\angle ABC$

When you are satisfied with your group's proof, discuss how it is similar to and different from Example B.

 **Exercises**

1. **DEVELOPING PROOF** Copy the flowchart. Provide each missing reason or statement in the proof.

Given: $\overline{SE} \cong \overline{SU}$
$\angle E \cong \angle U$

Show: $\triangle MOS$ is isosceles

Flowchart Proof

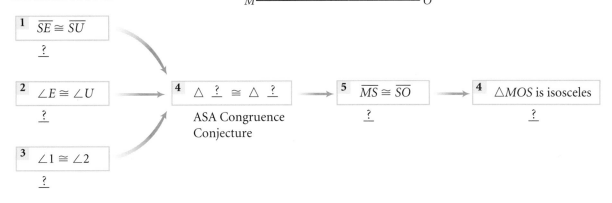

```
1  SE ≅ SU
   ?

2  ∠E ≅ ∠U         4  △ ? ≅ △ ?      5  MS ≅ SO       4  △MOS is isosceles
   ?                  ASA Congruence     ?                 ?
                      Conjecture
3  ∠1 ≅ ∠2
   ?
```

2. **DEVELOPING PROOF** Copy the flowchart. Provide each missing reason or statement in the proof.

Given: I is the midpoint of $\overline{CM}$
I is the midpoint of $\overline{BL}$

Show: $\overline{CL} \cong \overline{MB}$

Flowchart Proof

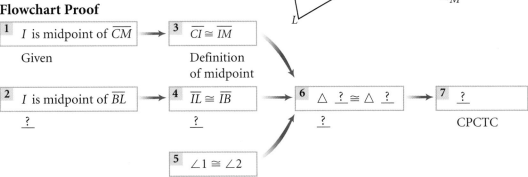

```
1  I is midpoint of CM  →  3  CI ≅ IM
   Given                    Definition
                           of midpoint

2  I is midpoint of BL  →  4  IL ≅ IB      6  △ ? ≅ △ ?    7  ?
   ?                         ?                ?               CPCTC

                           5  ∠1 ≅ ∠2
                              ?
```

DEVELOPING PROOF In Exercises 3–5, an auxiliary line segment has been added to the figure.

3. Complete this flowchart proof of the Isosceles Triangle Conjecture. Given that the triangle is isosceles, show that the base angles are congruent.

Given: △NEW is isosceles, with $\overline{WN} \cong \overline{EN}$ and median $\overline{NS}$

Show: ∠W ≅ ∠E

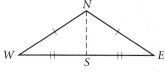

Flowchart Proof

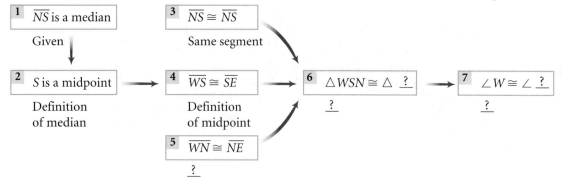
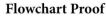

1	$\overline{NS}$ is a median

Given

| 2 | S is a midpoint |

Definition of median

| 3 | $\overline{NS} \cong \overline{NS}$ |

Same segment

| 4 | $\overline{WS} \cong \overline{SE}$ |

Definition of midpoint

| 5 | $\overline{WN} \cong \overline{NE}$ |

?

| 6 | △WSN ≅ △ ? |

?

| 7 | ∠W ≅ ∠ ? |

?

4. Complete this flowchart proof of the Converse of the Isosceles Triangle Conjecture.

Given: △NEW with ∠W ≅ ∠E
$\overline{NS}$ is an angle bisector

Show: △NEW is an isosceles triangle

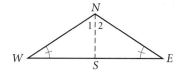

Flowchart Proof

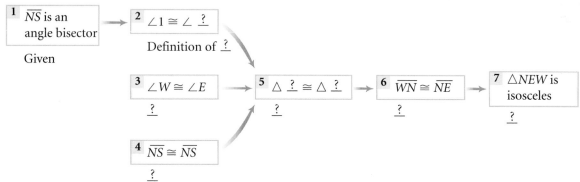

| 1 | $\overline{NS}$ is an angle bisector |

Given

| 2 | ∠1 ≅ ∠ ? |

Definition of ?

| 3 | ∠W ≅ ∠E |

?

| 4 | $\overline{NS} \cong \overline{NS}$ |

?

| 5 | △ ? ≅ △ ? |

?

| 6 | $\overline{WN} \cong \overline{NE}$ |

?

| 7 | △NEW is isosceles |

?

5. Complete the flowchart proof. What does this proof tell you about parallelograms?

Given: $\overline{SA} \parallel \overline{NE}$
$\overline{SE} \parallel \overline{NA}$

Show: $\overline{SA} \cong \overline{NE}$

Flowchart Proof

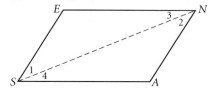

| 1 | $\overline{SA} \parallel \overline{NE}$ |

?

| 2 | $\overline{SE} \parallel \overline{NA}$ |

?

| 3 | ∠3 ≅ ∠4 |

AIA Conjecture

| 4 | ? |

?

| 5 | $\overline{SN} \cong \overline{SN}$ |

Same segment

| 6 | △ ? ≅ △ ? |

?

| 7 | ? |

?

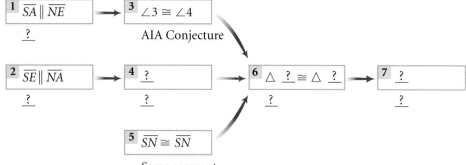

6. **DEVELOPING PROOF** In Chapter 3, you discovered how to construct a perpendicular through a point on a line. Perform this construction. Use a congruence shortcut to explain why the construction works.

7. Suppose you saw this step in a proof: Construct angle bisector *CD* to the midpoint of side *AB* in △*ABC*. What's wrong with that step? Explain.

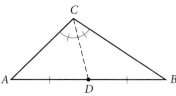

Review

8. **DEVELOPING PROOF** Which segment is the shortest? Explain. ⓗ

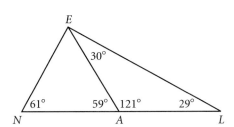

9. **DEVELOPING PROOF** What's wrong with this picture? Explain.

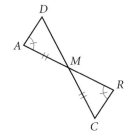

DEVELOPING PROOF For Exercises 10–12, name the congruent triangles and explain why the triangles are congruent. If you cannot show that they are congruent, write "cannot be determined."

10. $\overline{PO} \cong \overline{PR}$
△*POE* ≅ △ _?_
△*SON* ≅ △ _?_ ⓗ

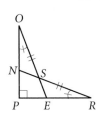

11. △ _?_ ≅ △ _?_ ⓗ

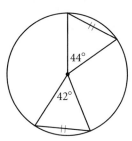

12. $\overline{AC} \cong \overline{CR}$, $\overline{CK}$ is a median of △*ARC*. △*RCK* ≅ △ _?_

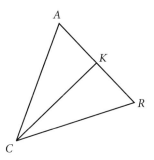

13. Copy the figure below. Calculate the measure of each lettered angle.

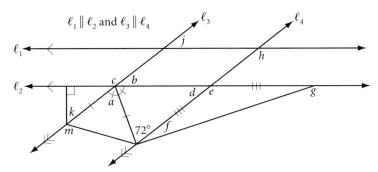

14. **DEVELOPING PROOF** Which point of concurrency is equidistant from all three vertices? Explain why. Which point of concurrency is equidistant from all three sides? Explain why. ⓗ

15. How wide is the stream?
Samantha is standing at the bank of a stream, wondering how wide the stream is. Remembering her geometry conjectures, she kneels down and holds her fishing pole perpendicular to the ground in front of her. She adjusts her hand on

the pole so that she can see the opposite bank of the stream along her line of sight through her hand. She then turns, keeping a firm grip on the pole, and uses the same line of sight to spot a boulder on her side of the stream. She measures the distance to the boulder and concludes that this equals the distance across the stream. What triangle congruence shortcut is Samantha using? Explain.

16. Sketch the solid shown with the red and green cubes removed. ⓗ

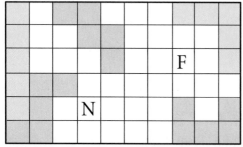

17. Rectangle *BOXY* has been rotated to create rectangle *B'O'X'Y'*. What are the coordinates of the center of rotation for the transformation?

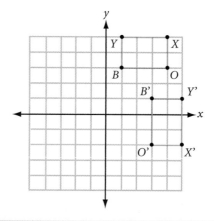

DEVELOPING MATHEMATICAL REASONING

Pentomino 6×10 Rectangle Puzzle

All 12 pentominoes can be arranged into a 6×10 rectangle. When completed every pentomino will touch an outer edge of the rectangle. The 12 pentomino shapes are identified by the letters *T, U, V, W, X, Y, Z, F, L, I, P,* and *N*. These letters are given as clues. If the letter *F*, for example, is in a square, then the *F*-pentomino covers that square. Use logical reasoning to determine the location of all the pentominoes.

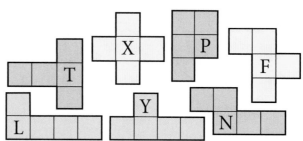

T U V W X Y Z F L I P N

Proving Special Triangle Conjectures

This boathouse is a symmetric structure with its isosceles triangle roofs and the identical doors on each side. What might this building reveal about the special properties of the line of symmetry in an isosceles triangle?

In this lesson you will investigate a special segment in isosceles triangles.

First, consider a scalene triangle. In $\triangle ARC$, $\overline{CD}$ is the altitude to the base $\overline{AR}$, $\overline{CE}$ is the angle bisector of $\angle ACR$, and $\overline{CF}$ is the median to the base $\overline{AR}$. From this example it is clear that the angle bisector, the altitude, and the median can all be different line segments. Is this true for all triangles? Can two of these ever be the same segment? Can they all be the same segment? Let's investigate.

If you constructed the angle bisector, the altitude, and the median in one of these roof windows, what would you notice?

INVESTIGATION

YOU WILL NEED

● a compass

● a straightedge

The Symmetry Line in an Isosceles Triangle

Each person in your group should draw a different isosceles triangle for this investigation.

Step 1 Construct a large isosceles triangle on a sheet of paper. Label it *ARK*, with *K* the vertex angle.

Step 2 Construct angle bisector $\overline{KD}$ with point *D* on $\overline{AR}$. Do △*ADK* and △*RDK* look congruent? If they are congruent, then $\overline{KD}$ is a line of symmetry.

Step 3 With your compass, compare $\overline{AD}$ and $\overline{RD}$. Is *D* the midpoint of $\overline{AR}$? If *D* is the midpoint, then what type of special segment is $\overline{KD}$?

Step 4 Compare ∠*ADK* and ∠*RDK*. Do they have equal measures? Are they supplementary? What conclusion can you make?

Step 5 Compare your conjectures with the results of other students. Now combine the two conjectures from Steps 3 and 4 into one.

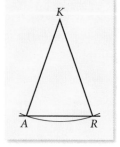

Vertex Angle Bisector Conjecture	C-28

In an isosceles triangle, the bisector of the vertex angle is also ? and ? .

DEVELOPING PROOF

Vertex Angle Bisector Conjecture

In the investigation you discovered that the symmetry of an isosceles triangle yields a number of special properties. Can you explain *why* these properties are true for all isosceles triangles? To prove the Vertex Angle Bisector Conjecture you need to prove two conjectures:

If a triangle is isosceles then the bisector of the vertex angle is also an altitude.
and,
If a triangle is isosceles then the bisector of the vertex angle is also a median.

To prove these two statements we first prove another "helper property." A statement that we prove so that we can use that property in the proof of other statements is called a **lemma**. Here is the lemma that will make the proving of both statements from the Vertex Angle Bisector Conjecture easier.

Lemma A: *The bisector of the vertex angle in an isosceles triangle divides the isosceles triangle into two congruent triangles.*

As a group, study the flowchart proof below and supply the missing statements and reasons for the proof of Lemma A.

Given: △ABC is isosceles
$\overline{AC} \cong \overline{BC}$, and $\overline{CD}$ is the bisector of ∠C

Show: △ADC ≅ △BDC

Flowchart Proof

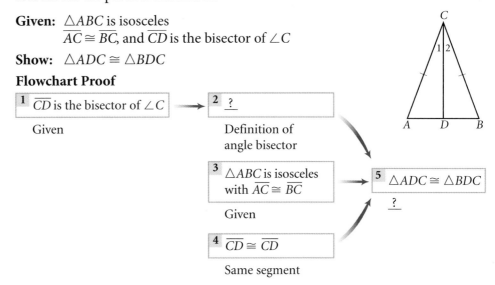

Once you have completed the proof of Lemma A you can use it to write the proof of the two statements for the Vertex Angle Bisector Conjecture. As a group, study the flowchart proof below and supply the missing statements and reasons for the proof of the conjecture:

If a triangle is isosceles then the bisector of the vertex angle is also an altitude to the base.

Given: △ABC is isosceles
$\overline{AC} \cong \overline{BC}$, and $\overline{CD}$ bisects ∠C

Show: $\overline{CD}$ is an altitude

Flowchart Proof

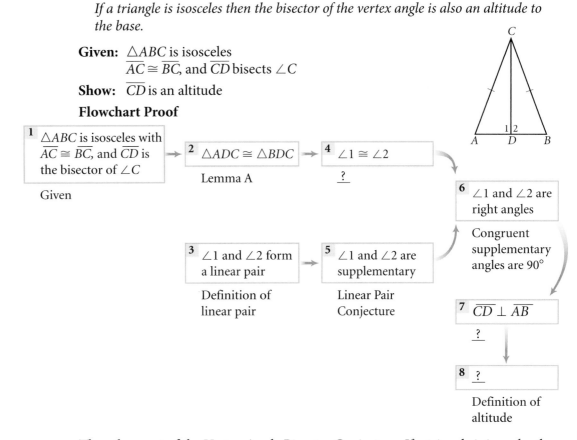

The other part of the Vertex Angle Bisector Conjecture, *If a triangle is isosceles then the bisector of the vertex angle is also a median,* is left as an exercise for you in the Exercise set.

4.8 Exercises

In Exercises 1–3, △ABC is isosceles with $\overline{AC} \cong \overline{BC}$.

1. Perimeter △ABC = 48 ⓗ
AC = 18
AD = ?

2. m∠ABC = 72°
m∠ADC = ?
m∠ACD = ?

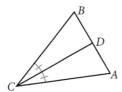

3. m∠CAB = 45°
m∠ACD = ?

4. $\overline{AC} \cong \overline{BC}$
F is what special point?

5. $\overline{PQ} \cong \overline{PR}$
V is what special point?

6. $\overline{GK} \cong \overline{GH}$
N is what special point?

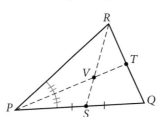

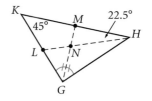

7. Create a flowchart proof for the statement: *If a triangle is isosceles then the bisector of the vertex angle is also a median.*

Given: △ABC is isosceles with $\overline{AC} \cong \overline{BC}$
$\overline{CD}$ is the bisector of ∠C

Show: $\overline{CD}$ is a median

8. In the Developing Proof section and Exercise 7, you completed proofs of these two conjectures: *The bisector of the vertex angle of an isosceles triangle is also the median to the base. The bisector of the vertex angle of an isosceles triangle is also the altitude to the base.*

To demonstrate that the altitude to the base, the median to the base, and the bisector of the vertex angle in an isosceles triangle are all the same segment, you really need to prove three statements. One possible sequence is diagrammed below.

You already proved one of them. Prove two more to complete the cycle.

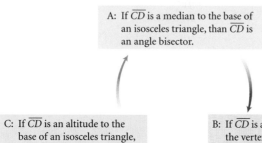

A: If $\overline{CD}$ is a median to the base of an isosceles triangle, than $\overline{CD}$ is an angle bisector.

C: If $\overline{CD}$ is an altitude to the base of an isosceles triangle, then $\overline{CD}$ is a median.

B: If $\overline{CD}$ is an angle bisector of the vertex angle of an isosceles triangle, then $\overline{CD}$ is an altitude.

9. **DEVELOPING PROOF** In the figure at right, $\triangle ABC$, the plumb level, is isosceles. A weight, called the plumb bob, hangs from a string attached at point C. If you place the level on a surface and the string is perpendicular to $\overline{AB}$, then the surface you are testing is level. To tell whether the string is perpendicular to $\overline{AB}$, check whether it passes through the midpoint of $\overline{AB}$. Create a flowchart proof to show that if D is the midpoint of $\overline{AB}$, then $\overline{CD}$ is perpendicular to $\overline{AB}$.

Given: $\triangle ABC$ is isosceles with $\overline{AC} \cong \overline{BC}$
D is the midpoint of $\overline{AB}$

Show: $\overline{CD} \perp \overline{AB}$

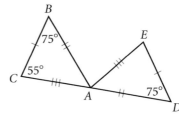

10. **DEVELOPING PROOF** $\triangle SNL$ is equilateral. Is $\triangle TIE$ equilateral? Explain. ⓗ

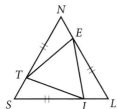

→ *History*
CONNECTION

Builders in ancient Egypt used a tool called a *plumb level* in building the great pyramids. With a plumb level, you can use the basic properties of isosceles triangles to determine whether a surface is level.

11. **DEVELOPING PROOF** Use Lemma A to write a paragraph proof of the Isosceles Triangle Conjecture. ⓗ

12. **DEVELOPING PROOF** Write a paragraph proof of the converse of the Isosceles Triangle Conjecture.

Review

13. **DEVELOPING PROOF** Trace the figure below. Calculate the measure of each lettered angle.

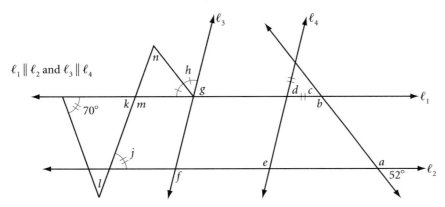

$\ell_1 \parallel \ell_2$ and $\ell_3 \parallel \ell_4$

14. How many minutes after 3:00 will the hands of a clock overlap? ⓗ

15. Sixty concurrent lines in a plane divide the plane into how many regions? ⓗ

16. If two vertices of a triangle have coordinates $A(1, 3)$ and $B(7, 3)$, find the coordinates of point C so that $\triangle ABC$ is a right triangle. Can you find any other points that would create a right triangle? Explain.

17. Points C, A, and D are collinear and $\triangle ABC \cong \triangle ADE$. How many degrees of clockwise rotation are needed for $\triangle ABC$ to be rotated onto $\triangle ADE$?

18. **Where are the fireworks coming from?** Hugo hears the sound of fireworks three seconds after he sees the flash. Duane hears the sound five seconds after he sees the flash. Hugo and Duane are 1.5 km apart. They know the flash was somewhere to the north. They also know that a flash can be seen almost instantly, but sound travels 340 m/s. Do Hugo and Duane have enough information to locate the site of the fireworks? Make a sketch and label all the distances that they know or can calculate.

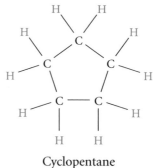

19. In an earlier exercise in Chapter 2, you found the rule for the family of hydrocarbons called alkanes, or paraffins. These contain a straight chain of carbons. Alkanes can also form rings of carbon atoms. These molecules are called cycloparaffins. The first three cycloparaffins are shown below. Sketch the molecule cycloheptane. Write the general rule for cycloparaffins ($C_nH_?$). ⓗ

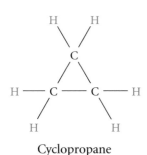 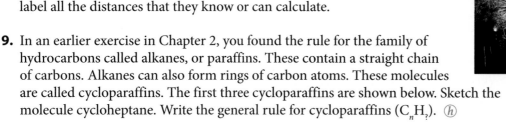

Cyclopropane   Cyclobutane   Cyclopentane

PERFORMANCE TASK

Buried Treasure

Pirate captain Lance Michaels is about to bury his latest plunder on Skull Island. The captain gives his first mate Angelina two ropes, the lengths of which only he knows. Captain Michaels then instructs Angelina to nail one end of the shorter rope to Hangman's Tree and one end of the longer rope through the eyes of Skull Rock. He then sends Angelina back to the ship. He takes the loose ends of the two ropes in one hand and tucked the treasure chest under his other arm and procedes to walk away from shore to the point where the two ropes become taut. He buries the treasure at that point, collects his ropes, and returns confidently to his ship and scallywag crew.

Has Pirate Lance Michaels given himself enough information to recover the treasure? Which congruence conjecture is he using to ensure the uniqueness of the location? If the ropes are 55 meters and 105 meters in length, where is the pirate treasure buried?

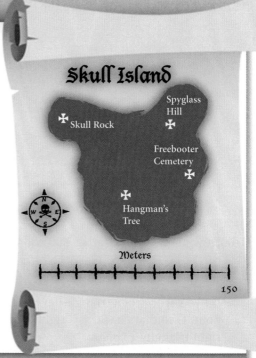

In this chapter you made many conjectures about triangles. You discovered some basic properties of isosceles and equilateral triangles. You learned different ways to show that two triangles are congruent. Do you remember them all? Triangle congruence shortcuts are an important idea in geometry. You can use them to explain why your constructions work. In later chapters, you will use your triangle conjectures to investigate properties of other polygons.

You also practiced reading and writing flowchart proofs. Can you sketch a diagram illustrating each conjecture you made in this chapter? Check your conjecture list to make sure it is up to date. Make sure you have a clear diagram illustrating each conjecture.

Exercises

YOU WILL NEED

Construction tools
for Exercises **35, 36,** and **38**

Geometry software
for Exercise **45**

1. **True-False**

    ____ **a.** The sum of the measures of the interior angles of a triangle is always less than the sum of the measures of one set of its exterior angles.

    ____ **b.** The base angles of an isosceles triangle are always acute.

    ____ **c.** It is possible for an obtuse triangle to have three congruent sides.

    ____ **d.** An exterior angle of a triangle is greater than each of the interior angles.

    ____ **e.** There are more true statements than false statements in a through e.

2. The first conjecture of this chapter is probably the most important so far. What is it? Why do you think it is so important?

3. What special properties do isosceles triangles have?

4. What does the statement "The shortest distance between two points is the straight line between them" have to do with the Triangle Inequality Conjecture?

5. What information do you need in order to determine that two triangles are congruent? That is, what are the four congruence shortcuts?

6. Explain why SSA is not a congruence shortcut.

7. A chopstick is twice as long as a swizzle stick. You break the chopstick randomly somewhere in the middle half of the stick. You now have three sticks. What is the probability that these three lengths form a triangle? *ⓗ*

8. Dan claims that the bisectors of two angles of a triangle can intersect at a right angle. Annie says, that is impossible! Who is right? Explain.

DEVELOPING PROOF For Exercises 9–26, if possible, name the congruent triangles. State the conjecture or definition that supports the congruence statement. If you cannot show the triangles to be congruent from the information given, write "cannot be determined."

9. △*PEA* ≅ △ _?_

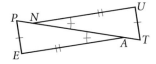

10. △*TOP* ≅ △ _?_

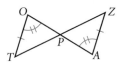

11. △*MSE* ≅ △ _?_

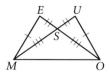

12. △*TIM* ≅ △ _?_

13. △*TRP* ≅ △ _?_

14. △*CGH* ≅ △ _?_

15. △ _?_ ≅ △ _?_
Is $\overline{WH}$ a median?

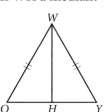

16. $\overleftrightarrow{AB} \parallel \overleftrightarrow{CD}$
△*ABE* ≅ △ _?_

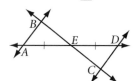

17. Polygon *CARBON* is a regular hexagon. △*ACN* ≅ △ _?_

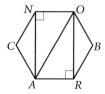

18. △ _?_ ≅ △ _?_ , $\overline{AD}$ ≅ _?_

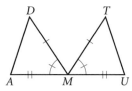

19. △ _?_ ≅ △ _?_

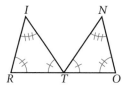

20. △ _?_ ≅ △ _?_

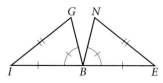

21. △ _?_ ≅ △ _?_ , $\overline{TR}$ ≅ _?_

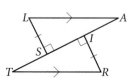

22. △ _?_ ≅ △ _?_ , $\overline{EI}$ ≅ _?_

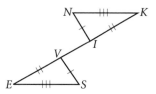

23. △*CAT* ≅ △ _?_

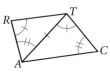

24. △ _?_ ≅ △ _?_
Is *NCTM* a parallelogram?

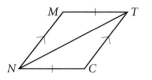

25. $\overline{IA}$ ≅ $\overline{LA}$
△ _?_ ≅ △ _?_

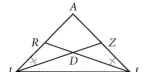

26. △ _?_ ≅ △ _?_
Is *STOP* a parallelogram?

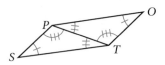

27. DEVELOPING PROOF What's wrong with this picture?

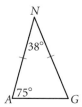

28. DEVELOPING PROOF What's wrong with this picture?

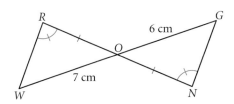

29. Quadrilateral *CAMP* has been divided into three triangles. Use the angle measures provided to determine the longest and shortest segments.

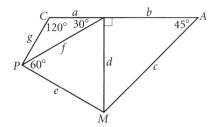

30. The measure of an angle formed by the bisectors of two angles in a triangle, as shown below, is 100°. What is angle measure *x*?

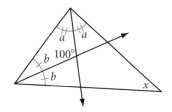

DEVELOPING PROOF In Exercises 31 and 32, decide whether there is enough information to prove congruence. If there is, write a proof. If not, explain what is missing.

31. In the figure below, $\overline{RE} \cong \overline{AE}$, $\angle S \cong \angle T$, and $\angle ERL \cong \angle EAL$. Is $\overline{SA} \cong \overline{TR}$?

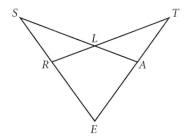

32. In the figure below, $\angle A \cong \angle M$, $\overline{AF} \perp \overline{FR}$, and $\overline{MR} \perp \overline{FR}$. Is $\triangle FRD$ isosceles?

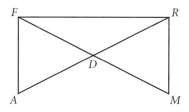

33. The measure of an angle formed by altitudes from two vertices of a triangle, as shown below, is 132°. What is angle measure *x*?

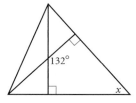

34. DEVELOPING PROOF Connecting the legs of the chair at their midpoints, as shown, guarantees that the seat is parallel to the floor. Explain why.

For Exercises 35 and 36, use the segments and the angles below. Use either patty paper or a compass and a straightedge. The lowercase letter above each segment represents the length of the segment.

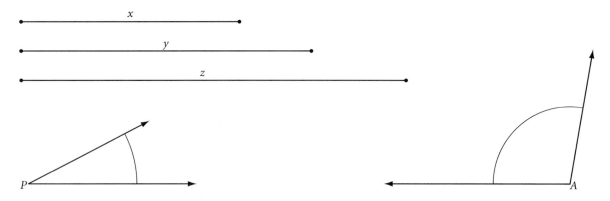

35. Construct △*PAL* given ∠*P*, ∠*A*, and *AL* = *y*.

36. Construct two triangles △*PBS* that are not congruent to each other given ∠*P*, *PB* = *z*, and *SB* = *x*.

37. **DEVELOPING PROOF** In the figure at right, is $\overline{TI} \parallel \overline{RE}$? Complete the flowchart proof or explain why they are not parallel.

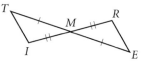

Given: *M* is the midpoint of both $\overline{TE}$ and $\overline{IR}$

Show: $\overline{TI} \parallel \overline{RE}$

Flowchart Proof

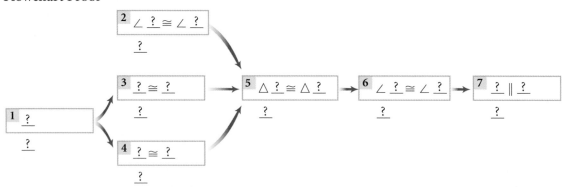

38. Use patty paper or compass and straightedge to construct a 75° angle. Explain your method.

39. In *ACBD* at the right, if *m*∠*CAD* > *m*∠*CBD*, arrange the six unknown angle measures in order from least to greatest.

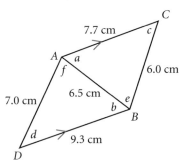

40. **TRUE OR FALSE?** The sum of the four sides of any quadrilateral is greater than the sum of the lengths of the two diagonals. Explain.

41. **TRUE OR FALSE?** If a line is drawn through any point on the bisector of an angle parallel to one of the sides of the angle, the line forms an isosceles triangle with the angle bisector and a side of the angle. Explain.

42. Is $\overrightarrow{AC}$ the bisector of $\angle BAD$? Explain how you know.

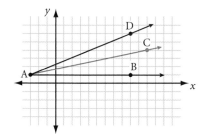

43. Given $\triangle ABC$ with vertices $A(-6, 2)$, $B(-3, 0)$, $C(-2, 4)$ and $\triangle DEF$ with vertices $D(2, 6)$, $E(0, 3)$, $F(4, 2)$.

   a. Rotate $\triangle ABC$ by the transformation rule $(x, y) \rightarrow (y, -x)$ to create $\triangle A'B'C'$.

   b. What happened? Does $\triangle A'B'C'$ appear to coincide with $\triangle DEF$?

   c. If they are congruent, what is the statement of congruence, $\triangle A'B'C' \cong \triangle(???)$?

   d. If they are not congruent explain why not.

44. Given quadrilateral $ABCD$ with vertices $A(3, -2)$, $B(6, 3)$, $C(4, 7)$, $D(1, 3)$ and quadrilateral $EFGH$ with vertices $E(-8, 3)$, $F(-6, -2)$, $G(-3, 3)$, $H(-6, 7)$.

   a. Reflect quadrilateral $ABCD$ by the transformation rule $(x, y) \rightarrow (-x - 2, y)$ to create quadrilateral $A'B'C'D'$.

   b. What happened? Does quadrilateral $A'B'C'D'$ appear to coincide with quadrilateral $EFGH$?

   c. If they are congruent, what is the statement of congruence, quadrilateral $A'B'C'D' \cong$ quadrilateral $(????)$?

   d. If they are not congruent explain why not.

45. GUESS-N-CHECK $\triangle ABC$ with vertices $A(-6, 3)$, $B(-4, 6)$, and $C(-1, 4)$, is rotated 90° clockwise about the origin to create image $\triangle A'B'C'$. Then $\triangle A'B'C'$ is reflected across the x-axis to create image $\triangle A''B''C''$. Which of the following are true? First, try this as a "mental experiment." Take a guess or explain how you know. Then create the diagram with your geometry software, perform the transformations, and see how good you were at visualization.

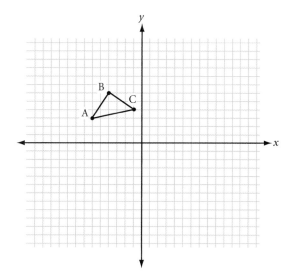

   a. $\angle A \cong \angle A' \cong \angle A''$

   b. $\overline{BC} \cong \overline{B'C'} \cong \overline{B''C''}$

   c. The points B, B', and B'' are all equally distant from the origin.

   d. The slope of $\overline{AB}$ is equal to the slope of $\overline{B'C'}$.

   e. The lines through $\overline{AC}$ and $\overline{A'C'}$ are perpendicular.

TAKE ANOTHER LOOK

The section that follows, Take Another Look, gives you a chance to extend, communicate, and assess your understanding of the work you did in the investigations in this chapter. Sometimes it will lead to new, related discoveries.

1. A friend claims that if the measure of one acute angle of a triangle is half the measure of another acute angle of the triangle, then the triangle can be divided into two isosceles triangles. Try this with a computer or other tools. Describe your method and explain why it works.

2. A friend claims that if one exterior angle has twice the measure of one of the remote interior angles, then the triangle is isosceles. Use a geometry software program or other tools to investigate this claim. Describe your findings.

3. **DEVELOPING PROOF** In the triangle to the right, ∠A measures 48°. The remainder of the measure of the 360° about point A, is the "reflex measure of angle A" as marked in the diagram. What is the sum of the reflex measures for ∠A, ∠B, and ∠C in △ABC? What is the sum of the measures of the three reflex angles of every triangle? Prove your conjecture.

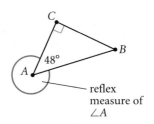

4. **DEVELOPING PROOF** In Chapter 3, you discovered how to construct the perpendicular bisector of a segment. Perform this construction. Now use what you've learned about congruence shortcuts to explain why this construction method works.

5. Is there a conjecture (similar to the Triangle Exterior Angle Conjecture) that you can make about exterior and remote interior angles of a convex quadrilateral? Experiment. Write about your findings.

6. Is there a conjecture you can make about inequalities among the sums of the lengths of sides and/or diagonals of a quadrilateral? Experiment. Write about your findings.

7. Is there a conjecture similar to the SSS Congruence Conjecture that you can make about congruence between quadrilaterals? For example, is SSSS a shortcut for quadrilateral congruence? Or, if three sides and a diagonal of one quadrilateral are congruent to the corresponding three sides and diagonal of another quadrilateral, must the two quadrilaterals be congruent (SSSD)? Investigate. Write a paragraph explaining how your conjectures follow from the triangle congruence conjectures you've learned.

8. Explore the Triangle Sum Conjecture on a sphere or a globe. Can you draw a triangle that has two or more obtuse angles? Three right angles? Write an illustrated report of your findings.

9. Investigate the Isosceles Triangle Conjecture and the Equilateral/Equiangular Triangle Conjecture on a sphere. Write an illustrated report of your findings.

CHAPTER

5

Discovering and Proving Polygon Properties

"The mathematicians may well nod their heads in a friendly and interested manner—I still am a tinkerer to them. And the "artistic" ones are primarily irritated. Still, maybe I'm on the right track if I experience more joy from my own little images than from the most beautiful camera in the world . . ."

M. C. ESCHER

OBJECTIVES

In this chapter you will

- study properties of convex polygons
- discover relationships among their angles, sides, and diagonals
- learn about real-world applications of special polygons

Polygon Sum Conjecture

There are many kinds of triangles, but in Chapter 4, you discovered that the sum of their angle measures is always 180°. In this lesson you'll investigate the sum of the angle measures in convex quadrilaterals, pentagons, and other polygons. Then you'll look for a pattern in the sum of the angle measures in *any* polygon.

"I find that the harder I work, the more luck I seem to have."

THOMAS JEFFERSON

INVESTIGATION

YOU WILL NEED
- protractor
- glue stick

Is There a Polygon Sum Formula?

For this investigation each person in your group should draw a different version of the same polygon. For example, if your group is investigating hexagons, try to think of different ways you could draw a hexagon.

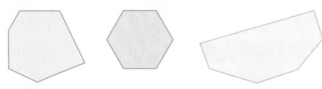

Step 1 Draw the polygon. Carefully measure all the interior angles, then find the sum.

Step 2 Share your results with your group. If you measured carefully, you should all have the same sum! If your answers aren't exactly the same, find the average.

Step 3 Copy the table below. Repeat Steps 1 and 2 with different polygons, or share results with other groups. Complete the table.

Number of sides of polygon	3	4	5	6	7	8	...	n
Sum of measures of angles	180°						...	

Step 4 Using a protractor may have given you approximate values for the angle sums. Let's check these polygon sums another way. Label the interior angles of one of the polygons in your group (Figure 1). Cut out the polygon and tear off (not cut with scissors) the angles (Figure 2). Draw a line and a point on the line on another piece of paper. With a glue stick, put a small swipe of glue in the region around the point. Arrange the torn-off angles around

the point to show their sum (Figure 3). (The swipe of glue will help hold the angles in position.) Two of the angles, have already been positioned. What do you think will happen when the remaining angles are added?

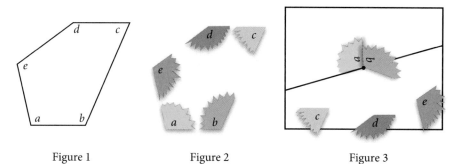

| Figure 1 | Figure 2 | Figure 3 |

Step 5 Compare your group's results with the results of other groups and adjust your table of values if necessary. Look for a pattern in the completed table. You can now make some conjectures.

Quadrilateral Sum Conjecture   C-29

The sum of the measures of the four interior angles of any quadrilateral is ?.

Pentagon Sum Conjecture   C-30

The sum of the measures of the five interior angles of any pentagon is ?.

Step 6 Using one of the polygons from your group, draw all the diagonals from *one* vertex of the polygon. How many triangles do the diagonals create? How many triangles do the diagonals create in the dodecagon (12-gon) at right? Try some other polygons. How do the number of triangles relate to the number of sides (*n*)? What is a general formula for the sum of the angle measures of a polygon in terms of the number of sides, *n*? State your observations as a conjecture.

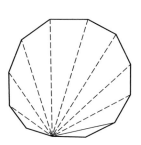

If a polygon has *n* sides, it is called an *n*-gon.

Polygon Sum Conjecture   C-31

The sum of the measures of the *n* interior angles of an *n*-gon is ?.

DEVELOPING PROOF

The investigation may have convinced you that the Polygon Sum Conjecture is true, but can you explain why it is true? You can use the Triangle Sum Conjecture that you proved true earlier to explain why the Quadrilateral Sum and Pentagon Sum Conjectures are true.

As a group, write a proof of the quadrilateral Sum Conjecture using the diagram at right.

Next, each group member writes a proof of the Pentagon Sum Conjecture using the diagram at right. Compare your proofs. Discuss any differences and create a final proof as a group.

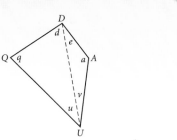

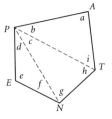

5.1 Exercises

YOU WILL NEED

Geometry software for Exercise **20**

1. Use the Polygon Sum Conjecture to complete the table.

Number of sides of polygon	7	8	9	10	11	12	...	k	100
Sum of measures of angles									

2. What is the measure of each angle of an equiangular pentagon? An equiangular hexagon? Complete the table. ⓗ

Number of sides of equiangular polygon	4	5	6	7	8	9	...	k	100
Measure of each angle of equiangular polygon									

In Exercises 3–8, use your conjectures to calculate the measure of each lettered angle.

3. $a = $?

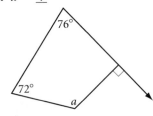

4. $b = $?

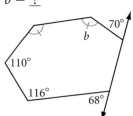

5. $e = $?
$f = $?

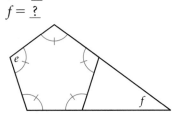

6. $c = $?
$d = $? ⓗ

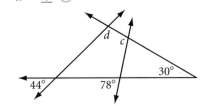

7. $g = $? ⓗ
$h = $?

8. $j = $?
$k = $?

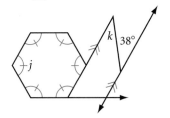

9. DEVELOPING PROOF What's wrong with this picture?

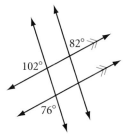

82°
102°
76°

10. DEVELOPING PROOF What's wrong with this picture?

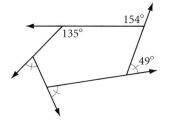

154°
135°
49°

11. Three regular polygons meet at point *A*. How many sides does the largest polygon have?

•*A*

12. DEVELOPING PROOF Trace the figure at right. Calculate each lettered angle measure. Explain how you determined the measures of angles *d, e,* and *f.*

13. How many sides does a polygon have if the sum of its angle measures is 2700°? ⓗ

14. How many sides does an equiangular polygon have if each interior angle measures 156°? ⓗ

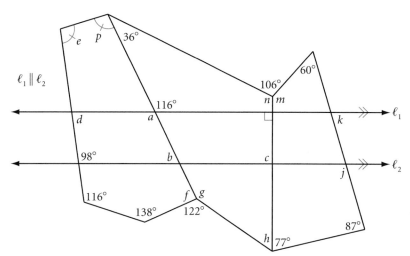

$\ell_1 \parallel \ell_2$

e *p* 36°
60°
106°
n *m*
116°
d *a* *k* ℓ_1
98° *b* *c*
j ℓ_2
116° *f* *g*
138° 122°
87°
h 77°

15. Archaeologist Ertha Diggs has uncovered a piece of a ceramic plate. She measures it and finds that each side has the same length and each angle has the same measure.

She conjectures that the original plate was the shape of a regular polygon. She knows that if the original plate was a regular 16-gon, it was probably a ceremonial dish from the third century. If it was a regular 18-gon, it was probably a palace dinner plate from the twelfth century.

If each angle measures 160°, from what century did the plate likely originate?

16. You need to build a window frame for an octagonal window like this one. To make the frame, you'll cut identical trapezoidal pieces. What are the measures of the angles of the trapezoids? Explain how you found these measures.

17. DEVELOPING PROOF Restate your proof of the Quadrilateral Sum Conjecture from the developing proof activity. Then use this diagram to show another way to prove the same conjecture. ⓗ

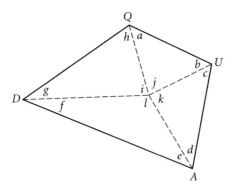

18. DEVELOPING PROOF You defined a rectangle as a parallelogram with all four angles congruent (an equiangular parallelogram). Now that you know the sum of the measures of the four angles of any quadrilateral is 360°, you can combine those two properties to prove (what you probably already knew) that the measure of each angle of a rectangle is 90°. Write a paragraph or Flowchart proof of this property.

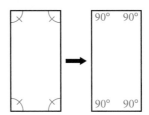

Review

19. This figure is a detail of one vertex of the tiling at the beginning of this lesson. Find the missing angle measure *x*.

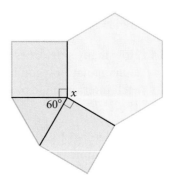

20. GUESS-N-CHECK Line ℓ is parallel to $\overleftrightarrow{AB}$. As *P* moves to the right along ℓ, which of these measures will always increase? First, try this as a "mental experiment." Take a guess, then create the diagram with your geometry software and see how good you were at visualization.

A. The distance *PA*

B. The perimeter of △*ABP*

C. The measure of ∠*APB*

D. The measure of ∠*ABP*

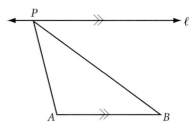

21. Draw a counterexample to show that this statement is false: If a triangle is isosceles, then its base angles are not complementary. Explain why your sketch demonstrates that the statement is false.

Exterior Angles of a Polygon

In Lesson 5.1, you discovered a formula for the sum of the measures of the *interior* angles of any convex polygon. In this lesson you will discover a formula for the sum of the measures of the *exterior* angles of a convex polygon.

Polygons with one set of exterior angles we will call "Pinwheel Polygons."

INVESTIGATION 1

Is There an Exterior Angle Sum?

YOU WILL NEED
- a straightedge
- a protractor
- glue stick

→ *Technology*
CONNECTION

The aperture of a camera is an opening shaped like a regular polygon surrounded by thin sheets that form a set of exterior angles. These sheets move together or apart to close or open the aperture, limiting the amount of light passing through the camera's lens. How does the sequence of closing apertures shown demonstrate the Exterior Angle Sum Conjecture?

Let's use some inductive and deductive reasoning to find the exterior angle measures in a polygon.

Each person in your group should draw a polygon with the same number of sides for Steps 1–4.

Step 1 Draw a large "pinwheel polygon" by extending one set of exterior angles on a polygon with the same orientation.

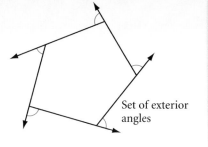

Set of exterior angles

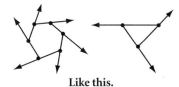 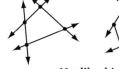

Like this.   Not like this.

Step 2 Measure all the *interior* angles of the polygon except one. Use the Polygon Sum Conjecture to calculate the measure of the remaining interior angle. Check your answer using your protractor.

Step 3 Use the Linear Pair Conjecture to calculate the measure of each exterior angle.

Step 4 Calculate the sum of the measures of the exterior angles. Share your results with your group members.

Step 5 Repeat Steps 1–4 with different kinds of polygons, or share results with other groups. Make a table to keep track of the number of sides and the sum of the exterior angle measures for each kind of polygon.

Step 6 Let's check these exterior angle sums another way. Create a polygon with one set of exterior angles and label the angles. Cut out the polygon with the exterior angles (Figure 1). Cut out each of the exterior angles (Figure 2). Draw a line and a point on the line on another piece of paper. Arrange the exterior angles around the point to show their sum (Figure 3). Use a small swipe of glue stick to hold them in position. Two of the exterior angles have already been positioned. What do you think will happen when the remaining angles are added?

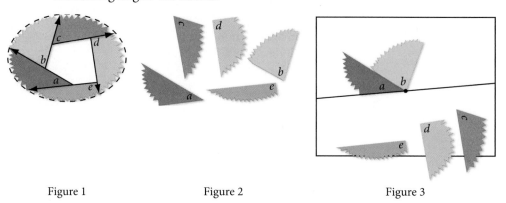

Figure 1   Figure 2   Figure 3

You should now be ready to state a conjecture for the sum of the measures of the exterior angles for any polygon.

Exterior Angle Sum Conjecture	C-32
For any polygon, the sum of the measures of a set of exterior angles is _?_ .	

DEVELOPING PROOF

Exterior Angle Sum

For an interactive version of the Exterior Angle Sum Conjecture, see the **Dynamic Geometry Exploration** in your ebook.

The investigation may have convinced you that the Exterior Angle Sum Conjecture is true, but can you explain why it is true? In the investigation you used the Polygon Sum Conjecture and the Linear Pair Conjecture to discover the Exterior Angle Sum Conjecture. You can use these properties to prove that the Exterior Angle Sum Conjecture is true for quadrilaterals and pentagons.

As a group, write a proof explaining why the Exterior Angle Sum Conjecture is true for quadrilaterals using the diagram at right.

Next, each group member will write a proof explaining why the Exterior Angle Sum Conjecture is true for pentagons using the diagram at right. Then compare the proofs.

INVESTIGATION 2

What is the Measure of an Equiangular Polygon Interior Angle?

Finally, use the steps below to derive formulas for the measure of each interior angle of an equiangular polygon.

Step 1 Using the Polygon Sum Conjecture, write a formula for the measure of each interior angle in an equiangular polygon.

Step 2 Using the Exterior Angle Sum Conjecture, write the formula for the measure of each exterior angle in an equiangular polygon.

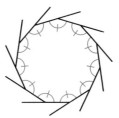 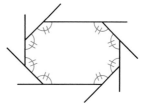 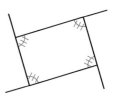

Step 3 Using your results from Step 2, you can write the formula for an interior angle of an equiangular polygon a different way. How do you find the measure of an interior angle if you know the measure of its exterior angle? Complete the next conjecture.

Equiangular Polygon Conjecture　　　　　　　　　**C-33**

You can find the measure of each interior angle of an equiangular n-gon by using either of these formulas: <u>?</u> or <u>?</u>.

(5.2) Exercises

1. What is the sum of the measures of the exterior angles of a decagon?

2. What is the measure of an exterior angle of an equiangular pentagon? An equiangular hexagon?

3. How many sides does a regular polygon have if each exterior angle measures 24°? *(h)*

4. How many sides does a polygon have if the sum of its interior angle measures is 7380°?

In Exercises 5–10, use your new conjectures to calculate the measure of each lettered angle.

5.

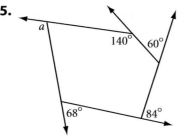

6.

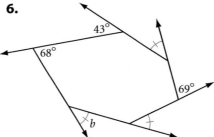

7. ⓗ

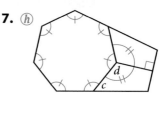

8.

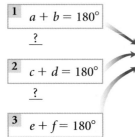

9.

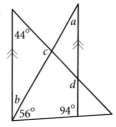

10.

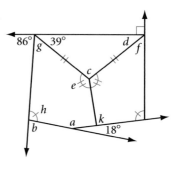

11. **DEVELOPING PROOF** Complete this flowchart proof of the Exterior Angle Sum Conjecture for a triangle.

Flowchart Proof

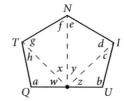

1 $a + b = 180°$

?

2 $c + d = 180°$

?

3 $e + f = 180°$

?

4 $a + b + c + d + e + f = \underline{?}°$

Addition property of equality

5 $a + c + e = \underline{?}°$

?

6 $b + d + f = \underline{?}°$

Subtraction property of equality

12. Is there a maximum number of obtuse exterior angles that any polygon can have? If so, what is the maximum? If not, why not? Is there a minimum number of acute interior angles that any polygon must have? If so, what is the minimum? If not, why not? ⓗ

Review

13. **DEVELOPING PROOF** In Lesson 5.1 you were asked to prove the Pentagon Sum Conjecture by drawing two diagonals from one vertex dividing the pentagon into three triangles. Prove the Pentagon Sum Conjecture using either one of the diagrams at right.

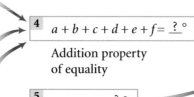

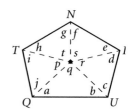

14. Name the regular polygons that appear in the tiling at right. Find the measures of the angles that surround point *A* in the tiling.

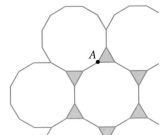

15. A regular dodecagon can be divided into different regions in a number of different ways.

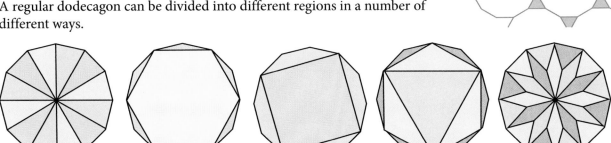

| Figure 1 | Figure 2 | Figure 3 | Figure 4 | Figure 5 |

   a. What is the measure of each angle of the isosceles triangles in Figure 1?

   b. What is the measure of each angle of the isosceles triangles in Figure 2?

   c. What is the measure of each angle of the isosceles trapezoids in Figure 3?

   d. What is the measure of each angle of one of the larger blue isosceles triangles in Figure 4?

   e. What is the measure of each angle of the rhombuses in Figure 5? The triangles are equilateral.

16. Given quadrilateral *ABCD* with vertices: $A(-6, -2)$, $B(6, -4)$, $C(1, 1)$, $D(-5, 2)$

   a. Translate quadrilateral *ABCD* by the translation rule $(x, y) \rightarrow (x - 3, y + 4)$ to create quadrilateral $A'B'C'D'$.

   b. What are the coordinates of the vertices of quadrilateral $A'B'C'D'$?

   c. Translate $A'B'C'D'$ by the translation rule $(x, y) \rightarrow (x + 3, y + 5)$ to create quadrilateral $A''B''C''D''$.

   d. What are the coordinates of the vertices of quadrilateral $A''B''C''D''$?

   e. What is the single transformation rule that takes quadrilateral *ABCD* onto quadrilateral $A''B''C''D''$?

   f. What is the single transformation rule that takes quadrilateral $A''B''C''D''$ back onto quadrilateral *ABCD*?

17. **DEVELOPING PROOF** $\angle RAC \cong \angle DCA$, $\overline{CD} \cong \overline{AR}$, $\overline{AC} \parallel \overline{DR}$. Is $\overline{AD} \cong \overline{CR}$? Why? ⓗ

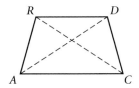

18. **DEVELOPING PROOF** $\overline{DT} \cong \overline{RT}$, $\overline{DA} \cong \overline{RA}$. Is $\angle D \cong \angle R$? Why? ⓗ

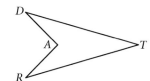

19. Quadrilateral $ABCD \cong$ quadrilateral $GFED$. How many degrees of counterclockwise rotation is needed for quadrilateral $ABCD$ to be rotated onto quadrilateral $GFED$?

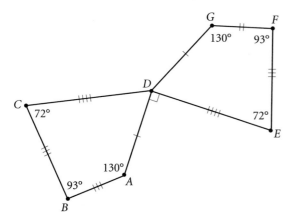

20. **GUESS-N-CHECK** $\triangle ABC$ with vertices $A(1, 2)$, $B(-4, -2)$, and $C(2, -3)$, is transformed by the ordered pair rule $(x, y) \rightarrow (3x, 3y)$ to create the image $\triangle A'B'C'$. Which of the statements below are true? First, try this as a "mental experiment." Take a guess or explain how you know. Then create the diagram with your geometry software, perform the transformation, and see how good you were at visualization.

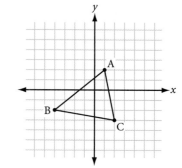

A. $\angle A \cong \angle A'$

B. $\overline{BC} \cong \overline{B'C'}$

C. The points B, B', and the origin are collinear.

D. The slope of $\overline{AB}$ is equal to the slope of $\overline{A'B'}$.

E. The perimeter of $\triangle A'B'C'$ is three times the perimeter of $\triangle ABC$.

DEVELOPING MATHEMATICAL REASONING

Dissecting a Hexagon

Make six copies of the hexagon at right by tracing it onto your paper. Find six different ways to divide a hexagon into twelve identical parts.

Star Polygons

If you arrange a set of eight points roughly around a circle or an oval, and then you connect *each* point to the next with segments, you should get a convex polygon. What do you get if you arrange a set of five points roughly around a circle or an oval, and then you connect every *second* point with segments? You get a star polygon like the one shown below left.

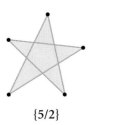

{5/2}

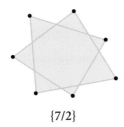

{7/2}

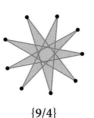

{9/4}

A star polygon is symbolized by {*n*/*k*} where *n* is the number of star point vertices and *k* is the count between points connected by a segment. The {9/4} star polygon for example, is created by starting at one of the nine points and counting four points clockwise and drawing a segment from your starting point to the fourth point then repeating the process from that point.

There are some special cases to look at. For example when you begin drawing the {6/2} star polygon, after three segments you are back to your starting point. So you move to the next point. Notice this star polygon is two overlapping triangles.

What star polygons are represented here? Describe them using the {*n*/*k*} notation.

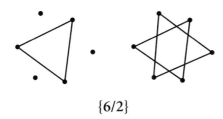

{6/2}

Sometimes you don't even get a star but more of an "asterisk." For example, when you draw the {6/3} star polygon after two moves you are back to your starting point, shown below.

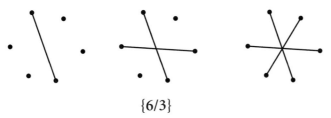

{6/3}

In this activity you'll create a number of star polygons and look for patterns among them.

Activity

Creating star polygons

Step 1 Sketch the star polygon for each set of points containing *n*, the number of star point vertices, ranging from 3 to 11 and *k*, the count between points connected by a segment, ranging from 1 to 10. Either create your own table for your set of star polygons or use the table provided for you by your teacher. Look for patterns.

k\n	1	2	3	4	5	6	7	8	9	10
3										
4										
5										
6										
7										
8										
9										
10										
11										

Step 2 Did you notice any duplicates in the rows? What symmetries did you find? State a rule for when two star polygons are the same.

Step 3 What did you notice about the *n* and *k* for the star polygons that are just convex polygons?

Step 4 What did you notice about the *n* and *k* for the "asterisk" star polygons?

Step 5 What did you notice about the *n* and *k* for the star polygons that were two or more overlapping triangles?

Step 6 Were there any star polygons that were made up of overlapping quadrilaterals or overlapping pentagons? What was the relationship between the *n* and *k* for these star polygons?

Step 7 What type of star polygon is {20/10} or {20/4} or {20/15} or {20/11}? Explain your reasoning.

Step 8 What star polygon is equivalent to a {20/10} or {20/4} or {20/15} or {20/11}? Explain how you know.

Kite and Trapezoid Properties

"Imagination is the highest kite we fly."

LAUREN BACALL

Recall that a **kite** is a quadrilateral with exactly two distinct pairs of congruent consecutive sides.

If you construct two different isosceles triangles on opposite sides of a common base and then remove the base, you have constructed a kite. In an isosceles triangle, the vertex angle is the angle between the two congruent sides. Therefore, let's call the two angles between each pair of congruent sides of a kite the **vertex angles** of the kite. Let's call the other pair the **nonvertex angles**.

A kite also has one line of reflectional symmetry, just like an isosceles triangle. You can use this property to discover other properties of kites. Let's investigate.

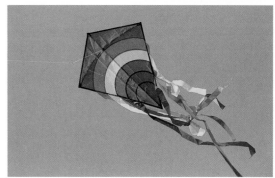

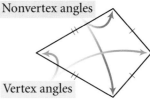

Nonvertex angles

Vertex angles

INVESTIGATION 1

What Are Some Properties of Kites?

YOU WILL NEED
- patty paper
- a straightedge

In this investigation you will look at angles and diagonals in a kite to see what special properties they have.

Step 1 On patty paper, draw two connected segments of different lengths, as shown. Fold through the endpoints and trace the two segments on the back of the patty paper.

Step 2 Compare the size of each pair of opposite angles in your kite by folding an angle onto the opposite angle. Are the vertex angles congruent? Are the nonvertex angles congruent? Share your observations with others near you and complete the conjecture.

Step 1

Step 2

> **Kite Angles Conjecture**   C-34
>
> The __?__ angles of a kite are __?__.

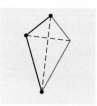
For an interactive version of this investigation, see the **Dynamic Geometry Exploration** Properties of Kites in your ebook.

Step 3 Draw the diagonals. How are the diagonals related? Share your observations with others in your group and complete the conjecture.

> ### Kite Diagonals Conjecture   C-35
>
> The diagonals of a kite are ? .

What else seems to be true about the diagonals of kites?

Step 4 Compare the lengths of the segments on both diagonals. Does either diagonal bisect the other? Share your observations with others near you. Copy and complete the conjecture.

> ### Kite Diagonal Bisector Conjecture   C-36
>
> The diagonal connecting the vertex angles of a kite is the ? of the other diagonal.

→ *Science*
CONNECTION

A *trapezium* is a quadrilateral with no two sides parallel.

Trapezium

The words *trapezoid* and *trapezium* come from the Greek word trapeza, meaning table. There are bones in your wrists that anatomists call trapezoid and trapezium because of their geometric shapes. Which bones are they?

Step 5 Fold along both diagonals. Does either diagonal bisect any angles? Share your observations with others and complete the conjecture.

> ### Kite Angle Bisector Conjecture   C-37
>
> The ? angles of a kite are ? by a ? .

You will prove the Kite Diagonal Bisector Conjecture and the Kite Angle Bisector Conjecture in the Exercise set.

Let's move on to trapezoids. Recall that a **trapezoid** is a quadrilateral with exactly one pair of parallel sides.

In a trapezoid the parallel sides are called **bases**. A pair of angles that share a base as a common side are called **base angles**.

In the next investigation you will discover some properties of trapezoids.

Pair of base angles

Bases

Pair of base angles

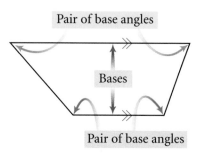

This is a view inside a deflating hot-air balloon. Notice the trapezoidal panels that make up the balloon.

INVESTIGATION 2

What Are Some Properties of Trapezoids?

YOU WILL NEED

- a double-edged straightedge
- a protractor
- a compass

Step 1 Use the two edges of your straightedge to draw parallel segments of unequal length. Draw two nonparallel sides connecting them to make a trapezoid.

Step 2 Use your protractor to find the sum of the measures of each pair of consecutive angles between the parallel bases. What do you notice about this sum? Share your observations with your group.

Find sum.

Step 3 Copy and complete the conjecture.

> **Trapezoid Consecutive Angles Conjecture**   C-38
>
> The consecutive angles between the bases of a trapezoid are ?.

Recall from Chapter 3 that a trapezoid whose two nonparallel sides are the same length is called an **isosceles trapezoid**. Next, you will discover a few properties of isosceles trapezoids.

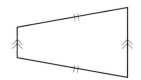

Like kites, isosceles trapezoids have one line of reflectional symmetry. Through what points does the line of symmetry pass?

Step 4 Use both edges of your straightedge to draw parallel lines. Using your compass, construct two congruent, nonparallel segments. Connect the four segments to make an isosceles trapezoid.

Step 5 Measure each pair of base angles. What do you notice about the pair of base angles in each trapezoid? Compare your observations with others near you.

Compare.
Compare.

Step 6 Copy and complete the conjecture.

> **Isosceles Trapezoid Conjecture** C-39
>
> The base angles of an isosceles trapezoid are ? .

What other parts of an isosceles trapezoid are congruent? Let's continue.

Step 7 Draw both diagonals. Compare their lengths. Share your observations with others near you.

Step 8 Copy and complete the conjecture.

> **Isosceles Trapezoid Diagonals Conjecture** C-40
>
> The diagonals of an isosceles trapezoid are ? .

DEVELOPING PROOF

As a group, write a flowchart proof that shows how the Isosceles Trapezoid Diagonals Conjecture follows logically from the Isosceles Trapezoid Conjecture. Use the diagrams below. As you saw earlier, separating the triangles makes it easier to see what triangles we wish to show congruent.

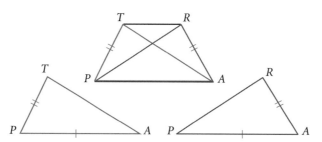

5.3 Exercises

Use your new conjectures to find the missing measures.

YOU WILL NEED

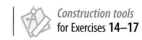
Construction tools
for Exercises **14–17**

1. *ABCD* is a kite.
perimeter = ?

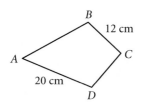

2. *x* = ?
y = ?

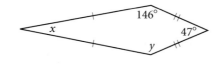

3. *x* = ?
y = ?

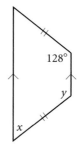

4. $x = \underline{\ ?\ }$
perimeter = 85 cm

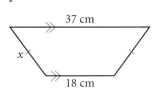

37 cm

x

18 cm

5. $x = \underline{\ ?\ }$
$y = \underline{\ ?\ }$

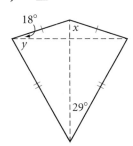

18°
y
x

29°

6. $x = \underline{\ ?\ }$
$y = \underline{\ ?\ }$
perimeter = 164 cm

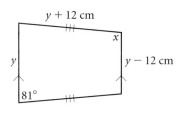

$y + 12$ cm

y x

$y - 12$ cm

81°

7. *ARTP* is an isosceles trapezoid with $RA = PT$.
Find *w*, *x*, and *y*. ⓗ

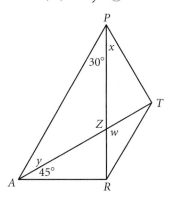

P
x
30°
T
Z w
y
45°
A   R

8. *FLYE* is a kite with $FL = LY$. Find *w*, *x*, and *y*.

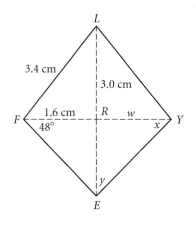

L
3.4 cm
3.0 cm
1.6 cm   R w
F 48° x Y
y
E

9. **DEVELOPING PROOF** Copy and complete the flowchart to show how the Kite Angle Bisector Conjecture follows logically from one of the triangle congruence conjectures.

Given: Kite *BENY* with $\overline{BE} \cong \overline{BY}$, $\overline{EN} \cong \overline{YN}$

Show: $\overline{BN}$ bisects $\angle B$
$\overline{BN}$ bisects $\angle N$

Flowchart Proof

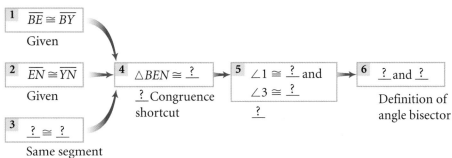

Y

B $\overset{2}{\underset{1}{\quad}}$ $\overset{4}{\underset{3}{\quad}}$ N

E

| 1 | $\overline{BE} \cong \overline{BY}$ |
Given

| 2 | $\overline{EN} \cong \overline{YN}$ |
Given

| 3 | $\underline{\ ?\ } \cong \underline{\ ?\ }$ |
Same segment

| 4 | $\triangle BEN \cong \underline{\ ?\ }$ |
$\underline{\ ?\ }$ Congruence shortcut

| 5 | $\angle 1 \cong \underline{\ ?\ }$ and $\angle 3 \cong \underline{\ ?\ }$
$\underline{\ ?\ }$ |

| 6 | $\underline{\ ?\ }$ and $\underline{\ ?\ }$ |
Definition of angle bisector

10. **DEVELOPING PROOF** Write a paragraph proof or flowchart proof of the Kite Diagonal Bisector Conjecture. Either show how it follows logically from the Kite Angle Bisector Conjecture that you just proved, or how it follows logically from the Converse of the Perpendicular Bisector Conjecture. ⓗ

11. Sketch and label kite *KITE* with vertex angles $\angle K$ and $\angle T$ and $KI > TE$. Which angles are congruent? Explain why.

12. Sketch and label trapezoid *QUIZ* with one base $\overline{QU}$. What is the other base? Name the two pairs of base angles.

13. Sketch and label isosceles trapezoid *SHOW* with one base $\overline{SH}$. What is the other base? Name the two pairs of base angles. Name the two sides of equal length.

In Exercises 14–16, use the properties of kites and trapezoids to construct each figure. You may use either patty paper or a compass and a straightedge.

14. Construct kite *BENF* given sides $\overline{BE}$ and $\overline{EN}$ and diagonal $\overline{BN}$. How many different kites are possible?

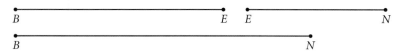

15. Given $\angle W$, $\angle I$, base $\overline{WI}$, and nonparallel side $\overline{IS}$, construct trapezoid *WISH*. ⓗ

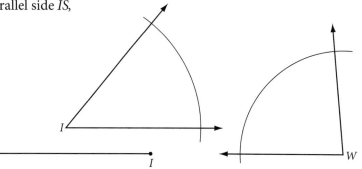

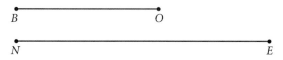

→ **Architecture**
CONNECTION

16. Construct a trapezoid *BONE* with $\overline{BO} \parallel \overline{NE}$. How many different trapezoids can you construct?

The Romans used the classical arch design in bridges, aqueducts, and buildings in the early centuries of the Common Era. The classical semicircular arch is really half of a regular polygon built with wedge-shaped blocks whose faces are isosceles trapezoids. Each block supports the blocks surrounding it.

17. The inner edge of the arch in the diagram below is half of a regular 18-gon. The inner edges of the arch are also the base of nine congruent isosceles triangles. Use either of the trapezoid properties to calculate the measures of all the angles in the nine isosceles trapezoids making up the arch. Then use your geometry tools to accurately draw a nine-stone arch like the one shown where each of the trapezoids is congruent.

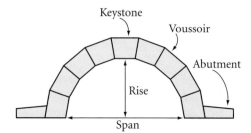

18. The take-out carton to the right is in the shape of an isosceles trapezoidal block, like the voussoirs shown in the previous exercise. If the angles on the face of the carton are 84° and 96°, how many of these cartons would be needed to create a semicircular arch?

This carton is shaped like an isosceles trapezoid block, like the voussoirs used in the arch above left.

19. The figure below shows the path of light through a trapezoidal prism and how an image is inverted. For the prism to work as shown, the trapezoid must be isosceles, $\angle AGF$ must be congruent to $\angle BHE$, and $\overline{GF}$ must be congruent to $\overline{EH}$. Show that if these conditions are met, then $\overline{AG}$ will be congruent to $\overline{BH}$. ⓗ

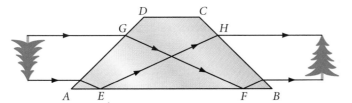

Review

20. DEVELOPING PROOF Trace the figure below. Calculate the measure of each lettered angle. Explain how you determined measures *e* and *g*.

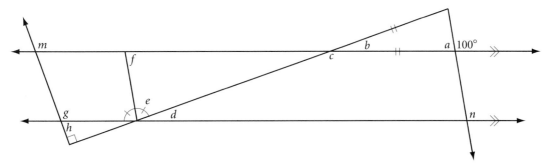

21. TRANSFORMATIONS. Given quadrilateral *ABCD* with vertices: $A(-8, 2)$, $B(-4, -2)$, $C(0, 2)$, $D(-4, 10)$

  a. Reflect quadrilateral *ABCD* across the *y*-axis to create quadrilateral $A'B'C'D'$.

  b. What are the coordinates of the vertices of quadrilateral $A'B'C'D'$?

  c. What is the transformation rule, $(x, y) \rightarrow (?, ?)$, that transforms quadrilateral *ABCD* to quadrilateral $A'B'C'D'$?

  d. Rotate quadrilateral $A'B'C'D'$ 90° clockwise about the origin to create quadrilateral $A''B''C''D''$.

  e. What are the coordinates of the vertices of quadrilateral $A''B''C''D''$?

  f. What is the transformation rule, $(x, y) \rightarrow (?, ?)$, that transforms quadrilateral $A'B'C'D'$ to quadrilateral $A''B''C''D''$?

  g. What is the single transformation rule that takes quadrilateral *ABCD* onto quadrilateral $A''B''C''D''$?

Properties of Parallelograms

"If there is an opinion, facts will be found to support it."

JUDY SPROLES

In this lesson you will discover some special properties of parallelograms. A parallelogram is a quadrilateral whose opposite sides are parallel.

Rhombuses, rectangles, and squares all fit this definition as well. Therefore, any properties you discover for parallelograms will also apply to these other shapes. However, to be sure that your conjectures will apply to *any* parallelogram, you should investigate parallelograms that don't have any other special properties such as right angles, all congruent angles, or all congruent sides.

INVESTIGATION

Four Parallelogram Properties

YOU WILL NEED

- graph paper
- patty paper or a compass
- a double-edged straightedge
- a protractor

First you'll create a parallelogram.

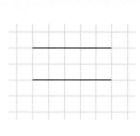

Step 1   Step 2

Step 1 Using the lines on a piece of graph paper as a guide, draw a pair of parallel lines that are at least 6 cm apart. Using the parallel edges of your double-edged straightedge, make a parallelogram. Label your parallelogram *LOVE*.

Step 2 Let's look at the opposite angles. Measure the angles of parallelogram *LOVE*. Compare a pair of opposite angles using patty paper or your protractor. Compare results with your group. Copy and complete the conjecture.

Parallelogram Opposite Angles Conjecture	C-41

The opposite angles of a parallelogram are _?_.

Two angles that share a common side in a polygon are consecutive angles. In parallelogram *LOVE*, ∠*LOV* and ∠*EVO* are a pair of consecutive angles. The consecutive angles of a parallelogram are also related.

Step 3 Find the sum of the measures of each pair of consecutive angles in parallelogram *LOVE*.

Share your observations with your group. Copy and complete the conjecture.

> ### Parallelogram Consecutive Angles Conjecture C-42
>
> The consecutive angles of a parallelogram are ? .

Step 4 Describe how to use the two conjectures you just made to find all the angles of a parallelogram with only one angle measure given.

Step 5 Next let's look at the opposite sides of a parallelogram. With your compass or patty paper, compare the lengths of the opposite sides of the parallelogram you made.

Share your results with your group. Copy and complete the conjecture.

For an interactive version of this investigation, see the **Dynamic Geometry Exploration** Properties of Parallelograms in your ebook.

> ### Parallelogram Opposite Sides Conjecture C-43
>
> The opposite sides of a parallelogram are ? .

Step 6 Finally, let's consider the diagonals of a parallelogram. Construct the diagonals $\overline{LV}$ and $\overline{EO}$, as shown below. Label the point where the two diagonals intersect point *M*.

Step 7 Measure $\overline{LM}$ and $\overline{VM}$. What can you conclude about point *M*? Is this conclusion also true for diagonal $\overline{EO}$? How do the diagonals relate?

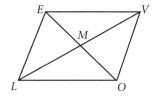

Share your results with your group. Copy and complete the conjecture.

> ### Parallelogram Diagonals Conjecture C-44
>
> The diagonals of a parallelogram ? .

DEVELOPING PROOF

The investigations may have convinced you that the parallelogram properties are true but what properties explain *why* they are true? To explain why, you first prove a **lemma**, another smaller theorem that you can use to prove some of the conjectures. The lemma you will prove says: *The diagonal of a parallelogram divides the parallelogram into two congruent triangles.* The following flowchart can be used to help explain why this conjecture is true. With your group members, study the flowchart and complete it or write your own paragraph proof that explains why the lemma is true.

Prove the lemma: The diagonal of a parallelogram divides the parallelogram into two congruent triangles.

Given: Parallelogram *SOAK* with diagonal $\overline{SA}$

Show: $\triangle SOA \cong \triangle AKS$

Flowchart Proof

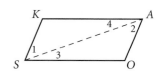

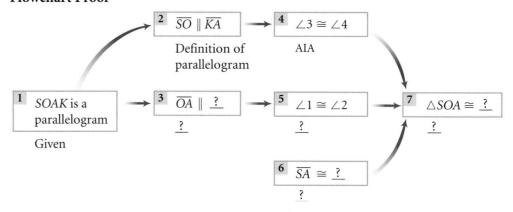

Next, prove the Parallelogram Opposite Angles Conjecture with your group members. Study the flowchart proof below and complete it or write your own paragraph proof that explains why the conjecture is true.

Prove the conjecture: The opposite angles of a parallelogram are congruent.

Given: Parallelogram *BATH* with diagonals $\overline{BT}$ and $\overline{HA}$

Show: $\angle HBA \cong \angle ATH$ and $\angle BAT \cong \angle THB$

Flowchart Proof

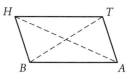

1 Parallelogram *BATH* with diagonal $\overline{BT}$ →	2 $\triangle BAT \cong \triangle THB$ →	3 $\angle BAT \cong \angle THB$
Given	Lemma just proved	CPCTC

4 Parallelogram *BATH* with diagonal $\overline{HA}$ →	5 $\triangle BAH = \triangle$ _?_ →	6 $\angle HBA \cong \angle$ _?_
_?_	_?_	_?_

5.4 Exercises

Use your new conjectures in the following exercises.
In Exercises 1–6, each figure is a parallelogram.

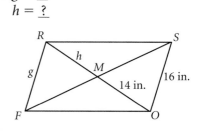

YOU WILL NEED

Construction tools
for Exercises **7, 8, 19, 20**

1. $c =$ _?_
   $d =$ _?_

2. $a =$ _?_
   $b =$ _?_

3. $g =$ _?_
   $h =$ _?_

4. $VF = 36$ m
$EF = 24$ m
$EI = 42$ m
What is the perimeter
of $\triangle NVI$? Ⓗ

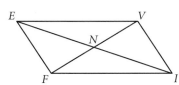

5. What is the perimeter?

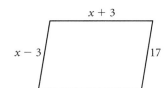

6. $e = \underline{\ ?\ }$
$f = \underline{\ ?\ }$

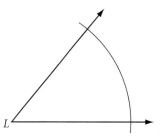

7. Given side $\overline{LA}$, side $\overline{AS}$, and $\angle L$, construct parallelogram *LAST*.

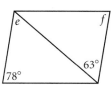

8. Given side $\overline{DR}$ and diagonals $\overline{DO}$ and $\overline{PR}$, construct parallelogram *DROP*. Ⓗ

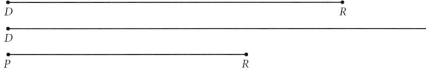

9. Find the coordinates of point *M* in parallelogram *PRAM*. Ⓗ

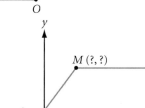

10. **DEVELOPING PROOF** Prove the conjecture: The opposite sides of a
parallelogram are congruent.

Given: Parallelogram *BATH* with diagonals $\overline{BT}$ and $\overline{HA}$

Show: $\overline{HT} \cong \overline{AB}$ and $\overline{HB} \cong \text{AT}$

Flowchart Proof

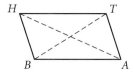

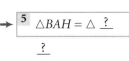

11. DEVELOPING PROOF Copy and complete the flowchart to show how the Parallelogram Diagonals Conjecture follows logically from other conjectures.

Given: *LEAN* is a parallelogram

Show: $\overline{EN}$ and $\overline{LA}$ bisect each other

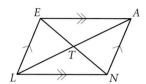

Flowchart Proof

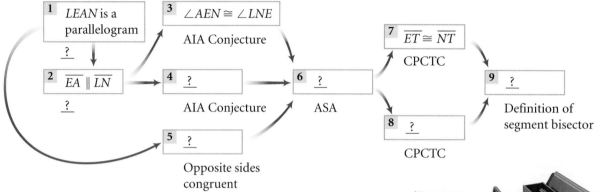

| 1 *LEAN* is a parallelogram | 3 $\angle AEN \cong \angle LNE$ |
| ? | AIA Conjecture |

| 2 $\overline{EA} \parallel \overline{LN}$ | 4 ? |
| ? | AIA Conjecture |

6 ?
ASA

7 $\overline{ET} \cong \overline{NT}$
CPCTC

8 ?
CPCTC

9 ?
Definition of segment bisector

5 ?
Opposite sides congruent

12. Study the tool box pictured here. Sketch the box as viewed from the side, and explain why a parallelogram linkage is used.

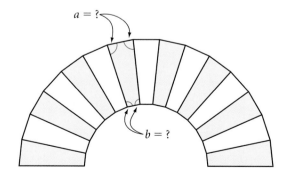

Review

13. Find the measures of the lettered angles in this tiling of regular polygons.

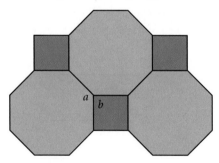

14. Trace the figure below. Calculate the measure of each lettered angle.

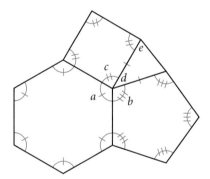

15. Find *x* and *y*. Explain.

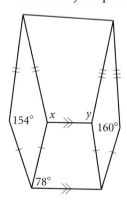

154°   x   y   160°

78°

16. What is the measure of each angle in the isosceles trapezoid face of a voussoir in this 15-stone arch?

$a = ?$

$b = ?$

17. DEVELOPING PROOF Is $\triangle XYW \cong \triangle WYZ$? Explain.

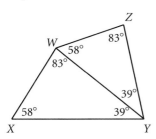

18. Sketch the cross-section formed when this pyramid is sliced by the plane.

19. DEVELOPING PROOF Construct two segments that bisect each other. Connect their endpoints. What type of quadrilateral is this? Draw a diagram and explain why.

20. DEVELOPING PROOF Construct two intersecting circles. Connect the two centers and the two points of intersection to form a quadrilateral. What type of quadrilateral is this? Draw a diagram and explain why.

DEVELOPING MATHEMATICAL REASONING

Lunar Lockout

The goal of this puzzle is to move the red piece into the center square. All of the pieces move according to these two rules:

▶ A piece can move only horizontally or vertically, not diagonally.

▶ A piece continues to move until its path is blocked by another piece.

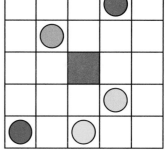

A piece can't move in a direction where there is no other piece to block its path. In the board at right, for example, you can move the blue piece up until it is stopped by the red piece, but you can't move it in any other direction. One possible solution to this puzzle is this sequence of moves: green right, green up, red down, red left, written symbolically as: G → ↑R↓ ←.

Try the puzzles below.

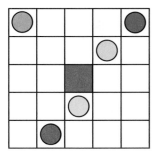

Beginner Puzzle

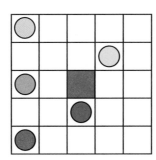

Intermediate Puzzle

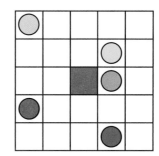

Advanced Puzzle

Properties of Special Parallelograms

"You must know a great deal about a subject to know how little is known about it."

LEO ROSTEN

The legs of the lifting platform shown at right form rhombuses. Can you visualize how this lift would work differently if the legs formed parallelograms that weren't rhombuses?

In this lesson you will discover some properties of rhombuses, rectangles, and squares. What you discover about the diagonals of these special parallelograms will help you understand why these lifts work the way they do.

 ## INVESTIGATION 1

YOU WILL NEED

- patty paper
- a double-edged straightedge

What Can You Draw with the Double-Edged Straightedge?

In this investigation you will discover the special parallelogram that you can draw using just the parallel edges of a straightedge.

 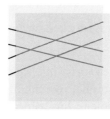 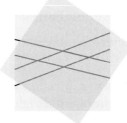

      Step 1   Step 2   Step 3

Step 1 On a piece of patty paper, use a double-edged straightedge to draw two pairs of parallel lines that intersect each other.

Step 2 Assuming that the two edges of your straightedge are parallel, you have drawn a parallelogram. Place a second patty paper over the first and copy one of the sides of the parallelogram.

Step 3 Compare the length of the side on the second patty paper with the lengths of the other three sides of the parallelogram. How do they compare? Share your results with your group. Copy and complete the conjecture.

Double-Edged Straightedge Conjecture	C-45
If two parallel lines are intersected by a second pair of parallel lines that are the same distance apart as the first pair, then the parallelogram formed is a _?_ .	

Recall that a **rhombus** is a parallelogram with four congruent sides, or an equilateral parallelogram. In Chapter 3, you learned how to construct a rhombus using a compass and straightedge, or using patty paper. Now you know a quicker and easier way, using a double-edged straightedge. To construct a parallelogram that is not a rhombus, you need two double-edged staightedges of different widths.

Now let's investigate some properties of rhombuses.

 ## INVESTIGATION 2

Do Rhombus Diagonals Have Special Properties?

YOU WILL NEED

● patty paper
● a straightedge
● a protractor
(optional)

View an interactive version of this lesson, see the **Dynamic Geometry Exploration** in your ebook.

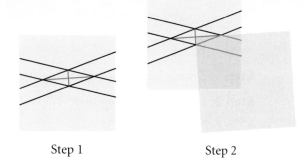

Step 1   Step 2

Step 1 Draw in both diagonals of the rhombus you created in Investigation 1.

Step 2 Use the corner of a patty paper or a protractor to measure the angles formed by the intersection of the two diagonals. Are the diagonals perpendicular?

Compare your results with your group. Also, recall that a rhombus is a parallelogram and that the diagonals of a parallelogram bisect each other. Combine these two ideas into your next conjecture.

> **Rhombus Diagonals Conjecture**   `C-46`
>
> The diagonals of a rhombus are _?_, and they _?_.

Step 3 The diagonals and the sides of the rhombus form two angles at each vertex. Fold your patty paper to compare each pair of angles. What do you observe? Compare your results with your group. Copy and complete the conjecture.

> **Rhombus Angles Conjecture**   `C-47`
>
> The _?_ of a rhombus _?_ the angles of the rhombus.

So far you've made conjectures about a rhombus, a quadrilateral with four congruent sides. Now let's look at quadrilaterals with four congruent angles. A rectangle is a parallelogram with four congruent angles, or an equiangular parallelogram. What special properties do they have?

 # INVESTIGATION 3

Do Rectangle Diagonals Have Special Properties?

Now let's look at the diagonals of rectangles.

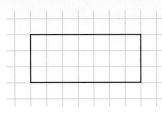

Step 1

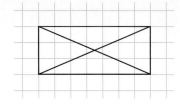

Step 2

Step 1 Draw a large rectangle using the lines on a piece of graph paper as a guide.

Step 2 Draw in both diagonals. With your compass, compare the lengths of the two diagonals.

Compare results with your group. In addition, recall that a rectangle is also a parallelogram. So its diagonals also have the properties of a parallelogram's diagonals. Combine these ideas to complete the conjecture.

> **Rectangle Diagonals Conjecture**　　　　　　　　`C-48`
>
> The diagonals of a rectangle are ? and ? .

INVESTIGATION 4

What Are the Properties of the Diagonals of a Square?

This final investigation is really a "thought experiment." What happens if you combine the properties of a rectangle and a rhombus? We call the shape a square. You can think of a square as a special rhombus and also a special rectangle. So you can define it in at least two different ways.

A **square** is an equiangular rhombus.

Or

A **square** is an equilateral rectangle.

A square is a parallelogram, as well as both a rectangle and a rhombus. Thus the square has the diagonal properties of all three. Discuss with your group members what you know about the diagonals of these three special parallelograms, then copy and complete this conjecture.

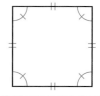

| Square Diagonals Conjecture | C-49 |

The diagonals of a square are _?_, _?_, and _?_.

 DEVELOPING PROOF

In Lesson 1.6 you arrived at the definitions for rhombuses and rectangles. It seemed like a neat organized way to categorize them as special parallelograms. You defined a rectangle as a parallelogram with all four angles congruent (an equiangular parallelogram). You defined a rhombus as a parallelogram with all four sides congruent (an equilateral parallelogram).

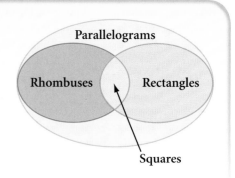

However, when we defined rhombus, we did not need the added condition of it being a parallelogram. We only needed to say that it is a quadrilateral with all four sides congruent (an equilateral quadrilateral). With your group members, follow along with the flowchart proof started for you below. Complete the flowchart proof by providing the missing reasons or write your own paragraph proof. The proof demonstrates logically that if a quadrilateral has four congruent sides then it is a parallelogram. If it is a parallelogram with four congruent sides then it is a rhombus.

Given: Quadrilateral $QUAD$ has $\overline{QU} \cong \overline{UA} \cong \overline{AD} \cong \overline{DQ}$ with diagonal $\overline{DU}$

Show: $QUAD$ is a rhombus

Flowchart Proof

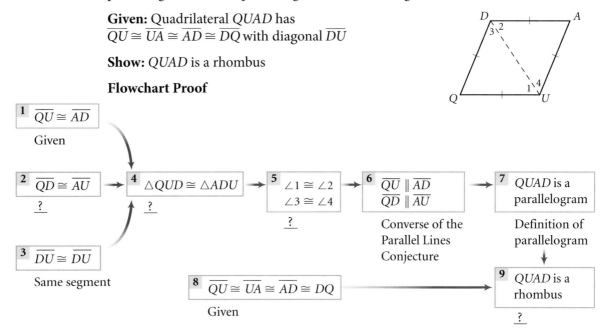

Likewise, when we defined rectangle, we did not need the added condition of it being a parallelogram. We only needed to say that it is a quadrilateral with all four angles congruent (an equiangular quadrilateral). With your group members, follow along with the flowchart proof started for you below. Complete the flowchart proof by providing the missing statements and reasons or write your own paragraph proof. The proof demonstrates logically that if a quadrilateral has four congruent angles then it is a parallelogram. If it is a parallelogram with four congruent angles then it is a rectangle.

Given: Quadrilateral $ABCD$ with $\angle 1 \cong \angle 2 \cong \angle 3 \cong \angle 4$ with side AD extended to form exterior $\angle 5$.

Show: $ABCD$ is a rectangle.

Flowchart Proof

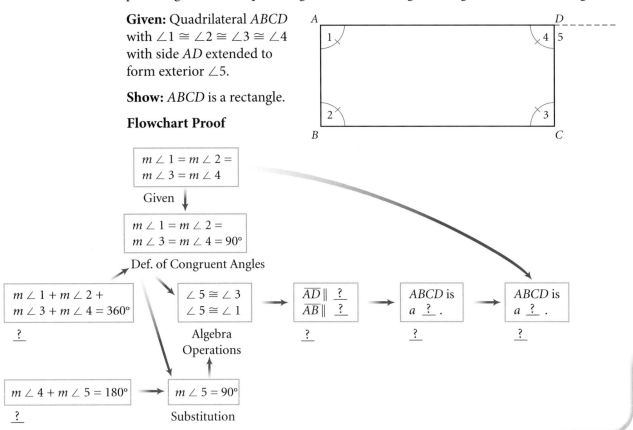

5.5 Exercises

YOU WILL NEED

Construction tools
for Exercises **17–19**

DEVELOPING PROOF For Exercises 1–10, state whether each statement is always true, sometimes true, or never true. Use sketches or explanations to support your answers.

1. The diagonals of a parallelogram are congruent. ⓗ

2. The consecutive angles of a rectangle are congruent and supplementary.

3. The diagonals of a rectangle bisect each other.

4. The diagonals of a rectangle bisect the angles.

5. The diagonals of a square are perpendicular bisectors of each other.

6. A rhombus is a square.

7. A square is a rectangle.

8. A diagonal divides a square into two isosceles right triangles.

9. Opposite angles in a parallelogram are congruent.

10. Consecutive angles in a parallelogram are congruent.

11. *WREK* is a rectangle.
   CR = 10
   WE = ?

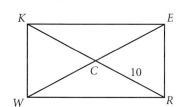

K   E

C   10

W   R

12. *PARL* is a parallelogram.
   y = ?   ⓗ

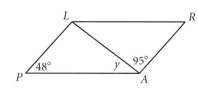

L   R

48°   y   95°

P   A

13. *SQRE* is a square.
   x = ?
   y = ?

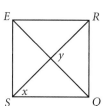

E   R

y

x

S   Q

DEVELOPING PROOF For Exercises 14–16, use deductive reasoning to explain your answers.

14. Is *DIAM* a rhombus? Why?

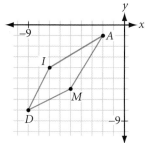

15. Is *BOXY* a rectangle? Why?

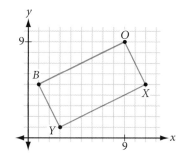

16. Is *TILE* a parallelogram? Why?

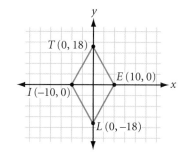

17. Given the diagonal $\overline{LV}$, construct square *LOVE*. ⓗ

L   V

18. Given diagonal $\overline{BK}$ and ∠*B*, construct rhombus *BAKE*. ⓗ

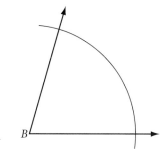

B   K   B

19. Given side $\overline{PS}$ and diagonal $\overline{PE}$, construct rectangle *PIES*.

P   S

P   E

20. **DEVELOPING PROOF** Write the converse of the Rectangle Diagonals Conjecture. Is it true? Prove it or show a counterexample. ⓗ

21. To make sure that a room is rectangular, builders check the two diagonals of the room as shown at right. Explain what they check about the diagonals, and why this works.

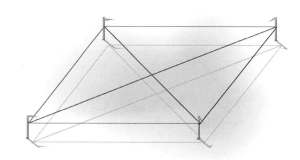

22. The platforms shown at the beginning of this lesson and here lift objects straight up. The platform also stays parallel to the floor. You can clearly see rhombuses in the picture, but you can also visualize the frame as the diagonals of rectangles. Explain why the diagonals of a rectangle guarantee this vertical movement.

Review

23. Trace the figure below. Calculate the measure of each lettered angle.

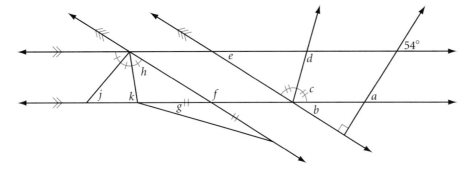

24. Find the coordinates of three more points that lie on the line passing through the points $(2, -1)$ and $(-3, 4)$.

25. Write the equation of the perpendicular bisector of the segment with endpoints $(-12, 15)$ and $(4, -3)$.

26. $\triangle ABC$ has vertices $A(0, 0)$, $B(-4, -2)$, and $C(8, -8)$. What is the equation of the median to side $\overline{AB}$?

DEVELOPING MATHEMATICAL REASONING

How Did the Farmer Get to the Other Side?

A farmer was taking her pet rabbit, a basket of prize-winning baby carrots, and her small—but hungry—rabbit-chasing dog to town. She came to a river and realized she had a problem. The little boat she found tied to the pier was big enough to carry only herself and one of the three possessions. She couldn't leave her dog on the bank with the little rabbit (the dog would frighten the poor rabbit), and she couldn't leave the rabbit alone with the carrots (the rabbit would eat all the carrots). But she still had to figure out how to cross the river safely with one possession at a time. How could she move back and forth across the river to get the three possessions safely to the other side?

EXPLORATION

Turning Two Quadrilaterals into a Parallelogram

Step 1 Draw a quadrilateral. Make a copy of it.

Step 2 Draw a diagonal in the first quadrilateral. Draw the other diagonal in the duplicate quadrilateral.

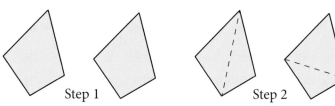

Step 1   Step 2

Step 3 Label all the congruent corresponding sides and angles

Step 4 Cut each quadrilateral into two triangles along the diagonals.

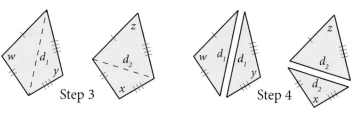

Step 3   Step 4

Step 5 Arrange the four triangles into a parallelogram.

Step 6 Explain how you did it. How do you know there are no gaps or overlaps? How do you know it is a parallelogram?

DEVELOPING MATHEMATICAL REASONING

Folding Cubes II

Each cube has designs on three faces. When unfolded, which figure at right could it become?

1.   **A.**   **B.**   **C.** 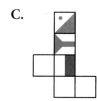   **D.**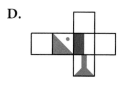

2. 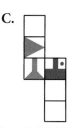   **A.** 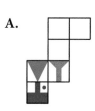   **B.** 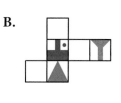   **C.** 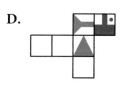   **D.**

Point of Concurrency: Circumcenter

You have constructed points of concurrency, which are intersections of lines in a triangle. You can also find these on a coordinate plane. Suppose you know the coordinates of the vertices of a triangle. How can you find the coordinates of the circumcenter? You can graph the triangle, construct the perpendicular bisectors of the sides, and then *estimate* the coordinates of the point of concurrency. However, to find the exact coordinates, you need to use algebra. Let's look at an example.

EXAMPLE

Find the coordinates of the circumcenter of $\triangle ZAP$ with $Z(0, -4)$, $A(-4, 4)$, and $P(8, 8)$.

Solution

To find the coordinates of the circumcenter, you need to write equations for the perpendicular bisectors of two of the sides of the triangle and then find the point where the bisectors intersect.

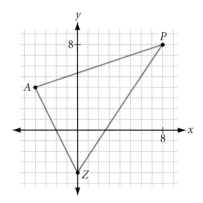

To find the equation for the perpendicular bisector of $\overline{ZA}$, first find the midpoint of $\overline{ZA}$, then find its slope.

$$\text{Midpoint of } \overline{ZA} = \left(\frac{0 + (-4)}{2}, \frac{-4 + 4}{2}\right)$$
$$= (-2, 0)$$

$$\text{Slope of } \overline{ZA} = \frac{4 - (-4)}{-4 - 0} = \frac{8}{-4} = -2$$

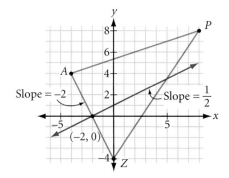

The slope of the perpendicular bisector of $\overline{ZA}$ is the opposite reciprocal of -2, or $\frac{1}{2}$, and it passes through point $(-2, 0)$. Substituting these values into the slope-intercept form of a line and solving for the y-intercept gives the equation of the perpendicular bisector.

$$y = mx + b$$
$$0 = \tfrac{1}{2}(-2) + b$$
$$1 = b$$
$$y = \tfrac{1}{2}x + 1$$

You can use the same technique to find the equation of the perpendicular bisector of $\overline{ZP}$. The midpoint of $\overline{ZP}$ is $(4, 2)$, and the slope is $\frac{3}{2}$. So the slope of the perpendicular bisector of $\overline{ZP}$ is $-\frac{2}{3}$ and it passes through the point $(4, 2)$. The equation of the perpendicular bisector is $y = -\frac{2}{3}x + \frac{14}{3}$.

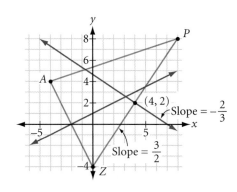

Since all the perpendicular bisectors intersect at the same point, you can solve these two equations to find that point.

$$\begin{cases} y = \frac{1}{2}x + 1 & \text{Perpendicular bisector of } \overline{ZA}. \\ y = -\frac{2}{3}x + \frac{14}{3} & \text{Perpendicular bisector of } \overline{ZP}. \end{cases}$$

The circumcenter is $\left(\frac{22}{7}, \frac{18}{7}\right)$. You can verify this result by finding the equation of the perpendicular bisector of $\overline{AP}$ and making sure that these values satisfy it.

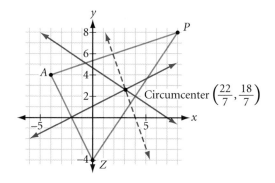

Exercises

1. The lines $y = 3 + \frac{2}{3}x$, $y = -\frac{1}{3}x$, and $y = -\frac{4}{3}x + 3$ intersect to form a triangle. Find the vertices of the triangle.

2. The vertices of parallelogram $ABCD$ are $A(2, 3)$, $B(8, 4)$, $C(10, 9)$, and $D(4, 8)$.

    a. Write the system of linear equations created by the diagonals of $ABCD$.

    b. Solve the system to find the point of intersection of the diagonals.

    c. Calculate the midpoint of each diagonal.

    d. Explain how your results to parts b and c confirm the Parallelogram Diagonals Conjecture.

3. Triangle RES has vertices $R(0, 0)$, $E(4, -6)$, and $S(8, 4)$. Find the equation of the perpendicular bisector of $\overline{RE}$.

In Exercises 4–6, find the coordinates of the circumcenter of each triangle.

4. Triangle TRM with vertices $T(-2, 1)$, $R(4, 3)$, and $M(-4, -1)$

5. Triangle FGH with vertices $F(0, -6)$, $G(3, 6)$, and $H(12, 0)$

6. Right triangle MNO with vertices $M(-4, 0)$, $N(0, 5)$, and $O(10, -3)$

7. For a right triangle, there is a shorter method for finding the circumcenter. What is it? Explain. (*Hint:* Graphing your work may help you recognize the method.)

In Chapter 3 you discovered that the three perpendicular bisectors of a triangle are concurrent in a point called the circumcenter. You then proved your conjecture using other properties of geometry. Now you have the skills to prove it using coordinate geometry.

8. **DEVELOPING PROOF** You prove that the perpendicular bisectors of the sides of a triangle are concurrent the same way you found the circumcenter in the previous exercises, except you use letters instead of numbers. To make the manipulating of symbols easier, you place the points on the coordinate grid at "nice" locations (usually on one of the axes). Locate the points of your diagram so that they correspond to the given information, but not assuming extra properties. The plan for the coordinate proof is started for you. Complete the proof that the perpendicular bisectors of the sides of a triangle are concurrent.

Given: $\triangle OAB$, without loss of generality, vertices $O(0, 0)$, $A(2a, 0)$, $B(2b, 2c)$

Show: The three perpendicular bisectors of the sides intersect at the same point.

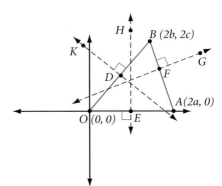

Plan:

- Find the slope of $\overline{OA}$, $\overline{OB}$, and $\overline{AB}$.
- Find the slope of $\perp$ bisectors $\overleftrightarrow{GF}$, $\overleftrightarrow{HE}$, and $\overleftrightarrow{KD}$.
- Find the midpoints of $\overline{OA}$, $\overline{OB}$, and $\overline{AB}$.
- Find the equations of $\perp$ bisectors $\overleftrightarrow{GF}$, $\overleftrightarrow{HE}$, and $\overleftrightarrow{KD}$.
- Find the point of intersection of $\perp$ bisectors $\overleftrightarrow{GF}$ and $\overleftrightarrow{HE}$.
- Find the point of intersection of $\perp$ bisectors $\overleftrightarrow{GF}$ and $\overleftrightarrow{KD}$.
- If the point of intersection of $\perp$ bisectors $\overleftrightarrow{GF}$ and $\overleftrightarrow{HE}$ and the point of intersection of $\perp$ bisectors $\overleftrightarrow{GF}$ and $\overleftrightarrow{KD}$ are the same, then you have proved the three perpendicular bisectors of the sides are concurrent!

DEVELOPING MATHEMATICAL REASONING

Pentomino 5×12 Rectangle Puzzle 1

The pentominoes shown below can be arranged into the 5×12 rectangle so that the letters form five geometry terms: *star polygons, tessellation, construction, golden spiral,* and *opposite side.* Place the pentominoes below in the grid to spell out the five geometry terms.

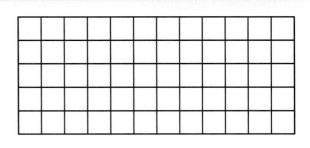

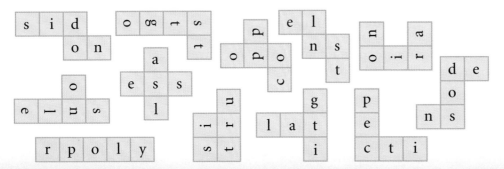

Proving Quadrilateral Properties

"For instance" is not a "proof."

JEWISH SAYING

Most of the paragraph proofs and flowchart proofs you have done so far have been set up for you to complete. Creating your own proofs requires good reasoning strategies and planning. One excellent reasoning strategy is "thinking backward." If you know where you are headed but are unsure where to start, start at the end of the problem and work your way back to the beginning one step at a time.

The firefighter below asks another firefighter to turn on one of the water hydrants. But which one? A mistake could mean disaster—a nozzle flying around loose under all that pressure. Which hydrant should the firefighter turn on?

Did you "think backward" to solve the puzzle? Thinking backward is a useful reasoning strategy to use when you write proofs which you may have already been using.

To help plan a proof and visualize the flow of reasoning, you can make a flowchart. As you think backward through a proof, you draw a flowchart backward to show the steps in your thinking.

Work with a partner when you first try planning your geometry proof. Think backward to make your plan: Start with the conclusion and reason back to the given. Let's look at an example.

A concave kite is sometimes called a **dart**.

EXAMPLE

Given: Dart $ADBC$ with $\overline{AC} \cong \overline{BC}$, $\overline{AD} \cong \overline{BD}$

Show: $\overline{CD}$ bisects $\angle ACB$

Solution

Plan: Begin by drawing a diagram and marking the given information on it. Next, construct your proof by reasoning backward and using other reasoning strategies. Then convert this reasoning into a flowchart. Your flowchart should start with boxes containing the given information and end with what you are trying to demonstrate. The arrows indicate the flow of your logical argument. Your thinking might go something like this:

"I can show $\overline{CD}$ is the bisector of $\angle ACB$ if I can show $\angle ACD \cong \angle BCD$."

"I can show $\angle ACD \cong \angle BCD$ if they are corresponding angles in congruent triangles."

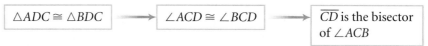

"Can I show $\triangle ADC \cong \triangle BDC$? Yes, I can, by SSS, because it is given that $\overline{AC} \cong \overline{BC}$ and $\overline{AD} \cong \overline{BD}$, and $\overline{CD} \cong \overline{CD}$ because it is the same segment in both triangles."

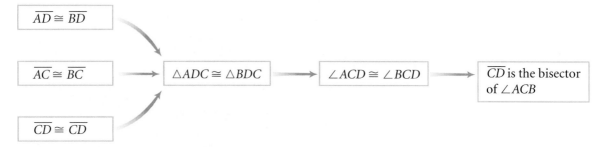

By adding the reason for each statement below each box in your flowchart, you can make the flowchart into a complete flowchart proof.

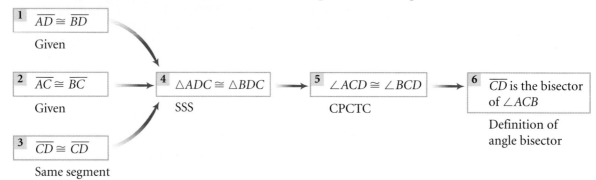

→ **Language**
CONNECTION

The abbreviation Q.E.D. at the end of a proof stands for the Latin phrase *quod erat demonstrandum*, meaning "which was to be demonstrated." This is a translation of the Greek phrase that Euclid used at the end of each of his proofs in the *Elements*.

Some students prefer to write their proofs in a flowchart format, and others prefer to write out the proof as an explanation in paragraph form. By reversing the reasoning in your plan, you can make the plan into a complete paragraph proof.

"It is given that $\overline{AC} \cong \overline{BC}$ and $\overline{AD} \cong \overline{BD}$. $\overline{CD} \cong \overline{CD}$ because it is the same segment in both triangles. So, $\triangle ADC \cong \triangle BDC$ by the SSS Congruence Conjecture, and $\angle ACD \cong \angle BCD$ by the definition of congruent triangles (CPCTC). Therefore, by the definition of angle bisectors, $\overline{CD}$ is the bisector of $\angle ACB$. Q.E.D."

INVESTIGATION

Finding the Square Route

Here is a puzzle for you to solve that has nothing to do with square roots. In the puzzle grid at right, the goal is to find a route—a path—that starts at 1 in the upper left and ends at 100 in the lower right.

You can move to an adjacent square horizontally, vertically, or diagonally. In order to move, you must be able to add, subtract, multiply, or divide the number in the square you occupy by 2 or 5 to get the number in the new square. For example, if you happen to be in square 11, you could move to square 9 by subtracting 2, or to square 55 by multiplying by 5.

Step 1 Using this puzzle's rule for moving, explain why there are three possible first moves.

Step 2 Solve the puzzle—which route will take you from 1 to 100? Show it with arrows.

Step 3 Think about any problem-solving strategies that were particularly helpful for solving this puzzle. How can these strategies help you in developing proofs?

5.6 Exercises

1. **DEVELOPING PROOF** Hopefully you discovered in the investigation *Finding the Square Route* that the quickest, most efficient way to solve the puzzle is to work backwards—starting at the 100 and reason backwards. This is a great strategy in puzzle solving and in doing proofs. Try this puzzle.

The Dealer's Dilemma In the game of bridge, the dealer deals 52 cards in a clockwise direction among four players. You are playing a game in which you are the dealer. You deal the cards, starting with the player on your left. However, in the middle of dealing, you stop to answer the phone. When you return, no one can remember where the last card was dealt. (And, of course, no cards have been touched.) Without counting the number of cards in anyone's hand or the number of cards yet to be dealt, how can you rapidly finish dealing, giving each player exactly the same cards she or he would have received if you hadn't been interrupted?

2. DEVELOPING PROOF Prove the conjecture: If the opposite sides of a quadrilateral are congruent, then the quadrilateral is a parallelogram. Complete the flow chart proof or write a paragraph proof.

Given: Quadrilateral *WATR*, with $\overline{WA} \cong \overline{RT}$ and $\overline{WR} \cong \overline{AT}$, and diagonal $\overline{WT}$

Show: *WATR* is a parallelogram

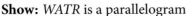

Flowchart Proof

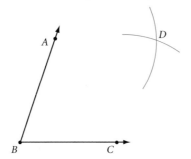

3. DEVELOPING PROOF The three steps below demonstrate the construction of a special quadrilateral. Which special quadrilateral is it? Explain how you know.

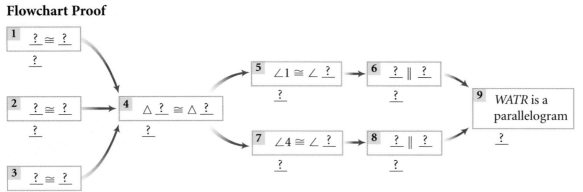

Step 1. Construct an arc with radius *BC* centered at *A*.

Step 2. Construct an arc with radius *AB* centered at *C*. Label point of intersection *D*.

Step 3. Construct segments *AD* and *DC* to form quadrilateral *ABCD*.

4. DEVELOPING PROOF Write a flowchart proof to demonstrate that quadrilateral *SOAP* is a parallelogram. ⓗ

Given: Quadrilateral *SOAP* with $\overline{SP} \parallel \overline{OA}$ and $\overline{SP} \cong \overline{OA}$

Show: *SOAP* is a parallelogram

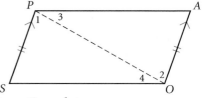

5. The results of the proof in Exercise 4 can now be stated as a proved conjecture. Complete this statement beneath your proof: "If one pair of opposite sides of a quadrilateral are both parallel and congruent, then the quadrilateral is a ? ."

DEVELOPING PROOF For Exercises 6–9, prove the conjecture.

6. Conjecture: The diagonals of a rectangle are congruent. ⓗ

Given: Rectangle *YOGI* with diagonals $\overline{YG}$ and $\overline{OI}$

Show: $\overline{YG} \cong \overline{OI}$

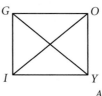

7. Conjecture: If the diagonals of a parallelogram are congruent, then the parallelogram is a rectangle. ⓗ

Given: Parallelogram *BEAR*, with diagonals $\overline{BA} \cong \overline{ER}$

Show: *BEAR* is a rectangle

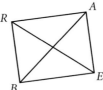

8. Isosceles Trapezoid Conjecture: The base angles of an isosceles trapezoid are congruent.

Given: Isosceles trapezoid *PART* with $\overline{PA} \parallel \overline{TR}$, $\overline{PT} \cong \overline{AR}$, and $\overline{TZ}$ constructed parallel to $\overline{RA}$

Show: $\angle TPA \cong \angle RAP$

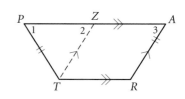

9. Isosceles Trapezoid Diagonals Conjecture: The diagonals of an isosceles trapezoid are congruent.

Given: Isosceles trapezoid *GTHR* with $\overline{GR} \cong \overline{TH}$ and diagonals $\overline{GH}$ and $\overline{TR}$

Show: $\overline{GH} \cong \overline{TR}$

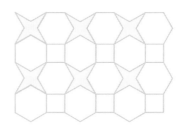

Review

10. Find the measure of the acute angles in the 4-pointed star in the Islamic tiling shown at right. The polygons are squares and regular hexagons. Find the measure of the acute angles in the 6-pointed star in the Islamic tiling on the far right. The 6-pointed star design is created by arranging six squares. Are the angles in both stars the same? ⓗ

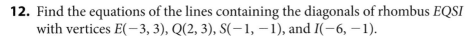

11. A contractor tacked one end of a string to each vertical edge of a window. He then handed a protractor to his apprentice and said, "Here, find out if the vertical edges are parallel." What should the apprentice do? Help him.

12. Find the equations of the lines containing the diagonals of rhombus *EQSI* with vertices $E(-3, 3)$, $Q(2, 3)$, $S(-1, -1)$, and $I(-6, -1)$.

13. The 3-by-9-by-12-inch clear plastic sealed container shown is resting on its smallest face. It is partially filled with a liquid to a height of 8 inches. Sketch the container resting on its middle-sized face. What will be the height of the liquid in the container in this position? ⓗ

14. Given quadrilateral *ABCD* with vertices: $A(-6, -1)$, $B(-2, 3)$, $C(-5, 6)$, $D(-7, 2)$ and quadrilateral *EFGH* with vertices: $E(3, -5)$, $F(7, -9)$, $G(8, -6)$, $H(6, -2)$.

   a. Reflect quadrilateral *ABCD* across the *y*-axis to create image $A'B'C'D'$.

   b. Translate quadrilateral *EFGH* by the translation vector $<-1, 8>$ to create image $E'F'G'H'$.

   c. Are quadrilaterals *ABCD* and *EFGH* congruent?

   d. If congruent, what is the statement of congruence (quadrilateral *ABCD* ≅ quadrilateral ????)?

   e. If congruent, what is the single transformation rule that takes one quadrilateral onto the other?

   f. If they are not congruent explain why not.

15. A treasure chest is buried on Castaway Island. The treasure map with a Cartesian grid on it hints that the buried treasure is located at a fourth vertex of the parallelogram having three of its vertices at $(-1, 4)$, $(1, 1)$, and $(3, 5)$. Pirate captain Shorty Jackson sends her first mate Fernando to dig at the location $(1, 8)$ on the map, but the treasure is not there. Why didn't they find the buried treasure? Where would you dig? Defend your decision.

Properties of Midsegments

As you learned in Chapter 3, the segment connecting the midpoints of two sides of a triangle is a midsegment of the triangle. The segment connecting the midpoints of the two nonparallel sides of a trapezoid is also called the midsegment of the trapezoid.

In this lesson you will discover special properties of midsegments.

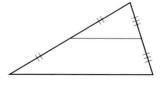

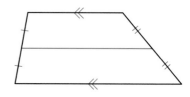

 INVESTIGATION 1

YOU WILL NEED

- patty paper
- a straightedge

Triangle Midsegment Properties

In this investigation you will discover two properties of triangle midsegments. Each person in your group can investigate a different triangle.

   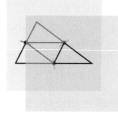   

Step 1   Step 2   Step 3

Step 1 Draw a triangle on a piece of patty paper. Pinch the patty paper to locate midpoints of the sides. Draw the midsegments. You should now have four small triangles.

Step 2 Place a second piece of patty paper over the first and copy one of the four triangles.

Step 3 Compare all four triangles by sliding the copy of one small triangle over the other three triangles. Compare your results with the results of your group. Copy and complete the conjecture.

Three Midsegments Conjecture	C-50

The three midsegments of a triangle divide it into ? .

Step 4 Mark all the congruent angles on the original patty paper. If you find it too cluttered, redraw the original triangle on regular paper with just one midsegment, as in the diagram at right, and then mark all the congruent angles. Using the Corresponding Angles Conjecture or its converse, what conclusions can you make about a midsegment and the large triangle's third side?

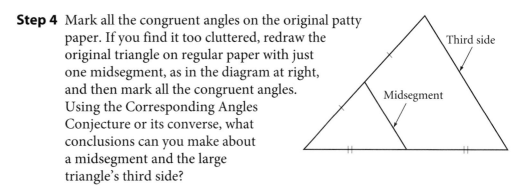

Step 5 Compare the length of the midsegment to the large triangle's third side. How do they relate? Copy and complete the conjecture.

Triangle Midsegment Conjecture `C-51`

A midsegment of a triangle is _?_ to the third side and _?_ the length of _?_.

In the next investigation you will discover two properties of the midsegment of a trapezoid.

 INVESTIGATION 2

YOU WILL NEED
• patty paper
• a straightedge

Trapezoid Midsegment Properties

Each person in your group can investigate a different trapezoid. Make sure you draw the two bases perfectly parallel.

Step 1   Step 2   Step 3

Step 1 Draw a small trapezoid on the left side of a piece of patty paper. Pinch the paper to locate the midpoints of the nonparallel sides. Draw the midsegment.

Step 2 Label the angles as shown. Place a second piece of patty paper over the first and copy the trapezoid and its midsegment.

Step 3 Compare the trapezoid's base angles with the corresponding angles at the midsegment by sliding the copy up over the original.

Step 4 Are the corresponding angles congruent? What can you conclude about the midsegment and the bases? Compare your results with the results of other students.

The midsegment of a triangle is half the length of the third side. How does the length of the midsegment of a trapezoid compare to the lengths of the two bases? Let's investigate.

Step 5 On the original trapezoid, extend the longer base to the right by at least the length of the shorter base.

Step 6 Slide the second patty paper under the first. Show the sum of the lengths of the two bases by marking a point on the extension of the longer base.

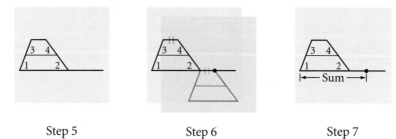

Step 5   Step 6   Step 7

Step 7 How many times does the midsegment fit onto the segment representing the sum of the lengths of the two bases? What do you notice about the length of the midsegment and the sum of the lengths of the two bases?

Step 8 Combine your conclusions from Steps 4 and 7 and complete this conjecture.

Trapezoid Midsegment Conjecture	C-52

The midsegment of a trapezoid is _?_ to the bases and is equal in length to _?_ .

What happens if one base of the trapezoid shrinks to a point? Then the trapezoid collapses into a triangle, the midsegment of the trapezoid becomes a midsegment of the triangle, and the Trapezoid Midsegment Conjecture becomes the Triangle Midsegment Conjecture. Do both of your midsegment conjectures work for the last figure?

 DEVELOPING PROOF

The first investigation may have convinced you that the Triangle Midsegment Conjecture is true but what properties have we proven earlier explain why it is true? The series of diagrams below can be used to explain why. With your group members, study these diagrams and explain to each other how they can be used to prove the Triangle Midsegment Conjecture.

We wish to prove: *If $\overline{DE}$ is a midsegment in $\triangle ABC$, then $\overline{DE} \parallel \overline{AB}$ and $DE = \left(\frac{1}{2}\right)AB$.*

We start with $\triangle ABC$ and segment $\overline{DE}$ a midsegment. We then construct an auxiliary line $\overleftrightarrow{DE}$ and find a point F on line $\overleftrightarrow{DE}$ so that $\overline{DE} \cong \overline{EF}$. Then we construct segment $\overline{BF}$.

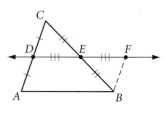

Thus $\triangle DEC \cong \triangle FEB$ (Why?)

If $\triangle DEC \cong \triangle FEB$ then $\overline{DC} \cong \overline{BF}$. (Why?)
Thus $\overline{DA} \cong \overline{BF}$. (Why?)

Likewise, $\angle DCE \cong \angle FBE$. (Why?)
Thus $\overline{DA} \parallel \overline{BF}$. (Why?)

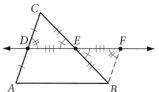

If $\overline{DA} \cong \overline{BF}$ and $\overline{DA} \parallel \overline{BF}$ then $ABFD$ is a parallelogram. (Why?)

If $ABFD$ is a parallelogram then midsegment $\overline{DE} \parallel \overline{AB}$. (Why?)

If $ABFD$ is a parallelogram then $\overline{AB} = \overline{DF}$. (Why?)

But, $DF = DE + EF$ and $DE = EF$. (Why?)

Therefore, $AB = DE + EF$ and thus $AB = 2DE$ or $DE = \left(\frac{1}{2}\right)AB$.

YOU WILL NEED

Geometry software
for Exercises **14** and **15**

Construction tools
for Exercises **11** and **22**

5.7 Exercises

1. How many midsegments does a triangle have? A trapezoid?

2. What is the perimeter of $\triangle TOP$? ⓗ

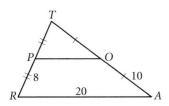

3. $x = $?
   $y = $?

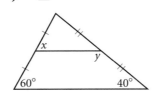

4. $z = $? ⓗ

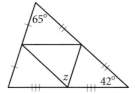

5. What is the perimeter of $\triangle TEN$?

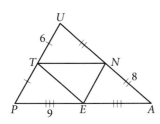

6. $m = $?
   $n = $?
   $p = $?

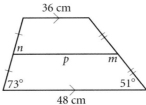

7. $q = $?

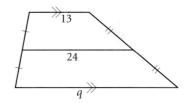

8. **DEVELOPING PROOF** Copy and complete the flowchart to show that $\overline{LN} \parallel \overline{RD}$.

   Given: Midsegment $\overline{LN}$ in $\triangle FOA$
   Midsegment $\overline{RD}$ in $\triangle IOA$

   Show: $\overline{LN} \parallel \overline{RD}$

   Flowchart Proof

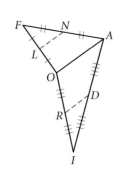

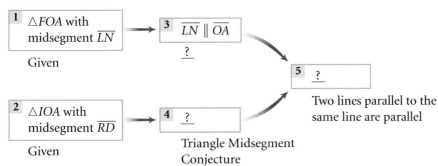

1. $\triangle FOA$ with midsegment $\overline{LN}$

   Given

3. $\overline{LN} \parallel \overline{OA}$

   ?

2. $\triangle IOA$ with midsegment $\overline{RD}$

   Given

4. ?

   Triangle Midsegment Conjecture

5. ?

   Two lines parallel to the same line are parallel

9. DEVELOPING PROOF Find the coordinates of midpoints E and Z. Show that the slope of the line containing midsegment $\overline{EZ}$ is equal to the slope of the line containing $\overline{YT}$.

10. DEVELOPING PROOF Find the coordinates of midpoints D and Z. Show that the slope of the midsegment is the same as the slope of both $\overline{TR}$ and $\overline{AP}$.

11. When you connected the midpoints of the three sides of a triangle in Investigation 1, you created four congruent triangles. Draw a quadrilateral on patty paper and pinch the paper to locate the midpoints of the four sides. Connect the midpoints to form a quadrilateral. What special type of quadrilateral do you get when you connect the midpoints? Use the Triangle Midsegment Conjecture to explain your answer. Ⓗ

12. Deep in a tropical rain forest, archaeologist Ertha Diggs and her assistant researchers have uncovered a square-based truncated pyramid (a square pyramid with the top part removed). The four lateral faces are isosceles trapezoids. A line of darker mortar runs along the midsegment of each lateral face. Ertha and her co-workers make some measurements and find that one of these midsegments measures 41 meters, and each bottom base measures 52 meters. Now that they have this information, Ertha and her team can calculate the length of the top base without having to climb up and measure it. Can you? What is the length of the top edge? How do you know?

13. Ladie and Casey pride themselves on their estimation skills and take turns estimating distances. Casey claims that two large redwood trees visible from where they are sitting are 180 feet apart, and Ladie says they are 275 feet apart.

The problem is, they can't measure the distance to see whose estimate is better, because their cabin is located between the trees. All of a sudden, Ladie recalls her geometry: "Oh yeah, the Triangle Midsegment Conjecture!" She collects a tape measure, a hammer, and some wooden stakes. What is she going to do?

14. DEVELOPING PROOF The midsegment $\overline{MN}$ of $\triangle ABC$ appears to bisect the altitude $\overline{CD}$. Is this true for all triangles? Investigate with patty paper or geometry software. Either find a counterexample or prove it is always true. ⓗ

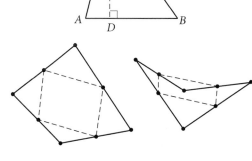

15. Use geometry software to construct a quadrilateral. Construct the midpoints of the four sides. Connect the midpoints to form a new quadrilateral. Drag a vertex or a side and observe what happens. What special type of quadrilateral do you get when you connect the midpoints? Is this still true when the quadrilateral is concave? Use the Triangle Midsegment Conjecture to prove it. ⓗ

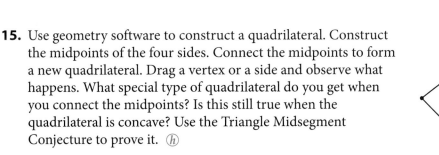

16. You are given the midpoints of the three sides of a triangle. How do you find the vertices of the triangle? ⓗ

Review

17. The 40-by-60-by-80 cm sealed rectangular container shown at right is resting on its largest face. It is filled with a liquid to a height of 30 cm. Sketch the container resting on its smallest face. Show the height of the liquid in this new position. Explain your method.

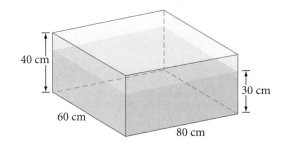

18. DEVELOPING PROOF Write the converse of this statement: If exactly one diagonal bisects a pair of opposite angles of a quadrilateral, then the quadrilateral is a kite. Is the converse true? Is the original statement true? If either statement is not true, sketch a counterexample and explain why it is not true.

19. DEVELOPING PROOF Trace the figure below. Calculate the measure of each lettered angle. Explain how you determined the measures h and k.

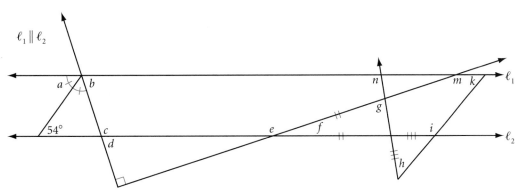

20. *CART* is an isosceles trapezoid. What are the coordinates of point *T*?

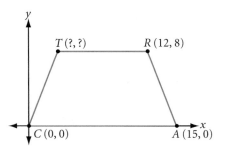

21. *HRSE* is a kite. What are the coordinates of point *R*?

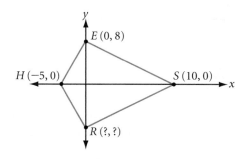

22. Use the kite properties you discovered in Lesson 5.3 to construct kite *FRNK* given diagonals $\overline{RK}$ and $\overline{FN}$ and side $\overline{NK}$. Is there only one solution?

PERFORMANCE TASK

In this lesson you discovered that you can use the parallel edges of a straightedge (let's call it the **D**ouble **E**dge **S**traight **E**dge, or **DESE**, tool) to *construct* a rhombus. The term *construct* is in italics because we originally defined construct to be what you can create with just compass and straightedge. To construct with the double-edged straightedge will mean what you can create using just the parallel edges of your ruler or straightedge. In this lesson you also discovered two important properties of a rhombus:

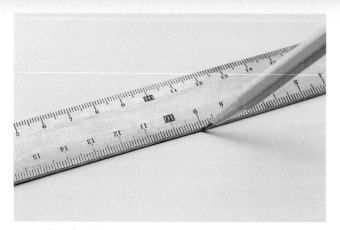

*   *The diagonals of a rhombus are perpendicular bisectors of each other.*

*   *The diagonals of a rhombus bisect the angles of the rhombus.*

In this performance task you are going to use a pencil and the DESE tool to *construct* two very important geometric constructions without the compass! You may not fold the paper, use a compass, or use any marks on the straightedge. You cannot use the lengths of the edges or the right angles of the straightedge: only the two parallel edges.

DESE construction #1: Draw an angle on your paper. Use your DESE tool to *construct* the bisector of the angle.

DESE construction #2: Draw a segment on your paper. Use your DESE tool to *construct* the perpendicular bisector of the segment.

In this chapter you extended your knowledge of triangles to other polygons. You discovered the interior and exterior angle sums for all polygons. You investigated the midsegments of triangles and trapezoids and the properties of parallelograms. You learned what distinguishes various quadrilaterals and what properties apply to each class of quadrilaterals.

Along the way you practiced proving conjectures with flowcharts and paragraph proofs. Be sure you've added the new conjectures to your list. Include diagrams for clarity.

How has your knowledge of triangles helped you make discoveries about other polygons?

Exercises

YOU WILL NEED

Construction tools for Exercises **20–24**

1. True-False

__ **a.** The ordered pairs (15, −10), (5, 10), (−15, 20), and (−5, 0) are the vertices of a rhombus.

__ **b.** The base angles of an isosceles trapezoid are sometimes 45°.

__ **c.** SAA is a congruence shortcut for quadrilaterals.

__ **d.** The midsegment of a trapezoid is perpendicular to both non-parallel sides of the trapezoid.

__ **e.** There are more false statements than true statements in a through e.

2. How do you find the measure of one exterior angle of a regular polygon?

3. How can you find the number of sides of an equiangular polygon by measuring one of its interior angles? By measuring one of its exterior angles?

4. How do you construct a rhombus by using only a ruler or double-edged straightedge?

5. How do you bisect an angle by using only a ruler or double-edged straightedge?

6. How can you use the converse of the Rectangle Diagonals Conjecture to determine if the corners of a room are right angles?

7. How can you use the Triangle Midsegment Conjecture to find a distance between two points that you can't measure directly?

8. Find x and y.

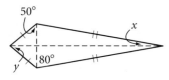

9. The perimeter is 266 cm. Find x.

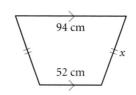

10. Find a and c.

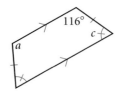

11. $\overline{MS}$ is a midsegment. Find the perimeter of *MOIS*.

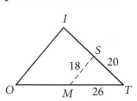

12. Find x.

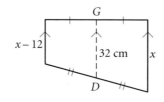

13. Find y and z.

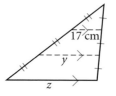

14. Copy and complete the table below by placing a yes (to mean always) or a no (to mean not always) in each empty space. Use what you know about special quadrilaterals.

	Kite	Isosceles Trapezoid	Parallelogram	Rhombus	Rectangle	Square
Opposite sides are parallel						
Opposite sides are congruent						
Opposite angles are congruent						
Diagonals bisect each other						
Diagonals are perpendicular						
Diagonals are congruent				No		
Exactly one line of symmetry	Yes					
Exactly two lines of symmetry						

15. A 2-inch-wide frame is to be built around the regular decagonal window shown. At what angles a and b should the corners of each piece be cut?

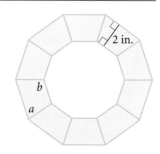

16. DEVELOPING PROOF Find the measure of each lettered angle. Explain how you determined measures *e*, *f*, and *g*.

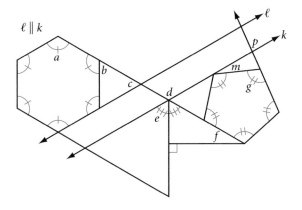

$\ell \parallel k$

17. Archaeologist Ertha Diggs has uncovered one stone that appears to be a voussoir from a semicircular stone arch. On each isosceles trapezoidal face, the obtuse angles measure 96°. Assuming all the stones were identical, how many stones were in the original arch?

18. Kite *ABCD* has vertices *A*(−3, −2), *B*(2, −2), *C*(3, 1), and *D*(0, 2). Find the coordinates of the point of intersection of the diagonals.

19. When you swing left to right on a swing, the seat stays parallel to the ground. Explain why.

20. The tiling of congruent pentagons shown below is created from a honeycomb grid (tiling of regular hexagons). What is the measure of each lettered angle? Re-create the design with compass and straightedge.

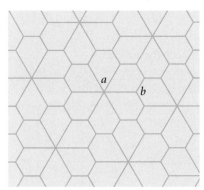

In Exercises 21–24, use the given segments and angles to construct each figure. Use either patty paper or a compass and a straightedge. The small letter above each segment represents the length of the segment.

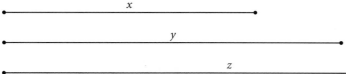

21. Construct rhombus *SQRE* with *SR* = *y* and *QE* = *x*.

22. Construct kite *FLYR* given ∠*F*, ∠*L*, and *FL* = *x*.

23. Given bases $\overline{LP}$ with length *z* and $\overline{EN}$ with length *y*, nonparallel side $\overline{LN}$ with length *x*, and ∠*L*, construct trapezoid *PENL*.

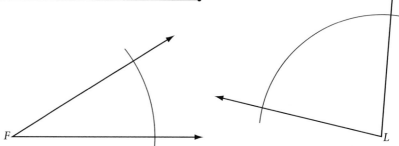

24. Given ∠*F*, *FR* = *x*, and *YD* = *z*, construct two trapezoids *FRYD* that are not congruent to each other.

25. Three regular polygons meet at point *B*. Only four sides of the third polygon are visible. How many sides does this polygon have?

26. Find *x*.

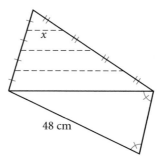

27. DEVELOPING PROOF Prove the conjecture: The diagonals of a rhombus bisect the angles.

Given: Rhombus *DENI*, with diagonal $\overline{DN}$

Show: Diagonal $\overline{DN}$ bisects ∠*D* and ∠*N*

Flowchart Proof

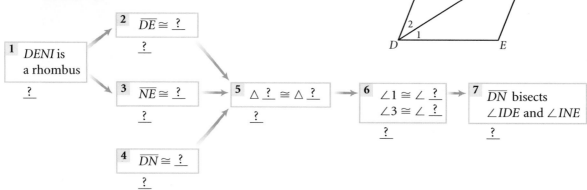

28. DEVELOPING PROOF Use a labeled diagram to prove the Parallelogram Opposite Sides Conjecture: The opposite sides of a parallelogram are congruent.

29. DEVELOPING PROOF The midsegment *MN* of trapezoid *ABCD* appears to bisect the altitude *CE*. Is this true for all trapezoids? Investigate with either patty paper or dynamic geometry software. Either find a counterexample or prove it is always true.

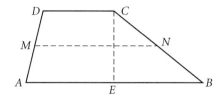

 TAKE ANOTHER LOOK

1. What is the sum of the measures of the reflex angles of a:

    a) convex quadrilateral?
        Prove your conjecture.

    b) convex pentagon?
        Prove your conjecture

    c) convex *n*-gon?
        Prove your conjecture

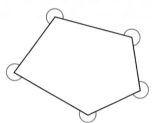

2. You discovered in Lesson 5.1 that the sum of the measures of the *n* interior angles of a convex *n*-gon is $(n - 2)180°$. What if the polygon is concave, with one "dent"? What is the sum? Investigate. Explain how you know.

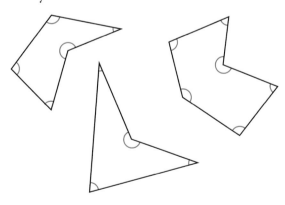

The small, precise polygons in the painting **Sunflowers** by Vincent van Gogh is a decorative colorful small mosaic

3. What if the polygon has more than one dent? Now what is the sum? Investigate. Make a conjecture and prove it.

4. You discovered earlier the formula for the sum of the measures of the *n* reflex angles of a convex *n*-gon. What if the polygon is concave, with one "dent"? Now what is the formula? What if the polygon has more than one dent? Investigate. Make a conjecture and prove it.

5. You discovered earlier that the sum of the measures of one set of exterior angles of a convex *n*-gon is 360°. What if the polygon is concave, with one "dent"? Is the sum still 360°? It turns out this will depend on how we define an exterior angle.

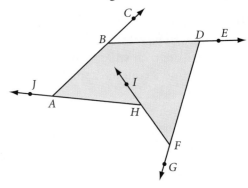

a) Consider the concave pentagon *ABDFH* with one dent at angle *H* shown to the right. If we define the measure of the exterior angle as *measured on the exterior of the polygon* then the exterior angle at the dent is the obtuse ∠*FHA*. You can use this definition to determine the sum of the measures of the angles of a concave polygon (with one dent). Investigate, make a conjecture and prove your conjecture.

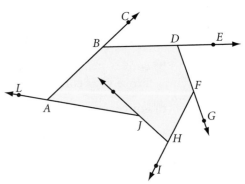

b) Consider the example of the concave hexagon *ABDFHJ* with one dent at angle *J* shown to the right. If we define the measure of the exterior angle *as measured from a side extended to the next side* then all the angles are measured clockwise except one, angle *J*. However when measuring angle *J*, the exterior angle at the dent, we are measuring counter-clockwise. If we consider some angles measured positive (measured clockwise) and other angles measured negative (measured counter clockwise) then you can determine the sum of the measures of the angles of a concave polygon (with one dent). Investigate, make a conjecture, and prove your conjecture.

6. Are the kite conjectures (C-34, C-35, C-36, and C-37) also true for darts (concave kites)? Choose your tools and investigate.

7. In Chapter 3 you discovered that the circumcenter of a right triangle is on the midpoint of the hypotenuse. This is equivalent to saying that the midpoint of the hypotenuse of a right triangle is equally distant to the three vertice of the triangle. In this chapter you discovered and proved that the diagonals of a rectangle are congruent and bisect each other. You can use those properties to now prove that the midpoint of the hypotenuse is equally distant to the three vertices.

Given: rectangle *ABCD* with diagonals *AC* and *BD* intersecting at *M*.

Show: *AM* = *BM* = *DM*. Or the midpoint *P* on the hypotenuse *BD* of right △*ABD* is equally distant to vertices *A, B,* and *D*.

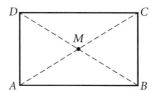

Applications of Transformations

"I believe that producing pictures, as I do, is almost solely a question of wanting so very much to do it well."

M. C. ESCHER

OBJECTIVES

In this chapter you will

- apply some basic properties of transformations and symmetry
- learn more about symmetry in art and nature
- use transformations to create tessellations
- confirm triangle congruence by transformations
- use coordinate geometry to describe composition of transformations

Symmetry and Transformations

"Symmetry is one idea by which man through the ages has tried to comprehend and create order, beauty, and perfection."

HERMANN WEYL

Symmetry is found in all cultures. It is ubiquitous in the decorative arts and historically the cornerstone of architectural design. Symmetry can be found in music, poetry, and dance. Symmetry is even essential to the structure of the DNA molecule.

Japanese Unit Origami Box

Navajo Rug Design

Pacific Northwest Art

If a figure can be reflected over a line in such a way that the resulting image coincides with the original, then the figure has **reflectional symmetry**. The reflection line is called the **line of symmetry**. The rug shown above has two lines of symmetry, thus two-fold reflectional symmetry.

If a figure can be rotated about a point in such a way that its rotated image coincides with the original figure before turning a full 360°, then the figure has **rotational symmetry**. Of course, every image is identical to the original figure after a rotation of any multiple of 360°. However, we don't call a figure symmetric if this is the only kind of symmetry it has. You can trace a figure to

test it for rotational symmetry. Place the copy exactly over the original, put your pen or pencil point on the center to hold it down, and rotate the copy. Count the number of times the copy and the original coincide until the copy is back in its original position. If an image takes 4 rotations to return to the original, this is known as four-fold rotational symmetry. Two-fold rotational symmetry is also called **point symmetry**.

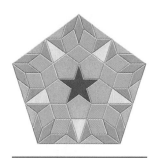

This tile pattern has both 5-fold rotational symmetry and 5-fold reflectional symmetry.

Some polygons have no symmetry or only one kind of symmetry.

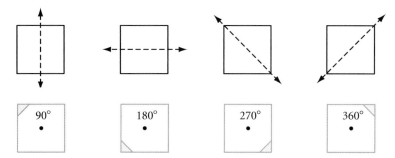

Polygon with no reflectional or rotational symmetries

Isosceles Triangle
One line of reflectional symmetry

Parallelogram
180° rotational symmetry

Regular polygons, however, are symmetric in many ways. A square, for example, has 4-fold reflectional symmetry and 4-fold rotational symmetry.

| 90° • | 180° • | 270° • | 360° • |

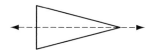 

INVESTIGATION

Symmetries of Regular Polygons

YOU WILL NEED
- patty paper
- mirror (optional)

Investigate the number of symmetries in regular polygons. Use the table to organize your information. To find the number of rotational symmetries, you may wish to trace each regular polygon onto patty paper and rotate it. If necessary, use a mirror to locate the lines of symmetry for each of the regular polygons. Then copy and complete the conjecture.

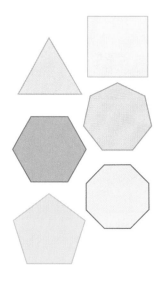

Number of sides of regular polygon	3	4	5	6	7	8	...	n
Number of reflectional symmetries		4					...	
Number of rotational symmetries ($\leq 360°$)		4					...	

Reflectional Symmetry of Regular Polygons Conjecture   `C-53`

A regular polygon of n sides has _?_ reflectional symmetries.

Rotational Symmetry of Regular Polygons Conjecture   `C-54`

A regular polygon of n sides has _?_ rotational symmetries.

A third type of symmetry is translational symmetry. We see translational symmetry in the arrangement of columns, or the slats in a picket fence, or the bricks on a wall.

Translational symmetry is the result of sliding a design or motif repeatedly by the same translation vector. If the image is translated by some multiple of the translation vector the image coincides with the original.

Yet another type of symmetry is glide-reflection symmetry. Combining a translation with a reflection gives a special two-step transformation called a **glide reflection**. A sequence of footsteps is a common example of a glide reflection. You will explore a few other examples of glide reflections in the exercises.

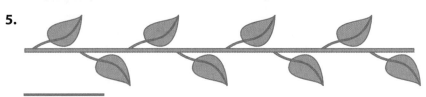

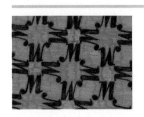

6.1 Exercises

In Exercises 1–5, identify the type (or types) of symmetry in each design.

1.

Butterfly

2.

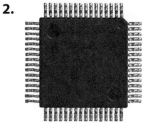

Computer chip

3.

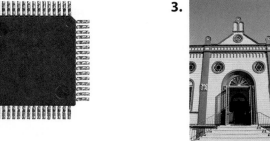

Temple Beth Israel

4.

Parking meters

5.

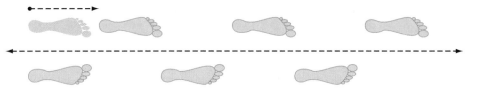

Branch of leaves

6. The diameter of this ceramic pot by a contemporary Native American artist is roughly 30 cm in diameter at its widest. The artist produced this translational symmetry design 28 times about the circumference. How much space did the artist need for each repeating unit?

7. The Maori culture brought *Kowhaiwhai* patterns with them from Polynesia to their new home in New Zealand. These patterns were painted on the rafters of the meeting houses or *Wharenui*. What type of transformation took the design in the triangle on the far left to the design in the second triangle and then to the design in the third triangle? Trace one of the triangles of this Maori wood rafter design onto patty paper. What would the next panel look like?

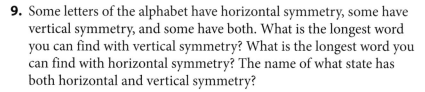

8. San Ildefonso Pueblos in New Mexico are known the world over for their beautiful pottery designs. Their designs exhibit a number of different types of transformations. What type of transformation took the design in the rectangle on the far left to the design in the second rectangle and then to the design in the third rectangle? Trace this San Ildefonso Pueblo design in one of the rectangles onto patty paper. What would the next panel look like?

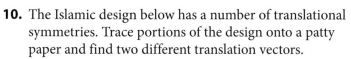

9. Some letters of the alphabet have horizontal symmetry, some have vertical symmetry, and some have both. What is the longest word you can find with vertical symmetry? What is the longest word you can find with horizontal symmetry? The name of what state has both horizontal and vertical symmetry?

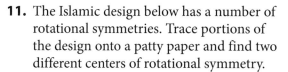

10. The Islamic design below has a number of translational symmetries. Trace portions of the design onto a patty paper and find two different translation vectors.

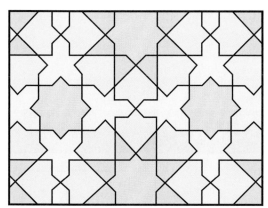

11. The Islamic design below has a number of rotational symmetries. Trace portions of the design onto a patty paper and find two different centers of rotational symmetry.

12. Which of the following is/are not possible:

   a. A trapezoid with exactly one line of symmetry.

   b. A rectangle with exactly one line of symmetry.

   c. A hexagon with exactly one line of symmetry.

   d. A hexagon with exactly two lines of symmetry.

   e. A hexagon with exactly three lines of symmetry.

13. Copy the two figures below onto graph paper. Each figure is the glide-reflected image of the other. Continue the pattern with two more glide-reflected figures. Identify the line of reflection.

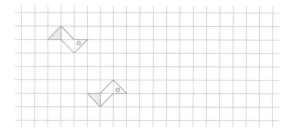

14. Words like MOM, WOW, TOOT, and OTTO all have a vertical line of symmetry when you write them in capital letters. Find another word that has a vertical line of symmetry.

Review

15. What you see in a mirror is actually light from an object bouncing off the mirror and traveling to your eye. The object's image seen in the mirror appears as if it were reflected behind the mirror, as far behind the mirror as the object is in front of the mirror. In the diagram at right, assume that the mirror is perpendicular to the ground. Use the fact that the light's incoming angle, $\angle 1$, is congruent to its outgoing angle, $\angle 2$, to explain why $BC = CE$.

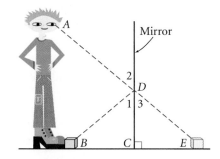

16. Which pairs of triangles are congruent? If congruent, write the statement of congruence and give the congruence shortcut that proves they are congruent.

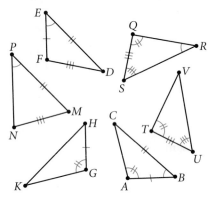

17. Copy the figure. Calculate the measure of each lettered angle. Explain how you determined measures h and s.

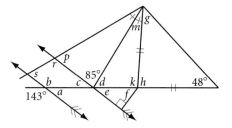

LESSON 6.2

Compositions of Reflections

In this lesson you will use patty paper to investigate what happens when a figure is reflected with two consecutive reflections. You will reflect a figure across one line of reflection and then reflect the image across a second line of reflection.

INVESTIGATION 1

Reflections across Two Parallel Lines

First, consider the case of parallel lines of reflection.

YOU WILL NEED
- patty paper
- a compass

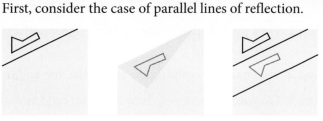

Step 1   Step 2   Step 3

"Why it's a looking-glass book, of course! And, if I hold it up to the glass, the words will all go the right way again"

ALICE IN *THROUGH THE LOOKING-GLASS* BY LEWIS CARROLL

Step 1 On a piece of patty paper, draw a figure and a line of reflection that does not intersect it.

Step 2 Fold to reflect your figure across the line of reflection and trace the image.

Step 3 On your patty paper, draw a second reflection line parallel to the first so that the image is between the two parallel reflection lines.

Step 4 Fold to reflect the image across the second line of reflection. Turn the patty paper over and trace the second image.

Step 4

Step 5 How does the second image compare to the original figure? Name the single transformation that transforms the original to the second image.

Step 6 Use a compass or patty paper to measure the distance between a point in the original figure and its second image point. Compare this distance with the distance between the parallel lines. How do they compare?

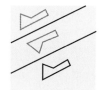

Step 5

Step 7 Compare your findings with those of others in your group and state your conjecture.

Reflections across Parallel Lines Conjecture   `C-55`

A composition of two reflections across two parallel lines is equivalent to a single <u>?</u>. In addition, the distance from any point to its second image under the two reflections is <u>?</u> the distance between the parallel lines.

Is a composition of reflections always equivalent to a single translation? If you reverse the process, start with the second or final image and reflect it across the second line, then reflect that image across the first line, do you get back to the original figure? If you reflect a figure across two intersecting lines rather than parallel lines, does this also result in a single transformation? Let's take a look.

INVESTIGATION 2

YOU WILL NEED
- patty paper
- a protractor

Reflections across Two Intersecting Lines

Next, you will explore the case of intersecting lines of reflection.

Step 1   Step 2   Step 3

Step 1 On a piece of patty paper, draw a figure and a reflection line that does not intersect it.

Step 2 Fold to reflect your figure across the line and trace the image.

Step 3 On your patty paper, draw a second reflection line intersecting the first so that the image is in an acute angle between the two intersecting reflection lines.

Step 4 Fold to reflect the first image across the second line and trace the second image.

Step 4

Step 5   Step 6   Step 7

Step 5 Draw two rays that start at the point of intersection of the two intersecting lines and that pass through corresponding points on the original figure and its second image.

Step 6 How does the second image compare to the original figure? Name the single transformation from the original to the second image.

Step 7 With a protractor or patty paper, compare the angle created in Step 5 with the acute angle formed by the intersecting reflection lines. How do the angles compare?

Step 8 Compare findings in your group and state your next conjecture.

Reflections across Intersecting Lines Conjecture	**C-56**

A composition of two reflections across a pair of intersecting lines is equivalent to a single _?_. The angle of _?_ is _?_ the acute angle between the pair of intersecting reflection lines.

You have just discovered that translations can be performed by a composition of reflections across parallel lines and rotations can be done by a composition of two reflections across intersecting lines. Thus all three isometries can be performed by some combination of reflections alone!

6.2 Exercises

YOU WILL NEED

Construction tools for Exercises **5–8**

1. Lines *m* and *n* are parallel and 10 cm apart.

a. Point *A* is 6 cm from line *m* and 16 cm from line *n*. Point *A* is reflected across line *m*, and then its image, *A′*, is reflected across line *n* to create a second image, point *A″*. How far is point *A* from point *A″*?

b. What if *A* is reflected across *n*, and then its image is reflected across *m*? Find the new image and distance from *A*.

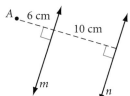

2. Lines *m* and *n* are parallel. △*ABC* is reflected across line *m* then its image, △*A′B′C′*, is reflected across the line *n* to create △*A″B″C″*. If *CC″* is 36 inches, how far apart are the parallel lines *m* and *n*? Explain how you found your answer.

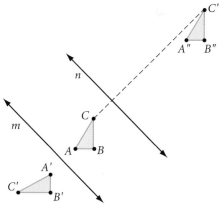

3. Two lines *m* and *n* intersect at point *P*, forming a 40° angle.

a. You reflect point *B* across line *m*, then reflect the image of *B* across line *n*. What angle of rotation about point *P* rotates the second image of point *B* back to its original position?

b. What if you reflect *B* first across *n*, and then reflect the image of *B* across *m*? Find the angle of rotation that rotates the second image back to the original position. What do you notice about the order of the reflections?

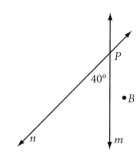

4. $\triangle ABC$ is reflected over $\overrightarrow{EF}$, and then $\triangle A'B'C'$, the image of $\triangle ABC$, is reflected over $\overrightarrow{ED}$ creating the second image $\triangle A''B''C''$. If the measure of the angle of rotation, $\angle BEB''$, is 152°, what is the measure of the angle between the intersecting reflection lines, $\angle DEF$? Explain your reasoning.

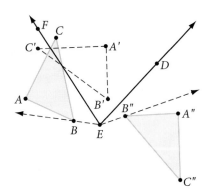

5. Copy the figure and $\angle PAL$ onto patty paper. If you reflect the figure across $\overrightarrow{AP}$, and then reflect the image across $\overrightarrow{AL}$, what is the measure of the equivalent rotation? Explain your answer. Complete the reflections to confirm your solution.

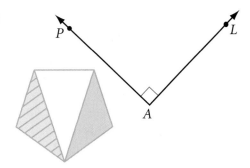

6. If the figure below is reflected across $\overleftrightarrow{PA}$ and then its image is reflected across $\overleftrightarrow{RL}$, predict where the final image will appear. If the distance between the parallel lines is 1.5 cm, what is the length of the equivalent translation vector? Copy the figure and perform the reflections to check your conjecture.

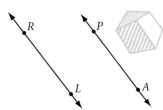

7. Copy the hexagonal figure and its translated image onto patty paper. Find a pair of parallel reflection lines that transform the original onto the image. ⓗ

8. Copy the original figure and its rotated image onto patty paper. Find a pair of intersecting reflection lines that transform the original onto the image.

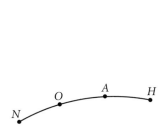

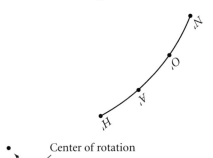

Center of rotation

9. Have you noticed that some letters have both horizontal and vertical symmetries? Have you also noticed that all the letters that have both horizontal and vertical symmetries also have point symmetry? Is this a coincidence? Use what you have learned about transformations to explain why.

Review

In Exercises 10 and 11, sketch the next two figures.

10.

11.

12. If you draw a figure on an uninflated balloon and then blow up the balloon, the figure will undergo a nonrigid transformation. Give another example of a nonrigid transformation.

13. List two objects in your home that have rotational symmetry, but not reflectional symmetry. List two objects in your classroom that have reflectional symmetry, but not rotational symmetry.

14. Is it possible for a triangle to have exactly one line of symmetry? Exactly two? Exactly three? Support your answers with sketches.

15. Draw two points onto a piece of paper and connect them with a curve that is point symmetric. Ⓗ

16. Preston Singletary is a contemporary glass artist with Northwest Native American Heritage (Tlingit). His vessel, *Peach Tlingit Glass Basket with Navy Rim*, is approximately 20 cm in diameter. After the glass vessel is blown, Preston and his team outline the motif (shown in the detail) and then they sandblast the design into the surface. If they plan to repeat the motif shown ten times, what is the space they need for each repeating unit? (Measurements and the number of repeating designs are approximations.)

17. **TRUE OR FALSE?** If two rectangles have congruent diagonals, the two rectangles are congruent. If true, prove it. If false, sketch a counterexample and explain how your sketch proves the statement false.

18. Given $\triangle ABC$ with vertices: $A(-6, -9)$, $B(6, -3)$, $C(-3, 6)$

   a. Transform $\triangle ABC$ by the rule $(x, y) \rightarrow (\frac{2}{3}x, \frac{2}{3}y)$ to create $\triangle A'B'C'$.

   b. What are the coordinates of the vertices of $\triangle A'B'C'$?

   c. How do the corresponding angles compare?

   d. Are the two triangles congruent?

Composition of Rotations

In this task you are going to look at all the possible compositions of rotations of an equilateral triangle such that the image coincides with the original. Each rotation will be about the center of the triangle. There are three rotational symmetries: 120°, 240°, and 360° (or 0° rotation). An equilateral triangle rotated any multiple of 360° is equivalent to not rotating it at all. This is called the **Identity** rotation.

To keep track of the new positions, the interiors of the triangles are marked as shown to the right. This is the equilateral triangle in its initial position before the first rotation. Copy this triangle onto heavy weight paper and cut it out. Use this cutout triangle to perform the compositions of rotations.

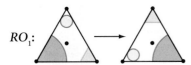

RO_1:

Counterclockwise rotation of 120°

RO_2:

Counterclockwise rotation of 240°

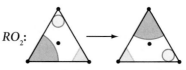

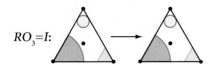

$RO_3 = I$:

Counterclockwise rotation of 360°
The identity rotation is symbolized with an I.

The composition of a 240° counterclockwise rotation followed by a 120° rotation is equivalent to a 360° rotation, or the identity rotation. This is written: $RO_1(RO_2) \rightarrow I$. The first transformation is written to the right in parentheses, and the second transformation is written to the left like a function statement. The composition of the two transformations $RO_2(I)$ would be the Identity rotation followed by the 240° rotation, which is equivalent to what single transformation?

Second rotation

		RO_1 (120°)	RO_2 (240°)	$RO_3 = I$ (360°)
First rotation	RO_1 (120°)	△	△	△
	RO_2 (240°)	*I*	△	△
	$RO_3 = I$ (360°)	△	△	△

Use your cutout equilateral triangle to complete the table of compositions of rotations of the equilateral triangle. Does the order of the rotations make a difference? For example, is $RO_1(RO_2)$ the same as $RO_2(RO_1)$? How many different orientations of the triangle are there in the table? Do any composition of rotations result in a single rotation? If so, identify them. If not, explain why it was not possible.

Composition of Reflections

Let's now continue our exploration and look at the composition of reflections of the equilateral triangle. For this task, RE_1 represents a reflection of the original triangle over the vertical line 1 as shown to the right. Does the order of the reflections make a difference? For example, is $RE_3(RE_2)$ the same as $RE_2(RE_3)$? How many different orientations of the triangle will there be? Will the results be similar to the results you found for rotations? Do any composition of reflections result in a single transformation?

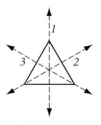

Before your exploration, make conjectures about the questions above. Compare your conjectures with your group and then plan and carry out a method to confirm or reject them.

EXPLORATION

Finding a Minimal Path

In Chapter 1, you used a protractor to find the path of the ball. In this exploration, you'll discover some other properties of reflections that have many applications in science and engineering. They may even help your pool game!

Activity

Step 1 Draw a segment, representing a pool table cushion, near the center of a piece of patty paper. Draw two points, *A* and *B*, on one side of the segment.

Step 2 Imagine you want to hit a ball at point *A* so that it bounces off the cushion and hits another ball at point *B*. Use your protractor and trial and error to find the point *C* on the cushion that you should aim for.

Step 3 Draw $\overline{AC}$ and $\overline{CB}$ to represent the ball's path.

Step 1   Step 2   Step 3

Step 4 Fold your patty paper to draw the reflection of point *B* across the line segment. Label the image point *B′*.

Step 5 Unfold the paper and draw a segment from point *A* to point *B′*. What do you notice? Does point *C* lie on segment $\overline{AB'}$? How does the path from *A* to *B′* compare to the two-part path from *A* to *C* to *B*?

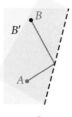
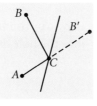

Step 4   Step 5

Step 6 Can you draw any other path from point *A* to the cushion to point *B* that is shorter than *AC* + *CB*? Why or why not? The shortest path from point *A* to the cushion to point *B* is called the minimal path. Copy and complete the conjecture.

> **Minimal Path Conjecture**
>
> If points *A* and *B* are on one side of line ℓ, then the minimal path from point *A* to line ℓ to point *B* is found by ? .

How can this discovery help your pool game? Suppose you need to hit a ball at point *A* into the cushion so that it will bounce off the cushion and pass through point *B*. To what point on the cushion should you aim? Visualize point *B* reflected across the cushion. Then aim directly at the reflected image.

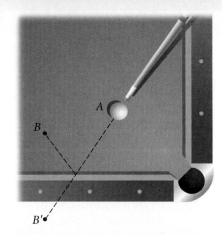

Miniature golf, like pool and billiards involves knowing your geometry, especially reflections. You discovered that on a pool table if you wish to strike a ball after hitting a cushion you visualize the ball reflected across the cushion, then aim for the reflected image. The same applies with miniature golf shots. If you need to bounce the ball off one of the walls to sink it into the cup, you need to visualize the cup being reflected over the wall. Then aim for the reflected image of the hole.

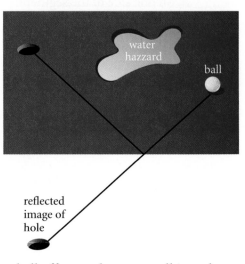

However, sometimes you need to bounce your ball off more than one wall in order to sink your ball on one shot. Let's look at an example.

EXAMPLE

How can you hit the ball at *T* around the corner and into the hole at *H* in one shot?

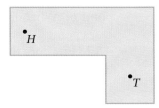

Solution

First, try to get a hole-in-one with a direct shot or with just one bounce off a wall. For one bounce, decide which wall the ball should hit. Visualize the image of the hole across that wall and aim for the reflected hole. There are two possibilities.

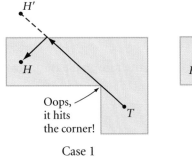

Case 1

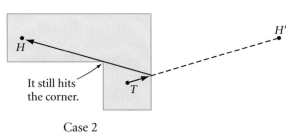

Case 2

In both cases the path is blocked. It looks like you need to try two bounces. Visualize a path from the tee hitting two walls and into the hole.

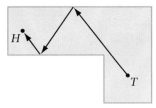

Visualize the path.

Now you can work backward. Which wall will the ball hit last? Reflect the hole across that wall creating image H'.

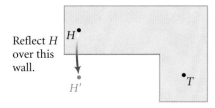

Reflect H over this wall.

Which wall will the ball hit before it approaches the second wall? Reflect the image of the hole H' across that wall creating image H''.

Draw the path from the tee to H'', H', and H. Can you visualize other possible paths with two bounces? Three bounces? What do you suppose is the minimal path from T to H?

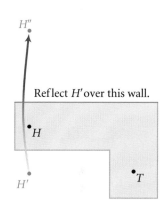

Reflect H' over this wall.

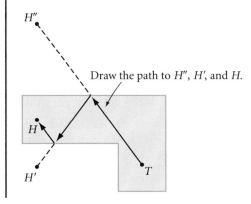

Draw the path to H'', H', and H.

Exercises

1. An 8×12 pool table has been "coordinatized" as shown to the right. If the ball is at $(3, 4)$, what are the coordinates of the point on the top cushion that the ball must hit so that it bounces off the cushion and into the pocket in the middle of the bottom cushion $(6, 0)$?

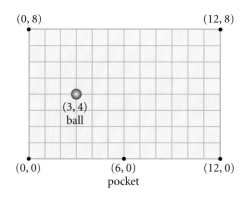

2. A new freeway is being built near the two towns of Perry and Mason. The two towns want to build roads to one junction point on the freeway. (One of the roads will be named Della Street.) Locate the junction point and draw the minimal path from Perry to the freeway to Mason. How do you know this is the shortest path?

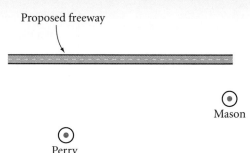

Proposed freeway

Mason

Perry

3. Each week Leona parks her United States Postal Service delivery truck at a different point along Dairy road. She delivers one large package to 2456 Dairy Road, returns to her vehicle, picks up another large package and delivers it to the neighboring farm house at 2460 Dairy Road. Where on Dairy road should she park to minimize her walking each week? (h)

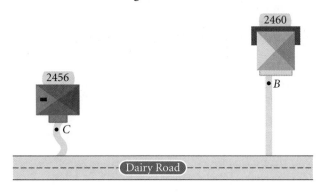

2460

2456

• B

• C

Dairy Road

4. Each morning the route of a rancher takes him from the house at point *A* to the south electrified fence, then over to the east electrified fence, then to the corral at point *B*. Copy the figure onto patty paper and locate the points on the south and east fences that minimize the rancher's route.

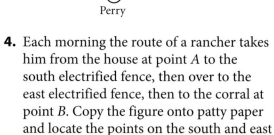

B •

E

•A

S

For Exercises 5 and 6, copy the miniature golf diagram for the two exercises below. Use patty paper to locate the hole-in-one path for each. A hole in one (also known as an ace) is when a player hits the ball from the tee into the cup with one shot.

5. Starting from the tee (point *T*), what point on a wall should a player aim for so that the golf ball bounces off the wall and goes into the hole at *H*?

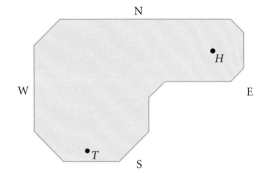

N

H

W

E

T

S

6. Starting from the tee (point *T*), plan a shot so that the golf ball goes into the hole at *H*. Show all your work.

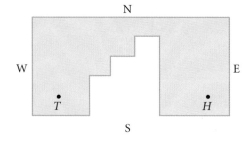

N

W

E

T

H

S

7. Design a miniature golf hole that requires the ball to bounce off at least two walls to get a hole in one. Then show your solution.

Ordered Pair Rules for Compositions of Transformations

In Lesson 6.2 you discovered two very important properties of compositions of reflections. The composition of two reflections across parallel lines is equivalent to a translation, and the composition of two reflections across intersecting lines is equivalent to a rotation. This means the three isometries can all be performed by some combination of reflections. We will use this idea in this lesson.

Parallel bathroom mirrors are the classic examples of reflections created by parallel mirrors.

In earlier coordinate geometry lessons, you reflected polygons across the x- or y-axes or rotated them about the origin. What happens if you reflect a figure across a line that is not an axis? What about rotations about other points besides the origin? In this lesson you will discover ordered pair rules for reflections across lines that are not x- or y-axes, and you will discover ordered pair rules for rotating figures about points that are not the origin.

In Example A you will look at a composition of two reflections across a pair of vertical and horizontal lines. From your discovery in Lesson 6.2, since the two lines are perpendicular, you should expect the resulting image to be a 180° rotation, but a rotation about what point?

EXAMPLE A

Reflect $\triangle ABC$ across the line $x = 2$.

a. What are the coordinates of the vertices of $\triangle A'B'C'$? What is the ordered pair rule $(x, y) \rightarrow (?, ?)$ that would take $\triangle ABC$ onto $\triangle A'B'C'$?

Reflect the image, $\triangle A'B'C'$, across the line $y = -3$ to get the image $\triangle A''B''C''$.

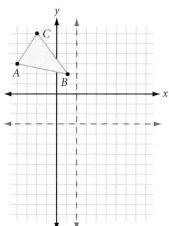

b. What are the coordinates of the vertices of $\triangle A''B''C''$? What is the ordered pair rule $(x, y) \rightarrow (?, ?)$ that would take $\triangle A'B'C'$ onto $\triangle A''B''C''$?

c. What single transformation is equivalent to the composition of these two transformations? What is the single ordered pair rule $(x, y) \rightarrow (?, ?)$ that would take $\triangle ABC$ onto $\triangle A''B''C''$?

Solution

a. Find the image of △*ABC* using the property of reflections that each point and its image point is equally distant from the line of reflection, $x = 2$, to get △*A'B'C'*. The coordinates of the vertices of △*A'B'C'* are *A'*(8, 3), *B'*(3, 2), *C'*(6, 6).

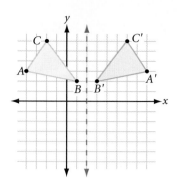

When you reflected across the vertical *y*-axis, the ordered pair rule was $(x, y) \rightarrow (-x, y)$. Notice that when you reflected across the vertical line $x = 2$ the *y*-coordinates are the same but each *x*-coordinate is not just the opposite sign. If we changed the sign of each *x*-coordinate of the vertices of △*ABC*, what else needs to be done?

If the vertices of △*ABC* are *A*(−4, 3), *B*(1, 2), and *C*(−2, 6) then reversing the sign of each *x*-coordinate and adding 4 to each gives you *A'*(8, 3), *B'*(3, 2), and *C'*(6, 6). Thus the ordered pair rule is $(x, y) \rightarrow (-x + 4, y)$.

b. Reflect △*A'B'C'* across the line $y = -3$ to get △*A"B"C"*. The coordinates of the vertices of △*A"B"C"* are *A"*(8, −9), *B"*(3, −8), and *C"*(6, −12).

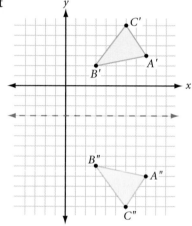

When you reflected across the horizontal *x*-axis, the ordered pair rule was $(x, y) \rightarrow (x, -y)$. Notice that when you reflected across the horizontal line $y = -3$ the *x*-coordinates are the same but each *y*-coordinate is not just the opposite sign. If we changed the sign of each *y*-coordinate of the vertices of △*A'B'C'*, what else needs to be done?

If the vertices of △*A'B'C'* are *A'*(8, 3), *B'*(3, 2), and *C'*(6, 6) then reversing the sign of each *y*-coordinate and adding −6 to each gives you *A"*(8, −9), *B"*(3, −8), and *C"*(6, −12). Thus the ordered pair rule is $(x, y) \rightarrow (x, -y - 6)$.

c. The composition of these two reflections appears to be a rotation of 180° about the point (2, −3) where the two lines of reflection intersect. Check this with patty paper. If the ordered pair rule is $(x, y) \rightarrow (-x + 4, y)$ when reflecting △*ABC* onto △*A'B'C'* and the ordered pair rule is $(x, y) \rightarrow (x, -y - 6)$ when reflecting △*A'B'C'* onto △*A"B"C"* then combining them gives an ordered pair rule: $(x, y) \rightarrow (-x + 4, -y - 6)$. To check, apply this ordered pair rule to the coordinates of the vertices of △*ABC* to see if the rule gives you the coordinates of the vertices of △*A"B"C"*.

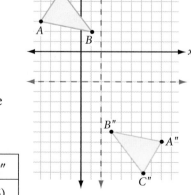

	A & A"	B & B"	C & C"
△*ABC*	(−4, 3)	(1, 2)	(−2, 6)
△*A"B"C"*	(8, −9)	(3, −8)	(6, −12)

In Example B you will look at a composition of two reflections across parallel lines. Since the two lines are parallel, you should expect the resulting image to be a translation. Will the translation distance still be twice the distance between the parallel lines? Is there a connection between the equations of the lines of reflection and the ordered pair rule?

EXAMPLE B

a. Triangle ABC with vertices $A(-4, 3)$, $B(-2, 6)$, and $C(1, 2)$ is reflected across the line $y = 2$. What are the coordinates of the vertices of $\triangle A'B'C'$? What is the ordered pair rule $(x, y) \rightarrow (?, ?)$ that would take $\triangle ABC$ onto $\triangle A'B'C'$?

b. The image, $\triangle A'B'C'$, is reflected across the line $y = -3$ to get the image $\triangle A''B''C''$. What are the coordinates of the vertices of $\triangle A''B''C''$? What is the ordered pair rule $(x, y) \rightarrow (?, ?)$ that would take $\triangle A'B'C'$ onto $\triangle A''B''C''$?

c. What single transformation is equivalent to the composition of these two transformations? What is the single ordered pair rule $(x, y) \rightarrow (?, ?)$ that would take $\triangle ABC$ onto $\triangle A''B''C''$?

Solution

a. Reflect $\triangle ABC$ across the line $y = 2$. The coordinates of the vertices $\triangle A'B'C'$ are $A'(-4, 1)$, $B'(-2, -2)$, and $C'(1, 2)$. Following similar reasoning to Example A, part a, the ordered pair rule is $(x, y) \rightarrow (x, -y + 4)$.

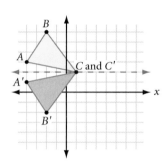

b. Reflect the vertices of $\triangle A'B'C'$ across $y = -3$ to get $\triangle A''B''C''$. The coordinates of the vertices of $\triangle A''B''C''$ are $A''(-4, -7)$, $B''(-2, -4)$, and $C''(1, -8)$. Using similar reasoning to part a, the ordered pair rule is $(x, y) \rightarrow (x, -y - 6)$.

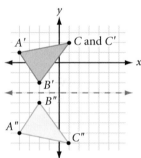

c. The composition of these two reflections appears to be, as expected, a translation of 10 units in the negative y-direction. Check this with patty paper. If the ordered pair rule is $(x, y) \rightarrow (x, -y + 4)$ when reflecting $\triangle ABC$ onto $\triangle A'B'C'$ and the ordered pair rule is $(x, y) \rightarrow (x, -y - 6)$ when reflecting $\triangle A'B'C'$ onto $\triangle A''B''C''$, then combining the two gives an ordered pair rule: $(x, y) \rightarrow (x, y - 10)$. To check, apply the ordered pair rule to the coordinates of the vertices of $\triangle ABC$ to see if the rule gives you the coordinates of the vertices of $\triangle A''B''C''$.

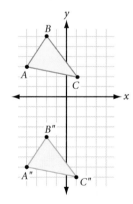

	A & A''	B & B''	C & C''
$\triangle ABC$	$(-4, 3)$	$(-2, 6)$	$(1, 2)$
$\triangle A''B''C''$	$(-4, -7)$	$(-2, -4)$	$(1, -8)$

Earlier you discovered that the ordered pair rule $(x, y) \rightarrow (-x, -y)$ results in a rotation 180° about the origin. In Example A the ordered pair rule $(x, y) \rightarrow (-x + 4, -y - 6)$ resulted in a rotation 180° about the point $(2, -3)$. Can you generalize this? What would be the ordered pair rule for a 180° rotation about the point $(3, 5)$? About the point (h, k)?

Furthermore, you also discovered earlier that the ordered pair rule $(x, y) \rightarrow (x, -y)$ results in a reflection across the x-axis. In Example B you found that a reflection across the line $y = 2$ is equivalent to an ordered pair rule $(x, y) \rightarrow (x, -y + 4)$. A reflection across the line $y = -3$ is equivalent to an ordered pair rule $(x, y) \rightarrow (x, -y - 6)$. Combining these two rules you get an ordered pair rule that produces a translation: $(x, y) \rightarrow (x, y - 10)$. Can you generalize these ideas? Let's investigate!

INVESTIGATION

Ordered Pair Rules for Compositions of Transformations

Perform the following investigations to discover how these ordered pair rules can transform a polygon.

Step 1 With graph paper and patty paper, or geometry software, perform the following compositions of transformations on a polygon and then match them to the ordered pair rules on the right.

a. A reflection across the line $y = x$ followed by a translation by the vector $<-1, 2>$.

b. A reflection across the x-axis and then a translation by the vector $<-2, 0>$.

c. A reflection across the line $y = -x$ and then a translation by the vector $<3, 2>$.

d. A reflection across the y-axis and then a translation by the vector $<0, 1>$.

e. A 180° rotation about the point $(1, 0)$.

f. A 90° counterclockwise rotation about the origin followed by a translation by the vector $<-2, -1>$.

g. A 90° clockwise rotation about the point $(1, -1)$.

i. $(x, y) \rightarrow (-x, y + 1)$

ii. $(x, y) \rightarrow (x - 2, -y)$

iii. $(x, y) \rightarrow (-x + 2, -y)$

iv. $(x, y) \rightarrow (y - 1, x + 2)$

v. $(x, y) \rightarrow (y + 2, -x)$

vi. $(x, y) \rightarrow (-y - 2, x - 1)$

vii. $(x, y) \rightarrow (-y + 3, -x + 2)$

Step 2 Next, generalize these compositions by completing the conjectures below.

a. The ordered pair rule $(x, y) \rightarrow (x + h, -y + k)$ is a ?.

b. The ordered pair rule $(x, y) \rightarrow (-x + h, y + k)$ is a ?.

c. The ordered pair rule $(x, y) \rightarrow (-x + h, -y + k)$ is a ?.

d. The ordered pair rule $(x, y) \rightarrow (y + h, x + k)$ is a ?.

e. The ordered pair rule $(x, y) \rightarrow (y + h, -x + k)$ is a ?.

f. The ordered pair rule $(x, y) \rightarrow (-y + h, x + k)$ is a ?.

g. The ordered pair rule $(x, y) \rightarrow (-y + h, -x + k)$ is a ?.

Step 3 In this lesson you discovered ordered pair rules for rigid transformations. All the ordered pair rules for these rigid transformations were of the form: $(x, y) \rightarrow (\pm x + h, \pm y + k)$ or $(x, y) \rightarrow (\pm y + h, \pm x + k)$. Let's generalize your findings by completing the following conjectures:

> **Coordinate Transformations Conjecture**
>
> If an ordered pair rule is of the form $(x, y) \rightarrow (\pm x + h, \pm y + k)$ or $(x, y) \rightarrow (\pm y + h, \pm x + k)$ then the transformation is a _?_ transformation.
>
> If an ordered pair rule is of the form $(x, y) \rightarrow (\pm x + h, \pm y + k)$ or $(x, y) \rightarrow (\pm y + h, \pm x + k)$ and the ordered pair rule transforms each vertex of a triangle to a corresponding vertex of another triangle then the two triangles are _?_ .

None of the ordered pair rules in this lesson had a number in front of the x or y. What type of transformation happens with an ordered pair rule such as $(x, y) \rightarrow (3x + 1, 3y - 2)$? These types of transformations will be explored in the next chapter.

Exercises

1. The ordered pair rule $(x, y) \rightarrow (x + 7, -y - 6)$ is what type of transformation?

2. The ordered pair rule $(x, y) \rightarrow (y - 7, -x + 6)$ is what type of transformation?

3. The ordered pair rule $(x, y) \rightarrow (-x, -y + 1)$ is what type of transformation?

4. What is the ordered pair rule for a composition of a reflection across the line $y = 4$ followed by a reflection across the line $y = -5$?

5. What is the ordered pair rule for a composition of a reflection across the line $y = x$ followed by a reflection across the line $y = -x$?

6. What is the ordered pair rule for a rotation of 180° about the point $(3, 1)$?

7. What is the ordered pair rule for a clockwise rotation of 90° about the origin?

8. In the graph at right, if $\triangle ABC \cong \triangle DEF$ what is the ordered pair rule that takes $\triangle ABC$ onto $\triangle DEF$?

9. Given $\triangle ABC$ with vertices: $A(-8, 2)$, $B(-7, -4)$, $C(-5, 7)$.

   a. Reflect $\triangle ABC$ across the line $x = -3$ to create image $\triangle A'B'C'$.

   b. Reflect $\triangle A'B'C''$ across the line $x = 3$ to create image $\triangle A''B''C''$.

   c. What are the coordinates of the vertices of $\triangle A''B''C''$?

   d What single transformation would take $\triangle ABC$ onto $\triangle A''B''C''$?

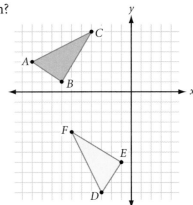

10. Given △ABC with vertices: A(−1, 7), B(−4, 2), C(−3, 1).

    a. Reflect △ABC across the line $y = -2$ to create image △A′B′C′.

    b. Reflect △A′B′C′ across the line $x = 2$ to create image △A″B″C″.

    c. What are the coordinates of the vertices of △A″B″C″?

    d What single transformation would take △ABC onto △A″B″C″?

11. Given the triangles on the coordinate grid to the right.

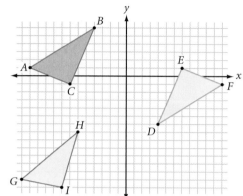

    a. Are any of the triangles congruent? What is the statement of congruence?

    b. If congruent, what transformations are necessary to transform one triangle onto the other?

    c. What is the ordered pair rule that takes one congruent triangle onto the other?

12. Given △COD with vertices C(−11, 4), O(−5, 3), D(−8, 8), △FIN with vertices F(6, −3), I(11, −4), N(8, −8), △ARM with vertices A(−2, −4), R(2, − 5), M(−1, −9), and △LEG with vertices L(0, 7), E(−1, 12), G(−4, 8).

    a. Are any of the triangles congruent? What is the statement of congruence?

    b. If congruent, what transformations are necessary to transform one triangle onto the other?

    c. What is the ordered pair rule that takes one congruent triangle onto the other?

DEVELOPING MATHEMATICAL REASONING

3-by-3 Inductive Reasoning Puzzle I

Sketch the figure missing in the lower-right corner of this 3-by-3 pattern.

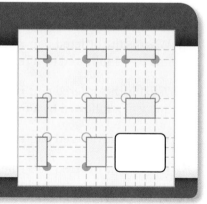

Congruence Shortcuts by Transformations

In earlier lessons you discovered a number of properties of rigid motions, or isometries. If a segment, angle, or polygon is reflected, rotated, or translated, then the image under that transformation is congruent to the original. In other words, angle measures and segment lengths are preserved under rigid motions.

If there is a sequence of transformations that transforms an image of one onto the other then we can say that the figure and its image are congruent. Let's look at an example of how to find a sequence of transformations to demonstrate two triangles are congruent.

EXAMPLE A If $\triangle ABC \cong \triangle DEF$, then you can perform a number of different sequences of transformations so that an image of $\triangle DEF$ coincides with $\triangle ABC$. Find one.

Solution Here is one sequence. Since the orientations of the corresponding congruent angles are the same, we will need two reflections to place the image of $\triangle DEF$ onto $\triangle ABC$.

Step 1 Construct two congruent triangles ($\triangle ABC \cong \triangle DEF$).

Step 2 We begin by translating $\triangle DEF$ to move the vertex of one of the pairs of congruent angles onto the other (F onto C). Translate $\triangle DEF$ by the translation vector $\overrightarrow{FC}$.

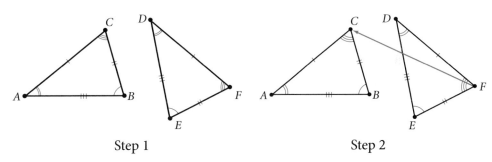

Step 1   Step 2

Step 3 Next, since $\overline{F'D'} \cong \overline{CA}$, construct the bisector of $\angle D'F'A$ and reflect $\triangle D'F'E'$ across it so that $\overline{F'D''}$ coincides with $\overline{F'A}$.

Step 4 Reflect $\triangle D'F'E'$ across the angle bisector.

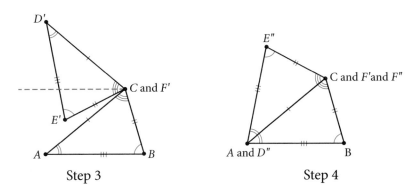

Step 3   Step 4

Step 5 Finally, since $\overline{F'E''} \cong \overline{CB}$ and $\overline{E''D''} \cong \overline{BA}$ we reflected $\triangle E''D''F'$ across $\overline{AC}$ which is the bisector of both $\angle E''AB$ and $\angle E''CB$. Reflect $\triangle E''D''F'$ across the angle bisector and the two triangles coincide.

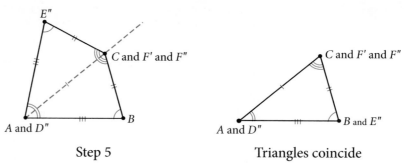

Step 5   Triangles coincide

In the above example, you knew that the two triangles were congruent. But in this sequence of transformations we actually used just the congruence between the three pairs of congruent sides. Thus we have confirmed the SSS congruence shortcut via transformations.

Almost an identical sequence of transformations could be performed using SAS, but let's look at a different example. This time we assume only three pairs of congruent corresponding parts.

EXAMPLE B

Given $\triangle PFG$ and $\triangle LGQ$ with $\overline{PG} \cong \overline{LQ}$, $\overline{FG} \cong \overline{GQ}$ and $\angle FGP \cong \angle Q$. Perform a sequence of transformations so that an image of $\triangle LGQ$ coincides with $\triangle PFG$.

Solution

Step 1 Construct two triangles $\triangle PFG$ and $\triangle LGQ$ with $\overline{PG} \cong \overline{LQ}$, $\overline{FG} \cong \overline{GQ}$ and $\angle FGP \cong \angle Q$.

Step 2 Since $\angle FGP \cong \angle Q$ and we want to transform the image of $\angle Q$ onto $\angle FGP$, translate $\triangle LGQ$ by the translation vector $\overline{QG}$. Does the direction of the vector matter? Why or why not?

Step 3 Since $\overline{FG} \cong \overline{GG'}$, rotate $\triangle L'G'Q'$ onto $\triangle PFG$ around center G using $\angle FGP$. Because we were able to use a sequence of transformations to make the two triangles coincide, we conclude that having two sides and the included angle, or SAS, is a valid congruence shortcut. In this example, points P, G, and Q were collinear. Does this sequence of transformations work if the points are not collinear? Explain your reasoning.

Steps 1 and 2

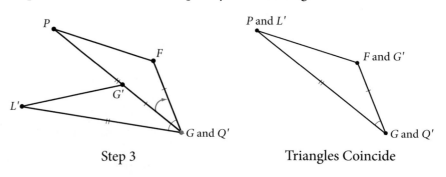

Step 3   Triangles Coincide

In Lesson 6.2, you discovered that the composition of two consecutive reflections across a pair of intersecting lines is equivalent to a single *rotation* transformation. In addition, the composition of two consecutive reflections across a pair of parallel lines is equivalent to a single *translation* transformation. If this is true, then perhaps any rigid transformation can be performed by one, two, or three reflections. For example, another solution to Example B is a sequence of reflections. What is that sequence? Is it always possible to find a sequence of reflections to complete any rigid transformation? How would you investigate this conjecture?

6.3 Exercises

YOU WILL NEED

Construction tools
for Exercises **2–7, 12**

1. In your own words, describe how the steps in Example B have confirmed the SAS congruence shortcut via transformations.

2. Given △ABC and △DEF with ∠A ≅ ∠D, $\overline{AC} \cong \overline{DF}$ and ∠C ≅ ∠F, perform a sequence of transformations so that an image of △DEF coincides with △ABC. Explain how your steps have confirmed the ASA congruence shortcut via transformations.

3. Given △ABC and △DEF with $\overline{AC} \cong \overline{DF}$, $\overline{AB} \cong \overline{DE}$, $\overline{BC} \cong \overline{EF}$, and the two triangles have *opposite* orientation, perform a sequence of transformations so that an image of △DEF coincides with △ABC.

For exercises 4–7, describe a sequence of transformations that could be used to confirm triangle congruence. What congruence shortcut did the sequence confirm? Patty paper may be helpful in finding what transformations were used.

4.

5.
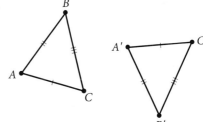

6.

7.
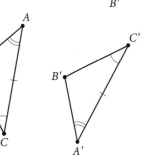

Review

In Exercises 8 and 9, sketch the next two figures.

8. , , , , , ?, ?

9.

10. The word DECODE remains unchanged when it is reflected across its horizontal line of symmetry. Find another such word with at least five letters.

◄--**DECODE**--►

11. How many reflectional symmetries does an isosceles triangle have?

12. Construct a square circumscribed about a circle.

Refer to the Cultural Connection for Exercises 13 and 14.

13. Use graph paper to design an arrangement of *tatami* for a 10-mat room. In how many different ways can you arrange the mats so that there are no places where four mats meet at a point (no cross patterns)? Assume that the mats measure 3-by-6 feet and that each room must be at least 9 feet wide. Show all your solutions.

14. There are at least two ways to arrange a 15-mat rectangle with no fault lines. One is shown. Can you find the other?

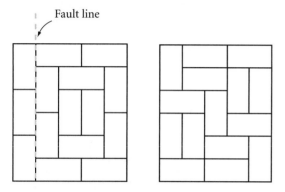
Fault line

Cultural
CONNECTION

Mats called *tatami* are used as a floor covering in traditional Japanese homes. *Tatami* is made from rush, a flowering plant with soft fibers, and has health benefits, such as removing carbon dioxide and regulating humidity and temperature. When arranging *tatami*, the seams form T-shapes. Arranging four at one vertex is avoided because it is difficult to get a good fit. Fault lines—straight seams passing all the way through a rectangular arrangement—are also avoided because they allow slippage. Room sizes are often given in *tatami* numbers.

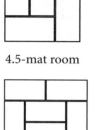
4.5-mat room

6-mat room

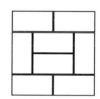
8-mat room

In Exercises 15 and 16, identify each statement as true or false. If true, explain why. If false, give a counterexample.

15. If two angles of a quadrilateral are right angles, then it is a rectangle.

16. If the diagonals of a quadrilateral are congruent, then it is a rectangle.

DEVELOPING MATHEMATICAL REASONING

Algebraic Magic Squares II

In this algebraic magic square, the sum of the entries in every row, column, and diagonal is the same. Find the value of x.

$8 - x$	15	14	$11 - x$
12	$x - 1$	x	9
8	$x + 3$	$x + 4$	5
$2x - 1$	3	2	$2x + 2$

Exploring Tessellations

Honeycombs are remarkably geometric structures. The hexagonal cells that bees make are ideal because they fit together perfectly without any gaps. The regular hexagon is one of many shapes that can completely cover a plane without gaps or overlaps. Mathematicians call such an arrangement of shapes a **tessellation** or a **tiling**. A tiling that uses only one shape is called a **monohedral tessellation**.

You can find tessellations in every home. Decorative floor tiles have tessellating patterns of squares. Brick walls, fireplaces, and wooden decks often display creative tessellations of rectangles. Where do you see tessellations every day?

The hexagon pattern in the honeycomb of the bee is a tessellation of regular hexagons.

Regular hexagons and equilateral triangles combine in this tiling from the 17th-century Topkapi Palace in Istanbul, Turkey.

You already know that squares and regular hexagons create monohedral tessellations. Because each regular hexagon can be divided into six equilateral triangles, we can logically conclude that equilateral triangles also create monohedral tessellations. Will other regular polygons tessellate? Let's investigate.

Activity 1

The Regular Tessellations

Step 1 For regular polygons to fill the plane without gaps or overlaps, their angles, when arranged around a point, must have measures that add up to exactly 360°. If the sum is less than 360°, there will be a gap. If the sum is greater, the shapes will overlap. Six 60° angles from six equilateral triangles add up to 360°, so regular triangles tessellate.

Triangles

Let's look at regular pentagons. Each angle in a regular pentagon measures 108° (360 is not divisible by 108). When three regular pentagons are arranged about a point their sum is 324°, so there is a gap. When four regular pentagons are arranged about a point their sum is 432°, so there is an

Pentagons

overlap. So regular pentagons cannot be arranged around a point without overlapping or leaving a gap. What about squares or regular heptagons? How many can you place about a point without a gap? Complete the table.

Number of sides of the regular polygon	3	4	5	6	7	8	9	10
Measure of each angle of the regular polygon	60°		108°					
Number of regular polygons about a point (without overlap)	6		3					
Will the regular polygon tessellate?	yes		no					

Step 2 In any regular polygon with more than six sides, each angle has a measure greater than _____°, therefore, no more than _____ angles can fit about a point without overlapping. The only regular polygons that create monohedral tessellations are _____, _____, and _____, State this as your next conjecture.

> **Regular Tessellations Conjecture**
>
> The only regular polygons that create monohedral tessellations are ?, ?, and ?.

A monohedral tessellation of congruent regular polygons is called a **regular tessellation**. What about tessellations of nonregular polygons? For example, will a scalene triangle tessellate? Let's investigate.

Activity 2

Do All Triangles Tessellate?

Step 1 Make 12 congruent scalene triangles, label the angles, and use them to try to create a tessellation.

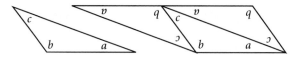

Step 2 Look at the angles about each vertex point. What do you notice?

Step 3 What is the sum of the measures of the three angles of a triangle? What is the sum of the measures of the angles that fit around each point? Compare your results with the results of others and state your next conjecture.

> **Tessellating Triangles Conjecture**
>
> ? triangle will create a monohedral tessellation.

You have seen that squares and rectangles tile the plane. Can you visualize tiling with parallelograms? Will any quadrilateral tessellate? Let's investigate.

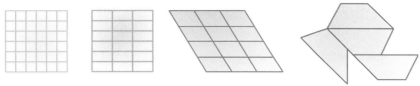

Activity 3

Do All Quadrilaterals Tessellate?

You want to find out if *any* quadrilateral can tessellate, so you should *not* choose a special quadrilateral for this investigation.

Step 1 Cut out 12 congruent quadrilaterals. Label the corresponding angles in each quadrilateral *a*, *b*, *c*, and *d*.

Step 2 Using your 12 congruent quadrilaterals, try to create a tessellation.

Step 3 Notice the angles about each vertex point. How many times does each angle of your quadrilateral fit at each point? What is the sum of the measures of the angles of a quadrilateral? Compare your results with others. State a conjecture.

> **Tessellating Quadrilaterals Conjecture**
>
> _?_ quadrilateral will create a monohedral tessellation.

→ *Mathematics*
CONNECTION

In 1975, when Martin Gardner wrote about pentagonal tessellations in *Scientific American*, experts thought that only eight kinds of pentagons would tessellate. Soon another type was found by Richard James III. After reading about this new discovery, Marjorie Rice began her own investigations.

With no formal training in mathematics beyond high school, Marjorie Rice investigated the tessellating problem and discovered four more types of pentagons that tessellate.

A regular pentagon does not tessellate, but are there *any* pentagons that tessellate? How many?

You will experiment with some pentagon tessellations in the exercises.

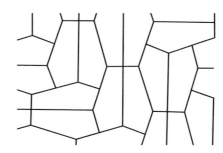

One of the pentagonal tessellations discovered by Marjorie Rice.

Exercises

1. Describe the transformations that take one square to an adjacent square in the tessellation of squares.

2. Describe the type(s) of transformations that take one equilateral triangle to an adjacent equilateral triangle in the tessellation of equilateral triangles.

3. Describe the type(s) of transformations that take one regular hexagon to an adjacent regular hexagon in the tessellation of regular hexagons.

4. The tessellation below has two different translation vectors. Copy the tessellation onto a patty paper and identify the translation vectors. (Ignore coloring.)

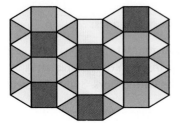

5. The tessellation below has two different centers of rotation. Copy the tessellation onto a patty paper and identify two centers of rotation. (Ignore coloring.)

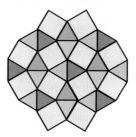

6. The beautiful Cairo street tiling shown below uses equilateral pentagons. One pentagon is shown below left. Use a ruler and a protractor to draw the equilateral pentagon on poster board or heavy cardboard. (For an added challenge, you can try to *construct* the pentagon, as Egyptian artisans likely would have done.) Cut out the pentagon and tessellate with it.

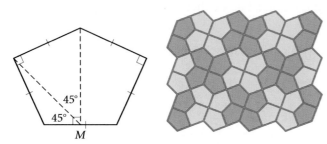

45°
45°
M

Point *M* is the midpoint of the base.

7. The figure at right is a detail of the Cairo tessellation from Exercise 6. A 90° clockwise rotation about the vertex of the right angle takes the yellow pentagon onto the green pentagon. Describe the transformation that takes the yellow pentagon onto the orange pentagon. Describe the transformation that takes the yellow pentagon onto the blue pentagon.

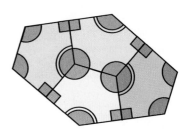

8. When you connect the center of each triangle across the common sides of the tessellating equilateral triangles at right, you get another tessellation. This new tessellation is called the **dual** of the original tessellation. Notice the dual of the equilateral triangle tessellation is the regular hexagon tessellation. Every regular tessellation of regular polygons has a dual.

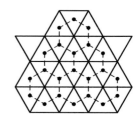

   a. Draw a regular square tessellation and make its dual. What is the dual?

   b. Draw a hexagon tessellation and make the dual of it. What is the dual?

   c. What do you notice about the duals?

Earlier you investigated compositions of rotations and compositions of reflections of an equilateral triangle. Let's put these transformations together. Copy the table shown below. Create an equilateral triangle on heavy stock paper. Reproduce the designs shown on the interior of the triangle. Do this on both sides as if the triangle were transparent.

Perform the compositions of these six transformations and draw the resulting design in each square of the table. Then find out what one transformation is equivalent to the composition of transformations just performed and write the name in the same square of the table. At right are a few examples.

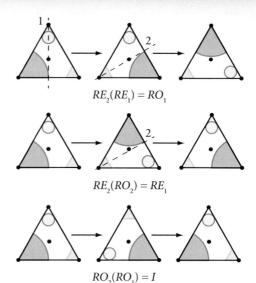

$$RE_2(RE_1) = RO_1$$

$$RE_2(RO_2) = RE_1$$

$$RO_2(RO_1) = I$$

Second transformation

First transformation

	I	RO_1 120°	RO_2 240°	RE_1	RE_2	RE_3
I	I	RO_1	RO_2	RE_1	RE_2	RE_3
RO_1 120°	RO_1	RO_2	I			
RO_2 240°	RO_2	I				
RE_1	RE_1			I		
RE_2	RE_2				I	
RE_3	RE_3					I

Does the order of the transformations make any difference? For example, is $RE_2(RO_1) = RO_1(RE_2)$? How many different orientations of the triangle are there in the table?

Tessellations Using Only Translations

So far this year you have had a lot of experience with the mathematics of transformations. In this lesson and the two to follow, you will get opportunities to use translations, reflections, rotations, and glide reflections to create tessellation art.

In 1936, M. C. Escher traveled to Spain and became fascinated with the tile patterns of the Alhambra. He spent days sketching the tessellations that Islamic masters had used to decorate the walls and ceilings. Some of his sketches are shown at right.

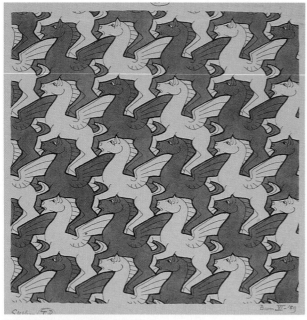

Escher wrote that the tessellations were "the richest source of inspiration" he had ever tapped.

Escher spent many years learning how to use translations, rotations, and glide reflections on grids of equilateral triangles and parallelograms. But he did not limit himself to pure geometric tessellations.

The four steps on the next page show how Escher may have created his Pegasus tessellation, shown at left. Notice how a partial outline of the Pegasus is translated from one side of a square to another to complete a single tile that fits with other tiles like itself. In Step 2, the original outline is translated by $\overrightarrow{AB}$. Step 4 uses translation vector $\overrightarrow{CD}$ to complete the Pegasus. How do these translation vectors compare to the original square? What do you notice?

You can use steps like this to create your own unique tessellation. Start with a tessellation of squares, rectangles, or parallelograms, and try translating curves on opposite sides of the tile. It may take a few tries to get a shape that looks like a person, animal, or plant. Use your imagination!

Step 1

Step 2

Step 3

Step 4

 INVESTIGATION

Creating a Tessellation Using Translations

YOU WILL NEED
- hexagonal grid paper
- straightedge

In Escher's Pegasus tessellation, corresponding points were selected to determine the translation vectors. The tessellation has horizontal and vertical translation vectors. Looking back at the original creation of the Pegasus, the translation vectors correspond with the sides of the original square used to create the image.

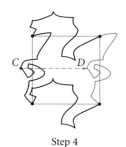

Step 1 Looking at the "Monster Mix" tessellation to the right, describe the translations used to create this tessellation. Draw the translation vectors on a copy of the tessellation.

Monster Mix **by Mark Purcell, former geometry student**

Step 2 Regular hexagons were used to create this tessellation. Rather than the two sets of opposite sides used in a square tessellation, this has three sets of opposite sides. Follow the six steps below to create the tessellation.

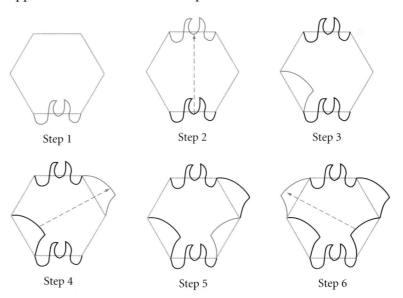

Step 1

Step 2

Step 3

Step 4

Step 5

Step 6

Step 3 Using the figure you created in Step 2, tessellate the figure across the page. Pick corresponding points of the original figure and its images and draw the translation vectors you used to create the tessellation. How do these translation vectors correspond to the regular hexagon?

Step 4 Do all tessellations that use only translations have translation vectors that correspond to the original shape? Explore other tessellations to test your conjecture.

The Escher designs and the student tessellations in this lesson took a great deal of time and practice. When you create your own tessellating designs of recognizable shapes, you'll appreciate the need for this practice!

6.4 Exercises

YOU WILL NEED

Construction tools
for Exercises **1–10**

In Exercises 1 and 2, copy each tessellating shape. Fill it in so that it becomes a recognizable figure. Use patty paper to create part of the tessellation. Draw the translation vectors that describe how the original figure was created and how the vectors were used to create the tessellation.

1.

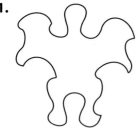

2.

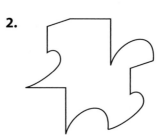

In Exercises 3–5, identify the basic tessellation grid (squares, parallelograms, or regular hexagons) that each geometry student used to create each translation tessellation. Copy one of the images onto patty paper. Draw the translation vectors showing the transformations that were used to create the tessellation.

3.

Cat Pack by Renee Chan,
former geometry student

4.

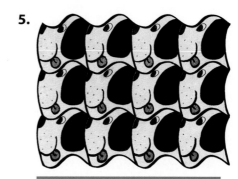

Snorty the Pig by Jonathon Benton,
former geometry student

5.

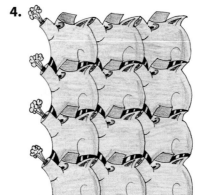

Dog Prints by Gary Murakam,
former geometry student

In Exercises 6 and 7, copy the figure and the grid onto patty paper. Create a tessellation on the grid with the figure. Describe the types of transformation(s) you used.

6.

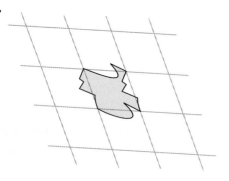

7.

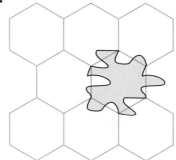

Now it's your turn. In Exercises 8 and 9, create a tessellation of recognizable shapes using the translation method you learned in this lesson. At first, you will probably end up with shapes that look like amoebas or spilled milk, but with practice and imagination, you will get recognizable images. Decorate and title your designs.

8. Use squares as the basic structure. ⓗ

9. Use regular hexagons as the basic structure.

Review

10. Frisco Fats needs to sink the 8-ball into the NW corner pocket, but he seems trapped. Can he hit the cue ball to a point on the N cushion so that it bounces out, strikes the S cushion, and taps the 8-ball into the corner pocket? Copy the table and construct the path of the ball. ⓗ

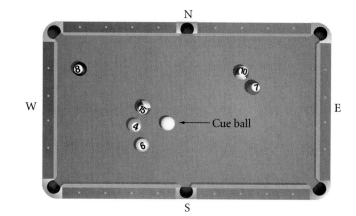

11. Identify each of the following statements as true or false. If true, explain why. If false, give a counterexample explaining why it is false.

a. If the two diagonals of a quadrilateral are congruent, but only one is the perpendicular bisector of the other, then the quadrilateral is a kite.

b. If the quadrilateral has exactly one line of reflectional symmetry, then the quadrilateral is a kite.

c. If the diagonals of a quadrilateral are congruent and bisect each other, then it is a square.

DEVELOPING MATHEMATICAL REASONING

Painted Faces I

Suppose some unit cubes are assembled into a large cube, then some of the faces of this large cube are painted. After the paint dries, the large cube is disassembled into the unit cubes, and you discover that 32 of these have no paint on any of their faces. How many faces of the large cube were painted?

Tessellations That Use Rotations

In Lesson 6.4, you created recognizable shapes by translating curves from opposite sides of a regular hexagon or square. In tessellations using only translations, all the figures face in the same direction. In this lesson you will use rotations of curves on a grid of parallelograms, equilateral triangles, or regular hexagons. The resulting tiles will fit together when you rotate them, and the designs will have rotational symmetry about points in the tiling. For example, in this Escher print, each reptile is made by rotating three different curves about three

M. C. Escher's *Symmetry Drawing E25* ©2014 The M. C. Escher Company—The Netherlands. All rights reserved. www. mcescher.com

alternating vertices of a regular hexagon. Let's look at how rotations were used to create this tessellation.

INVESTIGATION 1

Creating a Tessellation Using Rotations

Step 1 Construct regular hexagon *SIXGON*. Connect points *S* and *I* with a curve.

Step 2 Rotate curve *SI* about point *I* so that point *S* rotates to coincide with point *X*. How many degrees did you rotate the curve *SI*? Explain how you know.

Step 3 Connect points *G* and *X* with a curve.

Step 4 What point is the center of rotation to rotate curve *GX* so that point *X* rotates to coincide with point *O*? How many degrees must you rotate curve *GX*?

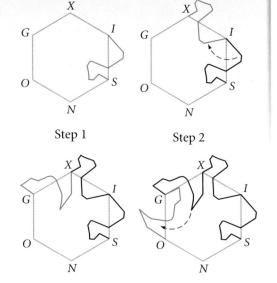

Step 5 Create curve *NO*. Describe the transformation that you must use to complete the final step.

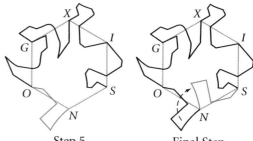

Step 5   Final Step

Step 6 Now that you have created the original figure, make several copies and create the tessellation. What are the centers and angles of rotation used to create the tessellation? How do these relate to the rotations used in the creation of the original figure?

Escher worked long and hard to adjust each curve until he got what he recognized as a reptile. When you are working on your own design, keep in mind that you may have to redraw your curves a few times until something you recognize appears.

Escher used his reptile drawing in this famous lithograph. Look closely at the reptiles in the drawing. Escher loved to play with our perceptions of reality!

M. C. Escher's *Reptiles* ©2014 The M. C. Escher Company—The Netherlands. All rights reserved. www.mcescher.com

Another method used by Escher utilizes rotations on an equilateral triangle grid. Two sides of each equilateral triangle have the same curve, rotated about their common point. The third side is a curve with point symmetry. The following steps demonstrate how you might create a tessellating flying fish like that created by Escher.

Flying Fish

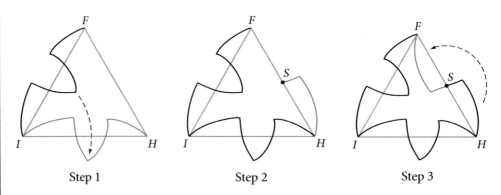

Step 1   Step 2   Step 3

Step 1 Connect points *F* and *I* with a curve. Then rotate the curve 60° clockwise about point *I* so that it becomes curve *IH*.

Step 2 Find the midpoint *S* of $\overline{FH}$ and draw curve *SH*.

Step 3 Rotate curve *SH* 180° about *S* to produce curve *FS*. Together curve *FS* and curve *SH* become the point-symmetric curve *FH*.

With a little added detail, the design becomes a flying fish.

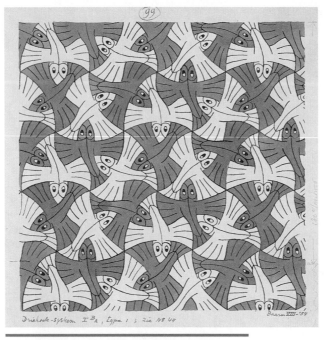

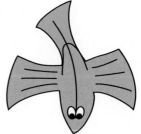

Or, with just a slight variation in the curves, the resulting shape will appear more like a bird than a flying fish.

The tessellations in this lesson are created solely from rotations. In Escher's Symmetry Drawing E99 (the flying fish tessellation) there are different centers of rotation with different degrees of rotation. Let's take a look at one of the centers of rotation in Escher's flying fish tessellation.

INVESTIGATION 2

Rotating Tessellations

Step 1 In Escher's flying fish tessellation, you can readily see one center of rotation where the wings of six flying fish touch. How many degrees of rotation are necessary to move one white flying fish onto another white flying fish? Use patty paper to confirm your solution.

Step 2 Describe the transformations for the set of three red flying fish.

Step 3 There is yet another center of rotation in this tessellation. How do you transform the white flying fish onto the red flying fish? What is the center of rotation? How many degrees of rotation about this point? Use patty paper to investigate.

6.5 Exercises

In Exercises 1 and 2, identify the basic grid (equilateral triangles or regular hexagons) that each geometry student used to create the tessellation.

1.

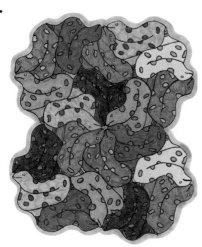

Snakes by Jack Chow, former geometry student

2.

Merlin by Aimee Plourdes, former geometry student

In Exercises 3 and 4, copy the figure and the grid onto patty paper. Show how you can use other pieces of patty paper to tessellate the figure on the grid. Label the centers of rotation used to create the tessellation. Find the angles of rotation used. Use patty paper to confirm your answers.

3.

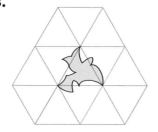

4.

In Exercises 5 and 6, create tessellation designs by using rotations. You will need patty paper or clear plastic, and grid paper or isometric dot paper.

5. Create a tessellating design of recognizable shapes by using a grid of regular hexagons. Decorate and color your art.

6. Create a tessellating design of recognizable shapes by using a grid of equilateral or isosceles triangles. Decorate and color your art.

Review

7. $\triangle ABC$ with vertices $A(1, 2)$, $B(-4, -2)$, and $C(2, -3)$, is transformed by the ordered pair rule $(x, y) \rightarrow (y, x)$ to create the image $\triangle A'B'C'$. Which of the following are true? First, try this as a "mental experiment." Take a guess or explain how you know. Then create the diagram with your geometry software, perform the transformation, and see how good you were at visualization.

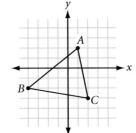

  a. $\angle A \cong \angle A'$

  b. $\overline{BC} \cong \overline{B'C'}$

  c. The points B, B', and the origin are collinear.

  d. The slope of $\overline{AB}$ is equal to the slope of $\overline{A'B'}$.

  e. The perimeter of $\triangle A'B'C'$ equals the perimeter of $\triangle ABC$.

8. Use geometry software to construct a line and two points A and B not on the line. Reflect A and B over the line and connect the four points to form a trapezoid.

  a. Explain why it is a trapezoid.

  b. Is it an isosceles trapezoid? Explain.

  c. Choose a random point C inside the trapezoid and connect it to the four vertices with segments. Calculate the sum of the distances from C to the four vertices. Drag point C around. Where is the sum of the distances the greatest? The least?

9. Given $\triangle ABC$ with vertices: $A(-4, -3)$, $B(4, -1)$, $C(3, 5)$

  a. Transform $\triangle ABC$ by the ordered pair rule $(x, y) \rightarrow (3x, 3y)$ to create $\triangle A'B'C'$.

  b. What are the coordinates of the vertices of $\triangle A'B'C'$?

  c. Are the two triangles congruent?

  d. How do the measures of the corresponding angles compare?

  e. How do the measures of the corresponding sides compare?

  f. What do you notice about the slopes of $\overline{AB}$ and $\overline{A'B'}$ and the slopes of $\overline{AC}$ and $\overline{A'C'}$?

DEVELOPING MATHEMATICAL REASONING

From Cube to Net Puzzle

The cube shown has had three holes drilled through it from three different directions. One hole is circular, a second is triangular, and the third is rectangular. Sketch the net of the cube.

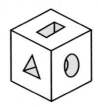

LESSON 6.6

Tessellations That Use Glide Reflections

"The young do not know enough to be prudent, and therefore they attempt the impossible, and achieve it, generation after generation."

PEARL S. BUCK

In this lesson you will use glide reflections to create tessellations. In Lesson 6.4, you saw Escher's translation tessellation of the winged horse Pegasus. All the horses are facing in the same direction. In the drawings below and below left, Escher used glide reflections on a grid of glide-reflected kites to get his horsemen facing in opposite directions.

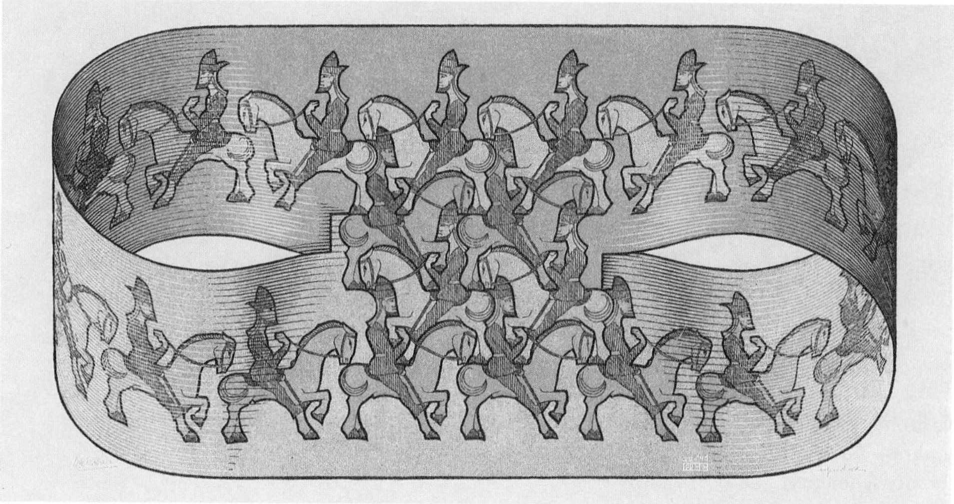

The steps below show how you can make a tessellating design similar to Escher's *Horseman*. (The symbol indicates a glide reflection.) What transformations are used to create Step 2?

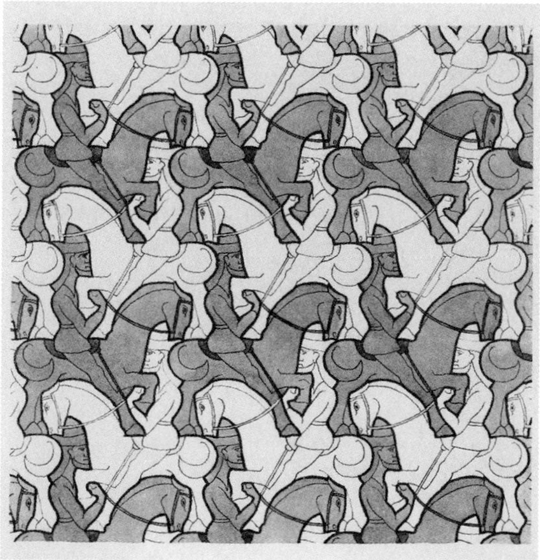

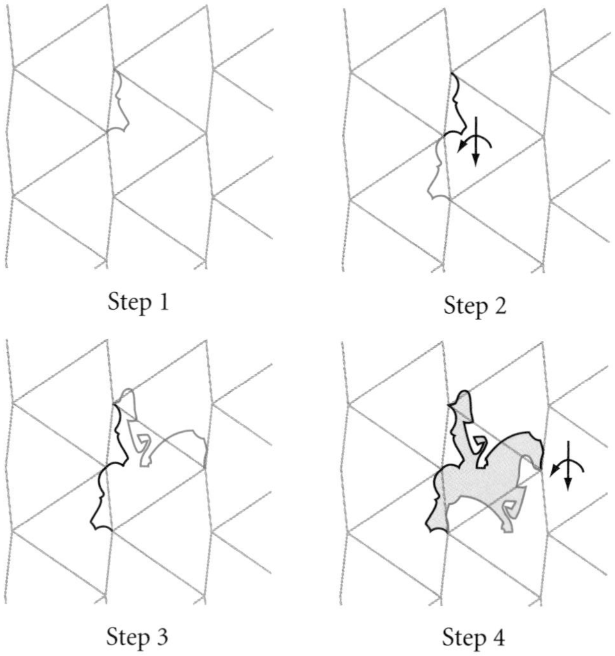

The curve in Step 1 is reflected across the polygon segment and then translated vertically down along the polygon. Step 4 has yet another set of transformations. Describe the sequence of transformations.

In the tessellation of birds below left, you can see that Escher used a grid of squares. You can use the same procedure on a grid of any type of glide-reflected parallelograms. The steps below show how you might create a tessellation of birds or fishes on a parallelogram grid rather than the square grid that Escher used.

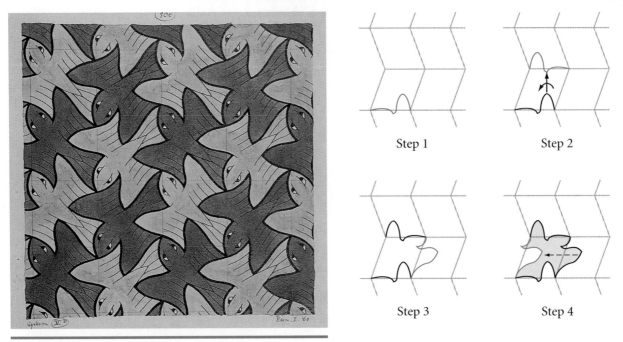

Step 1   Step 2

Step 3   Step 4

EXAMPLE

In Escher's Symmetry Drawing E108 (another flying fish tessellation), you can readily see the translations vertically as one white flying fish is translated up or down to its adjacent green flying fish. Describe the translation vectors that move a flying fish horizontally and vertically to another flying fish. How do the lengths of the translation vectors compare to the lengths of the sides of the square grid?

Solution

Using patty paper, you can see that indeed all the vertical translation vectors are half the length and at right angles to the horizontal translation vectors. The length of the vertical translation vectors is the same length as the sides of the square grid and the length of the horizontal translation vectors is twice the length of the sides of the squares.

In the exercise set you will look for lines of reflection in Escher's Symmetry Drawing E108.

(6.6) Exercises

In Exercises 1 and 2, identify the basic tessellation grid (kites or parallelograms) that the geometry student used to create the tessellation. Copy part of the tessellation with patty paper. Draw and describe the transformations that are used to create each tessellation.

Construction tools
for Exercises 1–7, 11

1.

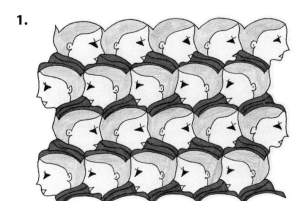

A Boy with a Red Scarf by Elina Uzin, former geometry student

2.

Glide Reflection by Alice Chan, former geometry student

In Exercises 3 and 4, copy the figure and the grid onto patty paper. Describe the transformations used to create the original figure. Use another piece of patty paper to tessellate the figure on the grid. Describe the transformations used to create the tessellation. How do these transformations relate to the grid used to create the original figure?

3.

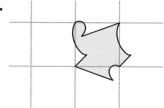

4.

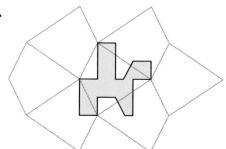

5. Here is another detail of Escher's flying fish tessellation (Symmetry Drawing E108) showing a flying fish and its adjacent glide-reflected image. Copy the image onto a patty paper. Make a second copy. Draw the line of reflection and the translation vector that moves the dark green flying fish onto the light green flying fish on one of the patty paper copies.

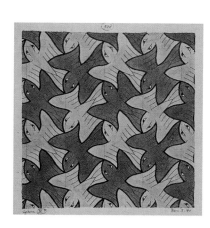

6. Create a glide-reflection tiling design of recognizable shapes by using a grid of kites. Decorate and color your art. Ⓗ

7. Create a glide-reflection tiling design of recognizable shapes by using a grid of parallelograms. Decorate and color your art.

Review

8. Find the coordinates of the circumcenter and centroid of △*FAN* with *F*(6, 0), *A*(7 7), and *N*(3, 9).

9. Find the measure of each lettered angle in the diagram below.

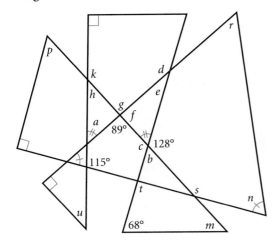

10. The green prism below right was built from the two solids below left. Copy the figure on the right onto isometric dot paper and shade in one of the two pieces to show how the complete figure was created.

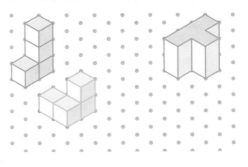

11. Copy △*TRY* and its rotated image onto patty paper. Locate the center of rotation by finding a pair of intersecting reflection lines that can be used to transform the original onto the image by a composition of two reflections.

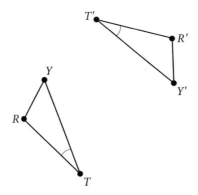

DEVELOPING MATHEMATICAL REASONING

Diamond Pattern Puzzle

If the pattern of number diamonds shown continues, what would be the sum of the numbers in the eighth diamond?

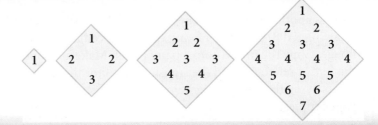

How is your memory? In this chapter you learned about rigid transformations in the plane—called isometries—and you revisited the principles of symmetry that you first learned in Chapter 0. You applied these concepts to create tessellations and described the transformations used to create them. Can you name the three rigid transformations? Can you describe how to compose transformations to make other transformations? How can you use reflections to improve your miniature-golf game? What types of symmetry do regular polygons have? What types of polygons will tile the plane? Review this chapter to be sure you can answer these questions.

Exercises

For Exercises 1–6, identify each statement as true or false. For each false statement, sketch a counterexample and explain why it is false.

YOU WILL NEED

Construction tools
for Exercises **11–18, 24**

1. The two transformations in which the orientation (the order of points as you move clockwise) does not change are translation and rotation.

2. The two transformations in which the image has the opposite orientation from the original are reflection and glide reflection.

3. A translation by (5, 12) followed by a translation by $(-8, -6)$ is equivalent to a single translation by $(-3, 6)$.

4. A rotation of $140°$ followed by a rotation of $260°$ about the same point is equivalent to a single rotation of $40°$ about that point.

5. A reflection across a line followed by a second reflection across a parallel line that is 12 cm from the first is equivalent to a translation of 24 cm.

6. A regular *n*-gon has *n* reflectional symmetries and *n* rotational symmetries.

In Exercises 7–9, identify the type or types of symmetry, including the number of symmetries, in each design. For Exercise 9, describe how you can move candles on the menorah to make the colors symmetrical, too.

7.

***Mandala* by Gary Chen, former geometry student**

8.

9.

10. The façade of Chartres Cathedral in France does not have reflectional symmetry. Why not? Sketch the portion of the façade that does have bilateral symmetry.

11. Find or create a logo that has reflectional symmetry. Sketch the logo and its line or lines of reflectional symmetry.

12. Find or create a logo that has rotational symmetry, but not reflectional symmetry. Sketch it.

13. Describe one transformation and also a sequence of more than one transformation that will make $\triangle ABC$ coincide with $\triangle A''B''C''$. What triangle congruence shortcut did you confirm?

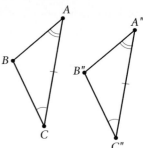

14. Describe the sequence of transformations completed below. What single transformation also describes the result?

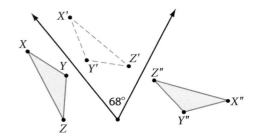

15. Copy the star $ABCDE$ and its rotated image onto a piece of patty paper. Locate the center and angle of rotation. Explain your method. Ⓗ

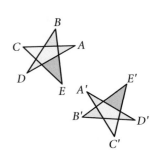

16. Given △*ABC* with vertices *A*(0, 3), *B*(4, 0), *C*(3, 7). Transform △*ABC* by the ordered pair rule (*x*, *y*) → (*x* − 3, −*y*) to create △*A′B′C′*. What are the coordinates of the vertices of △*A′B′C′*? Do the two triangles appear to be congruent?

17. Given △*ABC* with vertices *A*(−4, −3), *B*(−4, 1), *C*(−2, 0), △*DEF* with vertices *D*(−4, 2), *E*(−2, 4), *F*(1, 2), △*GHI* with vertices *G*(4, 1), *H*(2, 0), *I*(4, −3), and △*JKL* with vertices *J*(0, −2), *K*(−1, −4), *L*(3, −4).

   a. Are any of the triangles congruent? What is the statement of congruence?

   b. If congruent, what transformations are necessary to transform one triangle onto the other?

   c. What is the ordered pair rule that takes one congruent triangle onto the other?

18. Draw △*ABC* and △*DEF* with $\overline{AC} \cong \overline{DF}$, $\overline{AB} \cong \overline{DE}$, $\overline{BC} \cong \overline{EF}$. Then perform a sequence of transformations so that an image of △*DEF* coincides with △*ABC*.

In Exercises 19–21, identify the shape of the tessellation grid and describe the transformations that the student used to create each tessellation.

19.

***Perian Warriors* by Robert Bell, former geometry student**

20.

***Doves* by Serene Tam, former geometry student**

21.

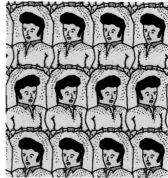

***Sightings* by Peter Chua and Monica Grant, former geometry students**

In Exercises 22 and 23, copy the figure and grid onto patty paper. Determine whether or not you can use the figure to create a tessellation on the grid. Explain your reasoning.

22.

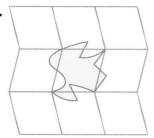

23.

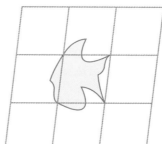

24. In his woodcut *Day and Night*, Escher gradually changes the shape of the patches of farmland into black and white birds. The birds are flying in opposite directions, so they appear to be glide reflections of each other. But notice that the tails of the white birds curve down, while the tails of the black birds curve up. So, on closer inspection, it's clear that this is not a glide-reflection tiling at all!

When two birds are taken together as one tile (a 2-motif tile), they create a translation tessellation. Use patty paper to find the 2-motif tile.

Mixed Review

In Exercises 25–41, identify the statement as true or false. For each false statement, explain why it is false and sketch a counterexample.

25. If a triangle has two angles of equal measure, then the third angle is acute.

26. If two sides of a triangle measure 45 cm and 36 cm, then the third side must be greater than 9 cm and less than 81 cm.

27. The diagonals of a parallelogram are congruent.

28. The measure of each angle of a regular dodecagon is 150°.

29. If $\overline{CD}$ is the midsegment of trapezoid *PLYR* with $\overline{PL}$ one of the bases, then $CD = \frac{1}{2}(PL + YR)$

30. In $\triangle BOY$, $BO = 36$ cm, $m\angle B = 42°$, and $m\angle O = 28°$. In $\triangle GRL$, $GR = 36$ cm, $m\angle R = 28°$, and $m\angle L = 110°$. Therefore, $\triangle BOY \cong \triangle GRL$.

31. If the sum of the measures of the interior angles of a polygon is less than 1000°, then the polygon has fewer than seven sides.

32. The sum of the measures of the three angles of an obtuse triangle is greater than the sum of the measures of the three angles of an acute triangle.

33. The sum of the measures of one set of exterior angles of a polygon is always less than the sum of the measures of interior angles.

34. Both pairs of base angles of an isosceles trapezoid are supplementary.

35. If the base angles of an isosceles triangle each measure 48°, then the vertex angle has a measure of 132°.

36. The diagonals of a rhombus bisect the angles of the rhombus.

37. The diagonals of a rectangle are perpendicular bisectors of each other.

38. If a triangle has two angles of equal measure, then the triangle is equilateral.

39. If a quadrilateral has three congruent angles, then it is a rectangle.

40. If the sum of the lengths of two consecutive sides of a kite is 48 cm, then the perimeter of the kite is 96 cm.

41. If the vertex angles of a kite measure 48° and 36°, then the nonvertex angles each measure 138°.

The concentric circles in the sky are actually a time exposure photograph of the movement of the stars in a night.

42. Find the measure of each lettered angle in the diagram below.

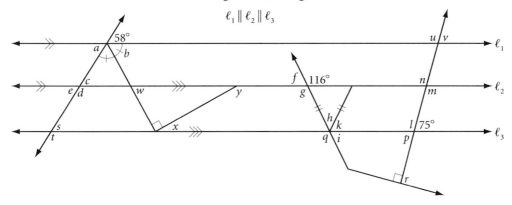

$\ell_1 \parallel \ell_2 \parallel \ell_3$

In Exercises 43–45, from the information given, determine which triangles, if any, are congruent. State the congruence conjecture that supports your congruence statement.

43. *STARY* is a regular pentagon.

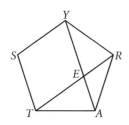

44. *FLYT* is a kite.

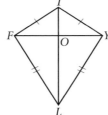

45. *PART* is an isosceles trapezoid.

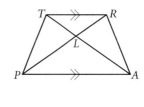

46. Archaeologist Dakota Diggs has uncovered a piece of triangular tile from a mosaic. A corner is broken off. Wishing to repair the mosaic, he lays the broken tile piece down on paper and traces the straight edges. With a ruler, he then extends the unbroken sides until they meet. What triangle congruence shortcut guarantees that the tracing reveals the original shape?

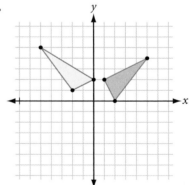

47. Use your protractor to draw and label a pair of supplementary angles that is not a linear pair.

48. Construct a rectangle whose length is twice its width.

49. If $AB = 15$ cm, C is the midpoint of $\overline{AB}$, D is the midpoint of $\overline{AC}$, and E is the midpoint of $\overline{DC}$, what is the length of $\overline{EB}$?

50. Draw the next shape in this pattern.

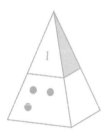 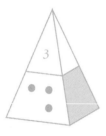 

For exercises 51–53 identify the type of transformation and then give the ordered pair rule for each. The original figure is in blue and its image is red.

51.

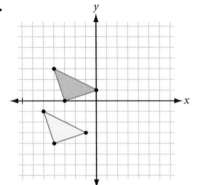

52. Ⓗ

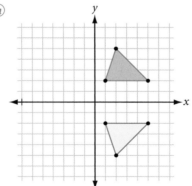

53.

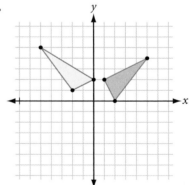

1. Assuming there are no other balls on a pool table, where should a player aim so that a randomly placed cue ball bounces off exactly three different cushions before returning to its original spot? How many different solutions can you find?

2. There are many books and websites devoted to the tessellation art of M. C. Escher. Make copies of three different Escher tessellation designs not found in this textbook. One should be a translation-type tessellation, one a rotation-type tessellation, and one a glide reflection-type tessellation. Label them with their tessellation type and use patty paper to locate the unit tessellation shape for each design.

3. There are four rotation transformations such that the image square coincides with the original square.

The interiors of the square are marked to help keep track of the new positions of the square after rotation transformations. Here is the square in its initial position before the first rotation.

The composition of a 270° counterclockwise rotation followed by a 90° rotation is equivalent to a 360° rotation, or the identity rotation. Symbolically, this is written: $RO_1(RO_3) \rightarrow I$. The composition of the two transformations $RO_2(RO_3)$ would be the 270° rotation followed by the 180° rotation, which is equivalent to what single transformation? Complete the table of compositions of rotations of the square. Does the order of the rotations make a difference? For example, is $RO_1(RO_3)$ the same as $RO_3(RO_1)$? How many different orientations of the square are there in the table?

Second transformation

First transformation		RO_1 cc 90°	RO_2 cc 180°	RO_3 cc 270°	$I=RO_4$ cc 360°
RO_1 cc 90°		RO_2	RO_3	$I=RO_4$	RO_1
RO_2 cc 180°		RO_3			
RO_3 cc 270°		$I=RO_4$			
$I=RO_4$ cc 360°		RO_1			

4. For squares there are four reflection transformations such that the image square coincides with the original square.

The composition of a reflection across the vertical symmetry line (line 1) followed by a reflection across the horizontal symmetry line (line 2) is written: $RE_2(RE_1)$. This would look like:

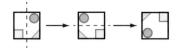

Complete a similar table to the one used in Exercise 3 that includes the compositions of reflections of the square. Does the order of the reflections make a difference? For example, is $RE_3(RE_1)$ the same as $RE_1(RE_3)$? How many different orientations of the square are there in the table?

5. There are four rotational symmetries for squares.

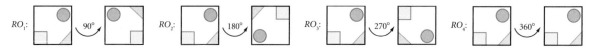

There are also four reflectional symmetries for squares.

In this exercise you will perform all the compositions of rotations and reflections of a square.

Using a table, perform the compositions of these eight transformations and record the resulting design in each square of the table. Then find out what one transformation is equivalent to the composition of transformations just performed. Write the name of that single transformation in the same square of the table. Half of the compositions were completed in the previous two Take Another Look exercises.

Does the order of the transformations make any difference? For example, is $RE_2(RO_1) = RO_1(RE_2)$? How many different orientations of the square are there in the table? You discovered earlier that *the composition of two consecutive reflections across intersecting lines is equivalent to a rotation and the amount of rotation is twice the angle between the lines of reflection.* How is that helpful in explaining the values in the table?

Establishing Similarity

> "Nobody can draw a line that is not a boundary line, every line separates a unity into a multiplicity. In addition, every closed contour no matter what its shape, pure circle or whimsical splash accidental in form, evokes the sensation of "inside" and "outside," followed quickly by the suggestion of "nearby" and "far off," of object and background."
>
> M. C. ESCHER

M. C. Escher's *Path of Life I* ©2014 The M. C. Escher Company—The Netherlands. All rights reserved. www.mcescher.com

OBJECTIVES

In this chapter you will

- use dilations in the coordinate plane
- define similar polygons
- discover shortcuts for similar triangles
- use the definition of similarity to solve problems
- use transformations to describe similarity

Dilations on the Coordinate Plane

In earlier lessons, you reflected, translated, and rotated polygons using ordered pair rules on the coordinate grid. Most of these were rigid transformations, or isometries. Occasionally they were non-rigid transformations. In this lesson you will discover properties of a special type of non-rigid transformation called a dilation. Let's look at a few examples.

How would you describe the transformation from the model biplane to the life size biplane?

EXAMPLE A

△*ABC* with vertices $A(-1, 0)$, $B(4, 2)$, and $C(2, 6)$ is transformed by the ordered pair rule $(x, y) \rightarrow (3x, y - 6)$ creating the image, △*A'B'C'*.

a. Graph the image of △*ABC* and label it △*A'B'C'*

b. Are any of the corresponding sides or angles congruent?

c. Is it a rigid transformation? Is △*ABC* ≅ △*A'B'C'*?

d. What appeared to happen?

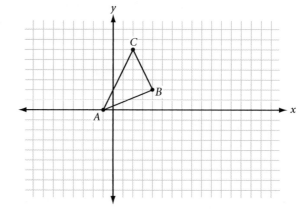

Solution

a. Draw △*ABC* on a set of axes and relocate its vertices using the ordered pair rule to get △*A'B'C'*.

b. A quick check with patty paper confirms that none of the corresponding angles or corresponding sides are congruent.

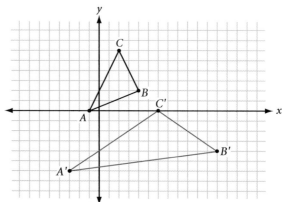

c. Since none of the corresponding angles or corresponding sides are congruent, the triangles are not congruent and the transformation is not a rigid transformation.

d. Since the *x*-values were tripled, it appears that △*ABC* was stretched three times as far apart in the horizontal direction and everything was 6 units lower in the *y*-direction.

What if both the *x*-coordinates and *y*-coordinates were multiplied by the same factor? In Example A we multiplied the *x*-coordinates by a number greater than one. This time let's see what happens when we multiply both *x*- and *y*-coordinates by the same positive number.

EXAMPLE B

△*ABC* with vertices *A*(−6, −6), *B*(12, −4), and *C*(4, 8) is transformed by the ordered pair rule $(x, y) \rightarrow (\frac{1}{2}x, \frac{1}{2}y)$ creating the image △*A'B'C'*.

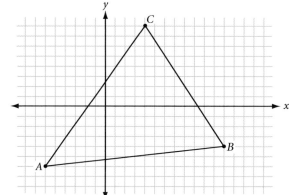

a. Graph the image of △*ABC* and label it △*A'B'C'*

b. Are any of the corresponding sides or angles congruent?

c. Is it a rigid transformation? Is △*ABC* ≅ △*A'B'C'*?

d. What appeared to happen?

Solution

a. Draw △*ABC* on a set of axes and relocate its vertices using the ordered pair rule to get △*A'B'C'*.

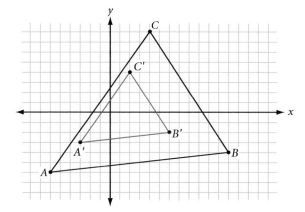

b. A quick check with patty paper confirms that all of the corresponding angles are congruent but none of the corresponding sides are congruent. The sides in the image triangle, △*A'B'C'*, are half the length of the corresponding sides of the original triangle, △*ABC*.

c. Since none of the corresponding sides are congruent, the triangles are not congruent and the transformation is not a rigid transformation.

d. Since the *x*- and *y*-coordinate values were cut in half, it appears that each side of △*A'B'C'* is half the length of the corresponding side of △*ABC*. The image triangle, △*A'B'C'*, appears to be a "scaled down" or reduction of the original triangle, △*ABC*.

This type of non-rigid transformation is called a **dilation**. A dilation is a non-rigid transformation that enlarges or reduces a geometric figure by a scale factor relative to a point. The ordered pair rule $(x, y) \rightarrow (rx, ry)$ describes a dilation in which the amount of increase or decrease in size, called the **scale factor**, is *r*, where *r* is a positive number. If *r* is greater than 1, then the dilation is an **enlargement** and if the scale factor *r* is less than 1, then the dilation is a **reduction**.

Let's extend our lesson on dilation to include circles. Are all circles dilations of one another? You will explore this idea in the investigation.

This satellite image is a scaled model of the actual hurricane. How would you estimate the actual size of the huricane?

 INVESTIGATION

Dilations of Circles

Given circle P with center at $P(-7, 5)$ and tangent to the x-axis at point A and circle Q with center at $Q(9, 3)$ and passing through the point $B(3, -5)$.

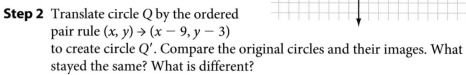

Step 1 Translate circle P by the ordered pair rule $(x, y) \rightarrow (x + 7, y - 5)$ to create circle P'. How did this translation affect the circle?

Step 2 Translate circle Q by the ordered pair rule $(x, y) \rightarrow (x - 9, y - 3)$ to create circle Q'. Compare the original circles and their images. What stayed the same? What is different?

Step 3 What is the dilation rule that transforms circle P' onto circle Q'?

In Steps 1–3, you translated two circles onto the origin. You then dilated one by the ratio of the two radii and the new dilated circles coincided.

Step 4 Can you do this for any two circles on the coordinate plane?

Step 5 If circle P has center at (a, b) and has a radius of r, and circle Q has center at (c, d) and a radius of s (with $r > s$), what would you do to transform one onto the other?

Step 6 Compare your responses with your group. You should be ready to state the conjecture.

> **Dilations of Circles Conjecture**
>
> All circles are _?_ of each other.

Exercises

Practice dilations by solving these exercises. Use patty paper to compare corresponding sides and angles.

1. Given $\triangle ABC$ with vertices $A(-2, -2)$, $B(1, -2)$, $C(-1, 1)$

   a. Dilate $\triangle ABC$ by the dilation rule $(x, y) \rightarrow (4x, 4y)$ to create $\triangle A'B'C'$.

   b. What are the coordinates of the vertices of $\triangle A'B'C'$?

c. How do the measures of the corresponding angles compare?

d. How do the measures of the corresponding sides compare?

e. What do you notice about the origin, A, and A' and the origin, B, and B'?

2. Given $\triangle ABC$ and $\triangle DEF$ at right.

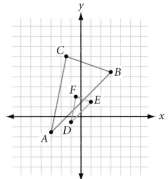

a. How do $\angle A$ and $\angle D$ compare? How do $\angle B$ and $\angle E$ compare? How do $\angle C$ and $\angle F$ compare?

b. How do $\overline{AB}$ and $\overline{DE}$ compare? How do $\overline{BC}$ and $\overline{EF}$ compare? How do $\overline{CA}$ and $\overline{FD}$ compare?

c. Is there a dilation rule that transforms $\triangle ABC$ onto $\triangle DEF$? If so, what is the dilation rule $(x, y) \rightarrow (?x, ?y)$? If not, explain why not.

3. Given Quadrilateral $ABCD$ with vertices $A(-8, 12)$, $B(0, 4)$, $C(8, 4)$ and $D(4, 16)$.

a. Dilate quadrilateral $ABCD$ by the dilation rule $(x, y) \rightarrow (\frac{1}{4}x, \frac{1}{4}y)$ to create quadrilateral $A'B'C'D'$.

b. What are the coordinates of the vertices of $A'B'C'D'$?

c. How do the measures of the corresponding angles compare?

d. How do the measures of the corresponding sides compare?

e. Are the corresponding sides parallel? Explain.

4. Given Quadrilateral $SQRE$ with vertices $S(0, 2)$, $Q(4, -2)$, $R(0, -6)$ and $E(-4, -2)$.

a. Is quadrilateral $SQRE$ a square? Explain how you know.

b. Dilate quadrilateral $SQRE$ by the dilation rule $(x, y) \rightarrow (\frac{3}{2}x, \frac{3}{2}y)$ to create quadrilateral $S'Q'R'E'$.

c. What are the coordinates of the vertices of quadrilateral $S'Q'R'E'$?

d. Is quadrilateral $S'Q'R'E'$ a square? Explain how you know.

e. Are the corresponding sides of $SQRE$ and $S'Q'R'E'$ parallel? Explain how you know.

5. Given rectangle $RECT$ with vertices $R(-7, 2)$, $E(-1, 2)$, $C(-1, 6)$ and $T(-7, 6)$.

a. How would you dilate rectangle $RECT$ to create the image $R'E'C'T'$ so that the length $R'E'$ is three times the length RE and the height $R'T'$ is half the height RT? What would be the dilation rule $(x, y) \rightarrow (?x, ?y)$ to create rectangle $R'E'C'T'$?

b. What are the coordinates of the vertices of $R'E'C'T'$?

c. Is the transformation of $RECT$ to $R'E'C'T'$ a dilation transformation? Explain.

d. What is the ratio of the perimeter of $RECT$ to $R'E'C'T'$?

6. Given circle P with center at $P(9, 6)$ that is tangent to the x-axis at point A.

a. Dilate circle P by the dilation rule $(x, y) \rightarrow (\frac{2}{3}x, \frac{2}{3}y)$ to create circle P'.

b. What are the coordinates of the center of circle P'?

c. Does circle P' touch the x-axis?

d. What are two other points on circle P'?

e. Are the points P, P', and the origin collinear?

f. What is the radius of circle P? What is the radius of circle P'?

g. What is the ratio of the radii?

Similar Polygons

"He that lets
the small things
bind him
Leaves the great
undone behind him."

PIET HEIN

You know that figures that have the same shape and size are congruent figures. Figures that have the same shape but not necessarily the same size are **similar** figures. To say that two figures have the same shape but not necessarily the same size is not, however, a precise definition of similarity.

Is your reflection in a fun-house mirror similar to a regular photograph of you? The images have a lot of features in common, but they are not mathematically similar. In mathematics, you can think of similar shapes as dilations (enlargements or reductions) of each other with no irregular distortions.

The uneven surface of a fun-house mirror creates a distorted image of you. Your true proportions look different in your reflection.

INVESTIGATION 1

YOU WILL NEED
- patty paper
- a ruler

What Makes Polygons Similar?

Let's explore what makes polygons similar. Hexagon *PQRSTU* is an enlargement of hexagon *ABCDEF*—they are similar.

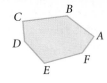
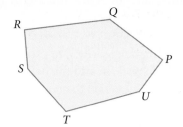

Step 1 Use patty paper to compare all corresponding angles. How do the corresponding angles compare?

Step 2 Measure the corresponding segments in both hexagons.

Step 3 Find the ratios of the lengths of corresponding sides. How do the ratios of corresponding sides compare?

Step 4 Calculate and compare these side length ratios within each polygon: $\frac{AB}{BC}$ with $\frac{PQ}{QR}$ and $\frac{EF}{CD}$ with $\frac{TU}{RS}$. What do you notice?

From Investigation 1, you should be ready to state a mathematical definition of similar polygons. Two polygons are similar if and only if the corresponding angles are congruent and the corresponding sides are in the same ratio.

Recall from algebra that a **proportion** is a statement of equality between two ratios. The equality $\frac{6}{18} = \frac{1}{3}$ is an example of a proportion. So our definition of similar polygons can be restated. Two polygons are **similar** if and only if the corresponding angles are congruent and the corresponding sides are proportional.

Are all rectangles similar? They have common characteristics, but they are not all similar. That is, you could not always enlarge or reduce a given rectangle to fit perfectly over every other rectangle. What about other geometric figures: squares, circles, triangles?

In this second investigation you will make the connection between similar polygons and dilated polygons.

INVESTIGATION 2

Similarity on the Coordinate Plane

YOU WILL NEED
- graph paper
- a straightedge
- patty paper
- a compass (optional)

In this investigation you will examine the effects of dilating a pentagon about the origin. Have each member of your group choose a different scale factor from these choices: $\frac{1}{2}$, $\frac{3}{4}$, 2, or 3.

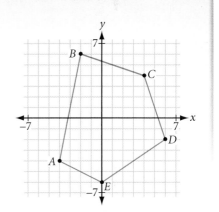

Step 1 Copy this pentagon onto your graph paper.

Step 2 Multiply the coordinates of the vertices by your scale factor.

Step 3 Locate these new coordinates on your graph paper and connect them. The new pentagon is a dilation of the original pentagon.

Step 4 Copy the original pentagon onto patty paper. Compare the corresponding angles of the two pentagons. What do you notice?

Step 5 Compare the corresponding sides with a compass or with patty paper. The length of each side of the new pentagon is how many times as long as the length of the corresponding side of the original pentagon?

Step 6 Compare results with your group. You should be ready to state a conjecture.

> **Dilation of a Polygon Conjecture** `C-57`
>
> If one polygon is a dilated image of another polygon, then _?_.

Step 7 Earlier you discovered that all circles are dilations of each other. How does that relate to the similarity of circles? Graph a circle with center (0, 0) and radius 8. Using the same scale factors that you used in the previous steps, find the new radii.

Step 8 Compare the corresponding radii. What do you notice?

Step 9 Compare your results with your group. You should be ready to state a conjecture.

> **Dilations of Circles Conjecture**   `C-58`
>
> Since one circle can be dilated to transform onto another circle, all circles are _?_ .

INVESTIGATION 3

Dilations with Construction Tools

Art
CONNECTION

Movie scenes are scaled down to small images on strips of film. Then they are scaled up to fit a large screen. So the film image and the projected image are similar. If the distance between the projector and the screen is decreased by half, each dimension of the screen image is cut in half.

Step 1 With your construction tools, construct quadrilateral *FOUR*, point *P*, and rays $\overrightarrow{PF}$, $\overrightarrow{PO}$, $\overrightarrow{PU}$, and $\overrightarrow{PR}$, as shown at right.

Step 2 With your compass, measure the distance *PF*. Use your compass to mark this distance two more times along $\overrightarrow{PF}$, and label point *F′* so that $\overline{PF'}$ is three times as long as $\overline{PF}$. Repeat this process on the other three rays to mark points *O′*, *U′*, and *R′* so that all the image points are three times as far from point *P* as the original points.

Step 3 Connect the image points to form quadrilateral *F′O′U′R′*, the image formed by dilating *FOUR* about point *P* by scale factor 3. Describe how the rays identify the center of dilation.

Step 4 Copy the original quadrilateral onto patty paper. Compare the corresponding angles of the two quadrilaterals. Explain what you observe.

Step 5 Compare the corresponding sides with a compass or patty paper. What is the ratio of each side length of the dilated quadrilateral to its corresponding side length of the original quadrilateral? Is the dilated image similar to the original? Explain why or why not.

In the three investigations you have seen that two polygons are similar if and only if the corresponding angles are congruent and the corresponding sides are proportional. You also discovered that if one polygon is a dilation of another polygon then they are similar and the ratio of corresponding sides is the scale factor of the dilation.

If $\triangle CAT$ is *congruent* to $\triangle MEW$, we write $\triangle CAT \cong \triangle MEW$. If two polygons are *similar* we use the symbol that sits above the equal sign in the congruent symbol: $\sim$.

For example, the statement $CORN \sim PEAS$ says that quadrilateral $CORN$ is similar to quadrilateral $PEAS$. Just as in statements of congruence, the order of the letters tells you which segments and which angles in the two polygons correspond.

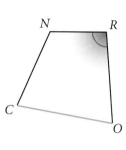

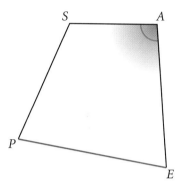

Corresponding angles are congruent:

$\angle C \cong \angle P \qquad \angle R \cong \angle A$
$\angle O \cong \angle E \qquad \angle N \cong \angle S$

Corresponding segments are proportional:

$$\frac{CO}{PE} = \frac{OR}{EA} = \frac{RN}{AS} = \frac{NC}{SP}$$

> **Art CONNECTION**
>
> This Spoonbridge and Cherry sculpture in Minneapolis was designed by Claes Oldenburg and Coosje van Bruggen. How did they use similarity to create this sculpture? Describe how you would estimate the size of this sculpture.

Notice also that the ratio of the lengths of any two segments in one polygon is equal to the ratio of the corresponding two segments in the similar polygon. For example, $\frac{CO}{OR} = \frac{PE}{EA}$ or $\frac{NR}{CO} = \frac{SA}{PE}$.

Do you need both conditions—congruent angles and proportional sides—to guarantee that the two polygons are similar? For example, if you know only that the corresponding angles of two polygons are congruent, can you conclude that the polygons have to be similar? Or, if corresponding sides of two polygons are proportional, are the polygons necessarily similar? These counterexamples show that both answers are no.

In the figures below, corresponding angles of square $SQUE$ and rectangle $RCTL$ are congruent, but their corresponding sides are not proportional.

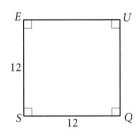

$$\frac{12}{10} \neq \frac{12}{18}$$

$$\left(\text{also, } \frac{12}{12} \neq \frac{10}{18}\right)$$

In the figures below, corresponding sides of square $SQUE$ and rhombus $RHOM$ are proportional, but their corresponding angles are not congruent.

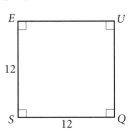

$$\frac{12}{18} = \frac{12}{18}$$

$$\left(\text{also, } \frac{12}{12} = \frac{18}{18}\right)$$

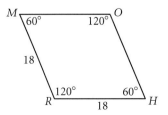

Clearly, neither pair of polygons is similar. You cannot conclude that two polygons are similar given only the fact that their corresponding angles are congruent or given only the fact that their corresponding sides are proportional.

You can use the definition of similar polygons to find missing measures in similar polygons.

EXAMPLE

$SMAL \sim BIGE$
Find x and y.

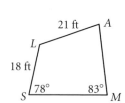 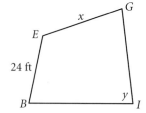

Solution

The quadrilaterals are similar, so you can use a proportion to find x.

$$\frac{18}{24} = \frac{21}{x} \qquad \text{A proportion of corresponding sides.}$$

$$18x = 24 \cdot 21 \qquad \text{Multiply both sides by 24x and simplify.}$$

$$x = 28 \qquad \text{Divide both sides by 18.}$$

The measure of the side labeled x is 28 ft.

In similar polygons, corresponding angles are congruent, so $\angle M \cong \angle I$. The measure of the angle labeled y is therefore 83°.

Notice that you could also use ratios *within* each quadrilateral to solve for x in this example: $\frac{x}{24} = \frac{21}{18}$. Check that you get the same result.

7.1 Exercises

For Exercises 1–3, match the similar figures.

YOU WILL NEED

Construction tools
for Exercise **23**

1.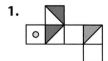

A.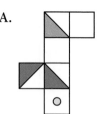

B.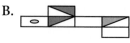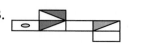

C.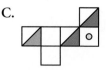

2.

A.

B.

C.

3.

A.

B.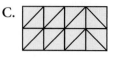

C.

For Exercises 4–6, sketch on graph paper a similar, but not congruent, figure.

4.

5.

6.

7. Complete the statement: If Figure A is similar to Figure B and Figure B is similar to Figure C, then ___?___. Draw and label figures to illustrate the statement.

8. What is the scale factor of a dilation in which the original polygon and its dilated image are congruent?

9. Are all isosceles triangles similar? Are all right triangles similar? Are all isosceles right triangles similar? Explain.

10. Draw rectangle *RECT* with sides of 8 cm and 12 cm. Draw rectangle *ANGL* with each side 3 cm shorter. Is *RECT* ∼ *ANGL*? Explain.

For Exercises 11–18, use the definition of similar polygons. All measurements are in centimeters.

11. *THINK* ∼ *LARGE*
Find *AL, RA, RG,* and *KN*.

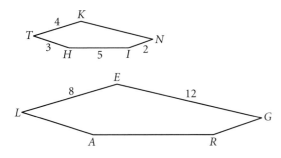

12. Are these polygons similar? Explain why or why not. ⓗ

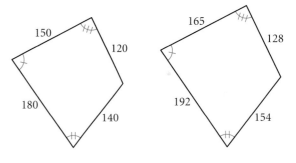

13. *SPIDER* ∼ *HNYCMB*
Find *NY, YC, CM,* and *MB*.

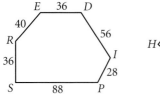

14. Are these polygons similar? Explain why or why not.

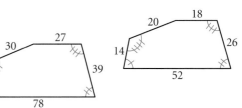

15. △*ACE* ∼ △*IKS*
Find *x* and *y*.

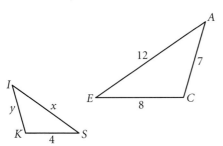

16. △*RAM* ∼ △*XAE*
Find *z*.

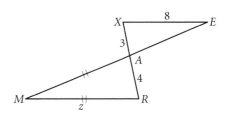

17. $\overline{DE} \parallel \overline{BC}$

Are the corresponding angles congruent in $\triangle AED$ and $\triangle ABC$? Are the corresponding sides proportional? Is $\triangle AED \sim \triangle ABC$? Explain your reasoning. ⓗ

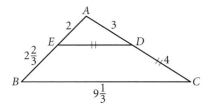

18. $\triangle ABC \sim \triangle DBA$

Find m and n.

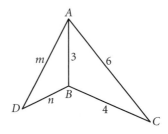

19. Copy $\triangle ROY$ onto your graph paper. Draw its dilation by a scale factor of 3. What is the center of dilation? What is the ratio of the perimeter of the dilated triangle to the perimeter of the original triangle? How does the ratio relate to the scale factor?

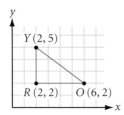

20. Copy this quadrilateral onto your graph paper. Draw its dilation by a scale factor of $\frac{1}{2}$. Is the dilation similar to the original quadrilateral? What is the center of dilation? Find the midpoints of the original quadrilateral and connect opposite midpoints to divide the quadrilateral into four quadrilaterals. How do these four quadrilaterals compare to the dilated quadrilateral?

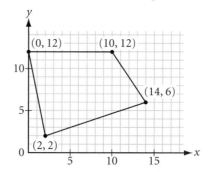

21. The photo at right shows the Crazy Horse Memorial and a scale model of the complete monument's design. The head of the Crazy Horse Memorial, from the chin to the top of the forehead, is 87.5 ft high. When the arms are carved, how long will each be? Use the photo and explain how you got your answer.

The Crazy Horse Memorial is located in South Dakota. Started in 1948, it will be the world's largest sculpture when complete.

Review

22. Jade and Omar each put in $1,000 to buy an old boat to fix up. Later Jade spent $825 on materials, and Omar spent $1,650 for parts. They worked an equal number of hours on the boat and eventually sold it for $6,800. How might they divide the $6,800 fairly? Explain your reasoning.

23. Use a compass and straightedge to construct

  a. A rhombus with a 60° angle.

  b. A second rhombus of different size with a 60° angle.

24. An 8×12 pool table has been "coordinatized" as shown to the right. If the cue ball is at (2, 6) and the eight ball is at (8, 2), what are the coordinates of the point on the top cushion that the ball must hit so that it bounces off the cushion and strikes the eight ball?

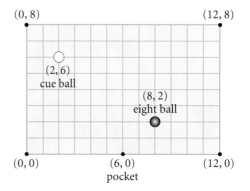

DEVELOPING MATHEMATICAL REASONING

3-by-3 Inductive Reasoning Puzzle II

Sketch the figure missing in the lower right corner of this pattern.

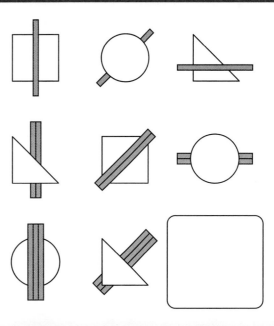

Similar Triangles

In Lesson 7.1, you concluded that you must know about both the angles and the sides of two quadrilaterals in order to make a valid conclusion about their similarity.

However, triangles are unique. Recall from Chapter 4 that you found four shortcuts for triangle congruence: SSS, SAS, ASA, and SAA. Are there shortcuts for triangle similarity as well? Let's first look for shortcuts using only angles.

The figures below illustrate that you cannot conclude that two triangles are similar given that only one set of corresponding angles is congruent. How about two sets of congruent angles?

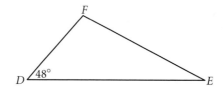

$\angle A \cong \angle D$, but $\triangle ABC$ is not similar to $\triangle DEF$ or to $\triangle DFE$.

INVESTIGATION 1

YOU WILL NEED

- a compass
- a ruler
- patty paper

Is AA a Similarity Shortcut?

If two angles of one triangle are congruent to two angles of another triangle, must the two triangles be similar?

Step 1 Draw any triangle *ABC*.

Step 2 Construct a second triangle, *DEF*, with $\angle D \cong \angle A$ and $\angle E \cong \angle B$. What will be true about $\angle C$ and $\angle F$? Why?

Step 3 Carefully measure the lengths of the sides of both triangles. Compare the ratios of the corresponding sides. Is $\frac{AB}{DE} \approx \frac{AC}{DF} \approx \frac{BC}{EF}$?

Step 4 Compare your results with the results of others near you. You should be ready to state a conjecture.

AA Similarity Conjecture   **C-59**

If _?_ angles of one triangle are congruent to _?_ angles of another triangle, then _?_.

Now let's look for shortcuts for similarity that use only sides. The figures at right illustrate that you cannot conclude that two triangles are similar given that two sets of corresponding sides are proportional.

$$\frac{54}{108} = \frac{1}{2}$$
$$\frac{48}{96} = \frac{1}{2}$$

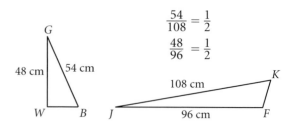

$\frac{GB}{JK} = \frac{GW}{JF}$, but $\triangle GWB$ is not similar to $\triangle JFK$.

How about all three sets of corresponding sides?

INVESTIGATION 2

Is SSS a Similarity Shortcut?

YOU WILL NEED

- a compass
- a straightedge
- a protractor
- patty paper

If three sides of one triangle are proportional to the three sides of another triangle, must the two triangles be similar?

Draw any triangle *ABC*. Then construct a second triangle, *DEF*, whose side lengths are a multiple of the original triangle. (Your second triangle can be larger or smaller.)

Compare the corresponding angles of the two triangles. Compare your results with the results of others near you and state a conjecture.

> **SSS Similarity Conjecture**   C-60
>
> If the three sides of one triangle are proportional to the three sides of another triangle, then the two triangles are _?_ .

So SSS and AA are shortcuts for triangle similarity. That leaves SAS and SSA as possible shortcuts to consider.

INVESTIGATION 3

Is SAS a Similarity Shortcut?

YOU WILL NEED

- a compass
- a protractor
- a ruler
- patty paper

Is SAS a shortcut for similarity? Try to construct two different triangles that are not similar but have two pairs of sides proportional and the pair of included angles equal in measure.

Compare the measures of corresponding sides and corresponding angles. Share your results with others near you and state a conjecture.

> **SAS Similarity Conjecture**   C-61
>
> If two sides of one triangle are proportional to two sides of another triangle and _?_ , then the _?_ .

DEVELOPING PROOF

Your group just performed three investigations leading to three similarity shortcut conjectures. In this *Developing Proof* section your group will select one or more of the three proofs below and together write the proof.

Proof 1   If AA is a similarity shortcut, explain why the AAA, ASA, and SAA are automatically similarity shortcuts as well.

Proof 2 Explain how SSS is a similarity shortcut using dilations. For example, dilate △*TUV* by a scale factor *r*, where *r* > 0. What is the ratio of each side in the image △*T'U'V'* to the corresponding side in the original △*TUV*?

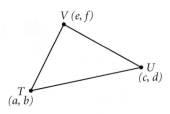

Is △*TUV* ~ △*T'U'V'*? As a group, write a convincing argument showing how SSS is a similarity shortcut.

Proof 3 One question remains: Is SSA a shortcut for similarity? SSA did not work as a congruence shortcut because you could create two different triangles with the given parts. Discuss if this is also true for similarity. Explain why SSA is or is not a similarity shortcut.

7.2 Exercises

For Exercises 1–14, use your new conjectures. All measurements are in centimeters.

1. *g* = ?

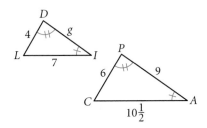

2. *h* = ?, *k* = ?

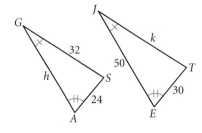

3. *m* = ? Ⓗ

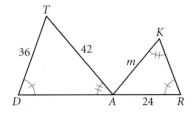

4. *n* = ?, *s* = ?

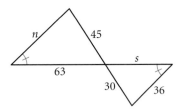

5. Is △*AUL* ~ △*MST*? Explain why or why not.

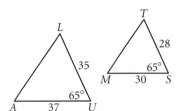

6. Is △*MOY* ~ △*NOT*? Explain why or why not.

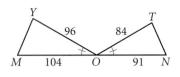

7. Why is △*TMR* ~ △*THM* ~ △*MHR*? Find *x*, *y*, and *h*. Ⓗ

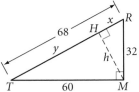

8. $\overline{TA} \parallel \overline{UR}$
Is ∠*QTA* ≅ ∠*TUR*?
Is ∠*QAT* ≅ ∠*ARU*?
Why is △*QTA* ~ △*QUR*?
e = ?

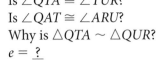

9. $\overline{OR} \parallel \overline{UE} \parallel \overline{NT}$
f = ?, *g* = ?

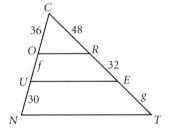

10. *FROG* is a trapezoid.
Is $\angle RGO \cong \angle FRG$?
Is $\angle GOF \cong \angle RFO$?
Why is $\triangle GOS \sim \triangle RFS$?
$t = \underline{?}\,, s = \underline{?}$

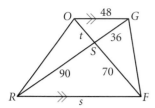

11. *TOAD* is a trapezoid.
$w = \underline{?}\,, x = \underline{?}$

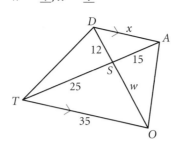

12. Find x and y. ⓗ

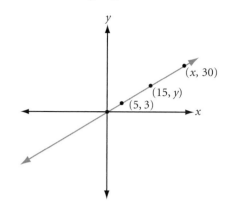

13. $\triangle MPL \sim \triangle FPV$.
$PF = \underline{?}\,, m\angle PFV = \underline{?}$

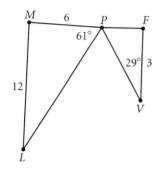

14. $\triangle ABC \sim \triangle$???. Why?

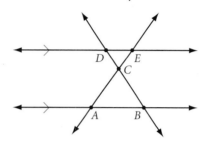

15. $\overline{BQ} \parallel \overline{RD}$, $\triangle R'D'X$ is a reflection of $\triangle RDX$.
Explain why $\triangle QBX \sim \triangle D'R'X$.

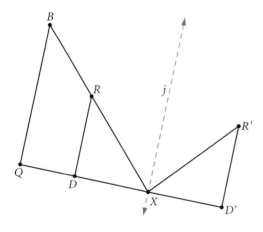

16. Show that $\triangle ABC$ is similar to $\triangle PQR$ by translating $\triangle ABC$ so that point B coincides with point Q. Find the scale factor that you need to use to dilate $\triangle A'B'C'$ so that its image $\triangle A''B''C''$ coincides with $\triangle PQR$. What was the ordered pair rule you used? What technique could you use to find the center of dilation? You will explore more about finding the center of dilation in the performance task at the end of this lesson.

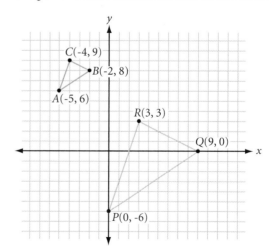

Review

17. Phoung volunteers at an SPCA that always houses 8 dogs. She notices that she uses seven 35-pound bags of dry dog food every two months. A new, larger SPCA facility that houses 20 dogs will open soon. Help Phoung estimate the amount of dry dog food that the facility should order every three months. Explain your reasoning.

18. In the Coordinate Geometry lesson, Dilations on the Coordinate Plane, you translated and dilated one circle to coincide with another circle. Thus, as you already knew, any two circles are similar. Equilateral $\triangle ABC$ is similar to equilateral $\triangle DEF$ by the AA similarity shortcut. Describe the steps necessary to transform equilateral $\triangle ABC$ so that its image $\triangle A'B'C'$ coincides with equilateral $\triangle DEF$, thus demonstrating by transformations that any two equilateral triangles are similar.

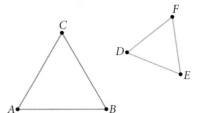

19. The photo at right shows a number of fragments of the Colossus of Constantine arranged in the courtyard of the Palazzo dei Conservatori of the Musei Capitolini, in Rome. Historians have determined that the statue had Constantine sitting on his throne. Use this photo to estimate how tall the entire statue was. List the measurements you need to make. List any assumptions you need to make. Explain your reasoning.

→ *History*
CONNECTION

Constantinople was named for the Emperor Constantine the Great (Roman Emperor 306–337 C.E.), depicted in this colossal statue built between 315 and 330 C.E. It broke when sculptors tried to add the extra weight of a beard to its face. The pieces of the statue remain close to its original location in Rome, Italy.

PERFORMANCE TASK

In this chapter, you have dilated figures in the coordinate plane, using the origin as the center of dilation. What happens if a different point in the plane is the center of dilation? Copy the polygon at right onto graph paper. Draw the polygon's image under a dilation with a scale factor of 2 and with point A as the center of dilation. Draw another image using a scale factor of $\frac{2}{3}$. Explain how you found the image points. How does dilating about point A differ from dilating about the origin?

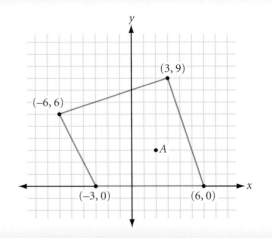

Indirect Measurement with Similar Triangles

"Never be afraid to sit awhile and think."

LORRAINE HANSBERRY

You can use similar triangles to calculate the height of tall objects that you can't reach. This is called **indirect measurement**. One method uses mirrors. Try it in the next investigation.

INVESTIGATION

YOU WILL NEED

- metersticks
- masking tape or a soluble pen
- a mirror

Mirror, Mirror

Choose a tall object with a height that would be difficult to measure directly, such as a football goalpost, a basketball hoop, a flagpole, or the height of your classroom.

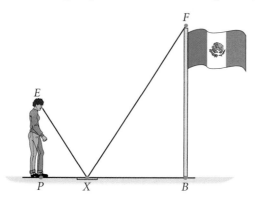

Step 1 Mark crosshairs on your mirror. Use tape or a soluble pen. Call the intersection point *X*. Place the mirror on the ground several meters from your object.

Step 2 An observer should move to a point *P* in line with the object and the mirror in order to see the reflection of an identifiable point *F* at the top of the object at point *X* on the mirror. Make a sketch of your setup, like this one.

Step 3 Measure the distance *PX* and the distance from *X* to a point *B* at the base of the object directly below *F*. Measure the distance from *P* to the observer's eye level, *E*.

Step 4 Think of $\overline{FX}$ as a light ray that bounces back to the observer's eye along $\overline{XE}$. Why is $\angle B \cong \angle P$? Name two similar triangles. Tell why they are similar.

Step 5 Set up a proportion using corresponding sides of similar triangles. Use it to calculate *FB*, the approximate height of the tall object.

Step 6 Write a summary of what you and your group did in this investigation. Discuss possible causes for error.

Another method of indirect measurement uses shadows.

EXAMPLE | A person 5 feet 3 inches tall casts a 6-foot shadow. At the same time of day, a lamppost casts an 18-foot shadow. What is the height of the lamppost?

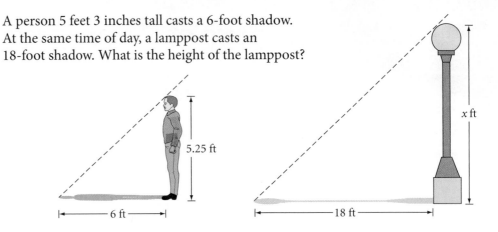

5.25 ft

x ft

6 ft   18 ft

Solution | The light rays that create the shadows hit the ground at congruent angles. Assuming both the person and the lamppost are perpendicular to the ground, you have similar triangles by the AA Similarity Conjecture. Solve a proportion that relates corresponding lengths.

$$\frac{5.25}{6} = \frac{x}{18}$$ Ratios of side lengths *within* similar triangles are equal.

$$18 \cdot \frac{5.25}{6} = x$$ Multiply both sides by 18.

$$15.75 = x$$ Simplify left side.

The height of the lamppost is 15 feet 9 inches.

(7.3) Exercises

YOU WILL NEED

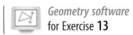

Geometry software
for Exercise **13**

1. A flagpole 4 meters tall casts a 6-meter shadow. At the same time of day, a nearby building casts a 24-meter shadow. How tall is the building?

2. Five-foot-tall Melody casts an 84-inch shadow. How tall is her friend if, at the same time of day, his shadow is 1 foot shorter than hers?

3. A 26-ft rope from the top of a flagpole reaches to the end of the flagpole's 10-ft shadow. How tall is the nearby football goalpost if, at the same moment, it has a shadow of 12.5 ft? *ⓗ*

4. Private eye Samantha Diamond places a mirror on the ground between herself and an apartment building and stands so that when she looks into the mirror, she sees into a window. The mirror's crosshairs are 1.22 meters from her feet and 7.32 meters from the base of the building. Sam's eye is 1.82 meters above the ground. How high is the window?

5. Juanita, who is 1.82 meters tall, wants to find the height of a tree in her backyard. From the tree's base, she walks 12.20 meters along the tree's shadow to a position where the end of her shadow exactly overlaps the end of the tree's shadow. She is now 6.10 meters from the end of the shadows. How tall is the tree?

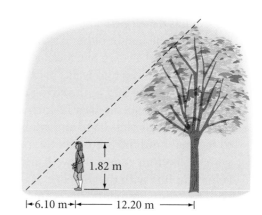

1.82 m

6.10 m — 12.20 m

6. While vacationing in Egypt, the Greek mathematician Thales calculated the height of the Great Pyramid. According to legend, Thales placed a pole at the tip of the pyramid's shadow and used similar triangles to calculate its height. This involved some estimating because he was unable to measure the distance from directly beneath the height of the pyramid to the tip of the shadow. From the diagram, explain his method. Calculate the height of the pyramid from the information given in the diagram.

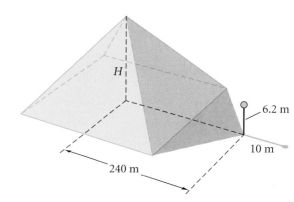

H

6.2 m

10 m

240 m

7. Calculate the distance across this river, *PR*, by sighting a pole, at point *P*, on the opposite bank. Points *R* and *O* are collinear with point *P*. Point *C* is chosen so that $\overline{OC} \perp \overline{PO}$. Lastly, point *E* is chosen so that *P*, *E*, and *C* are collinear and $\overline{RE} \perp \overline{PO}$. Also explain why $\triangle PRE \sim \triangle POC$. ⓗ

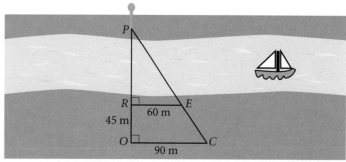

P

R ┐ 60 m E

45 m

O ┐ 90 m C

8. A pinhole camera is a simple device. Place unexposed film at one end of a shoe box, and make a pinhole at the opposite end. When light comes through the pinhole, an inverted image is produced on the film. Suppose you take a picture of a painting that is 30 cm wide by 45 cm high with a pinhole box camera that is 20 cm deep. How far from the painting should the pinhole be to make an image that is 2 cm wide by 3 cm high? Sketch a diagram of this situation. ⓗ

9. Kristin has developed a new method for indirectly measuring the height of her classroom. Her method uses string and a ruler. She tacks a piece of string to the base of the wall and walks back from the wall holding the other end of the string to her eye with her right hand. She holds a 12-inch ruler parallel to the wall in her left hand and adjusts her distance to the wall until the bottom of the ruler is in line with the bottom edge of the wall and the top of the ruler is in line with the top edge of the wall. Now with two measurements, she is able to calculate the height of the room. Explain her method. If the distance from her eye to the bottom of the ruler is 23 inches and the distance from her eye to the bottom of the wall is 276 inches, calculate the height of the room.

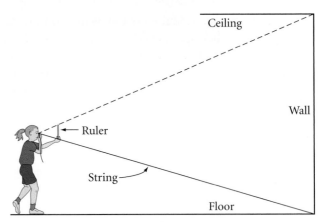

Review

For Exercises 10 and 11, first identify similar triangles and explain why they are similar. Then find the missing lengths. All measurements are in inches.

10. Find x. ⓗ

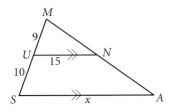

11. Find x, y, and h. ⓗ

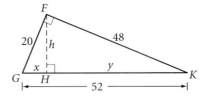

12. You are given the midpoints of the three sides of a triangle. How do you find the vertices of the triangle? Explain your method.

13. On a segment AB, point X is called the **golden cut** if $\frac{AB}{AX} = \frac{AX}{XB}$, where $AX > XB$. The **golden ratio** is the value of $\frac{AB}{AX}$ and $\frac{AX}{XB}$ when they are equal. Use geometry software to explore the location of the golden cut on any segment AB. What is the value of the golden ratio? Find a way to construct the golden cut. ⓗ

A •———————————— X •———————————— B

$$\frac{AB}{AX} = \frac{AX}{XB} = ?$$

14. Identify the point of concurrency E in △CON from the construction marks. Explain how you know.

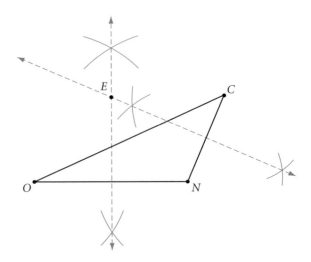

Corresponding Parts of Similar Triangles

Is there more to similar triangles than just proportional side lengths and congruent angles? For example, are there relationships between the lengths of corresponding altitudes, corresponding medians, or corresponding angle bisectors in similar triangles? Let's investigate.

INVESTIGATION 1

Corresponding Parts

YOU WILL NEED
- a compass
- a straightedge

Use unlined paper for this investigation. Have each member of your group pick a different scale factor.

Step 1 Draw any triangle. Using your scale factor, construct a similar triangle of a different size.

Step 2 Construct a pair of corresponding altitudes and use your compass to compare their lengths. How do they compare? How does the comparison relate to the scale factor you used?

Step 3 Construct a pair of corresponding medians. How do their lengths compare?

Step 4 Construct a pair of corresponding angle bisectors. How do their lengths compare?

Step 5 Compare your results with the results of others near you. You should be ready to make a conjecture.

Proportional Parts Conjecture	C-62
If two triangles are similar, then the lengths of the corresponding ?, ?, and ? are ? to the lengths of the corresponding sides.	

Recall when you first saw an angle bisector in a triangle. You may have thought that the bisector of an angle in a triangle divides the opposite side into two equal parts as well. A counterexample shows that this is not necessarily true. In $\triangle ROE$, $\overline{RT}$ bisects $\angle R$, but point T does not bisect $\overline{OE}$.

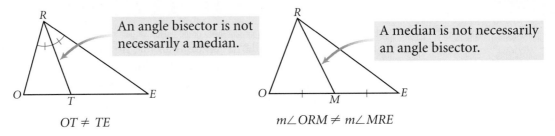

An angle bisector is not necessarily a median.

A median is not necessarily an angle bisector.

$OT \neq TE$

$m\angle ORM \neq m\angle MRE$

The angle bisector does, however, divide the opposite side in a particular way.

 INVESTIGATION 2

YOU WILL NEED

● a compass
● a ruler

Opposite Side Ratios

In this investigation you'll discover that there is a proportional relationship involving angle bisectors.

Step 1 Draw any angle. Label it A.

Step 2 On one ray, locate point C so that AC is 6 cm. Use the same compass setting and locate point B on the other ray so that AB is 12 cm. Draw $\overline{BC}$ to form $\triangle ABC$.

Step 3 Construct the bisector of $\angle A$. Locate point D where the bisector intersects side $\overline{BC}$.

Step 4 Measure and compare CD and BD.

Step 5 Calculate and compare the ratios $\frac{CA}{BA}$ and $\frac{CD}{BD}$.

Step 6 Repeat Steps 1–5 with $AC = 10$ cm and $AB = 15$ cm.

Step 7 Compare your results with the results of others near you. State a conjecture.

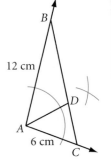

Angle Bisector/Opposite Side Conjecture	C-63

A bisector of an angle in a triangle divides the opposite side into two segments whose lengths are in the same ratio as ? .

Now let's look at how you can use deductive reasoning to prove one part of the Proportional Parts Conjecture that you discovered through inductive reasoning earlier in this lesson.

DEVELOPING PROOF

Your group just performed two investigations leading to two conjectures. In this *Developing Proof* section your group will select one or both of the two proofs below and together write the proof.

Proof 1 The flowchart proof shown below does not have the reasons for each step. In your group, study and discuss the flowchart proof. Prove that *the lengths of the corresponding medians of similar triangles are proportional to the lengths of the corresponding sides.* Either provide the reasons in the flowchart proof, or write your own proof.

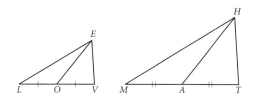

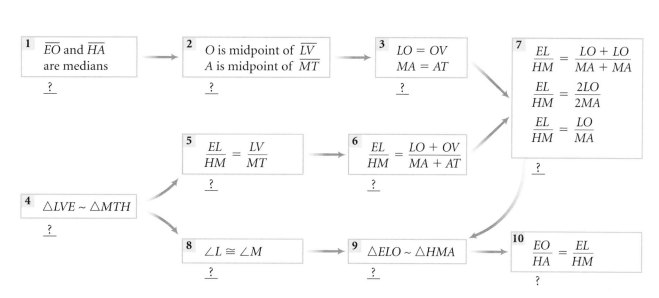

Proof 2 In the second investigation you discovered a proportional relationship in a triangle, but there didn't seem to be any similar triangles involved! In $\triangle ABC$ shown below left, none of the three triangles: $\triangle ABC$, $\triangle ACD$, or $\triangle ABD$ are similar. But with the help of a few auxiliary lines, you can create similar triangles. To create a proof of the Angle Bisector/Opposite Side Conjecture, drop perpendiculars to the angle bisector from the other two vertices as shown below right. This gives you two different pairs of similar right triangles. Use this diagram to prove the Angle Bisector/Opposite Side Conjecture.

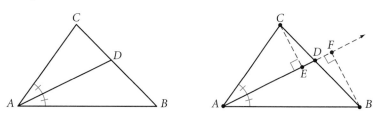

YOU WILL NEED

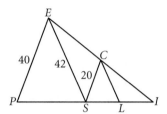

Geometry software
for Exercise **18**

For Exercises 1–13, use your new conjectures. All measurements are in centimeters.

1. △ICE ~ △AGE
h = ?

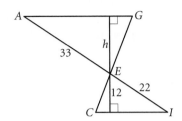

2. △SKI ~ △JMP
x = ?

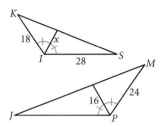

3. △PIE ~ △SIC
Point S is the midpoint of $\overline{PI}$.
Point L is the midpoint
of $\overline{SI}$. CL = ? ⓗ

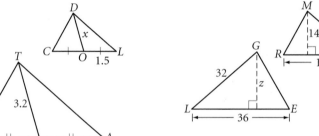

4. △CAP ~ △DAY
FD = ?

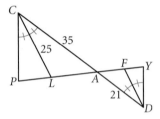

5. △HAT ~ △CLD
x = ?

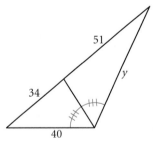

6. △ARM ~ △LEG
z = ?

7. v = ?

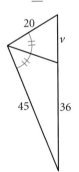

8. y = ?

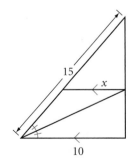

9. x = ? ⓗ

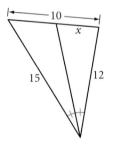

10. $\frac{a}{b}$ = ?, $\frac{a}{p}$ = ?

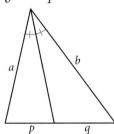

11. x = ? ⓗ

12. Prove that corresponding angle bisectors of similar triangles are proportional to corresponding sides. ⓗ

13. Triangle *PQR* is a dilated image of △*ABC*. Find the coordinates of *B* and *R*. Find the ratio $\frac{k}{h}$.

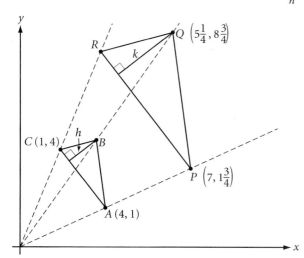

14. Do you think that proportional relationships exist between corresponding diagonals of similar quadrilaterals? Investigate, conjecture, and prove your conjecture.

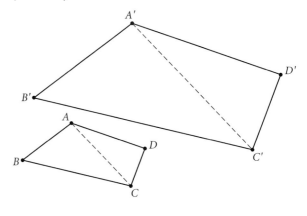

Review

15. A rectangle is divided into four rectangles, each similar to the original rectangle. What is the ratio of short side to long side in the rectangles?

16. In Chapter 5, you discovered that when you construct the three midsegments in a triangle, they divide the triangle into four congruent triangles. Are the four triangles similar to the original? Explain why or why not.

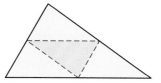

17. Assume $\frac{AB}{XY} = \frac{BC}{YZ}$. Find *AB* and *BC*.

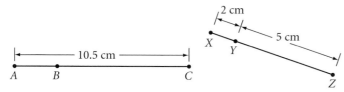

18. **GUESS-N-CHECK** As *B* moves from left to right along ℓ_1, describe what happens to each of the values below. First, try this as a "mental experiment." Take a guess, then create the diagram with your geometry software and see how good you were at visualization.

a. $m\angle ABP$

b. $m\angle PAB$

c. $m\angle APB$

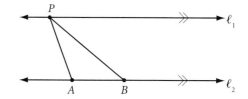

Proportional Segments Between Parallel Lines

In the figure below, $\overleftrightarrow{MT} \parallel \overline{LU}$. Is $\triangle LUV$ similar to $\triangle MTV$? Yes, it is. A short paragraph proof can support this observation.

Given: $\triangle LUV$ with $\overleftrightarrow{MT} \parallel \overline{LU}$

Show: $\triangle LUV \sim \triangle MTV$

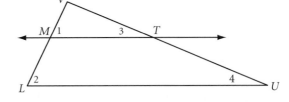

Paragraph Proof

First assume that the Corresponding Angles Conjecture and the AA Similarity Conjecture are true.

If $\overleftrightarrow{MT} \parallel \overline{LU}$, then $\angle 1 \cong \angle 2$ and $\angle 3 \cong \angle 4$ by the Corresponding Angles Conjecture.

If $\angle 1 \cong \angle 2$ and $\angle 3 \cong \angle 4$, then $\triangle LUV \sim \triangle MTV$ by the AA Similarity Conjecture.

Let's see how you can use this observation to solve problems.

EXAMPLE A

$\overline{EO} \parallel \overline{LN}$

$y = \underline{\ ?\ }$

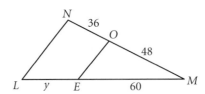

Solution

Separate $\triangle EMO$ and $\triangle LMN$ so that you can see the proportional relationships more clearly. Use the fact that $\triangle EMO \sim \triangle LMN$ to write a proportion with lengths of corresponding sides.

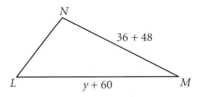

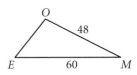

$$\frac{LM}{EM} = \frac{NM}{OM}$$ Corresponding sides of similar triangles are proportional.

$$\frac{y + 60}{60} = \frac{36 + 48}{48}$$ Substitute lengths given in the figure.

$$\frac{y + 60}{60} = \frac{7}{4}$$ Simplify the right side of the equation.

$$y + 60 = 105$$ Multiply both sides by 60 and simplify.

$$y = 45$$ Subtract 60 from both sides.

Notice that the ratio $\frac{LE}{EM}$ is the same as the ratio $\frac{NO}{OM}$. So there are more relationships in the figure than the ones we find in similar triangles. Let's investigate.

INVESTIGATION 1

YOU WILL NEED

● a ruler

● a protractor

Parallels and Proportionality

In this investigation we'll look at the ratios of segments that have been cut by parallel lines.

Step 1 Separate each figure below into two triangles. Then find x and numerical values for the given ratios.

a. $\overleftrightarrow{EC} \parallel \overline{AB}$

$x = \underline{?}$

$\dfrac{DE}{AE} = \underline{?}, \dfrac{DC}{BC} = \underline{?}$

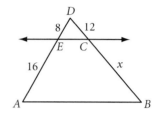

b. $\overleftrightarrow{KH} \parallel \overline{FG}$

$x = \underline{?}$

$\dfrac{JK}{KF} = \underline{?}, \dfrac{JH}{HG} = \underline{?}$

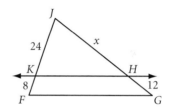

c. $\overleftrightarrow{QN} \parallel \overline{LM}$

$x = \underline{?}$

$\dfrac{PQ}{QL} = \underline{?}, \dfrac{PN}{MN} = \underline{?}$

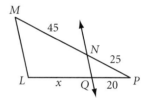

Step 2 What do you notice about the ratios of the lengths of the segments that have been cut by the parallel lines?

Is the converse true? That is, if a line divides two sides of a triangle proportionally, is it parallel to the third side? Let's see.

Step 3 Draw an acute angle, P.

Step 4 Beginning at point P, use your ruler to mark off lengths of 8 cm and 10 cm on one ray. Label the points A and B.

Step 5 Mark off lengths of 12 cm and 15 cm on the other ray. Label the points C and D. Notice that $\frac{8}{10} = \frac{12}{15}$.

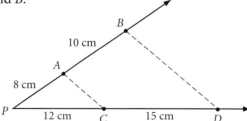

Step 6 Draw $\overline{AC}$ and $\overline{BD}$.

Step 7 With a protractor, measure $\angle PAC$ and $\angle PBD$. Are $\overline{AC}$ and $\overline{BD}$ parallel? How do you know?

Step 8 Repeat Steps 3–7, but this time use your ruler to create your own lengths such that $\frac{PA}{AB} = \frac{PC}{CD}$.

Step 9 Compare your results with the results of others near you.

You should be ready to combine your observations from Steps 2 and 9 into one conjecture.

Parallel/Proportionality Conjecture | C-64

If a line parallel to one side of a triangle passes through the other two sides, then it divides the other two sides _?_. Conversely, if a line cuts two sides of a triangle proportionally, then it is _?_ to the third side.

DEVELOPING PROOF

If you assume that the AA Similarity Conjecture is true, you can use algebra to prove the Parallel/Proportionality Conjecture. With your group members prove the first part of the conjecture. It is started for you below.

Given: $\triangle ABC$ with $\overleftrightarrow{XY} \parallel \overline{BC}$

Show: $\dfrac{a}{c} = \dfrac{b}{d}$

(Assume that the lengths a, b, c, and d are all nonzero.)

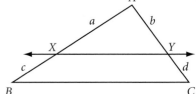

First, you know that $\triangle AXY \sim \triangle ABC$ (see the proof at the beginning of the lesson). Use a proportion of corresponding sides.

$$\frac{a}{a+c} = \frac{b}{b+d}$$ Lengths of corresponding sides of similar triangles are proportional.

From here you should be able to arrive at $\dfrac{a}{c} = \dfrac{b}{d}$.

Can the Parallel/Proportionality Conjecture help you divide segments into several proportional parts? Let's investigate.

INVESTIGATION 2

Extended Parallel/Proportionality

Step 1   Use the Parallel/Proportionality Conjecture to find each missing length. Are the ratios equal?

a. $\overline{FT} \parallel \overline{LA} \parallel \overline{GR}$

$x = \underline{?}$, $y = \underline{?}$

Is $\dfrac{FL}{LG} = \dfrac{TA}{AR}$?

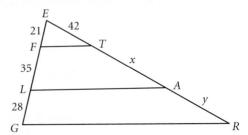

b. $\overline{ZE} \parallel \overline{OP} \parallel \overline{IA} \parallel \overline{DR}$

$a = \underline{?}, b = \underline{?}, c = \underline{?}$

Is $\dfrac{DI}{IO} = \dfrac{RA}{AP}$?

Is $\dfrac{IO}{OZ} = \dfrac{AP}{PE}$?

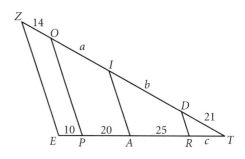

Step 2 Compare your results with the results of others near you. Complete the conjecture below.

> ### Extended Parallel/Proportionality Conjecture   C-65
>
> If two or more lines pass through two sides of a triangle parallel to the third side, then they divide the two sides $\underline{?}$.

Exploring the converse of this conjecture has been left for you as a Take Another Look activity.

You already know how to use a perpendicular bisector to divide a segment into two, four, or eight equal parts. Now you can use your new conjecture to divide a segment into *any* number of equal parts.

EXAMPLE B

Divide any segment *AB* into three congruent parts using only a compass and straightedge.

Solution

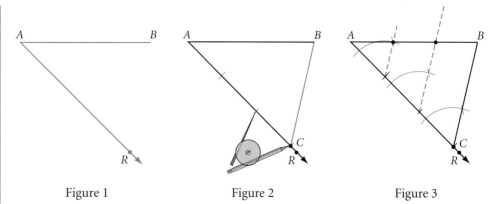

Figure 1   Figure 2   Figure 3

Draw segment *AB*. From one endpoint of $\overline{AB}$, draw any ray to form an angle (Figure 1). On the ray, mark off three congruent segments with your compass. Connect the third compass mark to the other endpoint of $\overline{AB}$ to form a triangle (Figure 2).

Finally, through the other two compass marks on the ray, construct lines parallel to the third side of the triangle (Figure 3). The two parallel lines divide $\overline{AB}$ into three equal parts.

7.5 Exercises

For Exercises 1–12, all measurements are in centimeters.

YOU WILL NEED

Construction tools
for Exercises **13** and **14**

Geometry software
for Exercise **23**

1. $\ell \parallel \overline{WE}$
$a = \underline{\ ?\ }$ (h)

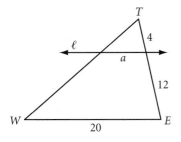

2. $m \parallel \overline{DR}$
$b = \underline{\ ?\ }$

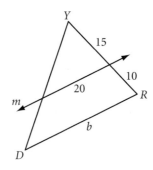

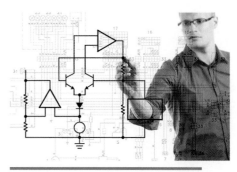

Similarity is used to create integrated circuits. Electrical engineers use large-scale maps of extremely small silicon chips. This engineer is making a scale drawing of a computer chip.

3. $n \parallel \overline{SN}$
$c = \underline{\ ?\ }$ (h)

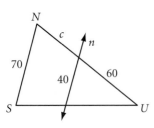

4. $\ell \parallel \overline{RA}$
$d = \underline{\ ?\ }$

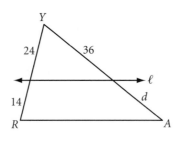

5. $m \parallel \overline{BA}$
$e = \underline{\ ?\ }$

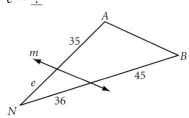

6. Is $r \parallel \overline{AN}$? (h)

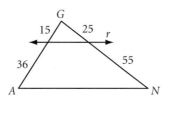

7. Alex and José have each found the value of x in the diagram at right in different ways and are explaining their methods. Alex says, "The proportion I used to solve this problem is $\frac{x}{14} = \frac{30}{12}$, so x is 35." José looks puzzled and responds, "I got x is 21 by using the proportion $\frac{x + 14}{30} = \frac{14}{12}$." Explain which method is correct and what is wrong with the incorrect method.

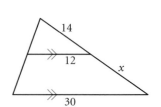

8. Is $m \parallel \overline{FL}$?

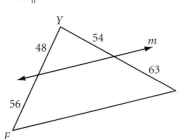

9. $r \parallel s \parallel \overline{OU}$
$m = \underline{?}, n = \underline{?}$

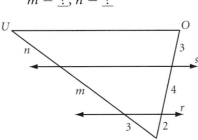

10. $\overline{MR} \parallel p \parallel q$
$w = \underline{?}, x = \underline{?}$

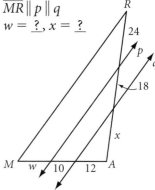

11. Is $m \parallel \overline{EA}$?
Is $n \parallel \overline{EA}$?
Is $m \parallel n$?

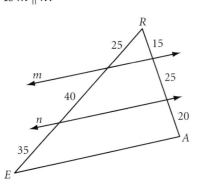

12. Is $\overline{XY} \parallel \overline{GO}$?
Is $\overline{XY} \parallel \overline{FR}$?
Is *FROG* a trapezoid?

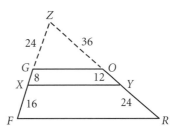

13. Draw segment *EF*. Use compass and straightedge to divide it into five equal parts.

14. Draw segment *IJ*. Construct a regular hexagon with *IJ* as the perimeter.

15. You can use a sheet of lined paper to divide a segment into equal parts. Draw a segment on a piece of patty paper, and divide it into five equal parts by placing it over lined paper. Which conjecture explains why this works?

16. The drafting tool shown at right is called a sector compass. You position a given segment between the 100-marks. What points on the compass should you connect to construct a segment that is three-fourths (or 75%) of *BC*? Explain why this works.

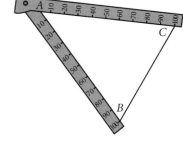

17. Assume that the SAS Similarity Conjecture and the Converse of the Parallel Lines Conjecture are true. Write a proof to show that if a line cuts two sides of a triangle proportionally, then it is parallel to the third side.

Given: $\dfrac{a}{c} = \dfrac{b}{d}$ (Assume $c \neq 0$ and $d \neq 0$.)

Show: $\overleftrightarrow{AB} \parallel \overline{YZ}$

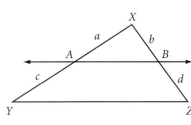

18. Another drafting tool used to construct segments is a pair of proportional dividers, shown at right. Two styluses of equal length are connected by a screw. The tool is adjusted for different proportions by moving the screw. Where should the screw be positioned so that *AB* is three-fourths of *CD*?

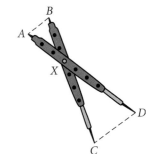

The Extended Parallel/Proportionality Conjecture can be extended even further. That is, you don't necessarily need a triangle. If three or more parallel lines intercept two other lines (transversals) in the same plane, they do so proportionally. For Exercises 19 and 20 use this extension.

19. Find x and y.

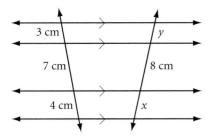

20. A real estate developer has parceled land between a river and River Road as shown. The land has been divided by segments perpendicular to the road. What is the "river frontage" (lengths x, y, and z) for each of the three lots?

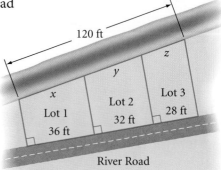

Review

21. Find the measure of each lettered angle in the diagram below.

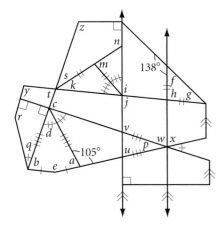

22. Copy the figure below onto your own paper. Divide it into four figures similar to the original figure. Explain how you know they are similar.

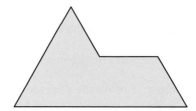

23. In Lesson 7.3, Exercise 13, you learned about the golden cut and the golden ratio. A **golden rectangle** is a rectangle in which the ratio of the length to the width is the golden ratio. That is, a golden rectangle's length, l, and width, w, satisfy the proportion

$$\frac{w}{l} = \frac{l}{w+1}$$

a. Use geometry software to construct a golden rectangle. Your construction for Exercise 13 in Lesson 7.3 will help.

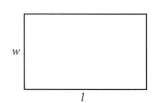

A golden rectangle

b. When a square is cut off one end of a golden rectangle, the remaining rectangle is a smaller, similar golden rectangle. If you continue this process over and over again, and then connect opposite vertices of the squares with quarter-circles, you create a curve called the **golden spiral**. Use geometry software to construct a golden spiral. The first three quarter-circles are shown below.

Some researchers believe Greek architects used golden rectangles to design the Parthenon.

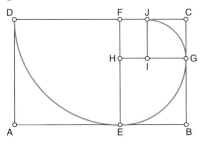

ABCD is a golden rectangle.

EBCF is a golden rectangle.

HGCF is a golden rectangle.

IJFH is a golden rectangle.

The curve from D to E to G to J is the beginning of a golden spiral.

DEVELOPING MATHEMATICAL REASONING

Color Code Puzzle I

Color Code Puzzles are very similar to the Bagels puzzles you have solved earlier. One player (*code creator*) picks a set of four colored discs (colors may be repeated) and hides them in a row, visible only to the *code creator* and hidden from the opponent (*code breaker*).

Like Bagels puzzles, your task with Color Code puzzles is to guess the order and color of the four colored circles that have been hidden. The *code breaker* takes a guess by selecting four colored discs from the set of six colors and places them in the first row nearest them in whatever order they wish (for example red-green-yellow-yellow). The *code creator* gives the *code breaker* a clue after each guess. As the game progresses, the *code breaker's* guesses become more educated or logical with the help of the clues. Here are the clues.

◯ Nothing is correct.

⊖ One color disc is correct but in the wrong position.

⊕ One color disc is correct and in the correct position.

In the game below, a number of guesses have been made, with the clue for each guess shown to its right. From the given set of guesses and clues, determine the four-color arrangement.

Answer	?	?	?	?	
Guess #4	◯	◯	◯	◯	⊖⊖⊖⊖
Guess #3	◯	◯	◯	◯	⊕⊖
Guess #2	◯	◯	◯	◯	⊕⊖⊖
Guess #1	◯	◯	◯	◯	⊖

Similarity has many applications. Any scale drawing or model, anything that is reduced or enlarged, is governed by the properties of similar figures. So engineers, visual artists, and film-makers all use similarity. It is also useful in indirect measurement. Do you recall the two indirect measurement methods you learned in this chapter? How do you use dilations to create similar figures? What are the ordered pair rules that describe dilations? Are all polygons similar? Are all circles similar?

Exercises

In Exercises 1–5, identify the statement as true or false. For each true statement, explain why it is true. For each false statement, explain why it is false and sketch a counterexample.

YOU WILL NEED

Construction tools
for Exercise **19**

1. All equiangular hexagons are similar.

2. If a polygon is dilated by a scale factor of 1, then the original polygon and its image are congruent.

3. If a polygon is dilated by a scale factor of 3, then the ratio of the perimeter of the original polygon to the image polygon is 1 to 3.

4. Circle P with center at $(2, 3)$ is tangent to the x-axis. Circle Q with center at $(-5, -7)$ is tangent to the y-axis. If circle P is transformed by the ordered pair rule $(x, y) \rightarrow (\frac{5}{3}x - 7, \frac{5}{3}y - 10)$ then the image of P will coincide with circle Q.

5. If you can measure the length of a shadow of an object, you can determine the height of the object.

For exercises 6 and 7, sketch on graph paper a similar, but not congruent figure.

6.
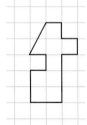

7.
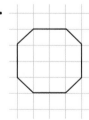

8. Given △DEF and △QRT. What is the dilation rule $(x, y) \rightarrow (?, ?)$ used to create the image △QRT? What is the center of dilation?

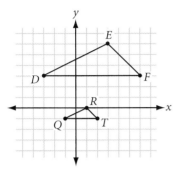

9. Given the rectangles below, which rectangles are similar? Which are congruent? Explain your reasoning for each.

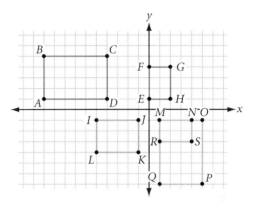

10. Given △SLZ and △BLD. Are the triangles similar? If they are, explain why. If not, explain why not.

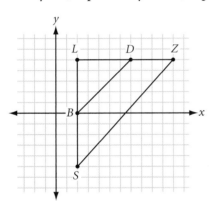

11. $\overline{MA} \parallel t$.
$z = ?$

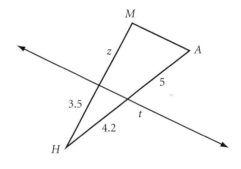

In Exercises 12 and 13, measurements are in centimeters.

12. ABCDE ~ FGHIJ
$w = ?, x = ?, y = ?, z = ?$

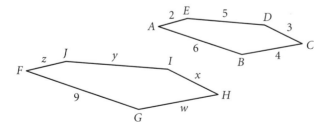

13. △ABC ~ △DBA
$x = ?, y = ?$

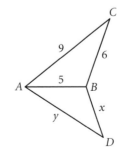

14. $\overline{TU} \parallel \overline{WX}$

$\triangle TUV \sim \triangle$???

Explain why.

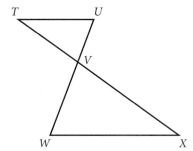

15. Are these polygons similar? Explain why or why not.

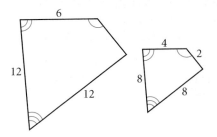

16. Katie is 6 feet tall and casts a shadow that is 2.5 feet. If the palm tree next to her casts a shadow of 8.75 feet, how tall is the palm tree?

17. David is 5 ft 8 in. tall and wants to find the height of an oak tree in his front yard. He walks along the shadow of the tree until his head is in a position where the end of his shadow exactly overlaps the end of the tree's shadow. He is now 11 ft 3 in. from the foot of the tree and 8 ft 6 in. from the end of the shadows. How tall is the oak tree?

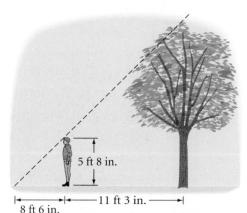

18. A certain magnifying glass, when held 6 in. from an object, creates an image that is 10 times the size of the object being viewed. What is the measure of a 20° angle under this magnifying glass?

19. Construct $\overline{KL}$. Then find a point P that divides $\overline{KL}$ into two segments that have a ratio $\frac{3}{4}$.

20. If two triangles are congruent, are they similar? Explain.

21. Suppose you had a real ice cream cone spill similar to the sculpture at right. What measurements would you make to calculate the height and width of the sculpture? Explain your reasoning.

This sculpture, called Dropped Cone, was also created by Swedish-American sculptors Claes Oldenburg and Coosje van Bruggen. Their art reflects how everyday objects can be intriguing.

22. How do you know $\triangle JFM \sim \triangle FZM$? Find h.

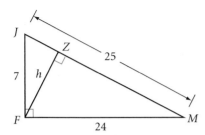

23. $LRTU$ is a trapezoid. Which triangles are similar? Explain why. Find x.

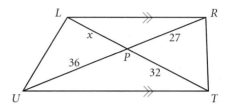

24. For the two quadrilaterals shown in the coordinate grid to the right, what point is the center of dilation? What is the ordered pair rule that transforms $QUAD$ to $Q'U'A'D'$?

25. $\overline{BD}$ bisects $\angle CDA$. Find x.

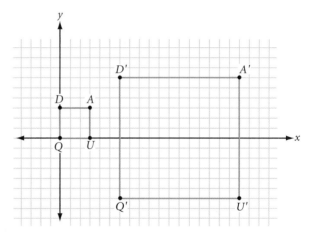

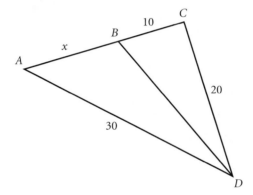

26. $\triangle ABC \sim \triangle EFG$. $x =$?
Which other triangles are similar? Why?

27. $z \parallel \ell \parallel g \parallel h$
$w =$?, $x =$?, $y =$?, $z =$?

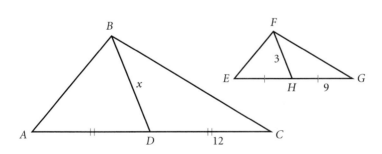

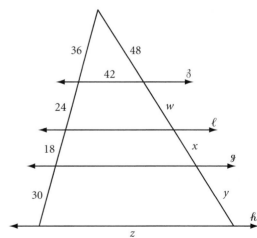

TAKE ANOTHER LOOK

1. You've learned that an ordered pair rule such as $(x, y) \rightarrow (x + h, y + k)$ is a translation and the ordered pair rule $(x, y) \rightarrow (-x + h, y + k)$ is a composition of a reflection across the y-axis and a translation.

   In this chapter you learned about dilation transformations. The ordered pair rule $(x, y) \rightarrow (rx, ry)$ is a dilation and the coefficient r is the scale factor of the dilation. Show an example of each composition of dilation and rigid transformation for each ordered pair rule below:

   a. $(x, y) \rightarrow (rx + h, ry + k)$

   b. $(x, y) \rightarrow (rx + h, -ry + k)$

   c. $(x, y) \rightarrow (-rx + h, -ry + k)$

2. A total eclipse of the Sun can occur because the ratio of the Moon's diameter to its distance from Earth is about the same as the ratio of the Sun's diameter to its distance to Earth. Draw a diagram and use similar triangles to explain why it works.

   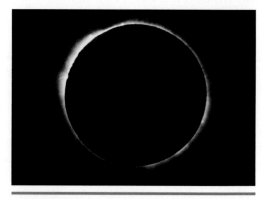

   A solar eclipse

3. It is possible for the three angles and two of the sides of one triangle to be congruent to the three angles and two of the sides of another triangle, and yet for the two triangles not to be congruent. Two such triangles are shown below. Use geometry software or patty paper to find another pair of similar (but not congruent) triangles in which five parts of one are congruent to five parts of the other.

   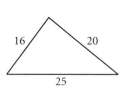 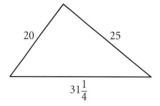

   Explain why these sets of side lengths work. Use algebra to explain your reasoning.

4. Is the converse of the Extended Parallel Proportionality Conjecture true? That is, if two lines intersect two sides of a triangle, dividing the two sides proportionally, must the two lines be parallel to the third side? Prove that it is true or find a counterexample showing that it is not true.

5. If the three sides of one triangle are each parallel to one of the three sides of another triangle, what might be true about the two triangles? Use geometry software to investigate. Make a conjecture and explain why you think your conjecture is true.

Area

"I could fill an entire second life with working on my prints."
M. C. ESCHER

OBJECTIVES

In this chapter you will

- discover area formulas for rectangles, parallelograms, triangles, trapezoids, kites, regular polygons, circles, and other shapes
- use area formulas to solve problems
- learn how to find the surface areas of prisms, pyramids, cylinders, and cones
- learn about area relationships in similar polygons

Areas of Triangles and Special Quadrilaterals

"A little learning is a dangerous thing— almost as dangerous as a lot of ignorance."

ANONYMOUS

People work with areas in many occupations. Carpenters calculate the areas of walls, floors, and roofs before they purchase materials for construction. Painters calculate surface areas so that they know how much paint to buy for a job. Decorators calculate the areas of floors and windows to know how much carpeting and drapery they will need. In this chapter you will discover, or perhaps rediscover,

Tile layers need to find floor area to determine how many tiles to buy.

formulas for finding the areas of the regions within triangles, parallelograms, trapezoids, kites, regular polygons, and circles. In this chapter you will also review how transformations are used to derive these different area formulas.

Recall that the **area** of a plane figure is the measure of the region enclosed by the figure. You could measure the area of a figure by counting the number of square units that you can arrange to fill the figure completely.

For example, to find the area of a rectangle you can simply count squares, but there's another method. Since the squares are arranged in rows and columns you can multiply the number of squares in each row by the number of rows.

Any side of a rectangle can be called a **base**. A rectangle's **height** is the length of the side that is perpendicular to the base. For each pair of parallel bases, there is a corresponding height.

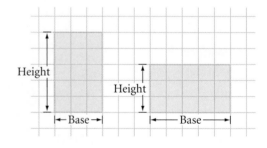

If we call the bottom side of each rectangle in the figure the base, then the length of the base is the number of squares in each row and the height is the number of rows. So you can use these terms to state a formula for the area. Add this conjecture to your list.

Rectangle Area Conjecture   *C-66*

The area of a rectangle is given by the formula _?_, where A is the area, b is the length of the base, and h is the height of the rectangle.

INVESTIGATION 1

YOU WILL NEED

- graph paper
- a straightedge
- a compass
- scissors

Area Formulas for Parallelograms and Triangles

Recall that the area formula for a parallelogram was derived from the area formula for a rectangle. On your graph paper, draw a parallelogram. Construct one altitude. Label your parallelogram like the one shown below. Cut out the parallelogram.

Step 1 Describe how the diagrams below demonstrate the area formula for a parallelogram.

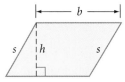
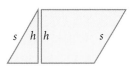

Step 2 What type of transformation was used to move the right triangle that was cut from the left side of the parallelogram to the right side to turn a parallelogram into a rectangle? What was the translation distance? How do you know there was no gap or overlap?

Step 3 You are now ready to state a formula for the area of a parallelogram.

Parallelogram Area Conjecture | **C-67**

The area of a parallelogram is given by the formula _?_ , where A is the area, b is the length of the base, and h is the height of the parallelogram.

We can also derive the area formula for a triangle from the area formula for a parallelogram.

Step 4 On your graph paper, draw a triangle. Cut out the triangle and label its parts as shown. Make and label a copy.

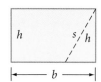

Step 5 Arrange the triangles to form a parallelogram. What is the area of this new figure?

Step 6 What type of transformation was used to move a copy of the original triangle to create a parallelogram? Describe the transformation. How do you know there was no gap or overlap?

Step 7 What is the area of one of the triangles? Make a conjecture. Write a brief description in your notebook of how you arrived at the formula.

Triangle Area Conjecture | **C-68**

The area of a triangle is given by the formula _?_ , where A is the area, b is the length of the base, and h is the height of the triangle.

INVESTIGATION 2

Area Formula for Trapezoids

YOU WILL NEED
- graph paper
- a straightedge
- a compass
- scissors

Using the conjectures you created in Investigation 1, let's derive the formula for a trapezoid.

Step 1 On your graph paper, draw a trapezoid. Cut out the trapezoid, construct its altitude, and label its parts as shown. Make and label a copy.

Step 2 Arrange the two trapezoids to form a parallelogram. What is its area?

Step 3 What type of transformation was used to move a copy of the original trapezoid to create a parallelogram? Describe the transformation. How do you know there was no gap or overlap?

Step 4 What is the area of one of the trapezoids? Make a conjecture.

Trapezoid Area Conjecture　　　　　　　　　　　　　**C-69**

The area of a trapezoid is given by the formula __?__, where A is the area, b_1 and b_2 are the lengths of the two bases, and h is the height of the trapezoid.

If the dimensions of a figure are measured in inches, feet, or yards, the area is measured in in² (square inches), ft² (square feet), or yd² (square yards). If the dimensions are measured in centimeters or meters, the area is measured in cm² (square centimeters) or m² (square meters). Can you explain why?

In earlier courses you discovered the area formulas for rectangles, parallelograms, triangles, and trapezoids but probably not the formula for the area of a kite. Here is an investigation leading to the formula for the area of a kite.

INVESTIGATION 3

Area Formula for Kites

YOU WILL NEED
- Heavy paper or cardboard
- Scissors

Can you rearrange a kite into shapes for which you already have the area formula? Do you recall some of the properties of a kite?

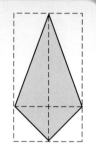

Create and carry out your own investigation to discover a formula for the area of a kite. What transformations did you use? Discuss your results with your group. State a conjecture.

Kite Area Conjecture　　　　　　　　　　　　　**C-70**

The area of a kite is given by the formula __?__.

8.1 Exercises

YOU WILL NEED

Construction tools
for Exercise **25**

In Exercises 1–15, use your new area conjectures to solve for the unknown measures.

1. $A = 273$ cm^2
$h = \underline{?}$

13 cm

2. $P = 40$ ft
$A = \underline{?}$

7 ft

3. Shaded area $= \underline{?}$

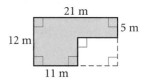

21 m
5 m
12 m
11 m

4. $A = \underline{?}$

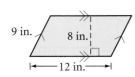

9 in.
8 in.
12 in.

5. $A = 2508$ cm^2
$P = \underline{?}$

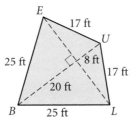

44 cm
48 cm

6. Find the area of the shaded region.

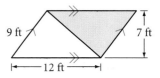

9 ft
7 ft
12 ft

7. $A = \underline{?}$

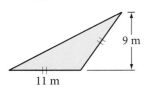

9 m
11 m

8. $A = \underline{?}$

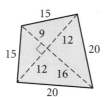

15
9
12
15
20
12
16
20

9. $A = \underline{?}$

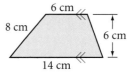

6 cm
8 cm
6 cm
14 cm

10. $A = 39$ cm^2
$h = \underline{?}$

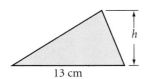

h
13 cm

11. $A = 420$ ft^2
$LE = \underline{?}$

E
17 ft
U
25 ft
8 ft
17 ft
20 ft
B
25 ft
L

12. $A = 50$ cm^2
$h = \underline{?}$

7 cm
6 cm
h
13 cm

13. $A = 180$ m^2
$b = \underline{?}$

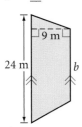

9 m
24 m
b

14. $A = 204$ cm^2
$P = 62$ cm
$h = \underline{?}$

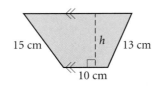

15 cm
h
13 cm
10 cm

15. $x = \underline{?}$ ⓗ
$y = \underline{?}$

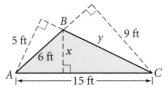

B
5 ft
9 ft
y
6 ft
x
A
15 ft
C

16. Sketch and label two different rectangles, each with area 48 cm^2.

17. Sketch and label two different parallelograms, each with area 64 cm^2.

18. Draw and label a figure with area 64 cm^2 and perimeter 64 cm.

For Exercises 19 and 20, you may choose to use a coordinate grid.

19. Find the area of quadrilateral *ABCD* with vertices *A*(0, 0), *B*(6, 0), *C*(14, 16), and *D*(8, 16).

20. Find the area of quadrilateral *EFGH* with vertices *E*(0, 0), *F*(6, −4), *G*(8, 0), and *H*(6, 4).

21. Sketch and label two different triangles, each with area 54 cm².

22. Sketch and label two different trapezoids, each with area 56 cm².

Review

23. △*DEF* is a dilated image of △*ABC* in the coordinate grid on the right. Find the dilation ratio. Explain your method.

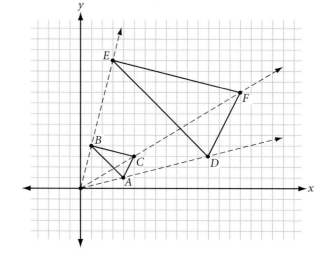

24. Identify the point of concurrency from the construction marks.

a. 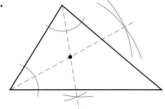   b.    c.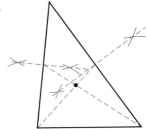

25. Given *AM* as the length of the altitude of an equilateral triangle, construct the triangle.

A •——————————————• *M*

DEVELOPING MATHEMATICAL REASONING

Dissecting a Dodecagon Puzzle

Show how you can divide the regular dodecagon into regular hexagon(s), square(s) and equilateral triangle(s). There will be at least one of each.

Applications of Area

By now, you know formulas for finding the areas of rectangles, parallelograms, triangles, trapezoids, and kites. Now let's see if you can use these area formulas to approximate the areas of irregularly shaped figures.

The *Crooked House* in Sopot, Poland, was designed by Szotyńscy & Zaleski. In order to buy enough paint, how would they find the area to cover?

INVESTIGATION

YOU WILL NEED
- Figures A–H
- rulers

Solving Problems with Area Formulas

Which of these shapes has the greatest area? Which of these shapes has the least area? Estimate the area of each geometric figure and rank the areas from greatest to least. Before you begin to measure, discuss with your group a measurement strategy. Discuss what units you should use. Different group members might get different results. However, your results should be close. Decide as a group how you will determine one group answer. For each figure, write a sentence or two explaining how you measured the area and how accurate you think it is.

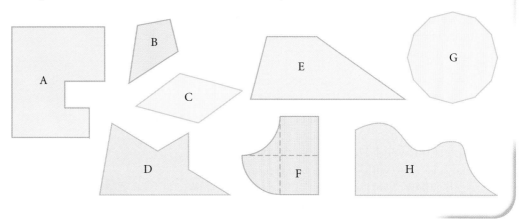

Now that you have practiced measuring and calculating area, you're ready to try some application problems. Many everyday projects require you to find the areas of flat surfaces on three-dimensional objects. You'll learn more about surface area in Lesson 8.5.

In the exercises you will learn how to use area in buying rolls of wallpaper, gallons of paint, bundles of shingles, square yards of carpet, and square feet of tile. Keep in mind that you can't buy $12\frac{11}{16}$ gallons of paint! You must buy 13 gallons. If your calculations tell you that you need 5.25 bundles of shingles, you have to buy 6 bundles.

1. Tammy is estimating how much she should charge for painting 148 rooms in a new hotel with one coat of base paint and one coat of finishing paint. The four walls and the ceiling of each room must be painted. Each room measures 14 ft by 16 ft by 10 ft.

   a. Calculate the total area of all the surfaces to be painted with each coat. Ignore doors and windows.

   b. One gallon of base paint covers 500 square feet. One gallon of finishing paint covers 250 square feet. How many gallons of each will Tammy need for the job?

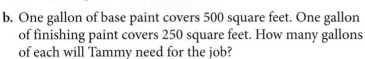

2. Rashad wants to wallpaper the four walls of his bedroom. The room is rectangular and measures 11 feet by 13 feet. The ceiling is 10 feet high. A roll of wallpaper at the store is 2.5 feet wide and 50 feet long. How many rolls should he buy? (Wallpaper is hung from ceiling to floor. Ignore doors and windows.)

3. It takes 65,000 solar cells, each 1.25 in. by 2.75 in., to power the Helios Prototype, shown at right. How much surface area, in square feet, must be covered with the cells? The cells on Helios are 18% efficient. Suppose they were only 12% efficient, like solar cells used in homes. How much more surface area would need to be covered to deliver the same amount of power?

→ *Technology*
CONNECTION

In August 2001, the Helios Prototype, a remotely controlled, nonpolluting solar-powered aircraft, reached 96,500 feet—a record for nonrocket aircraft.

4. Harold works at a state park. He needs to seal the redwood deck at the information center to protect the wood. He measures the deck and finds that it is a kite with diagonals 40 feet and 70 feet. Each gallon of sealant covers 400 square feet, and the sealant needs to be applied every six months. How many gallon containers should he buy to protect the deck for the next three years?

40 ft

70 ft

5. A landscape architect is designing three trapezoidal flowerbeds to wrap around three sides of a hexagonal flagstone patio, as shown. What is the area of the entire flowerbed? The landscape architect's fee is $300 plus $5 per square foot. What will the flowerbed cost?

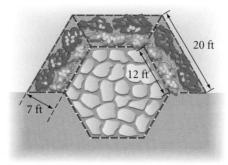
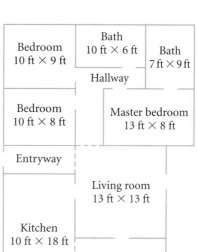

Career CONNECTION

Landscape architects have a keen eye for natural beauty. They study the grade and direction of land slopes, stability of the soil, drainage patterns, and existing structures and vegetation. They use science and engineering to plan environments that harmonize land features with structures, reducing the impact of urban development upon nature.

For Exercises 6 and 7, refer to the floor plan at right.

6. Dareen's family is ready to have wall-to-wall carpeting installed. The carpeting they chose costs $14 per square yard, the padding $3 per square yard, and the installation $3 per square yard. What will it cost them to carpet the three bedrooms and the hallway shown? *(h)*

7. Dareen's family now wants to install 1-foot-square terra-cotta tiles in the entryway and kitchen, and 4-inch-square blue tiles on each bathroom floor. The terra-cotta tiles cost $5 each, and the bathroom tiles cost 45¢ each. How many of each kind will they need? What will all the tiles cost?

Floor plan:
- Bedroom 10 ft × 9 ft
- Bath 10 ft × 6 ft
- Bath 7 ft × 9 ft
- Hallway
- Bedroom 10 ft × 8 ft
- Master bedroom 13 ft × 8 ft
- Entryway
- Living room 13 ft × 13 ft
- Kitchen 10 ft × 18 ft
- Dining room 13 ft × 9 ft

8. Sarah is tiling a wall in her bathroom. It is rectangular and measures 4 feet by 7 feet. The tiles are square and measure 6 inches on each side. How many tiles does Sarah need? *(h)*

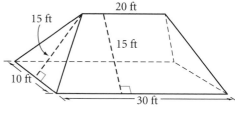

9. The roof on Crystal's house is formed by two congruent trapezoids and two congruent isosceles triangles, as shown. She wants to put new wood shingles on her roof. Each shingle will cover 0.25 square foot of area. (The shingles are 1 foot by 1 foot, but they overlap by 0.75 square foot.) How many shingles should Crystal buy?

10. Three college students are planning to share a 3-bedroom 1-bath apartment near the campus. The rent is $1,475 per month. The three bedrooms measure 12 ft by 10 ft, 10 ft by 12 ft, and 12 ft by 12 ft 6 in. How should they fairly divide the cost of the rent? Explain your reasoning.

Review

11. Two different sized rectangles are cut from a rectangular piece of cardboard leaving a smaller rectangle 5 cm by 8 cm in size. What is the largest possible size for the original piece of cardboard?

12. *P* is a random point on side $\overline{AY}$ of rectangle *ARTY*. The shaded area is what fraction of the area of the rectangle? Why?

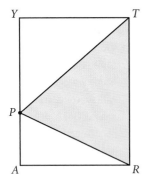

13. One playing card is placed over another, as shown. Is the top card covering half, less than half, or more than half of the bottom card? Explain.

14. $A = \underline{?}$
$P = \underline{?}$

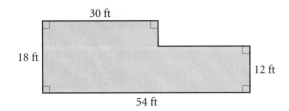

15. **GUESS-N-CHECK** As *P* moves from left to right along ℓ which of the following values changes? First, try this as a "mental experiment." Take a guess, then create the diagram with your geometry software and see how good you were at visualization.

a. The area of $\triangle ABP$

b. The area of $\triangle PDC$

c. The area of trapezoid *ABCD*

d. $m\angle A + m\angle PCD + m\angle CPD$

e. None of these

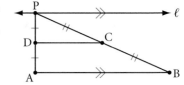

In Exercises 16–18, identify each statement as true or false. If true, explain why. If false, give a counterexample.

16. If the measure of each exterior angle of a regular polygon is 24°, then the polygon has 15 sides.

17. If the diagonals of a parallelogram bisect its angles, then the parallelogram is a square.

18. If two sides of a triangle measure 25 cm and 30 cm, then the third side must be greater than 5 cm, but less than 55 cm.

DEVELOPING MATHEMATICAL REASONING

Knight's Tour Puzzle II

The goal of a knight's tour puzzle is to fill the grid with consecutive numbers that are connected by the knight's L-move from one square to the next (a knight's tour). The circles represent the locations of the smallest and the largest numbers on the grid (1 and 36).

		7	16		14
				28	
11					
			◯		
				◯	
32		34	25		23

Areas of Circles and Regular Polygons

"The moon is a dream of the sun."

PAUL KLEE

So far in this chapter, you have discovered the formulas for the areas of various polygons. In this lesson you'll discover the formulas for the area of a circle and for regular polygons. Most of the shapes you have investigated could be divided into rectangles or triangles. Can a circle be divided into rectangles or triangles? Not exactly, but in this investigation you will see an interesting way to think about the area of a circle.

INVESTIGATION 1

YOU WILL NEED

- a compass
- scissors

Area Formula for Circles

Circles do not have straight sides like polygons do. However, the area of a circle can be rearranged. Let's investigate.

Step 1 Use your compass to make a large circle. Cut out the circular region.

Step 2 Fold the circular region in half. Fold it in half a second time, then a third time and a fourth time. Unfold your circle and cut it along the folds into 16 wedges.

Step 3 Arrange the wedges in a row, alternating the tips up and down to form a shape that resembles a parallelogram.

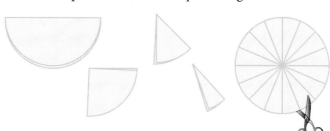

If you cut the circle into more wedges, you could rearrange these thinner wedges to look even more like a rectangle, with fewer bumps. You would not lose or gain any area in this change, so the area of this new "rectangle," skimming off the bumps as you measure its length, would be closer to the area of the original circle.

If you could cut an infinite number of wedges, you'd actually have a rectangle with smooth sides. What would its base length be? What would its height be in terms of C, the circumference of the circle?

Step 4 The radius of the original circle is r and the circumference is $2\pi r$. What are the base and the height of a rectangle made of a circle cut into an infinite number of wedges? Find its area in terms of r. State your next conjecture.

Circle Area Conjecture   **C-71**

The area of a circle is given by the formula _?_, where A is the area and r is the radius of the circle.

Just as you divided the circle into a number of sectors, you can divide a regular polygon into congruent isosceles triangles by drawing segments from the center of the polygon to each vertex. The center of the polygon is actually the center of a circumscribed circle, so these congruent segments are sometimes called the radii of a regular polygon.

In this investigation you will divide regular polygons into triangles. Then you will write a formula for the area of any regular polygon.

INVESTIGATION 2

Area Formula for Regular Polygons

Consider a regular pentagon with side length s, divided into congruent isosceles triangles. Each triangle has a base s and a height a.

Step 1 What is the area of one isosceles triangle in terms of a and s?

Step 2 What is the area of this pentagon in terms of a and s?

Step 3 Repeat Steps 1 and 2 with other regular polygons and complete the table below.

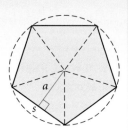

Regular pentagon

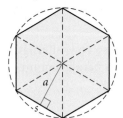

Regular hexagon

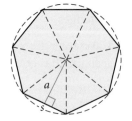

Regular heptagon

Number of sides	5	6	7	8	9	10	...	n	...	50
Area of regular polygon							...		...	

The distance a appears in the area formula for a regular polygon, and it has a special name—apothem. An **apothem** of a regular polygon is a perpendicular segment from the center of the polygon's circumscribed circle to a side of the polygon. You may also refer to the length of the segment as the apothem.

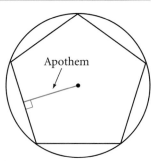

Apothem

Step 4 What is the perimeter of a regular polygon in terms of n and s? Use your answer to this question and your last entry in the table to state your next conjecture.

Regular Polygon Area Conjecture C-72

The area of a regular polygon is given by the formula _?_ or _?_, where A is the area, P is the perimeter, a is the apothem, s is the length of each side, and n is the number of sides.

How do you use these new conjectures? Let's look at a few examples.

EXAMPLE A | The small apple pie has a diameter of 8 inches, and the large cherry pie has a radius of 5 inches. How much larger is the large pie?

Solution | First, find each area.

Small pie	**Large pie**
$A = \pi r^2$	$A = \pi r^2$
$= \pi(4)^2$	$= \pi(5)^2$
$= \pi(16)$	$= \pi(25)$
≈ 50.2	≈ 78.5

The large pie is 78.5 in², and the small pie is 50.2 in². The difference in area is about 28.3 square inches. So the large pie is more than 50% larger than the small pie, assuming they have the same thickness. Notice that we used 3.14 as an approximate value for π.

EXAMPLE B | If the area of the circle at right is 256π m², what is the circumference of the circle?

Solution | Use the area to find the radius. Then, use the radius to find the circumference.

$$A = \pi r^2 \qquad C = 2\pi r$$
$$256\pi = \pi r^2 \qquad = 2\pi(16)$$
$$256 = r^2 \qquad = 32\pi$$
$$r = 16 \qquad \approx 100.5 \text{ m}$$

The circumference is 32π meters, or approximately 100.5 meters.

EXAMPLE C | Genie and Ray are planning to build a foam safety ring that will surround the family trampoline for their two kids, Casey and Ginger. The outside perimeter is a regular dodecagon with each side measuring approximately 7 feet and the inner perimeter is a regular octagon with each side measuring approximately 8.2 feet. The approximate length of the apothem of the dodecagon is 13 feet and the approximate length of the apothem of the octagon is 10 feet. What is the approximate area they will need to cover in foam?

Solution | To find the area between the two regular polygons, find their areas and subtract the smaller from the larger.

$$\text{Area of dodecagon} = \tfrac{1}{2}aP$$
$$= \tfrac{1}{2}(13)[(12)(7)]$$
$$= 546 \text{ ft}^2$$

$$\text{Area of octagon} = \tfrac{1}{2}aP$$
$$= \tfrac{1}{2}(10)[(8)(8.2)]$$
$$= 328 \text{ ft}^2$$

$$\text{Area of the foam ring} = (546 \text{ ft}^2 - 328 \text{ ft}^2)$$
$$= 218 \text{ ft}^2$$

8.3 Exercises

YOU WILL NEED

Geometry software
for Exercise 25

Solve for the unknown measures in Exercises 1–8. Leave your answers in terms of π, unless the problem asks for an approximation. For approximations, use the π key on your calculator. Recall that the symbol $\approx$ is used for measurements or calculations that are approximations.

1. If $r = 3$ in., $A = $ _?_.

2. If $r = 7$ cm, $A = $ _?_.

3. If $r = 0.5$ m, $A \approx $ _?_.

4. If $A = 9\pi$ cm^2, then $r = $ _?_.

5. If $A = 3\pi$ in^2, then $r = $ _?_.

6. If $A = 0.785$ m^2, then $r \approx $ _?_.

7. If $C = 12\pi$ in., then $A = $ _?_.

8. If $C = 314$ m, then $A \approx $ _?_.

In Exercises 9–16, find the unknown length accurate to the nearest unit, or the unknown area accurate to the nearest square unit.

9. $A \approx $ _?_
  $s = 24$ cm
  $a \approx 24.9$ cm

10. $a \approx $ _?_
  $s = 107.5$ cm
  $A \approx 19,887.5$ cm^2

11. $P \approx $ _?_
  $a = 38.6$ cm
  $A \approx 4940.8$ cm^2

12. Regular pentagon: $a = 3$ cm and $s \approx 4.4$ cm, $A \approx $ _?_

13. Regular nonagon: $a = 9.6$ cm and $A \approx 302.4$ cm^2, $P \approx $ _?_

14. Regular n-gon: $a = 12$ cm and $P \approx 81.6$ cm, $A \approx $ _?_

15. Find the approximate perimeter of a regular polygon if $a = 9$ m and $A \approx 259.2$ m^2.

16. Find the approximate length of each side of a regular n-gon if $a = 80$ feet, $n = 20$, and $A \approx 20,000$ square feet.

17. What is the area of the shaded region between the circle and the rectangle?

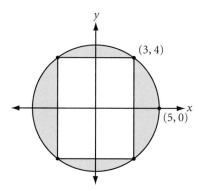

18. What is the area of the shaded region between the circle and the triangle?

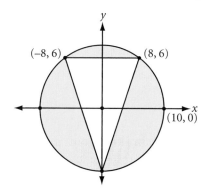

19. Find the approximate area of the shaded region of the regular octagon *ROADSIGN*. The apothem measures 20 cm. Segment *GI* measures about 16.6 cm. ⓗ

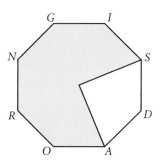

20. Find the approximate area of the shaded regular hexagonal donut. The apothem and sides of the smaller hexagon are half as long as the apothem and sides of the large hexagon. $a \approx 6.9$ cm and $r \approx 8$ cm ⓗ

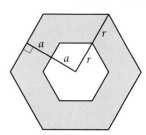

21. Sketch and label a circle with an area of 324π cm². Be sure to label the length of the radius.

22. An interior designer created the kitchen plan shown. The countertop will be constructed of colored concrete. What is its total surface area? If concrete countertops 1.5 inches thick cost $85 per square foot, what will be the total cost of this countertop?

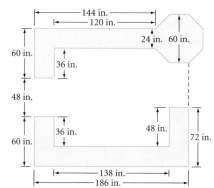

Career

CONNECTION

Interior designers, unlike interior decorators, are concerned with the larger planning and technical considerations of interiors, as well as with style and color selection. They have an intuitive sense of spatial relationships. They prepare sketches, schedules, and budgets for client approval and inspect the site until the job is complete.

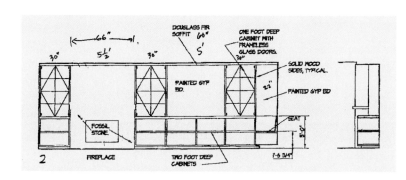

Review

23. $A = \underline{\ ?\ }$

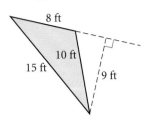

8 ft
10 ft
15 ft
9 ft

24. *GHJK* is a rectangle. Find the area of pentagon *GHIJK*.

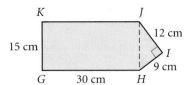
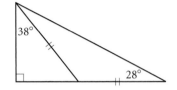

K   J
15 cm
12 cm
I
9 cm
G   30 cm   H

25. Construct a parallelogram and a point in its interior. Construct segments from this point to each vertex, forming four triangles. Measure the area of each triangle. Move the point to find a location where all four triangles have equal area. Is there more than one such location? Explain your findings.

26. Find the area of the shaded region. Assume all the squares are congruent.

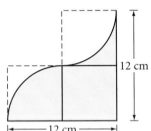

12 cm

12 cm

27. What's wrong with this picture?

38°

28°

28. The 6 cm by 18 cm by 24 cm clear plastic sealed container is resting on a cylinder. It is partially filled with liquid, as shown. Sketch the container resting on its smallest face. Show the liquid level in this position.

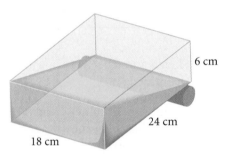

6 cm

24 cm

18 cm

29. △*ABC* with vertices *A*(−10, 4), *B*(−3, 4), and *C*(−7, 8), is rotated 90° counterclockwise to create the image △*A′B′C′*. What is the area of △*A′B′C′*? Explain your reasoning.

DEVELOPING MATHEMATICAL REASONING

Connecting Cubes

The two objects shown at right can be placed together to form each of the shapes below except one. Which one?

A.

B.

C.

D.

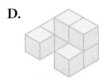

Areas of Sectors

In Lesson 8.3, you discovered a formula for calculating the area of a circle. With the help of your visual thinking and problem-solving skills, you can calculate the areas of different sections of a circle.

If you cut a slice of pizza, each slice would probably be a sector of a circle. If you could make only one straight cut with your knife, your slice would be a segment of a circle. If you don't like the crust, you'd cut out the center of the pizza; the crust shape that would remain is called an annulus.

"Cut my pie into four pieces—I don't think I could eat eight."

YOGI BERRA

Sector of a circle

Segment of a circle

Annulus

A **sector of a circle** is the region between two radii and an arc of the circle.

A **segment of a circle** is the region between a chord and an arc of the circle.

An **annulus** is the region between two concentric circles.

"Picture equations" are helpful when you try to visualize the areas of these regions. The picture equations below show you how to find the area of a sector of a circle, the area of a segment of a circle, and the area of an annulus.

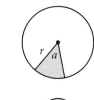

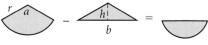

$$\frac{a}{360} \cdot \pi r^2 = A_{sector}$$

$$\frac{a}{360} \pi r^2 - \frac{1}{2}bh = A_{segment}$$

$$\pi R^2 - \pi r^2 = A_{annulus}$$

EXAMPLE A

Find the area of the shaded sector.

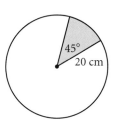

45°
20 cm

Solution

The sector is $\frac{45°}{360°}$, or $\frac{1}{8}$, of the circle.

$$A_{sector} = \frac{a}{360} \cdot \pi r^2 \qquad \text{The area formula for a sector.}$$

$$= \frac{45}{360} \cdot \pi(20)^2 \qquad \text{Substitute } r = 20 \text{ and } a = 45.$$

$$= \frac{1}{8} \cdot 400\pi \qquad \text{Simplify the fraction and square 20.}$$

$$= 50\pi \qquad \text{Multiply.}$$

The area is 50π cm².

EXAMPLE B | Find the area of the shaded segment.

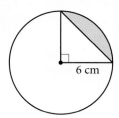

6 cm

Solution | According to the picture equation on page 425, the area of a segment is equivalent to the area of the sector minus the area of the triangle. You can use the method in Example A to find that the area of the sector is $\frac{1}{4} \cdot 36\pi$ cm², or 9π cm². The area of the triangle is $\frac{1}{2} \cdot 6 \cdot 6$, or 18 cm². So the area of the segment is $9\pi - 18$ cm².

EXAMPLE C | The shaded area is 14π cm², and the radius is 6 cm. Find x.

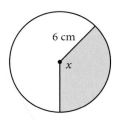

6 cm

x

Solution | The sector's area is $\frac{x}{360}$ of the circle's area, which is 36π.

$$14\pi = \frac{x}{360} \cdot 36\pi$$

$$\frac{360 \cdot 14\pi}{36\pi} = x$$

$$x = 140$$

The central angle measures 140°.

8.4 Exercises

In Exercises 1–8, find the area of the shaded region. The radius of each circle is r. If two circles are shown, r is the radius of the smaller circle and R is the radius of the larger circle.

1. $r = 6$ cm

60°

2. $r = 8$ cm

240°

3. $r = 16$ cm

4. $r = 2$ cm

5. $r = 8$ cm

6. $R = 7$ cm
$r = 4$ cm ⓗ

r

R

7. $r = 2$ cm

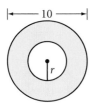

8. $R = 12$ cm
$r = 9$ cm

9. The shaded area is 12π cm². Find r.

10. The shaded area is 32π cm². Find r.

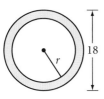

11. The shaded area is 120π cm², and the radius is 24 cm. Find x.

12. The shaded area is 10π cm². The radius of the large circle is 10 cm, and the radius of the small circle is 8 cm. Find x. ⓗ

13. *Which slice would you prefer?* Pentomino Pizza is offering a Columbus Day sale on its individual slices. For the price of a slice of a regular 6 in. radius pizza you can choose either:

a. a slice with the same central angle but twice the radius, or

b. a slice with the same radius but twice the central angle, or

c. a slice with twice the central angle and twice the radius for triple the price.

Which pizza offer is the best deal? Explain.

14. Utopia Park has just installed a circular fountain 8 meters in diameter. The Park Committee wants to pave a 1.5-meter-wide path around the fountain. If paving costs $10 per square meter, find the cost to the nearest dollar of the paved path around the fountain.

This circular fountain in Peshtera, Bulgaria, shares a center with the circular path around it. How many concentric circles do you see in the picture?

Review

15. Which one of the figures (a–d) has the greatest amount of shaded area? Which has the least? All the squares are congruent. Each set of circles is externally tangent. ⓗ

a.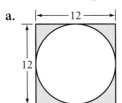

b.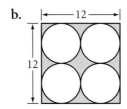

c.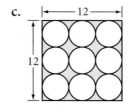

d.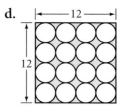

16. The height of a trapezoid is 15 m and the midsegment is 32 m. What is the area of the trapezoid? ⓗ

17. $\overline{CE}$, $\overline{BH}$, and $\overline{AG}$ are altitudes. Find AB and AG.

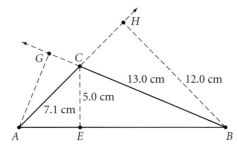

18. A 4-by-16 rectangle can be cut into two pieces and reassembled to form a square.

  a. What is the area of the square?

  b. What is the length of each side of the square?

  c. The perimeter of the square is how much less than that of the rectangle?

  d. Sketch how the 4×16 rectangle can be cut into two pieces and reassembled to form a square.

  e. Using transformations, describe how to reassemble the pieces to precisely create the square.

DEVELOPING MATHEMATICAL REASONING

Bordered Magic Square Puzzle

A *normal* $n \times n$ magic square is a square arrangement of consecutive numbers from 1 to n^2 such that every row, column, and both main diagonals sum to the same number called the magic sum. Magic squares that do not use just the first n^2 positive integers are called *simple* magic squares. When a 5×5 *normal* magic square also has a *simple* 3×3 magic square centered in the middle of the grid that special magic square is a bordered magic square. Fill in the missing numbers to the 5×5 grid shown to create a bordered 5×5 magic square.

24	19	1	3	18
	10		12	4
6		13		
			16	

Pick's Formula for Area

You know how to find the area of polygon regions, but how would you find the area of the dinosaur footprint at right?

You know how to place a polygon on a grid and count squares to find the area. About a hundred years ago, Austrian mathematician Georg Alexander Pick (1859–1943) discovered a relationship, now known as Pick's formula, for finding the area of figures on a square dot grid.

Let's start by looking at polygons on a square dot grid. The dots are called lattice points. Let's count the lattice points in the interior of the polygon and those on its boundary and compare our findings to the areas of the polygon that you get by dividing them into rectangles and triangles.

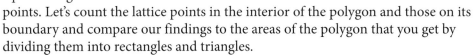

Polygon A	**Polygon B**	**Polygon C**
5 boundary points	5 boundary points	3 boundary points
1 interior point	0 interior points	5 interior points

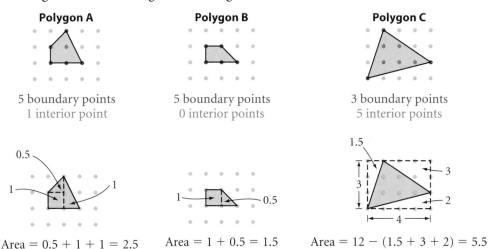

Area = 0.5 + 1 + 1 = 2.5   Area = 1 + 0.5 = 1.5   Area = 12 − (1.5 + 3 + 2) = 5.5

How can the boundary points and interior points help us find the area? An important technique for finding patterns is to hold one variable constant and see what happens with the other variables. That's what you'll do in the next activity.

In this activity you will first investigate patterns that emerge when you hold the area constant. Then you will investigate patterns that emerge when you hold the number of interior or boundary points constant. The goal is to find a formula that relates the area of a polygon to the number of interior and boundary points.

Activity

Dinosaur Footprints and Other Shapes

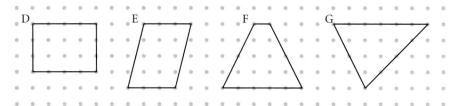

Step 1 Confirm that each polygon D through G above has area $A = 12$.

Step 2 Let b be the number of boundary points and i be the number of interior points. Create and complete a table like this one for polygons with $A = 12$.

	D	E	F	G
Number of boundary points (b)				
Number of interior points (i)				

Step 3 Study the table for patterns. Do you see a relationship between b and i? Graph the pairs (b, i) from your table and label each point. What do you notice? Write an equation that fits the points.

Now investigate what happens if you hold the interior points constant.

Step 4 Polygon B has $b = 5$, $i = 0$, and $A = 1.5$. On square dot paper draw other polygons with *no* interior points. Calculate the area of each polygon.

Step 5 Copy and complete this table for polygons with $i = 0$.

Number of boundary points (b)	3	4	5	6	7	8
Area			1.5			

Step 6 Polygon A has $b = 5$, $i = 1$, and $A = 2.5$. On square dot paper draw other polygons with exactly *one* interior point. Calculate the area of each polygon.

Step 7 Make a table like the one in Step 5, but for polygons with $i = 1$. When you hold the interior points constant, what happens to the area each time one boundary point is added?

Now investigate what happens if you hold the boundary points constant.

Step 8 Polygon C has $b = 3$, $i = 5$, and $A = 5.5$. On square dot paper draw other polygons with exactly *three* boundary points. Calculate the area of each polygon.

Step 9 Copy and complete this table for polygons with $b = 3$. When you hold the boundary points constant, what happens to the area each time one interior point is added?

Number of interior points (i)	0	1	2	3	4	5
Area						5.5

To find Pick's formula, it can be helpful to organize all your data in one place.

Step 10 Copy and complete the table below. Check the patterns by drawing more polygons on square dot paper.

		Number of boundary points (*b*)					
		3	**4**	**5**	**6**	**7**	**8**
	0			1.5			
	1			2.5			
Number of interior points (*i*)	**2**						
	3						
	4						
	5	5.5					

Step 11 Generalize the formula to find the area if you know the number of boundary points and the number of interior points. Copy and complete the conjecture.

> **Pick's Formula**
>
> If *A* is the area of a polygon whose vertices are lattice points, *b* is the number of lattice points on the boundary of the polygon, and *i* is the number of interior lattice points, then $A = \underline{?}\, b + \underline{?}\, i + \underline{?}$.

Pick's formula is useful for approximating the area of an irregularly shaped region.

Step 12 Use Pick's formula to find the approximate areas of these irregular shapes.

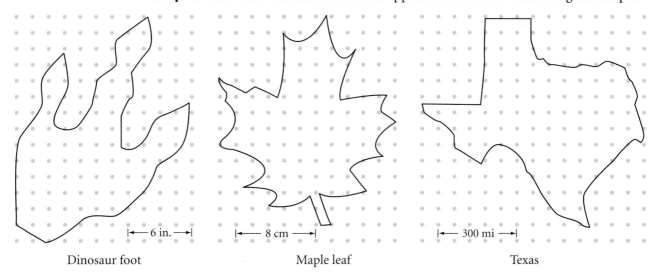

|←— 6 in. —→| |←— 8 cm —→| |←— 300 mi —→|

Dinosaur foot   Maple leaf   Texas

Surface Area

In previous lessons, you calculated the surface areas of walls and roofs. But not all building surfaces are rectangular. How would you calculate the amount of glass necessary to cover a pyramid-shaped building? Or the number of tiles needed to cover a cone-shaped roof?

In this lesson you will learn how to find the surface areas of prisms, pyramids, cylinders, and cones. The **surface area** of each of these solids is the sum of the areas of all the faces or surfaces that enclose the solid. For prisms and pyramids, the faces include the solid's **bases** and its **lateral faces**.

In a prism, the bases are two congruent polygons and the lateral faces are rectangles or other parallelograms.

In a pyramid, the base can be any polygon. The lateral faces are triangles.

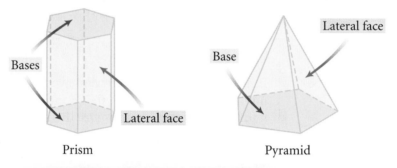

Prism   Pyramid

"No pessimist ever discovered the secrets of the stars, or sailed to an uncharted land, or opened a new doorway for the human spirit."

HELEN KELLER

This glass pyramid was designed by I. M. Pei for the entrance of the Louvre museum in Paris, France.

This skyscraper in Chicago, Illinois, is an example of a prism.

A cone is part of the roof design of this Victorian house.

The Round Tower in Copenhagen was built in 1637 as a large cylinder.

To find the surface areas of prisms and pyramids, follow these steps.

> **Steps for Finding Surface Area**
>
> 1. Draw and label each face of the solid as if you had cut the solid apart along its edges and laid it flat. Label the dimensions.
> 2. Calculate the area of each face. If some faces are identical, you only need to find the area of one.
> 3. Find the total area of all the faces.

EXAMPLE A

Find the surface area of the rectangular prism.

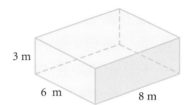

These shipping containers are rectangular prisms.

Solution

Draw and label the two congruent bases, and the four lateral faces unfolded into one rectangle. Then find the areas of all the rectangular faces.

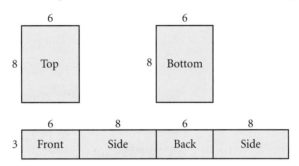

$$\begin{aligned} \text{surface area} &= 2(\text{base area}) + (\text{lateral surface area}) \\ &= 2(6 \cdot 8) + 3(6 + 8 + 6 + 8) \\ &= 2(48) + 3(28) \\ &= 96 + 84 \\ &= 180 \end{aligned}$$

The surface area of the prism is 180 m².

EXAMPLE B

Find the surface area of the cylinder.

Solution

Imagine cutting apart the cylinder. The two bases are circular regions, so you need to find the areas of two circles. Think of the lateral surface as a wrapper. Slice it and lay it flat to get a rectangular region. You'll need the area of this rectangle. The height of the rectangle is the height of the cylinder. The base of the rectangle is the circumference of the circular base.

12 in.

|——— 10 in. ———|

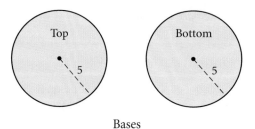

Top
5

Bottom
5

Bases

$b = C = 2\pi r$

$h = 12$

Lateral surface

$$\text{surface area} = 2(\pi r^2) + (2\pi r)h$$
$$= 2(\pi \cdot 5^2) + (2 \cdot \pi \cdot 5) \cdot 12$$
$$\approx 534$$

The surface area of the cylinder is about 534 in².

This ice cream plant in Burlington, Vermont, uses cylindrical containers for its milk and cream.

These conservatories in Edmonton, Canada, are glass pyramids.

The surface area of a pyramid is the area of the base plus the areas of the triangular faces. The height of each triangular lateral face is called the **slant height**. The slant height is labeled l and the pyramid height is labeled h.

Height   Slant height

In the investigation you'll find out how to calculate the surface area of a pyramid with a regular polygon base. A **regular pyramid** is a pyramid with a regular polygon base and the altitude of the pyramid meets the center of the regular polygon. A regular square pyramid is shown above right and a regular hexagonal pyramid is shown to the right.

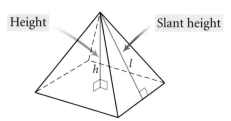

INVESTIGATION 1

Surface Area of a Regular Pyramid

You can cut and unfold the surface of a regular pyramid into these shapes.

 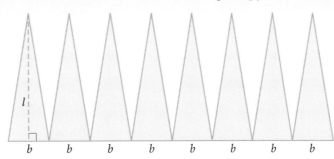 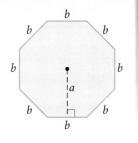

Step 1 Each lateral face is a triangle with base b and height l. What is the area of each lateral face?

Step 2 What is the total lateral surface area? What is the total lateral surface area for any pyramid with a regular n-gon base?

Step 3 What is the area of the base for any regular n-gon pyramid?

Step 4 Use your expressions from Steps 2 and 3 to write a formula for the surface area of a regular n-gon pyramid in terms of n, base length b, slant height l, and apothem a.

If the number of sides on the regular polygon base of a regular pyramid is *even* then the lateral faces can be arranged into a parallelogram as shown below left. If the number of sides on the regular polygon base of a regular pyramid is *odd* then the lateral faces can be arranged into a trapezoid as shown below right.

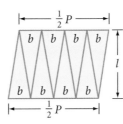 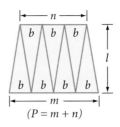

Step 5 If the regular polygon base of a regular pyramid has an even number of sides, what is the total area of the lateral faces in terms of the perimeter P and slant height l? If the regular polygon base has an odd number of sides, what is the total area of the lateral faces in terms of P and l? Are the two expressions the same? Write another expression for the total surface area of a regular n-gon pyramid in terms of the perimeter of the base, P, height l, and apothem a.

You can find the surface area of a cone using a method similar to the one you used to find the surface area of a pyramid.

INVESTIGATION 2

Surface Area of a Cone

Architecture
CONNECTION

Is this Native American tepee shaped more like a cone or a pyramid?

As the number of faces of a pyramid increases, it begins to look like a cone. You can think of the lateral surface as many small triangles or as a sector of a circle.

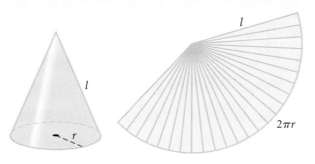
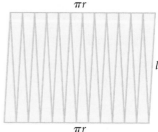

Step 1 What is the area of the base?

Step 2 What is the lateral surface area in terms of l and r? What portion of the circle is the sector? What is the area of the sector?

Step 3 Write the formula for the surface area of a cone.

EXAMPLE C | Find the total surface area of the cone.

Solution |
$SA = \pi rl + \pi r^2$
$= (\pi)(5)(10) + \pi(5)^2$
$= 75\pi$
≈ 235.6

The surface area of the cone is about 236 cm².

10 cm
5 cm

(8.5) Exercises

In Exercises 1–10, find the surface area of each solid. All quadrilaterals are rectangles, and all given measurements are in centimeters. Round your answers to the nearest 0.1 cm².

1.

5
5
5

2.

37
37
9

3.

10
7
8
6

4.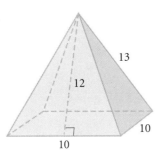

13

12

10

10

5.

8

3

6. |←— 14 —→|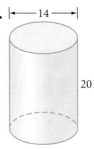

20

7. The base is a regular hexagon with apothem $a \approx 12.1$, side $s = 14$, and height $h = 7$. ⓗ

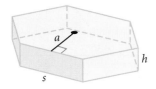

a

h

s

8. The base is a regular pentagon with apothem $a \approx 11$ and side $s = 16$. Each lateral edge $t = 17$, and the height of a face $l = 15$.

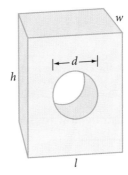

t

l

a

s

9. $D = 8, d = 4, h = 9$ ⓗ

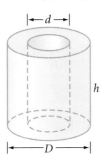

|←— d —→|

h

|←——— D ———→|

10. $l = 8, w = 4, h = 10, d = 4$

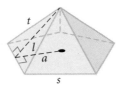

w

|←— d —→|

h

l

11. Explain how you would find the surface area of this obelisk.

12. Claudette and Marie are planning to paint the exterior walls of their country farmhouse (all vertical surfaces) and to put new cedar shingles on the roof. The paint they like best costs $25 per gallon and covers 250 square feet per gallon. The wood shingles cost $65 per bundle, and each bundle covers 100 square feet. How much will this home improvement cost? All measurements are in feet.

6.5   6.5

12

15   15

12

38.5

24

End view

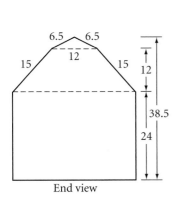

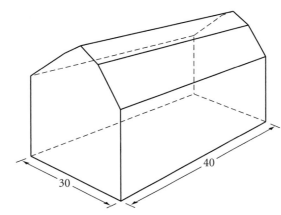

30

40

Review

13. $\triangle ABC$ with vertices $A(-4, 10)$, $B(3, 6)$, and $C(3, 10)$, is transformed by the ordered pair rule $(x, y) \to (2x, y)$ to create the image $\triangle A'B'C'$. What is the area of $\triangle A'B'C'$?

14. $\triangle ABC$ with vertices $A(3, -2)$, $B(-3, -3)$, and $C(3, 3)$, is transformed by the ordered pair rule $(x, y) \to (3x, 3y)$ to create the image $\triangle A'B'C'$. What is the area of $\triangle A'B'C'$?

15. Trace the figure at right. Find the lettered angle measures. Explain how you determined measures f and k.

16. If the pattern of blocks continues, what will be the surface area of the 50th solid in the pattern? (Every edge of each block has length 1 unit.)

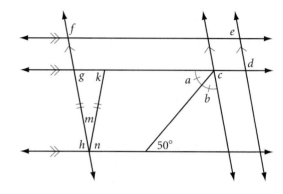

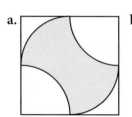 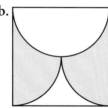 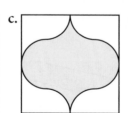 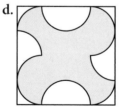

PERFORMANCE TASK

The illustrations below demonstrate how to find a rectangle with the same area as the shaded figure.

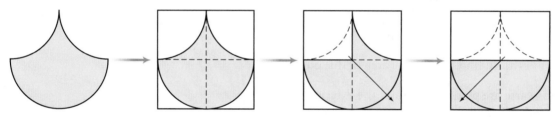

In a series of diagrams, demonstrate how to find a rectangle with the same area as each shaded figure below.

a. **b.** **c.** **d.**

Reverse the process you used above. On graph paper, draw a 12-by-6 rectangle. Use your compass to divide it into at least four parts, then rearrange the parts into a new curved figure. Draw its outline on graph paper. Find the area of your figure.

> **Mathematics**
> **CONNECTION**
>
> Attempts to solve the famous problem of squaring a circle—finding a square with the same area as a given circle—led to the creation of some special shapes made up of parts of circles. These diagrams are based on some that Leonardo da Vinci sketched while attempting to solve this problem.

Area and Similarity

"All my life I've always wanted to be somebody. But I see now I should have been more specific."

JANE WAGNER

Suppose an artist uses 200 tiles to create a tessellation design that covers a rectangle with dimensions 2 ft by 3 ft. He is hired to cover a wall with dimensions 10 ft by 15 ft using the same design and tiles of the same size. Even though the wall is five times as long as the rectangle in each dimension, he finds that 1000 tiles cover only a small part of the wall. In this lesson you will discover why.

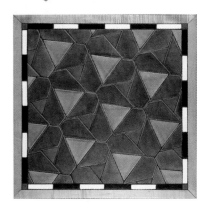

INVESTIGATION 1

YOU WILL NEED
- graph paper

Area Ratios

In this investigation you will find the relationship between areas of similar figures. Have each member of your group pick a different whole number scale factor.

Step 1 Draw a rectangle on graph paper. Calculate its area.

Step 2 Multiply each dimension of your rectangle by your scale factor and draw the enlarged similar rectangle. Calculate its area.

Step 3 What is the ratio of side lengths (larger to smaller) for your two rectangles? What is the ratio of their areas (larger to smaller)?

Step 4 How many copies of the smaller rectangle would you need to fill the larger rectangle? Draw lines in your larger rectangle to show how you would place the copies to fill the area.

Step 5 Find the areas of these two similar triangles. Write the ratio of the smaller area to the larger area as a fraction and simplify. Do the same with the side lengths. Compare these two ratios.

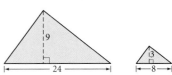

Step 6 Find the exact areas of these two circles in terms of π, not as approximate decimals. Write the ratio of the smaller area to the larger area as a fraction and simplify. Do the same with the radii. Compare these two ratios.

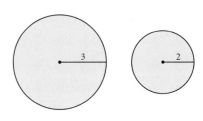

Step 7 Compare your results with those of others in your group and look for a pattern. This relationship between the ratio of corresponding sides (or radii) and the ratio of areas can be generalized to all similar polygons because all polygons can be divided into triangles. You should be ready to state a conjecture.

Proportional Areas Conjecture	C-73

If corresponding side lengths of two similar polygons or the radii of two circles compare in the ratio $\frac{m}{n}$, then their areas compare in the ratio __?__.

DEVELOPING PROOF

Proportional Areas

The sides of the larger triangle are two times those of the smaller triangle. How much larger is the area of the larger triangle?

In the investigation your group members calculated the areas of a pair of similar triangles given the lengths of their bases and heights. As a group, use algebra to prove the Proportional Areas Conjecture restated for triangles: *If two triangles are similar and their ratio of corresponding parts are m to n, then their areas are in the ratio of* $\left(\frac{m}{n}\right)^2$.

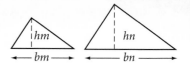

INVESTIGATION 2

Surface Area Ratios

YOU WILL NEED
- interlocking cubes
- isometric dot paper

In this investigation you will investigate whether the Proportional Areas Conjecture is also true for surface areas.

Step 1 Use cubes to construct a 3-by-2-by-1 rectangular prism. Calculate its surface area.

Step 2 Multiply each dimension by a scale factor of 2 and build the enlarged prism. Calculate its surface area.

Step 3 What is the ratio of the lengths of corresponding edges of the larger prism to the smaller prism? What is the ratio of their surface areas?

Step 4 Draw the solid at right on isometric dot paper. Calculate its surface area.

Step 5 Multiply each segment length by a scale factor of 4 and draw the resulting enlarged solid. Calculate its surface area.

Step 6 Calculate the ratio of lengths of corresponding edges and the ratio of surface areas of the two solids. Is the Proportional Areas Conjecture true for surface areas?

Let's look at an application of the Proportional Areas Conjecture.

EXAMPLE

If you need 3 oz of shredded cheese to cover a medium 12 in. diameter pizza, how much shredded cheese would you need to cover a large 16 in. diameter pizza?

Solution

The ratio of the pizza diameters is $\frac{16}{12}$, or $\frac{4}{3}$. Therefore the ratio of the pizza areas is $\left(\frac{4}{3}\right)^2$, or $\frac{16}{9}$. Let x represent the amount of cheese needed for a large pizza and set up a proportion.

$$\frac{\text{area of large pizza}}{\text{area of small pizza}} = \frac{\text{amount of cheese for large pizza}}{\text{amount of cheese for small pizza}}$$

$$\frac{16}{9} = \frac{x}{3}$$

By solving for x, you find that a large pizza requires $5\frac{1}{3}$ oz of shredded cheese.

8.6 Exercises

YOU WILL NEED

Construction tools
for Exercise **22**

1. $\triangle CAT \sim \triangle MSE$
area of $\triangle CAT = 72$ cm²
area of $\triangle MSE = \underline{\ ?\ }$ ⓗ

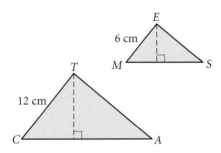

2. $RECT \sim ANGL$
$\dfrac{\text{area of } RECT}{\text{area of } ANGL} = \dfrac{9}{16}$
$TR = \underline{\ ?\ }$

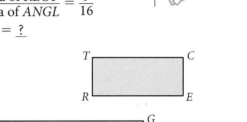

3. $TRAP \sim ZOID$
$\dfrac{\text{area of } ZOID}{\text{area of } TRAP} = \dfrac{16}{25}$
$a = \underline{\ ?\ }, b = \underline{\ ?\ }$ ⓗ

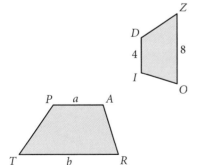

4. semicircle $R \sim$ semicircle S
$\dfrac{r}{s} = \dfrac{3}{5}$
area of semicircle $S = 75\pi$ cm²
area of semicircle $R = \underline{\ ?\ }$

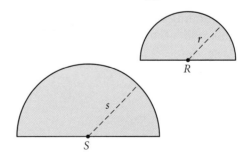

5. The ratio of the lengths of corresponding diagonals of two similar kites is $\frac{1}{7}$. What is the ratio of their areas?

6. The smaller parallelogram has sides with lengths a and b. The larger parallelogram has sides three times as large and has been divided by parallel lines into small parallelograms congruent to the small parallelogram. Sketch a triangle with side lengths of x, y, and z. Sketch a second triangle with sides four times larger: $4x$, $4y$, and $4z$. Draw lines in the larger triangle to show how many of the small triangles fit in the larger triangle.

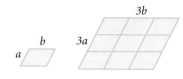

7. The ratio of the lengths of the edges of two cubes is $\frac{m}{n}$. What is the ratio of their surface areas? ⓗ

8. Annie works in a magazine's advertising department. A client has requested that his 5 cm by 12 cm ad be enlarged: "Double the length and double the width, then send me the bill." The original ad cost $1500. How much should Annie charge for the larger ad? Explain your reasoning.

9. Solve the problem posed at the beginning of the lesson. An artist uses 200 tiles to create a tessellation design that covers a rectangle with dimensions 2 ft by 3 ft. He will cover a wall with dimensions 10 ft by 15 ft using the same design and tiles of the same size. How many tiles will he need to cover the entire wall?

10. Circle O is dilated by a scale factor $r = 3$. The image, circle O', has an area of 225π cm². What is the radius of circle O?

11. Make four copies of the trapezoid at right. Arrange them into a larger trapezoid. Sketch the final trapezoid and show how the smaller trapezoids fit inside it. Describe the transformations you used to create the larger trapezoid. Are the smaller trapezoids similar to the larger one? Explain why or why not.

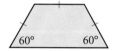

12. Consider a rectangle with base 2 cm and height 1 cm.

  a. Imagine stretching the base by multiplying it by scale factor x, without changing the height. Make a table of the area of the rectangle for values of x from 1 to 6. Plot the points on a graph and write the function $a(x)$ that gives the area as a function of x.

  b. Now imagine stretching both the base *and* the height by multiplying them by scale factor x. As before, make a table of the new area of the rectangle for values of x from 1 to 6, plot the points, and write the function $A(x)$ that gives the new area as a function of x.

  c. How do the equations for $a(x)$ and $A(x)$ differ? How do their graphs differ?

13. In the diagram at right, the second rectangle is a dilation of the first rectangle by scale factor r. Given that the ratio of the corresponding sides of the similar rectangles is r, prove that the ratio of their areas is r^2.

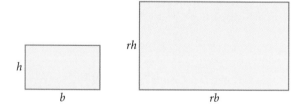

Review

14. $x = \underline{\ ?\ }, y = \underline{\ ?\ }$

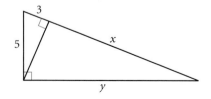

15. $XY = \underline{\ ?\ }$

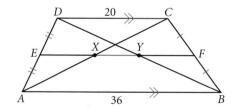

16. Sara rents her goat, Munchie, as a lawn mower. Munchie is tied to a stake with a 10 m rope. Sara wants to find an efficient pattern for Munchie's stake positions so that all grass in a field 42 m by 42 m is mowed but overlap is minimized. Make a sketch showing all the stake positions needed.

17. Prove that corresponding altitudes of similar triangles are proportional to corresponding sides.

18. *True or false?* The angle bisector of one of the nonvertex angles of a kite will divide the diagonal connecting the vertex angles into two segments whose lengths are in the same ratio as two unequal sides of the kite. If true, explain why. If false, show a counterexample that proves it false.

19. Find *x* and explain how you know.

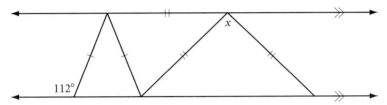

20. Find the area of a regular decagon with an apothem about 5.7 cm and a perimeter 37 cm.

21. Find the area of a triangle whose sides measure 13 feet, 13 feet, and 10 feet. ⓗ

22. Given side $\overline{AB}$, median $\overline{CM}$ to $\overline{AB}$, and altitude $\overline{CD}$ to $\overline{AB}$, construct $\triangle ABC$.

DEVELOPING MATHEMATICAL REASONING

Bagels Puzzle II

In the original computer game of bagels, a player determines a three-digit number (no digit repeated) by making educated guesses. After each guess, the computer gives a clue about the guess. Here are the clues.

bagels: no digit is correct
pico: one digit is correct but in the wrong position
fermi: one digit is correct and in the correct position

In games 1 and 2 below, a number of guesses have been made, with the clue for each guess shown to its right. From the given set of guesses and clues, determine the three-digit number. If there is more than one solution, find them all.

Game 1: 012 *pico fermi*
345 *bagels*
678 *pico*
081 *pico*
702 *pico pico*
???

Game 2: 901 *bagels*
245 *pico*
367 *fermi*
498 *pico fermi*
348 *pico pico*
???

You should know area formulas for rectangles, parallelograms, triangles, trapezoids, regular polygons, and circles. You should also be able to show where these formulas come from and how they're related to one another. Most importantly, you should be able to apply them to solve practical problems involving area, including the surface areas of solid figures. The ratios of area in similar figures are related to the ratios of their dimensions. But recall that as the dimensions increase, the area increases by a squared factor.

When you use area formulas for real-world applications, you have to consider units of measurement and accuracy. Should you use inches, feet, centimeters, meters, or some other unit? If you work with a circle or a regular polygon, is your answer exact or an approximation?

Exercises

1. True-False

__ **a.** The area of a kite is half the area of a rectangle that circumscribes it.

__ **b.** If the length and width of a rectangle are doubled then the area of the rectangle is doubled.

__ **c.** If the perimeter of a square is 48 cm and the circumference of a circle is 12π cm, then the area of the circle is less than the area of the square.

__ **d.** If the length of the midsegment of a trapezoid is 36 m and its height is 20 m, then the area of the trapezoid is equal to that of a rectangle with a base of 72 m and height of 10 m.

__ **e.** If the area of a sector of a circle with a radius of 12 cm is 16π cm², then the central angle of the sector is 36°.

__ **f.** If the area of $\triangle MAS$ is 36 cm², then the area of the image of $\triangle MAS$ after a reflection is also 36 cm².

__ **g.** Rectangle *PEAR* has an area of 160 cm². If it is transformed by the ordered pair rule, $(x, y) \rightarrow (2x, 2y)$, then its image, $P'E'A'R'$, has an area of 640 cm².

__ **h.** There are three times as many true statements as false statements in a through h.

For Exercises 2–11, match the area formula with the shaded area.

2. $A = bh$

3. $A = 0.5bh$

4. $A = 0.5h(b_1 + b_2)$

5. $A = 0.5d_1d_2$

6. $A = 0.5aP$

7. $A = \pi r^2$

8. $A = \dfrac{x}{360}\pi r^2$

9. $A = \pi(R^2 - r^2)$

10. $SA = 2\pi rl + 2\pi r^2$

11. $SA = \pi rl + \pi r^2$

A.

B.

C.

D.

E.

F.

G.

H.

I.

J.

For Exercises 12–14, illustrate each term.

12. Apothem

13. Annulus

14. Sector of a circle

For Exercises 15–17, draw a diagram and explain in a paragraph how you derived the area formula for each figure.

15. Parallelogram

16. Trapezoid

17. Circle

Solve for the unknown measures in Exercises 18–26. All measurements are in centimeters.

18. $A = \underline{\ ?\ }$

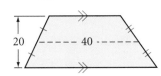

19. $A \approx \underline{\ ?\ }$
$a = 36$
$s \approx 41.6$

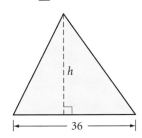

20. $A = \underline{\ ?\ }$
$R = 8$
$r = 2$

21. $A = 576\ \text{cm}^2$
$h = \underline{\ ?\ }$

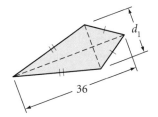

22. $A = 576\ \text{cm}^2$
$d_1 = \underline{\ ?\ }$

23. $A = 126\ \text{cm}^2$
$a = 13\ \text{cm}$
$h = 9\ \text{cm}$
$b = \underline{\ ?\ }$

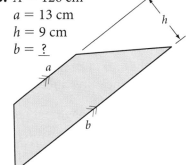

24. $C = 18\pi$ cm
$A = \underline{\ ?\ }$

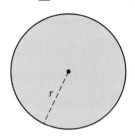

25. $A = 576\pi$ cm²
The circumference is $= \underline{\ ?\ }$.

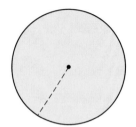

26. $A_{sector} = 16\pi$ cm²
$m\angle FAN = \underline{\ ?\ }$.

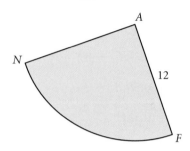

In Exercises 27–29, find the shaded area to the nearest 0.1 cm². In Exercises 28 and 29, the quadrilateral is a square and all arcs are arcs of a circle of radius 6 cm.

27.

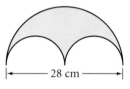

|← 28 cm →|

28.

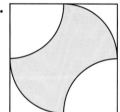

29.

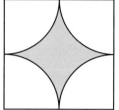

In Exercises 30–32, find the surface area of each prism or pyramid. All given measurements are in centimeters. All quadrilaterals are rectangles, unless otherwise labeled.

30.

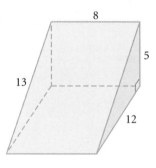

31. The base is a trapezoid.

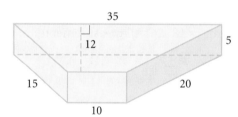

32.

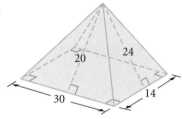

For Exercises 33 and 34, plot the vertices of each figure on graph paper, then find its area.

33. Parallelogram $ABCD$ with vertices $A(0, 0)$, $B(14, 0)$, and $D(6, 8)$

34. Quadrilateral $FOUR$ with vertices $F(0, 0)$, $O(4, -3)$, $U(9, 5)$, and $R(4, 15)$

35. The sum of the lengths of the two bases of a trapezoid is 22 cm, and its area is 66 cm². What is the height of the trapezoid?

36. Find the area of a regular pentagon to the nearest tenth of a square centimeter if the apothem measures about 6.9 cm and each side measures 10 cm.

37. Find three noncongruent polygons, each with an area of 24 square units, on a 6-by-6 geoboard or a 6-by-6 square dot grid.

38. The ratio of the perimeters of two similar parallelograms is 3:7. What is the ratio of their areas?

39. The Jones family paid $150 to a painting contractor to stain their 12 ft by 15 ft deck. The Smiths have a similar deck that measures 16 ft by 20 ft. What price should the Smith family expect to pay to have their deck stained?

40. Lancelot wants to make a pen for his pet, Isosceles. What is the area of the largest rectangular pen that Lancelot can make with 100 meters of fencing if he uses a straight wall of the castle for one side of the pen?

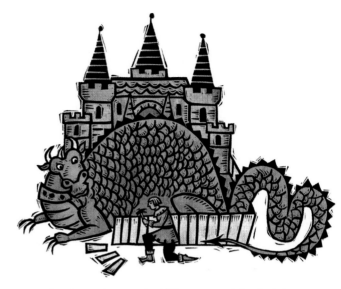

41. **Which shape will give you the maximum area?** If you have a hundred feet of rope to arrange into the perimeter of either a square or a circle, which shape will give you the maximum area? Explain.

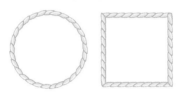

Ropes

42. **Which is a better fit** (fills more of the hole): a round peg in a square hole or a square peg in a round hole? Explain.

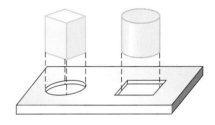

43. **What's the best deal?** The Pizzeria sells pizza by the slice, according to the sign. Which slice is the best deal (the most pizza per dollar)?

44. If you need 8 oz of dough to make a 12-inch diameter pizza, how much dough will you need to make a 16-inch pizza on a crust of the same thickness?

45. Which is the biggest slice of pie: one-fourth of a 6-inch diameter pie, one-sixth of an 8-inch diameter pie, or one-eighth of a 12-inch diameter pie? Which slice has the most crust along the curved edge?

46. Using the figure at right, calculate the ratio of the area of the square, the area of the circle, and the area of the isosceles triangle. Copy and complete this statement of proportionality.

Area of square to Area of circle to Area of triangle is _?_ to _?_ to _?_.

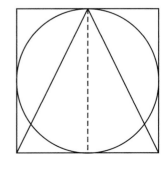

47. The Hot-Air Balloon Club at Da Vinci High School has designed a balloon for the annual race. The panels are a regular octagon, eight squares, and sixteen isosceles trapezoids, and club members will sew them together to construct the balloon. They have built a scale model, as shown at right. The approximate dimensions of the four types of panels are below, shown in feet.

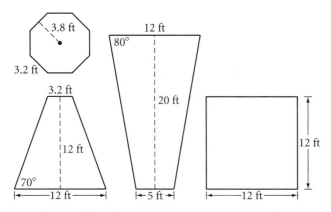

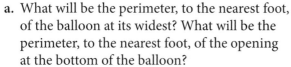

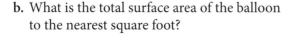

a. What will be the perimeter, to the nearest foot, of the balloon at its widest? What will be the perimeter, to the nearest foot, of the opening at the bottom of the balloon?

b. What is the total surface area of the balloon to the nearest square foot?

48. You are producing 10,000 of these metal wedges, and you must electroplate them with a thin layer of high-conducting silver. The measurements shown are in centimeters. Find the total cost for silver, if silver plating costs $1 for each 200 square centimeters. Assume each quadrilateral is a rectangle.

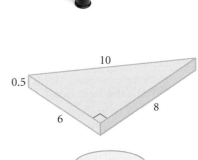

49. The measurements of a chemical storage container are shown in meters. Find the cost of painting the exterior of nine of these large cylindrical containers with sealant. The sealant costs $32 per gallon. Each gallon covers 18 square meters. Do not paint the bottom faces.

50. Hector is a very cost-conscious produce buyer. He usually buys asparagus in large bundles, each 44 cm in circumference. But today there are only small bundles that are 22 cm in circumference. Two 22 cm bundles are the same price as one 44 cm bundle. Is this a good deal or a bad deal? Why?

51. The measurements of a copper cone are shown in inches. Find the cost of spraying an oxidizer on 100 of these copper cones. The oxidizer costs $26 per pint. Each pint covers approximately 5000 square inches. Spray only the lateral surface.

52. Tom and Betty are planning to paint the exterior walls of their cabin (all vertical surfaces). The paint they have selected costs $24 per gallon and, according to the label, covers 150 to 300 square feet per gallon. Because the wood is very dry, they assume the paint will cover 150 square feet per gallon. How much will the project cost? (All measurements shown are in feet.)

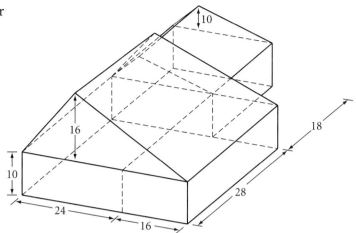

 TAKE ANOTHER LOOK

1. Use geometry software to construct these shapes:

   a. A triangle whose perimeter can vary, but whose area stays constant

   b. A parallelogram whose perimeter can vary, but whose area stays constant

2. *True or false?* The area of a triangle is equal to half the perimeter of the triangle times the radius of the inscribed circle. Support your conclusion with a convincing argument.

3. Does the area formula for a kite hold for a dart? Support your conclusion with a convincing argument.

4. How can you use the Regular Polygon Area Conjecture to arrive at a formula for the area of a circle? Use a series of diagrams to help explain your reasoning.

5. Use algebra to show that the total surface area of a prism with a regular polygon base is given by the formula $SA = P(h + a)$, where h is height of the prism, a is the apothem of the base, and P is the perimeter of the base.

6. Use algebra to show that the total surface area of a cylinder is given by the formula $SA = C(h + r)$, where h is the height of the cylinder, r is the radius of the base, and C is the circumference of the base.

7. Here is a different formula for the area of a trapezoid: $A = mh$, where m is the length of the midsegment and h is the height. Does the formula work? Use algebra or a diagram to explain why or why not. Does it work for a triangle?

8. *True or false?* If the diagonals of a quadrilateral are perpendicular, then the area of the quadrilateral is half the product of the diagonals. Support your conclusion with either a counterexample or a convincing argument.

9. In Lesson 8.4, Exercise 15, you were asked to find the shaded area between the circles inscribed within a square. Did you notice that the ratio of the sum of the areas of all the circles to the area of the square was always the same? Is this always true? Can you prove it?

10. *True or false?* If the diagonals of a convex quadrilateral are perpendicular to each other then one of the diagonals divides the quadrilateral into two triangles of equal area. Investigate, conjecture, and prove true or false.

11. *True or false?* If one diagonal of a convex quadrilateral bisects the other diagonal then one of the diagonals divides the quadrilateral into two triangles of equal area. Investigate, conjecture, and prove true or false.

12. The midsegment of a triangle divides the triangle into a smaller triangle and a trapezoid. The smaller triangle can be rotated so that the trapezoid and triangle can form a parallelogram. Create a geometry software document that demonstrates the transformation of a triangle into a parallelogram. ⓗ

13. The midsegment of a trapezoid divides the trapezoid into two smaller trapezoids. One of the trapezoids can be rotated so that the two trapezoids can form a parallelogram. Then the parallelogram can be dissected into a triangle and trapezoid and the two can be transformed into a rectangle. Create a geometry software document that demonstrates the transformation of a trapezoid into a parallelogram then into a rectangle. Describe the types of transformations involved. ⓗ

Discovering and Proving Circle Properties

> *"I am the only one who can judge how far I constantly remain below the quality I would like to attain."*
> M. C. ESCHER

OBJECTIVES

In this chapter you will

- discover properties of tangent lines
- learn relationships among chords, arcs, and angles
- learn how to calculate the length of an arc
- define the radian measure of an angle
- prove circle conjectures

Tangent Properties

Let's review some basic terms from Chapter 1 before you begin discovering the properties of circles. You should be able to identify the terms below.

Match the figures at the right with the terms at the left.

1. Congruent circles
2. Concentric circles
3. Radius
4. Chord
5. Diameter
6. Tangent
7. Central angle
8. Minor arc
9. Major arc
10. Semicircle

A. $\overline{DC}$
B. $\overleftrightarrow{TG}$
C. $\overline{OE}$
D. $\overline{AB}$
E.
F.
G. $\overarc{RQ}$
H. $\overarc{PRQ}$
I. $\overarc{PQR}$
J. $\angle PTR$

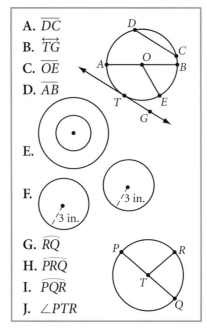

In this lesson you will investigate the relationship between a tangent line to a circle and the radius of the circle, and between two tangent segments to a common point outside the circle.

Rails act as tangent lines to the wheels of a train. Each wheel of a train theoretically touches only one point on the rail. The point where the rail and the wheel meet is a point of tangency. Why can't a train wheel touch more than one point at a time on the rail? How is the radius of the wheel to the point of tangency related to the rail? Let's investigate.

The rail is tangent to the wheels of the train.
The adult penguins' heads are tangent to each other.

INVESTIGATION 1

Going Off on a Tangent

YOU WILL NEED
- a compass
- a straightedge

In this investigation you will discover the relationship between a tangent line and the radius drawn to the point of tangency.

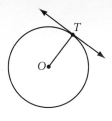

Step 1 Construct a large circle. Label the center O.

Step 2 Using your straightedge, draw a line that appears to touch the circle at only one point. Label the point T. Construct $\overline{OT}$.

Step 3 Use your protractor to measure the angles at T. What can you conclude about the radius $\overline{OT}$ and the tangent line at T?

Step 4 Share your results with your group. Then copy and complete the conjecture.

> **Tangent Conjecture**   C-74
>
> A tangent to a circle ? the radius drawn to the point of tangency.

Technology
CONNECTION

The International Space Station has been orbiting the earth since 2000. According to the United States Space Command, there are over 8,000 objects larger than a softball circling Earth at speeds of over 18,000 miles per hour! If gravity were suddenly "turned off" somehow, these objects would travel off into space on a straight line tangent to their orbits, and not continue in a curved path.

You can also show that the converse of the Tangent Conjecture is true. If you construct a line perpendicular to a radius at the point where it touches the circle, the line will be tangent to the circle.

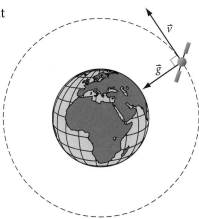

The Tangent Conjecture has important applications related to circular motion. For example, a satellite maintains its velocity in a direction tangent to its circular orbit. This velocity vector is perpendicular to the force of gravity, which keeps the satellite in orbit.

INVESTIGATION 2

Tangent Segments

YOU WILL NEED
- a compass
- a straightedge

In this investigation you will discover something about the lengths of segments tangent to a circle from a point outside the circle.

Step 1 Construct a circle. Label the center E.

Step 2 Choose a point outside the circle and label it N.

Step 3 Draw two rays from point N tangent to the circle. Mark the points where these lines appear to touch the circle and label them A and G.

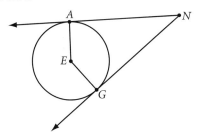

Step 4 Use your compass to compare segments NA and NG. Segments such as these are called **tangent segments**.

Step 5 Share your results with your group. Copy and complete the conjecture.

> **Tangent Segments Conjecture**   C-75
>
> Tangent segments to a circle from a point outside the circle are __?__.

DEVELOPING PROOF

Tangent Segments

The investigation may have convinced you that the conjecture is true, but can you explain why? What other properties does this conjecture depend upon? One important property you proved earlier is the Converse of the Isosceles Triangle Conjecture. As a group, look over the diagrams below, answer the questions, and then prove the Tangent Segments Conjecture. You will use reasoning strategies such as drawing an auxiliary line, drawing and labeling a diagram, and applying previous conjectures.

Given: ⊙O with tangents $\overrightarrow{TA}$ and $\overrightarrow{TN}$.

Show: $\overline{TA} \cong \overline{TN}$

An important auxiliary line is segment $\overline{AN}$. Why is $\overline{OA} \cong \overline{ON}$? Why is $\triangle OAN$ isosceles? Why is $\angle x \cong \angle y$? Why is $\angle w \cong \angle z$? Why is $\overline{TA} \cong \overline{TN}$?

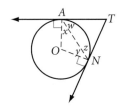

In the figure at right, the central angle, $\angle BOA$, determines the minor arc, $\overset{\frown}{AB}$. $\angle BOA$ is said to intercept $\overset{\frown}{AB}$ because the arc is within the angle. This arc is referred to as the **intercepted arc**. The measure of a minor arc is defined as the measure of its central angle, so $m\overset{\frown}{AB} = 40°$. The measure of a major arc is the reflex measure of $\angle BOA$, or 360° minus the measure of the minor arc, so $m\overset{\frown}{BCA} = 320°$.

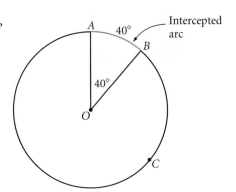

Let's look at an example involving arc measures and tangent segments.

EXAMPLE

In the figure at right, $\overrightarrow{TA}$ and $\overrightarrow{TG}$ are both tangent to circle N. If the major arc formed by the two tangents measures 220°, find the measure of $\angle T$.

Solution

The minor arc intercepted by $\angle N$ measures $360° - 220°$, or 140°. Thus, $m\angle N = 140°$. By the Tangent Conjecture, both $\angle A$ and $\angle G$ must be right angles, and by the Quadrilateral Sum Conjecture, the sum of the angles in quadrilateral $TANG$ is 360°.

So, $m\angle T + 90° + 140° + 90° = 360°$, which means that $m\angle T = 40°$.

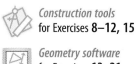

Tangent circles are two circles that are tangent to the same line at the same point. They can be **internally tangent** or **externally tangent**, as shown. What conjectures can you make about tangent circles? You will explore more about them in the exercise set.

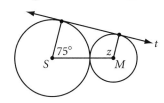

Externally tangent circles   Internally tangent circles

9.1 Exercises

YOU WILL NEED

Construction tools
for Exercises 8–12, 15

Geometry software
for Exercises 13, 21

Solve Exercises 1–5. Explain how you determined your solution.

1. Rays m and n are tangent to circle P. $w = $?

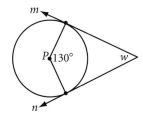

2. Rays r and s are tangent to circle Q. $x = $? ⓗ

3. Ray k is tangent to circle R. $y = $?

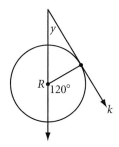

4. Line t is tangent to both tangent circles. $z = $?

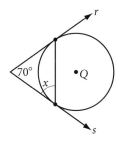

5. Quadrilateral $POST$ is circumscribed about circle Y. $OR = 13$ in. and $ST = 12$ in. Find the perimeter of $POST$. ⓗ

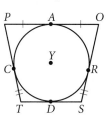

6. Pam participates in the hammer-throw event. She swings a 16 lb ball at arm's length, about eye-level. Then she releases the ball at the precise moment when the ball will travel in a straight line toward the target area. Draw an overhead view that shows the ball's circular path, her arms at the moment she releases it, and the ball's straight path toward the target area.

7. Explain how you could use only a T-square, like the one shown at right, to find the center of a Frisbee.

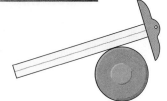

For Exercises 8–12, first make a sketch of what you are trying to construct and label it. Then use the segments below, with lengths *r, s,* and *t.*

```
•————————————•   •————————•   •————————•
       r              s             t
```

8. Construct a circle with radius *r*. Mark a point on the circle. Construct a tangent through this point. ⓗ

9. Construct a circle with radius *t*. Choose three points on the circle that divide it into three minor arcs and label points *X, Y,* and *Z*. Construct a triangle that is circumscribed about the circle and tangent at points *X, Y,* and *Z*.

10. Construct two congruent, externally tangent circles with radius *s*. Then construct a third circle that is both congruent and externally tangent to the two circles.

11. Construct two internally tangent circles with radii *r* and *t*.

12. Construct a third circle with radius *s* that is externally tangent to both the circles you constructed in Exercise 11.

13. Use geometry software to construct a circle. Label three points on the circle and construct tangents through them. Drag the three points and write your observations about where the tangent lines intersect and the figures they form. What happens if two of the three points are on opposite ends of a diameter? What happens if the three points are on the same semicircle?

14. Find real-world examples (different from the example shown at the right) of two internally tangent circles and of two externally tangent circles. Either sketch or make copies of the examples for your notebook.

This astronomical clock in Prague, Czech Republic, has one pair of internally tangent circles. What other circle relationships can you find in the clock photo?

15. In Taoist philosophy, all things are governed by one of two natural principles, yin and yang. Yin represents the earth, characterized by darkness, cold, or wetness. Yang represents the heavens, characterized by light, heat, or dryness. The two principles, when balanced, combine to produce the harmony of nature. The symbol for the balance of yin and yang is shown at right. Construct the yin and yang symbol. Start with one large circle. Then construct two circles with half the diameter that are internally tangent to the large circle and externally tangent to each other. Finally, construct small circles that are concentric to the two inside circles. Shade or color your construction. ⓗ

16. A satellite in geostationary orbit remains above the same point on Earth's surface even as Earth turns. If such a satellite has a 30° view of the equator, what percentage of the equator is observable from the satellite? ⓗ

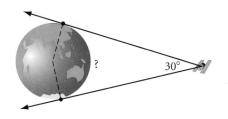

17. $\overrightarrow{TA}$ and $\overrightarrow{TB}$ are tangent to circle O. What's wrong with this picture?

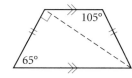

Review

18. Identify each quadrilateral from the given characteristics.

   a. Diagonals are perpendicular and bisect each other.

   b. Diagonals are congruent and bisect each other, but it is not a square.

   c. Only one diagonal is the perpendicular bisector of the other diagonal.

   d. Diagonals bisect each other.

19. Explain why x equals y.

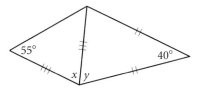

20. What's wrong with this picture?

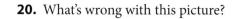

21. Use geometry software to explore the following. Circle O with center at $O(3, -2)$ passes through $A(7, 1)$ and circle Q with center at $Q(-3, 8)$ passes through $B(0, 4)$. ⓗ

   a. Are the two circles congruent? How do you know?

   b. If congruent, what is the single transformation rule that takes circle O onto circle Q?

   c. If they are not congruent explain why not.

> **→ Astronomy**
> **CONNECTION**
>
> Tangent lines can help you locate where a solar eclipse will occur on the surface of Earth. The diagram shows how rays tangent to both the sun and moon will determine the boundaries of regions that experience total shadow, called the umbra, and partial shadow, called the penumbra. This diagram is not drawn to scale. The diameter of the sun is roughly 400 times larger than that of the moon, but the sun is also about 400 times farther away from Earth than the moon, making them appear roughly the same size in the sky.

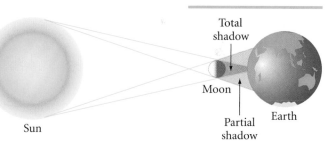

DEVELOPING MATHEMATICAL REASONING

Colored Cubes

Sketch the solid shown, but with the red cubes removed and the blue cube moved to cover the starred face of the green cube.

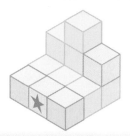

Chord Properties

In the last lesson you discovered some properties of a tangent, a line that intersects the circle only once. In this lesson you will investigate properties of a chord, a line segment whose endpoints lie on the circle.

In a person with correct vision, light rays from distant objects are focused to a point on the retina. If the eye represents a circle, then the path of the light from the lens to the retina represents a chord. The angle formed by two of these chords to the same point on the retina represents an inscribed angle. How would you define an inscribed angle?

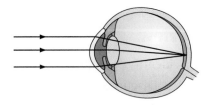

Before investigating the properties of chords in a circle, let's define two types of angles in a circle.

INVESTIGATION 1

Defining Angles in a Circle

Write a good definition of each boldfaced term. Discuss your definitions with others in your group. Agree on a common set of definitions as a class and add them to your definition list. In your notebook, draw and label a figure to illustrate each term.

Step 1 **Central Angle**

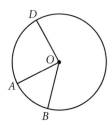

∠AOB, ∠DOA, and ∠DOB are central angles of circle O.

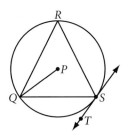

∠PQR, ∠PQS, ∠RST, ∠QST, and ∠QSR are not central angles of circle P

Step 2 **Inscribed Angle**

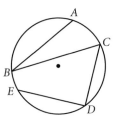

∠ABC, ∠BCD, and ∠CDE are inscribed angles.

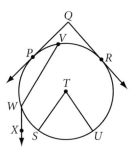

∠PQR, ∠STU, and ∠VWX are not inscribed angles.

INVESTIGATION 2

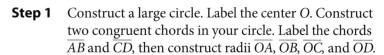

Chords and Their Central Angles

YOU WILL NEED

- a compass
- a straightedge
- a protractor
- patty paper (optional)

Next you will discover some properties of chords and central angles. You will also see a relationship between chords and arcs.

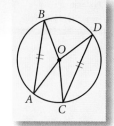

Step 1 Construct a large circle. Label the center *O*. Construct two congruent chords in your circle. Label the chords $\overline{AB}$ and $\overline{CD}$, then construct radii $\overline{OA}$, $\overline{OB}$, $\overline{OC}$, and $\overline{OD}$.

Step 2 With your protractor, measure ∠*BOA* and ∠*COD*. How do they compare? Share your results with others in your group. Then copy and complete the conjecture.

> **Chord Central Angles Conjecture**   C-76
>
> If two chords in a circle are congruent, then they determine two central angles that are _?_ .

Step 3 How can you fold your circle construction to check the conjecture?

Step 4 Recall that the measure of an arc is defined as the measure of its central angle. If two central angles are congruent, their intercepted arcs must be congruent. Combine this fact with the Chord Central Angles Conjecture to complete the next conjecture.

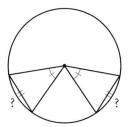

> **Chord Arcs Conjecture**   C-77
>
> If two chords in a circle are congruent, then their _?_ are congruent.

INVESTIGATION 3

Chords and the Center of the Circle

YOU WILL NEED

- a compass
- a straightedge
- patty paper (optional)

In this investigation you will discover relationships about a chord and the center of its circle.

Step 1 Construct a large circle and mark the center. Construct two nonparallel congruent chords. Then construct the perpendiculars from the center to each chord.

Step 2 How does the perpendicular from the center of a circle to a chord divide the chord? Copy and complete the conjecture.

For interactive versions of these investigations, see the **Dynamic Geometry Exploration** Chord Properties in your ebook.

Perpendicular to a Chord Conjecture	C-78

The perpendicular from the center of a circle to a chord is the ? of the chord.

Let's continue this investigation to discover a relationship between the length of congruent chords and their distances from the center of the circle.

Step 3 Compare the distances (measured along the perpendicular) from the center to the chords. Are the results the same if you change the size of the circle and the length of the chords? State your observations as your next conjecture.

Chord Distance to Center Conjecture	C-79

Two congruent chords in a circle are ? from the center of the circle.

INVESTIGATION 4

Perpendicular Bisector of a Chord

YOU WILL NEED

- a compass
- a straightedge
- patty paper (optional)

Next, you will discover a property of perpendicular bisectors of chords.

Step 1 Construct a large circle and mark the center. Construct two nonparallel chords that are not diameters. Then construct the perpendicular bisector of each chord and extend the bisectors until they intersect.

Step 2 What do you notice about the point of intersection? Compare your results with the results of others near you. Copy and complete the conjecture.

Perpendicular Bisector of a Chord Conjecture	C-80

The perpendicular bisector of a chord ? .

With the perpendicular bisector of a chord, you can find the center of any circle, and therefore the vertex of the central angle to any arc. All you have to do is construct the perpendicular bisectors of nonparallel chords.

"Pull the cord?! Don't I need to construct it first?"

DEVELOPING PROOF

Chords Central Angles

The investigation may have convinced you that the Chords Central Angles Conjecture is true but what properties proven earlier explain why they are true? The flowchart below can be used to help explain why this conjecture is true. With your group members, complete the flowchart proof or write your own paragraph proof that explains why the conjecture is true.

Given: Circle O with chords $\overline{AB} \cong \overline{CD}$

Show: $\angle AOB \cong \angle COD$

Flowchart Proof

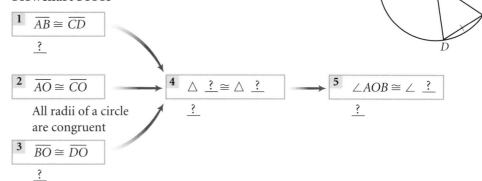

1 $\overline{AB} \cong \overline{CD}$
    ?

2 $\overline{AO} \cong \overline{CO}$
    All radii of a circle are congruent

3 $\overline{BO} \cong \overline{DO}$
    ?

4 $\triangle\ ?\ \cong \triangle\ ?$
    ?

5 $\angle AOB \cong \angle\ ?$
    ?

9.2 Exercises

Solve Exercises 1–10. State which conjectures or definitions you used.

1. $x = \underline{?}$

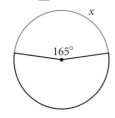

165°

2. $z = \underline{?}$

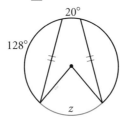

20°
128°
z

3. $w = \underline{?}$

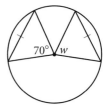

70° w

4. $AB = CD$
$PO = 8$ cm
$OQ = \underline{?}$

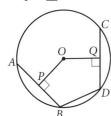

5. $\overline{AB}$ is a diameter.
Find $m\widehat{AC}$ and $m\angle B$.

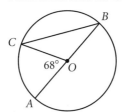

68°

6. $GIAN$ is a kite.
Find w, x, and y.

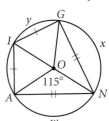

115°

7. $AB = 6$ cm $OP = 4$ cm
$CD = 8$ cm $OQ = 3$ cm
$BD = 6$ cm
What is the perimeter of
$OPBDQ$?

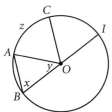

8. $m\widehat{AC} = 130°$
Find w, x, y, and z.

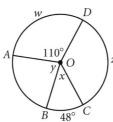

9. $x = $?
$y = $? $\textcircled{h}$
$z = $?

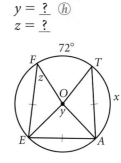

10. $\overline{AB} \parallel \overline{CO}$, $m\widehat{CI} = 66°$
Find x, y, and z.

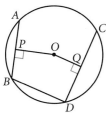

11. What's wrong with this
picture?

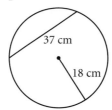

12. What's wrong with this
picture?

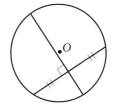

13. Draw a circle and two chords of unequal length. Which is closer to the center of the circle, the longer chord or the shorter chord? Explain.

14. Draw two circles with unequal radii. In each circle, draw a chord so that the chords have the same length. Draw the central angle determined by each chord. Which central angle is larger? Explain.

15. Polygon *MNOP* is a rectangle inscribed in a circle centered at the origin. Find the coordinates of points *M*, *N*, and *O*.

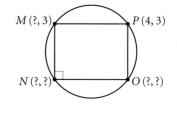

16. Construct a triangle. Using the sides of the triangle as chords, construct a circle passing through all three vertices. Explain your method. Why does this seem familiar?

17. Trace a circle onto a blank sheet of paper without using your compass. Locate the center of the circle using a compass and straightedge. Trace another circle onto patty paper and find the center by folding.

18. Adventurer Ertha Diggs digs up a piece of a circular ceramic plate. Suppose she believes that some ancient plates with this particular design have a diameter of 15 cm. She wants to calculate the diameter of the original plate to see if the piece she found is part of such a plate.

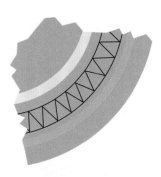

She has only this piece of the circular plate, shown at right, to make her calculations. Trace the outer edge of the plate onto a sheet of paper. Help her find the diameter.

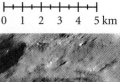

19. The satellite photo at right shows only a portion of a lunar crater. How can cartographers use the photo to find its center? Trace the crater and locate its center. Using the scale shown, find its radius.

20. Complete the flowchart proof or write a paragraph proof of the Perpendicular to a Chord Conjecture: The perpendicular from the center of a circle to a chord is the bisector of the chord.

Given: Circle O with chord $\overline{CD}$, radii $\overline{OC}$ and $\overline{OD}$, and $\overline{OR} \perp \overline{CD}$

Show: $\overline{OR}$ bisects $\overline{CD}$

Flowchart Proof

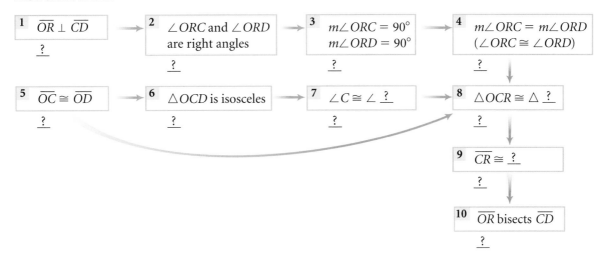

21. Circle O has center $(0, 0)$ and passes through points $A(3, 4)$ and $B(4, -3)$. Find an equation to show that the perpendicular bisector of $\overline{AB}$ passes through the center of the circle. Explain your reasoning. ⓗ

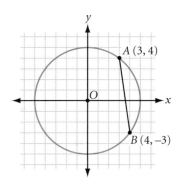

Review

22. Identify each of these statements as true or false. If the statement is true, explain why. If it is false, explain why and give a counterexample.

   a. If the diagonals of a quadrilateral are congruent but only one is the perpendicular bisector of the other, then the quadrilateral is a kite.

   b. If the quadrilateral has exactly one line of reflectional symmetry, then the quadrilateral is a kite.

   c. If the diagonals of a quadrilateral are congruent and bisect each other, then it is a square.

23. Rachel and Yulia are building an art studio above their back bedroom. There will be doors on three sides leading to a small deck that surrounds the studio. They need to place an electrical junction box in the ceiling of the studio so that it is equidistant from the three light switches shown by the doors. Copy the diagram of the room and find the location of the junction box. ⓗ

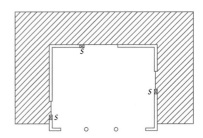

For Exercises 24–26, use the ordered pair rule shown to relocate the four points on the given circle. Does the new figure appear congruent to the original circle?

24. $(x, y) \rightarrow (x - 1, y + 2)$

25. $(x, y) \rightarrow (-x, y)$

26. $(x, y) \rightarrow (2x, 2y)$

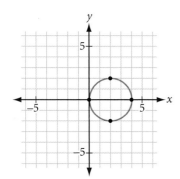

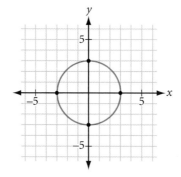

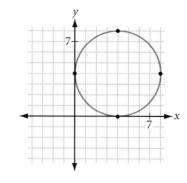

27. GUESS-N-CHECK Consider the figure below with line $\ell \parallel \overline{AB}$. As P moves from left to right along line ℓ, which of these values does not remain constant? First, try this as a "mental experiment." Take a guess, then create the diagram with your geometry software and see how good you were at visual thinking.

A. The length of $\overline{DC}$

B. The distance from D to $\overline{AB}$

C. The ratio $DC : AB$

D. The perimeter of $\triangle ABP$

E. None of the above

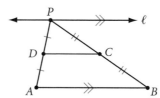

PERFORMANCE TASK

Intersecting Tangents

What is the relationship between the measure of the angle formed by two tangents to a circle, $\angle P$, and the measure of the intercepted arc AB? Investigate this relationship with your group and make a conjecture.

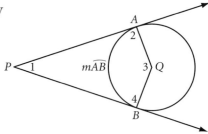

Conjecture: The measure of the angle formed by two intersecting tangents to a circle is _?_ (Intersecting Tangents Conjecture).

Given that $\overrightarrow{PA}$ and $\overrightarrow{PB}$ are both tangent to circle Q in the diagram at right, prove the conjecture you made.

Arcs and Angles

Many arches that you see in structures are semicircular, but Chinese builders long ago discovered that arches don't have to have this shape. The Zhaozhou bridge, shown below, was completed in 605 c.e. It is the world's first stone arched bridge in the shape of a minor arc, predating other minor-arc arches by about 800 years.

In this lesson you'll discover properties of arcs and the angles associated with them.

"Learning by experience is good, but in the case of mushrooms and toadstools, hearsay evidence is better."

ANONYMOUS

INVESTIGATION 1

Inscribed Angle Properties

YOU WILL NEED

- a compass
- a straightedge
- a protractor

In this investigation you will compare an inscribed angle and a central angle, both inscribed in the same arc. Refer to the diagram of circle O, with central angle COR and inscribed angle CAR.

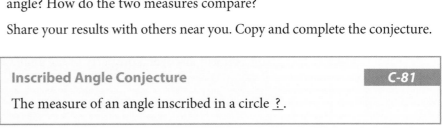

Step 1   Measure $\angle COR$ with your protractor to find $m\overset{\frown}{CR}$, the intercepted arc. Measure $\angle CAR$. How does $m\angle CAR$ compare with $m\overset{\frown}{CR}$?

Step 2   Construct a circle of your own with an inscribed angle. Draw and measure the central angle that intercepts the same arc. What is the measure of the inscribed angle? How do the two measures compare?

Step 3   Share your results with others near you. Copy and complete the conjecture.

Inscribed Angle Conjecture	C-81
The measure of an angle inscribed in a circle ? .	

INVESTIGATION 2

Inscribed Angles Intercepting the Same Arc

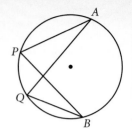

Next, let's consider two inscribed angles that intercept the same arc. In the figure at right, $\angle AQB$ and $\angle APB$ both intercept $\overarc{AB}$. Angles AQB and APB are both inscribed in $\overarc{APB}$.

Step 1 Construct a large circle. Select two points on the circle. Label them A and B. Select a point P on the major arc and construct inscribed angle APB. With your protractor, measure $\angle APB$.

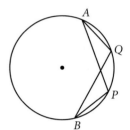

Step 2 Select another point Q on $\overarc{APB}$ and construct inscribed angle AQB. Measure $\angle AQB$.

Step 3 How does $m\angle AQB$ compare with $m\angle APB$?

Step 4 Repeat Steps 1–3 with points P and Q selected on minor arc AB. Compare results with your group. Then copy and complete the conjecture.

> **Inscribed Angles Intercepting Arcs Conjecture**   `C-82`
>
> Inscribed angles that intercept the same arc __?__ .

INVESTIGATION 3

Angles Inscribed in a Semicircle

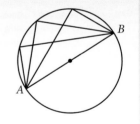

Next, you will investigate a property of angles inscribed in semicircles. This will lead you to a third important conjecture about inscribed angles.

Step 1 Construct a large circle. Construct a diameter $\overline{AB}$. Inscribe three angles in the same semicircle. Make sure the sides of each angle pass through A and B.

Step 2 Measure each angle with your protractor. What do you notice? Compare your results with the results of others and make a conjecture.

> **Angles Inscribed in a Semicircle Conjecture**   `C-83`
>
> Angles inscribed in a semicircle __?__ .

Now you will discover a property of the angles of a quadrilateral inscribed in a circle.

INVESTIGATION 4

Cyclic Quadrilaterals

YOU WILL NEED

- a compass
- a straightedge
- a protractor

A quadrilateral inscribed in a circle is called a **cyclic quadrilateral**. Each of its angles is inscribed in the circle, and each of its sides is a chord of the circle.

Step 1 Construct a large circle. Construct a cyclic quadrilateral by connecting four points anywhere on the circle.

Step 2 Measure each of the four inscribed angles. Write the measure in each angle. Look carefully at the sums of various angles. Share your observations with students near you. Then copy and complete the conjecture.

> **Cyclic Quadrilateral Conjecture** `C-84`
>
> The _?_ angles of a cyclic quadrilateral are _?_ .

INVESTIGATION 5

Arcs by Parallel Lines

YOU WILL NEED

- patty paper
- a compass
- a double-edged straightedge

Next, you will investigate arcs formed by parallel lines that intersect a circle.

A line that intersects a circle in two points is called a **secant**. A secant contains a chord of the circle, and passes through the interior of a circle, while a tangent line does not. Note that a secant is a line while a chord is a segment.

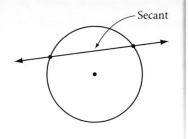

Secant

Step 1 On a piece of patty paper, construct a large circle. Lay your straightedge across the circle so that its parallel edges pass through the circle. Draw secants $\overleftrightarrow{AB}$ and $\overleftrightarrow{DC}$ along both edges of the straightedge.

Step 2 Fold your patty paper to compare $\overset{\frown}{AD}$ and $\overset{\frown}{BC}$. What can you say about $\overset{\frown}{AD}$ and $\overset{\frown}{BC}$?

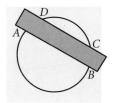

Step 3 Repeat Steps 1 and 2, using either lined paper or another object with parallel edges to construct different parallel secants. Share your results with other students. Then copy and complete the conjecture.

> **Parallel Lines Intercepted Arcs Conjecture** `C-85`
>
> Parallel lines intercept _?_ arcs on a circle.

Review these conjectures and ask yourself which quadrilaterals can be inscribed in a circle. Can any parallelogram be a cyclic quadrilateral? If two sides of a cyclic quadrilateral are parallel, then what kind of quadrilateral will it be?

YOU WILL NEED

Geometry software
for Exercises **20** and **22**

Construction tools
for Exercise **25**

Use your new conjectures to solve Exercises 1–17. For each exercise, explain how you determined your answer.

1. $a = \underline{\ ?\ }$

2. $b = \underline{\ ?\ }$

3. $c = \underline{\ ?\ }$ ⓗ

4. $h = \underline{\ ?\ }$ ⓗ

5. $d = \underline{\ ?\ }$
$e = \underline{\ ?\ }$

6. $f = \underline{\ ?\ }$
$g = \underline{\ ?\ }$

7. JUST is a rhombus.
$w = \underline{\ ?\ }$

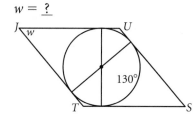

8. CALM is a rectangle.
$x = \underline{\ ?\ }$

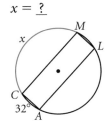

9. DOWN is a kite.
$y = \underline{\ ?\ }$

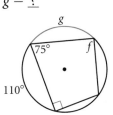

10. $k = \underline{\ ?\ }$

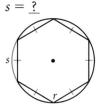

11. $r = \underline{\ ?\ }$
$s = \underline{\ ?\ }$

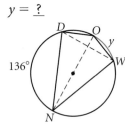

12. $m = \underline{\ ?\ }$
$n = \underline{\ ?\ }$

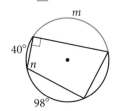

13. $\overline{AB} \parallel \overline{CD}$
$p = \underline{\ ?\ }$
$q = \underline{\ ?\ }$

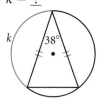

14. What is the sum of a, b, c, d, and e? ⓗ

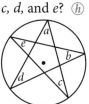

15. $y = \underline{\ ?\ }$ ⓗ

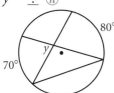

80°

70°

y

16. What's wrong with this picture?

37°   35°

17. Is $\overset{\frown}{AC} \cong \overset{\frown}{CE}$? Explain.

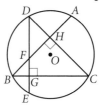

D   A

H

F

O

B   G   C

E

18. What is the difference between "an angle inscribed in an arc" and "an angle that intercepts an arc"? Draw and label an example of each.

19. How can you find the center of a circle, using only the corner of a piece of paper?

20. Chris Chisholm, a high school student in Whitmore, California, used the Angles Inscribed in a Semicircle Conjecture to discover a simpler way to find the orthocenter in a triangle. Chris constructs a circle using one of the sides of the triangle as the diameter, then immediately finds an altitude to each of the triangle's other two sides. Use geometry software and Chris's method to find the orthocenter of a triangle. Does this method work on all kinds of triangles? ⓗ

21. The width of a view that can be captured in a photo depends on the camera's *picture angle*. Suppose a photographer takes a photo of your class standing in one straight row with a camera that has a 46° picture angle. Draw a line segment to represent the row. Draw a 46° angle on a piece of patty paper. Locate at least eight different points on your paper where a camera could be positioned to include all the students, filling as much of the picture as possible. What is the locus of all such camera positions? What conjecture does this activity illustrate? ⓗ

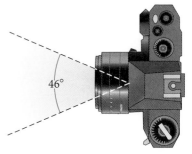

46°

22. **GUESS-N-CHECK** Construct a circle and a diameter. Construct a point on one of the semicircles, and construct two chords from it to the endpoints of the diameter to create a right triangle. Locate the midpoint of each of the two chords. Predict the locus of the two midpoints as the vertex of the right angle is moved around the circle. Finally, use geometry software to animate the point on the circle and trace the locus of the two midpoints. What do you get?

Review

23. Find the measure of each lettered angle. State your reasoning for each measure.

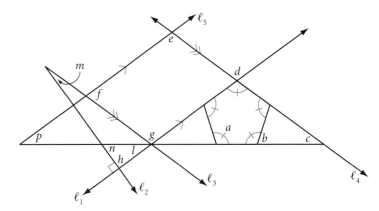

ℓ_5

m

e

f

d

a

p   *g*   *b*   *c*

n   *l*

h

ℓ_1 ℓ_2 ℓ_3 ℓ_4

24. Circle U passes through points $(3, 11)$, $(11, -1)$, and $(-14, 4)$. Find the coordinates of its center. Explain your method.

25. Use your construction tools to re-create this design of three congruent circles, all tangent to each other and internally tangent to a larger circle. What information do you need to know to calculate the blue area? ⓗ

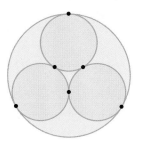

26. What's wrong with this picture?

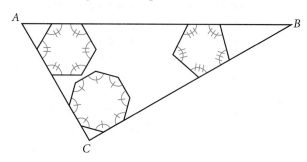

27. What percent of the rectangle is shaded orange?

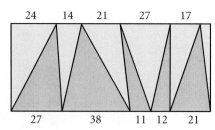

DEVELOPING MATHEMATICAL REASONING

Picture Patterns

Draw the next picture in each pattern. Then write the rule for the total number of squares in the nth picture of the pattern.

1.

2.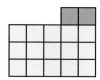

Proving Circle Conjectures

In the previous lesson you first discovered the Inscribed Angle Conjecture: The measure of an angle inscribed in a circle equals half the measure of its intercepted arc. You then discovered four other conjectures related to inscribed angles. In this lesson you will prove that all four of these conjectures are logical consequences of the Inscribed Angle Conjecture.

First we must prove the Inscribed Angle Conjecture itself, but how? Let's use our reasoning strategies to make a plan. By thinking backward, we see that a central angle gives us something to compare an inscribed angle with. If one side of the inscribed angle is a diameter, then we can form a central angle by adding an auxiliary line. But what if the circle's center is not on the inscribed angle? There are three possible cases.

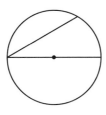

Case 1

The circle's center is on the angle.

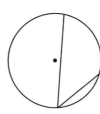

Case 2

The center is outside the angle.

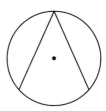

Case 3

The center is inside the angle.

Let's break the problem into parts and consider one case at a time. We'll start with the easiest case first.

Case 1: The circle's center is on the inscribed angle.

This proof uses the variables x, y, and z to represent the measures of the angles as shown in the diagram at right.

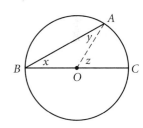

Given: Circle O with inscribed angle ABC on diameter $\overline{BC}$

Show: $m\angle ABC = \frac{1}{2}m\widehat{AC}$

Flowchart Proof of Case 1

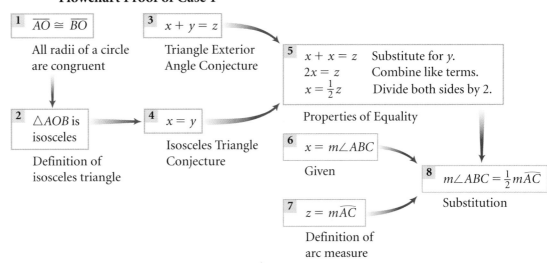

DEVELOPING PROOF

Inscribed Angles

Case 1: As a group, go through the flowchart proof of Case 1, one box at a time. What does each statement mean? How does it relate to the given diagram? How does the reason below the box support the statement? How do the arrows connect the flow of ideas? Discuss the logic of the proof with your group members.

The proof of Case 1 allows us now to prove the other two cases. By adding an auxiliary line, we can use the proof of Case 1 to show that the measures of the inscribed angles that *do* contain the diameter are half those of their intercepted arcs. The proof of Case 2 requires us to accept angle addition and arc addition, or that the measures of adjacent angles and arcs on the same circle can be added.

Case 2: The circle's center is outside the inscribed angle.

This proof uses x, y, and z to represent the measures of the angles, and p and q to represent the measures of the arcs as shown in the diagram at right.

Given: Circle O with inscribed angle ABC on one side of diameter $\overline{BD}$

Show: $m\angle ABC = \frac{1}{2}m\widehat{AC}$

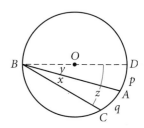

Flowchart Proof of Case 2

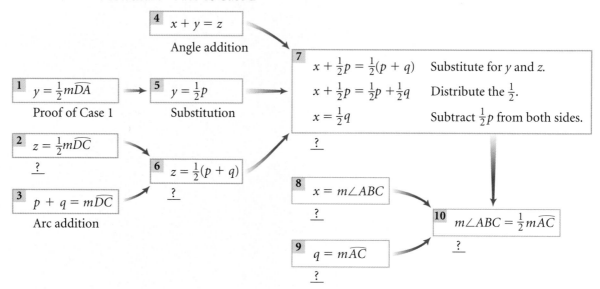

As a group, go through the flowchart proof of Case 2 and fill in the missing reasons. Then work together to create a flowchart proof for Case 3, similar to the proof of Case 2.

Case 3: The circle's center is inside the inscribed angle.

This proof uses x, y, and z to represent the measures of the angles, and p and q to represent the measures of the arcs, as shown in the diagram at right.

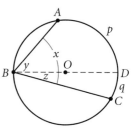

Given: Circle O with inscribed angle ABC whose sides lie on either side of diameter $\overline{BD}$

Show: $m\angle ABC = \frac{1}{2}m\widehat{AC}$

Once we have proved all three cases, we have proved the Inscribed Angle Conjecture. You can now accept it as true to write proofs of other conjectures in the exercises.

9.4 Exercises

In Exercises 1–4, the four conjectures are consequences of the Inscribed Angle Conjecture. Prove each conjecture by writing a paragraph proof or a flowchart proof. Use reasoning strategies, such as think backwards, apply previous conjectures and definitions, and break a problem into parts to develop your proofs.

1. Inscribed angles that intercept the same arc are congruent. ⓗ
   Given: Circle O with $\angle ACD$ and $\angle ABD$ inscribed in $\overset{\frown}{ACD}$
   Show: $\angle ACD \cong \angle ABD$

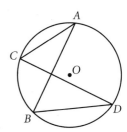

2. Angles inscribed in a semicircle are right angles. ⓗ
   Given: Circle O with diameter $\overline{AB}$, and $\angle ACB$ inscribed in semicircle ACB
   Show: $\angle ACB$ is a right angle

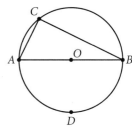

3. The opposite angles of a cyclic quadrilateral are supplementary. ⓗ
   Given: Circle O with inscribed quadrilateral $LICY$
   Show: $\angle L$ and $\angle C$ are supplementary

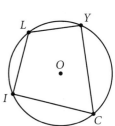

4. Parallel lines intercept congruent arcs on a circle. ⓗ
   Given: Circle O with chord $\overline{BD}$ and $\overleftrightarrow{AB} \parallel \overleftrightarrow{CD}$
   Show: $\overset{\frown}{BC} \cong \overset{\frown}{DA}$

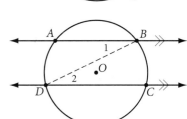

For Exercises 5–7, determine whether each conjecture is true or false. If the conjecture is false, explain why and draw a counterexample. If the conjecture is true, prove it by writing either a paragraph or flowchart proof.

5. If a parallelogram is inscribed within a circle, then the parallelogram is a rectangle. ⓗ
   Given: Circle Y with inscribed parallelogram $GOLD$
   Show: $GOLD$ is a rectangle

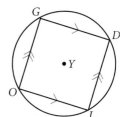

6. If a kite is inscribed in a circle, then one of the diagonals of the kite is a diameter of the circle.

Given: *BRDG* is a kite inscribed in a circle with *BR* = *RD*, *BG* = *DG*

Show: $\overline{RG}$ is a diameter.

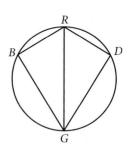

7. If a trapezoid is inscribed within a circle, then the trapezoid is isosceles. ⓗ

Given: Circle *R* with inscribed trapezoid *GATE*

Show: *GATE* is an isosceles trapezoid

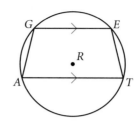

Review

8. Use what you know about isosceles triangles and the angle formed by a tangent and a radius to find the missing arc measure or angle measure in each diagram. Examine these cases to find a relationship between the measure of the angle formed by a tangent and chord at the point of tangency, ∠*ABC*, and the measure of the intercepted arc, $\overset{\frown}{AB}$. Then copy and complete the conjecture below.

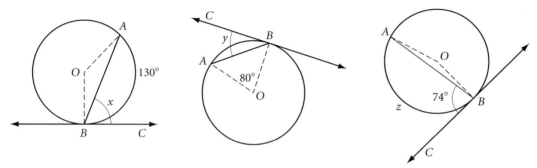

Conjecture: The measure of the angle formed by the intersection of a tangent and chord at the point of tangency is _?_. (Tangent-Chord Conjecture)

9. Given circle *O* with chord $\overline{AB}$ and tangent $\overleftrightarrow{BC}$ in the diagram at right, prove the conjecture you made in the last exercise. ⓗ

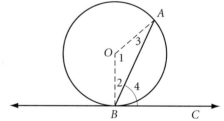

10. For each of the statements below, choose the letter for the word that best fits (A stands for always, S for sometimes, and N for never). If the answer is S, give two examples, one showing how the statement can be true and one showing how the statement can be false.

a. An equilateral polygon is (A/S/N) equiangular.

b. If a triangle is a right triangle, then the acute angles are (A/S/N) complementary.

c. The diagonals of a kite are (A/S/N) perpendicular bisectors of each other.

d. A regular polygon (A/S/N) has both reflectional symmetry and rotational symmetry.

e. If a polygon has rotational symmetry, then it (A/S/N) has more than one line of reflectional symmetry.

Match each term in Exercises 11–19 with one of the figures A–N.

11. Minor arc

12. Major arc

13. Semicircle

14. Central angle

15. Inscribed angle

16. Chord

17. Secant

18. Tangent

19. Inscribed triangle

A. $\overline{OC}$

B. $\overline{AB}$

C. $\overline{OF}$

D. $\angle COD$

E. $\angle DAC$

F. $\angle ACF$

G. $\overleftrightarrow{CF}$

H. $\overleftrightarrow{AC}$

I. $\overrightarrow{GB}$

J. $\widehat{BAD}$

K. $\widehat{ABD}$

L. $\widehat{CD}$

M. $\triangle OCD$

N. $\triangle ACD$

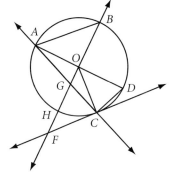

20. Use the diagram at right and the flowchart below to write a paragraph proof explaining why two congruent chords in a circle are equidistant from the center of the circle. ⓗ

Given: Circle O with $\overline{PQ} \cong \overline{RS}$ and $\overline{OT} \perp \overline{PQ}$ and $\overline{OV} \perp \overline{RS}$

Show: $\overline{OT} \cong \overline{OV}$

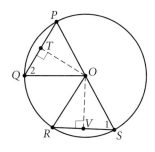

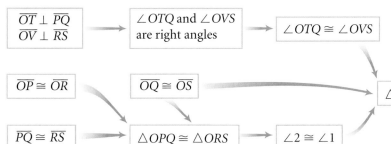

21. Given $\triangle ABC$ with vertices $A(-6, -5)$, $B(6, -3)$, $C(3, 8)$

  a. Transform $\triangle ABC$ by the rule $(x, y) \to (2x, 2y)$ to create $\triangle A'B'C'$.

  b. What are the coordinates of the vertices of $\triangle A'B'C'$?

  c. Are the two triangles congruent?

  d. How do the corresponding angles compare? Use patty paper to compare.

DEVELOPING MATHEMATICAL REASONING

Rolling Quarters

One of two quarters remains motionless while the other rotates around it, never slipping and always tangent to it. When the rotating quarter has completed a turn around the stationary quarter, how many turns has it made around its own center point? Try it!

The Circumference/ Diameter Ratio

The distance around a polygon is called the perimeter. The distance around a circle is called the **circumference**. Here is a nice visual puzzle. Which is greater, the height of a tennis-ball can or the circumference of the can? The height is approximately three tennis-ball diameters tall. The diameter of the can is approximately one tennis-ball diameter. If you have a tennis-ball can handy, try it. Wrap a string around the can to measure its circumference, then compare this measurement with the height of the can. Surprised?

If you actually compared the measurements, you discovered that the circumference of the can is greater than three diameters of the can. In this lesson you are going to discover (or perhaps rediscover) the relationship between the diameter and the circumference of every circle. Once you know this relationship, you can measure a circle's diameter and calculate its circumference.

If you measure the circumference and diameter of a circle and divide the circumference by the diameter, you get a number slightly larger than 3. The more accurate your measurements, the closer your ratio will come to a special number called π (pi), pronounced "pie," like the dessert.

INVESTIGATION

A Taste of Pi

YOU WILL NEED

- several round objects (cans, mugs, bike wheel, plates, balloons)
- a meterstick or metric measuring tape
- sewing thread or thin string

In this investigation you will find an approximate value of π by measuring circular objects and calculating the ratio of the circumference to the diameter. Let's see how close you come to the actual value of π.

Step 1 Measure the circumference of each round object by wrapping the measuring tape or string around its perimeter. Then measure the diameter of each object with the meterstick or tape. Record each measurement to the nearest millimeter.

Step 2 Make a table like the one below and record the circumference (C) and diameter (d) measurements for each round object.

Object	Circumference (C)	Diameter (d)	Ratio $\frac{C}{d}$
Can			
Mug			
Wheel			

Mathematics
CONNECTION

The number π is an irrational number—its decimal form never ends and the pattern of digits does not repeat. The symbol π is a letter of the Greek alphabet. Perhaps no other number has more fascinated mathematicians throughout history. Mathematicians in ancient Egypt used $\left(\frac{4}{3}\right)^4$ as their approximation of circumference to diameter. Early Chinese and Hindu mathematicians used $\sqrt{10}$. By 408 C.E., Chinese mathematicians were using $\frac{355}{113}$. Today, computers have calculated approximations of π to billions of decimal places, and there are websites devoted to π!

Step 3 Calculate the ratio $\frac{C}{d}$ for each object. Record the answers in your table.

Step 4 Calculate the average of your ratios of $\frac{C}{d}$.

Compare your average with the averages of other groups. Are the $\frac{C}{d}$ ratios close? You should now be convinced that the ratio $\frac{C}{d}$ is very close to 3 for every circle. We define π as the ratio $\frac{C}{d}$. If you solve this formula for C, you get a formula for the circumference of a circle in terms of the diameter, d. The diameter is twice the radius ($d = 2r$), so you can *also* get a formula for the circumference in terms of the radius, r.

Step 5 Copy and complete the conjecture.

> **Circumference Conjecture** `C-86`
>
> If C is the circumference and d is the diameter of a circle, then there is a number π such that $C =$ _?_. If $d = 2r$ where r is the radius, then $C =$ _?_.

Accurate approximations of π have been of more interest intellectually than practically. Still, what would a carpenter say if you asked her to cut a board 3π feet long? Most calculators have a π button that gives π to eight or ten decimal places. You can use this value for most calculations, then round your answer to a specified decimal place. If your calculator doesn't have a π button, or if you don't have access to a calculator, use the value 3.14 for π. If you're asked for an exact answer instead of an approximation, state your answer in terms of π.

How do you use the Circumference Conjecture? Let's look at an example.

EXAMPLE | If we estimate the diameter of Earth is 8000 miles, find the average speed in miles per hour Phileas Fogg must travel to circumnavigate Earth about the equator in 80 days.

Solution | To find the speed, you need to know the distance and the time. The distance around the equator is equal to the circumference C of a circle with a diameter of 8,000 miles.

$$C = \pi d \qquad \text{The equation for circumference.}$$
$$= \pi(8,000) \qquad \text{Substitute 8,000 for } d.$$
$$\approx 25,133 \qquad \text{Round to nearest mile.}$$

So, Phileas must travel 25,133 miles in 80 days. To find the speed v in mi/h, you need to divide distance by time and convert days into hours.

$$v = \frac{distance}{time}$$ The formula for speed, or velocity.

$$\approx \frac{25{,}133\ mi}{80\ days} \cdot \frac{1\ day}{24\ h}$$ Substitute values and convert units of time.

$$\approx 13\ mi/h$$ Evaluate and round to the nearest mile per hour.

If Earth's diameter were *exactly* 8,000 miles, you could evaluate $\frac{8{,}000\pi}{80 \cdot 24}$ and get an exact answer of $\frac{25\pi}{6}$ in terms of π.

9.5 Exercises

In Exercises 1–6, leave your answer in terms of π.

1. If $C = 5\pi$ cm, find d.

2. If $r = 5$ cm, find C.

3. If $C = 24$ m, find r.

4. If $d = 5.5$ m, find C.

5. If a circle has a diameter of 12 cm, what is its circumference?

6. If a circle has a circumference of 46π m, what is its diameter?

7. What's the circumference of a bicycle wheel with a 27-inch diameter?

8. If the distance from the center of a Ferris wheel to one of the seats is approximately 90 feet, what is the distance traveled by a seated person, to the nearest foot, in one revolution?

9. If a circle is inscribed in a square with a perimeter of 24 cm, what is the circumference of the circle? ⓗ

10. If a circle with a circumference of 16π inches is circumscribed about a square, what is the length of a diagonal of the square?

11. A satellite in a nearly circular orbit is 2000 km above Earth's surface. The radius of Earth is approximately 6400 km. If the satellite completes its orbit in 12 hours, calculate the speed of the satellite in kilometers per hour. ⓗ

12. Wilbur Wrong is flying his remote-control plane in a circle with a radius of 28 meters. His brother, Orville Wrong, clocks the plane at 16 seconds per revolution. What is the speed of the plane? Express your answer in meters per second. The brothers may be wrong, but you could be right!

13. Here is a tiring problem. The diameter of a car tire is approximately 60 cm. The warranty is good for 70,000 km. About how many revolutions will the tire make before the warranty is up? More than a million? A billion?

14. Each year a growing tree adds a new ring to its cross-section. Some years the ring is thicker than others. Why do you suppose this happens?

Suppose the average thickness of growth rings in the Flintstones National Forest is 0.5 cm. About how old is "Old Fred," a famous tree in the forest, if its circumference measures 766 cm?

15. Pool contractor Peter Tileson needs to determine the number of 1-inch tiles to put around the edge of a pool. The pool is a rectangle with two semicircular ends as shown. How many tiles will he need?

→ **Science**
CONNECTION

Trees can live hundreds to thousands of years, and we can determine the age of one tree by counting its growth rings. A pair of rings—a light ring formed in the spring and summer and a dark one formed in the fall and early winter—represent the growth for one year. We can learn a lot about the climate of a region over a period of years by studying tree growth rings. This study is called *dendroclimatology*.

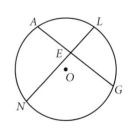

Review

16. Use what you know about inscribed angles and exterior angles of a triangle to find the missing angle measures in each diagram. Examine these cases to find a relationship between the measure of ∠AEN and the measures of the two intercepted arcs, $\widehat{AN}$ and $\widehat{LG}$. Then copy and complete the conjecture below.

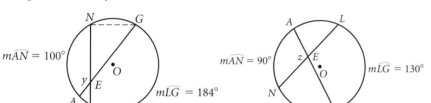

Conjecture: The measure of an angle formed by two intersecting chords is **?**. (Intersecting Chords Conjecture)

17. Given circle O with chords $\overline{AG}$ and $\overline{LN}$ in the diagram at right, prove the conjecture you made in the last exercise. Start by drawing the auxiliary line $\overline{NG}$. ⓗ

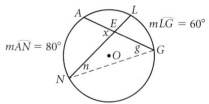

18. Find z. Explain your method.

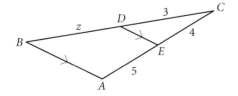

19. Explain why a and b are complementary.

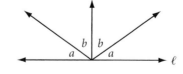

20. Prove the conjecture: If two circles intersect at two points, then the segment connecting the centers is the perpendicular bisector of the common chord, the segment connecting the points of intersection.

> **Given:** Circle *M* and circle *S* intersect at points *A* and *T* with radii $\overline{MA} \cong \overline{MT}$ and $\overline{SA} \cong \overline{ST}$
>
> **Show:** $\overline{MS}$ is the perpendicular bisector of $\overline{AT}$

Flowchart Proof

1	?

Given

3	*MAST* is a kite

?

4	?

?

2	?

Given

21. Trace the figure below. Calculate the measure of each lettered angle.

ℓ_1 and ℓ_2 are tangents.

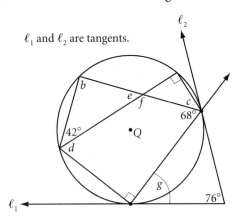

22. Explain why *m* is parallel to *n*. ⓗ

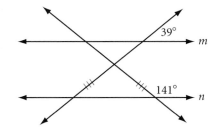

23. Given circle *P* with center at *P*(6, 3) and tangent to the *x*-axis at point *A*. ⓗ

   a. What is the radius of circle *P*?

   b. Name three other points on circle *P*.

   c. Transform circle *P* by the transformation rule $(x, y) \rightarrow (\frac{x}{3}, \frac{y}{3})$ to create circle *P'*.

   d. What are the coordinates of the center of circle *P'*?

   e. Is $\odot P' \cong \odot P$?

   f. Are the points *P*, *P'*, and the origin collinear?

   g. What is the radius of circle *P*? What is the radius of circle *P'*?

   h. What is the ratio of the circumference of circle *P'* to the circumference of circle *P*?

24. Zach wants a circular table so that 12 chairs, each 16 inches wide, can be placed around it with at least 8 inches between chairs. What should be the diameter of the table? Will the table fit in a 12 foot by 14 foot dining room? Explain.

25. Construct a scalene acute triangle. Construct the inscribed circle.

Arc Length

You have learned that the *measure* of a minor arc is equal to the measure of its central angle. On a clock, the measure of the arc from 12:00 to 4:00 is equal to the measure of the angle formed by the hour and minute hands. A circular clock is divided into 12 equal arcs, so the measure of each hour is $\frac{360°}{12}$, or 30°. The measure of the arc from 12:00 to 4:00 is four times 30°, or 120°.

Notice that because the minute hand is longer, the tip of the minute hand must travel farther than the tip of the hour hand even though they both move 120° from 12:00 to 4:00. So the arc *length* is different even though the arc *measure* is the same!

Let's take another look at the arc measure.

EXAMPLE A

What fraction of its circle is each arc?

a. $\overset{\frown}{AB}$ is what fraction of circle *T*?

b. $\overset{\frown}{CED}$ is what fraction of circle *O*?

c. $\overset{\frown}{EF}$ is what fraction of circle *P*?

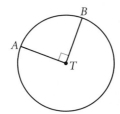

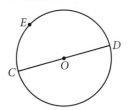

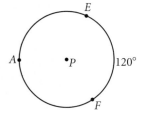

Solution

In part a, you probably "just knew" that the arc is one-fourth of the circle because you have seen one-fourth of a circle so many times. Why is it one-fourth? The arc measure is 90°, a full circle measures 360°, and $\frac{90°}{360°} = \frac{1}{4}$. The arc in part b is half of the circle because $\frac{180°}{360°} = \frac{1}{2}$. In part c, you may or may not have recognized right away that the arc is one-third of the circle. The arc is one-third of the circle because $\frac{120°}{360°} = \frac{1}{3}$.

What do these fractions have to do with arc length? If you traveled halfway around a circle, you would cover $\frac{1}{2}$ of its perimeter, or circumference. If you went a quarter of the way around, you would travel $\frac{1}{4}$ of its circumference. The **arc length** is some fraction of the circumference of its circle.

The measure of an arc is calculated in units of degrees, but arc length is calculated in units of distance.

INVESTIGATION

Finding the Arcs

In this investigation you will find a method for calculating the arc length.

Step 1 For $\overset{\frown}{AB}$, $\overset{\frown}{CED}$, and $\overset{\frown}{GH}$, find what fraction of the circle each arc is.

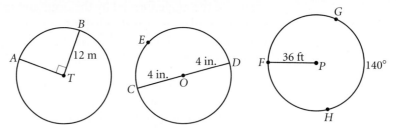

Step 2 Find the circumference of each circle.

Step 3 Combine the results of Steps 1 and 2 to find the length of each arc.

Step 4 Share your ideas for finding the length of an arc. Generalize this method for finding the length of *any* arc, and state it as a conjecture.

Arc Length Conjecture   **C-87**

The length of an arc equals the ?.

How do you use this new conjecture? Let's look at a few examples.

EXAMPLE B | If the radius of the circle is 24 cm and $m\angle BTA = 60°$, what is the length of $\overset{\frown}{AB}$?

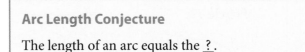

Solution | $m\angle BTA = 60°$, so $m\overset{\frown}{AB} = 120°$ by the Inscribed Angle Conjecture. Then $\frac{120}{360} = \frac{1}{3}$, so the arc length is $\frac{1}{3}$ of the circumference, by the Arc Length Conjecture.

$$\text{arc length} = \frac{1}{3}C$$
$$= \frac{1}{3}(48\pi) \quad \text{Substitute } 2\pi r \text{ for } C, \text{ where } r = 24.$$
$$= 16\pi \quad \text{Simplify.}$$

The arc length is 16π cm, or approximately 50.3 cm.

In this lesson, you learned the difference between the terms arc measure and arc length and learned how to find the arc length in degrees or linear units of measurement. Arc measure can also be measured in radians. A **radian measure** is calculated by dividing the length of the arc by its radius.

EXAMPLE C | For Example B, find the radian measure of $\overset{\frown}{AB}$.

Solution | Using the definition of radian measure and the information from Example B, we can calculate the radian measure.

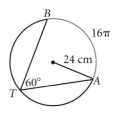

$$\text{radian measure} = \frac{\text{arc length}}{\text{radius}} \qquad \text{Definition of radian measure}$$

$$= \frac{16\pi \text{ cm}}{24 \text{ cm}} \qquad \text{Substitute } 16\pi \text{ for arc length and } r = 24$$

$$= \frac{2\pi}{3} \text{ radians} \qquad \text{Simplify}$$

The radian measure of $\overset{\frown}{AB}$ is $\frac{2\pi}{3}$ radians. Since both the arc length and radius were in cm the units cancel, so there are no units associated with radians.

What do you notice about the radian measure in comparison to the semicircle? If we draw the diameter and the radius to point B, the relationship between the arc and the semicircle seems to be defined by the radian measure. What do you think the radian measure of the semicircle would be? How does the radius affect the radian measure? You will explore these ideas in the exercise set.

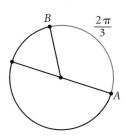

9.6 Exercises

YOU WILL NEED

Construction tools
for Exercise **14**

Geometry software
for Exercises **25** and **27**

For Exercises 1–8, state your answers in terms of π.

1. Length of $\overset{\frown}{CD}$ is _?_.

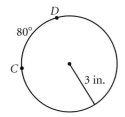

2. Length of $\overset{\frown}{EF}$ is _?_.

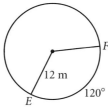

3. Length of $\overset{\frown}{BIG}$ is _?_. ⓗ

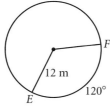

4. Length of $\overset{\frown}{AB}$ is 6π m. The radius is _?_.

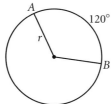

5. The radius is 18 ft. Length of $\overset{\frown}{RT}$ is _?_.

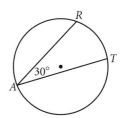

6. The radius is 9 m. Length of $\overset{\frown}{SO}$ is _?_.

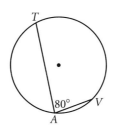

7. Length of $\overset{\frown}{TV}$ is 12π in. The diameter is _?_.

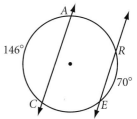

8. Length of $\overset{\frown}{AR}$ is 40π cm. $\overleftrightarrow{CA} \parallel \overrightarrow{RE}$. The radius is _?_. ⓗ

9. A go-cart racetrack has 100-meter straightaways and semicircular ends with diameters of 40 meters. Calculate the average speed in meters per minute of a go-cart if it completes 4 laps in 6 minutes. Round your answer to the nearest m/min. ⓗ

10. Astronaut Polly Hedra circles Earth every 90 minutes in a path above the equator. If the diameter of Earth is approximately 8000 miles, what distance along the equator will she pass directly over while eating a quick 15-minute lunch?

11. The Library of Congress reading room has desks along arcs of concentric circles. If an arc on the outermost circle with eight desks is about 12 meters long and makes up $\frac{1}{9}$ of the circle, how far are these desks from the center of the circle? How many desks would fit along an arc with the same central angle, but that is half as far from the center? Explain. ⓗ

The Library of Congress, Washington, D.C.

12. Recall that the radian measure is calculated by finding the ratio of the arc length to the radius. How does the size of the circle affect the radian measure? How does the central angle affect the radian measure? Calculate the radian measure for these three 45° angles. Write a conjecture about your results. Use different central angles to test your conjecture.

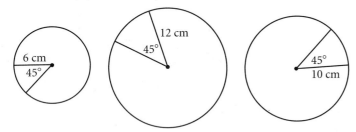

13. A Greek mathematician who lived in the 3rd century B.C.E., Eratosthenes, devised a clever method to calculate the circumference of Earth. He knew that the distance between Aswan (then called Syene) and Alexandria was 5000 Greek stadia (a stadium was a unit of distance at that time), or about 500 miles. At noon of the summer solstice, the Sun cast no shadow on a vertical pole in Syene, but at the same time in Alexandria a vertical pole did cast a shadow. Eratosthenes found that the angle between the vertical pole and the ray from the tip of the pole to the end of the shadow was 7.2°. From this he was able to calculate the ratio of the distance between the two cities to the circumference of Earth. Use this diagram to explain Eratosthenes' method, then use it to calculate the circumference of Earth in miles.

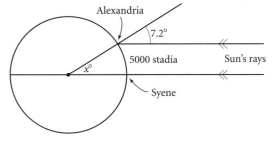

14. The diagrams below show the sequence of steps to construct a curly-4-gon. Construct your own curly-4-gon. If the radius of each circle is 1 unit, what is the perimeter of the curly-4-gon?

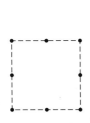

Construct a square with both diagonals. Locate the midpoints of the sides.

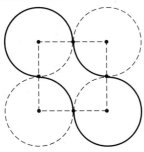

Construct a circle from each vertex of the square with radius half the length of the side of the square.

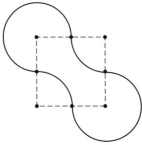

Hide construction of alternating interior and exterior portions of the circles to create a curly-4-gon.

15. Earlier in this lesson and exercise set, you found that the radian measure for a 120° arc was $\frac{2\pi}{3}$ radians and for a 45° arc was $\frac{\pi}{4}$ radians. What is the radian measure for a semicircle? What is the radian measure for a complete circle?

16. Using your results from Exercise 15, calculate how many degrees are in 1 radian. ⓗ

Review

17. Angular velocity is a measure of the rate at which an object revolves around an axis, and can be expressed in degrees per second. Suppose a carousel horse completes a revolution in 20 seconds. What is its angular velocity? Would another horse on the carousel have a different angular velocity? Why or why not?

18. Tangential velocity is a measure of the distance an object travels along a circular path in a given amount of time. Like speed, it can be expressed in meters per second. Suppose two carousel horses complete a revolution in 20 seconds. The horses are 8 m and 6 m from the center of the carousel, respectively. What are the tangential velocities of the two horses? Round your answers to the nearest 0.1 m/s. Explain why the horses have equal angular velocities but different tangential velocities.

19. Use what you learned about the angle formed by a tangent and a chord in Lesson 9.4, Exercise 8, as well as what you know about inscribed angles and exterior angles of a triangle to find the missing angle measures in each diagram. Examine these cases to find a relationship between the measure of the angle formed by a tangent and a secant to a circle, $\angle BPA$, and the measures of the two intercepted arcs, $\overset{\frown}{AB}$ and $\overset{\frown}{BC}$. Then copy and complete the conjecture below.

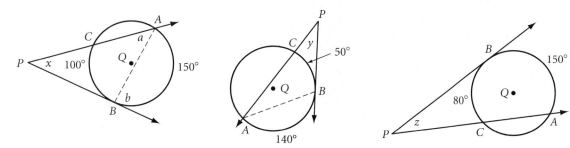

Conjecture: The measure of the angle formed by an intersecting tangent and secant to a circle is _?_ . (Tangent-Secant Conjecture)

20. Given circle Q with secant $\overleftrightarrow{PA}$ and tangent $\overleftrightarrow{PB}$ in the diagram at right, prove the conjecture you made in the last exercise. Start by drawing auxiliary line $\overline{AB}$. ⓗ

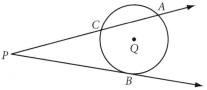

21. Calculate the measure of each lettered angle. ⓗ

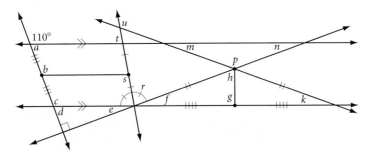

22. Find the measure of the angle formed by a clock's hands at 10:20. ⓗ

23. Circle P is centered at the origin. $\overleftrightarrow{AT}$ is tangent to circle P at $A(8, 15)$. Find the equation of $\overleftrightarrow{AT}$.

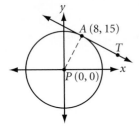

24. $\overrightarrow{PA}$ is tangent to circle Q. The line containing chord $\overline{CB}$ passes through P. Find $m\angle P$.

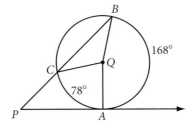

25. **GUESS-N-CHECK** $\triangle ABC$ with vertices $A(1, 2)$, $B(-4, -2)$, and $C(2, -3)$, is transformed by the ordered pair rule $(x, y) \rightarrow (-y, x)$ to create the image $\triangle A'B'C'$. Which of the following statements A–E below are true? First, try this as a "mental experiment." Take a guess or explain how you know. Then create the diagram with your geometry software, perform the transformation, and see how good you were at visualization.

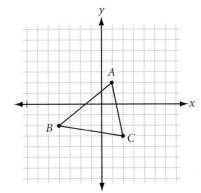

    A. $\angle A \cong \angle A'$

    B. $\overline{BC} \cong \overline{B'C'}$

    C. The equation of the line of reflection is $y = x$.

    D. The slope of $\overline{AB}$ is equal to the slope of $\overline{A'B'}$.

    E. The area of $\triangle A'B'C'$ is four times the area of $\triangle ABC$.

26. How many different 3-edge routes are possible from R to G along the wire frame shown? ⓗ

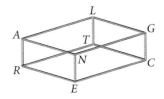

27. Use geometry software to pick any three points. Construct an arc through all three points. (Can it be done?) How do you find the center of the circle that passes through all three points?

28. $EFGH$ is a square divided into a grid of 25 squares. The area of the shaded figure is 156 cm². What is the perimeter of the shaded figure? Explain.

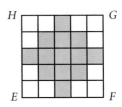

29. *JKLM* is a square divided into a grid of 36 squares. The perimeter of the shaded figure is 168 cm. What is the area of the shaded figure? Explain.

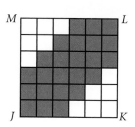

DEVELOPING MATHEMATICAL REASONING

Cover the Square

Trace each diagram below onto another sheet of paper.

Cut out the four triangles in each of the two small equal squares and arrange them to exactly cover the large square.

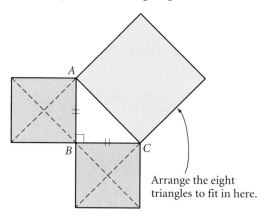

Arrange the eight triangles to fit in here.

Cut out the small square and the four triangles from the square on leg $\overline{EF}$ and arrange them to exactly cover the large square.

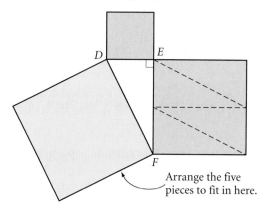

Arrange the five pieces to fit in here.

Two squares with areas x^2 and y^2 are divided into the five regions as shown. Cut out the five regions and arrange them to exactly cover a larger square with an area of z^2.

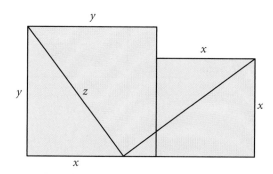

Two squares have been divided into three right triangles and two quadrilaterals. Cut out the five regions and arrange them to exactly cover a larger square.

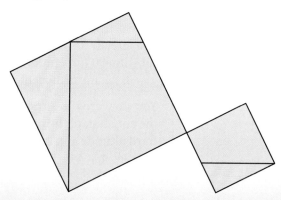

Points of Concurrency: Orthocenter

Suppose you know the coordinates of the vertices of a triangle. In Chapter 5, you saw that you can find the coordinates of the circumcenter by writing equations for the perpendicular bisectors of two of the sides and solving the system. Similarly, you can find the coordinates of the orthocenter by finding equations for two lines containing altitudes of the triangle and solving the system.

EXAMPLE A

Find the coordinates of the orthocenter of $\triangle PDQ$ with $P(0, -4)$, $D(-4, 4)$, and $Q(8, 4)$.

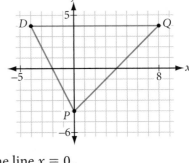

Solution

The orthocenter is the intersection of two altitudes of the triangle. An altitude passes through a vertex and is perpendicular to the opposite side. Because $\overline{DQ}$ is horizontal, the altitude from P to $\overline{DQ}$ must be a vertical line. The line that is vertical and passes through P is the line $x = 0$.

Next, find the equation of the line containing one of the other altitudes. You can find the equation of the line containing the altitude from Q to $\overline{DP}$ by finding the line that is perpendicular to $\overline{DP}$ and that passes through Q.

The slope of $\overline{DP}$ is $\frac{-4-4}{0-(-4)}$, or -2. The altitude is perpendicular to $\overline{DP}$, so the slope of the altitude is $\frac{1}{2}$, the opposite reciprocal of -2. Using the definition of slope and the coordinates of Q, the equation of the dashed line is $\frac{y-4}{x-8} = \frac{1}{2}$. Solving for y gives $y = \frac{1}{2}x$ as the equation of the line containing the altitude.

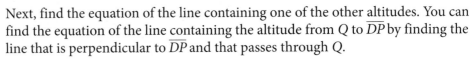

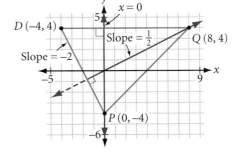

To find the point where the altitudes intersect, solve the system of equations. You already know $x = 0$. If you substitute 0 for x into $y = \frac{1}{2}x$, you get $y = 0$. So, the orthocenter is $(0, 0)$.

You can verify this result by writing the equation of the line containing the third altitude and making sure $(0, 0)$ satisfies it.

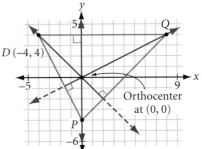

Exercises

1. Given △RES with vertices R(0, 0), E(4, −6), and S(8, 4). Find the equation of the line containing the altitude from E to $\overline{RS}$.

In Exercises 2–4, find the coordinates of the orthocenter for each triangle.

2. Right triangle MNO

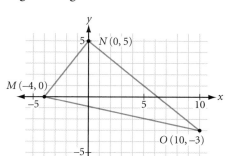

3. Isosceles triangle CDE

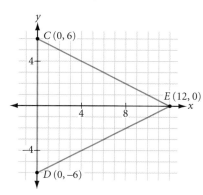

4. Obtuse isosceles △PAT

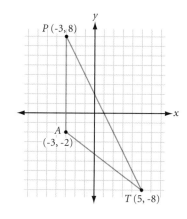

In Chapter 3 you discovered that the three altitudes of a triangle are concurrent in a point called the orthocenter. Now you have the coordinate geometry skills to prove it.

5. You prove that the altitudes of a triangle are concurrent the same way you found the orthocenter in the previous exercises, except you use letters instead of numbers. To make the manipulating of symbols easier you place the points on the coordinate grid at "nice" locations (usually on one of the axes). You must locate the points of your diagram so that they correspond to the given information, yet you are not assuming extra properties. The plan for the coordinate proof is started for you. Complete the proof that the altitudes of a triangle are concurrent.

Given: △OAB, without loss of generality, vertices O(0, 0), A(a, 0), B(b, c)

Show: △OAB, the three altitudes intersect at the same point.

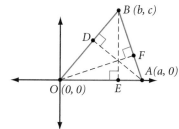

Plan:
- Find the slope of $\overline{OA}$, $\overline{OB}$, and $\overline{AB}$.
- Find the slope of altitudes $\overline{OF}$, $\overline{BE}$, and $\overline{AD}$.
- Find the equations of altitudes $\overline{OF}$, $\overline{BE}$, and $\overline{AD}$.
- Find the point of intersection of altitudes $\overline{OF}$ and $\overline{BE}$.
- Find the point of intersection of altitudes $\overline{OF}$ and $\overline{AD}$.
- If the point of intersection of altitudes $\overline{OF}$ and $\overline{BE}$ and the point of intersection of altitudes $\overline{OF}$ and $\overline{AD}$ are the same, then you have proved the three altitudes are concurrent!

In this chapter you learned some new circle vocabulary and solved real-world application problems involving circles. You discovered the relationship between a radius and a tangent line. You discovered special relationships between angles and their intercepted arcs. You defined the radian measure of an angle. And you learned about the special ratio π and how to use it to calculate the circumference of a circle and the length of an arc.

You should be able to sketch these terms from memory: *chord, tangent, central angle, inscribed angle,* and *intercepted arc.* And you should be able to explain the difference between arc measure and arc length.

Exercises

YOU WILL NEED

Construction tools
for Exercises **21–24, 34**

1. What do you think is the most important or useful circle property you learned in this chapter? Why?

2. How can you find the center of a circle with a compass and a straightedge? With patty paper? With the right-angled corner of a carpenter's square?

3. What does the path of a satellite have to do with the Tangent Conjecture?

4. Explain the difference between the degree measure of an arc and its arc length.

Solve Exercises 5–19. If the exercise uses the "=" sign, answer in terms of π. If the exercise uses the "≈" sign, give your answer accurate to one decimal place.

5. $b = \underline{\ ?\ }$

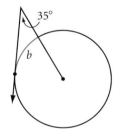

35°

b

6. $a = \underline{\ ?\ }$

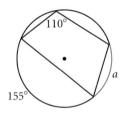

110°

155°

a

7. $c = \underline{\ ?\ }$

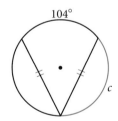

104°

c

8. $e = \underline{\ ?\ }$

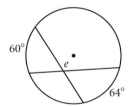

60°

e

64°

9. $d = \underline{\ ?\ }$

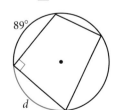

89°

d

10. $f = \underline{\ ?\ }$

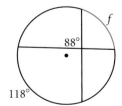

f

88°

118°

11. circumference ≈ _?_

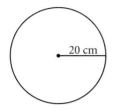
20 cm

12. circumference = 132 cm
d ≈ _?_

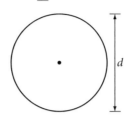
d

13. r = 27 cm. The length
of $\overarc{AB}$ is _?_ .

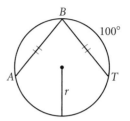
B
100°
A
T
r

14. r = 36 ft. The length
of $\overarc{CD}$ is _?_

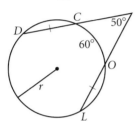
C
50°
D
60°
O
r
L

15. What's wrong with this picture?

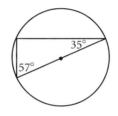
35°
57°

16. What's wrong with this picture?

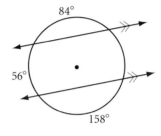
84°
56°
158°

17. Explain why $\overline{KE} \parallel \overline{YL}$.

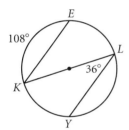
E
108°
L
36°
K
Y

18. Explain why △JIM is isosceles.

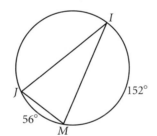
I
J
152°
56°
M

19. Explain why △KIM is isosceles.

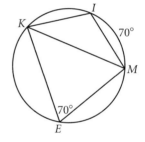
I
K
70°
M
70°
E

20. On her latest archaeological dig, Ertha Diggs has unearthed a portion of a cylindrical column. All she has with her is a pad of paper. How can she use it to locate the diameter of the column?

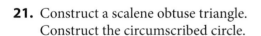

21. Construct a scalene obtuse triangle. Construct the circumscribed circle.

22. Construct a scalene acute triangle. Construct the inscribed circle.

23. Construct a rectangle. Is it possible to construct the circumscribed circle, the inscribed circle, neither, or both?

24. Find the radian measure of the arc of a circle with a central angle measure of 135° and a radius of 5 cm. How does the radian measure change if the radius changes to 10 cm? Explain.

25. What is the radian measure for each of the following angles?

    a. 60°   **b.** 180°   **c.** 270°   **d.** 315°

26. Find the center of the circle passing through the points (−7, 5), (0, 6), and (1, −1).

27. Rashid is an apprentice on a road crew for a civil engineer. He needs to find a trundle wheel similar to but larger than the one shown at right. If each rotation is to be 1 m, what should be the diameter of the trundle wheel?

28. Melanie rides the merry-go-round on her favorite horse on the outer edge, 8 meters from the center of the merry-go-round. Her sister, Melody, sits in the inner ring of horses, 3 meters in from Melanie. In 10 minutes, they go around 30 times. What is the average speed of each sister?

29. While talking to his friend Tara on the phone, Dmitri sees a lightning flash, and 5 seconds later he hears thunder. Two seconds after that, Tara, who lives 1 mile away, hears it. Sound travels at 1100 feet per second. Draw and label a diagram showing the possible locations of the lightning strike.

30. King Arthur wishes to seat all his knights at a round table. He instructs Merlin to design and create an oak table large enough to seat 100 people. Each knight is to have 2 ft along the edge of the table. Help Merlin calculate the diameter of the table.

→ **Geography**
CONNECTION

One nautical mile was originally defined to be the length of one minute of arc of a great circle of Earth. (A great circle is the intersection of the sphere and a plane that cuts through its center. There are 60 minutes of arc in each degree.) But Earth is not a perfect sphere. It is wider at the great circle of the equator than it is at the great circle through the poles. So defined as one minute of arc, one nautical mile could take on a range of values. To remedy this, an international nautical mile was defined as 1.852 kilometers (about 1.15 miles).

31. If a circular moat should have been a circle of radius 10 meters instead of radius 6 meters, how much greater should the larger moat's circumference have been?

32. The sector of a circle shown at right can be curled into a cone by bringing the two straight 45 cm edges together. What will be the diameter of the base of the cone?

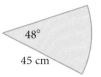

48°

45 cm

33. Read the Geography Connection at right. Given that the polar radius of Earth is 6357 kilometers and that the equatorial radius of Earth is 6378 kilometers, use the original definition to calculate one nautical mile near a pole and one nautical mile near the equator. Show that the international nautical mile is between both values.

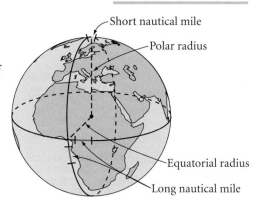

Short nautical mile

Polar radius

Equatorial radius

Long nautical mile

Mixed Review

34. Construct an isosceles triangle that has a base length equal to half the length of one leg.

35. In a regular octagon inscribed in a circle, how many diagonals pass through the center of the circle? In a regular nonagon? A regular 20-gon? What is the general rule?

36. A bug clings to a point two inches from the center of a spinning fan blade. The blade spins around once per second. How fast does the bug travel in inches per second?

In Exercises 37–44, identify the statement as true or false. For each false statement, explain why it is false and sketch a counterexample.

37. The area of a rectangle and the area of a parallelogram are both given by the formula $A = bh$, where A is the area, b is the length of the base, and h is the height.

38. When a figure is reflected over a line, the line of reflection is perpendicular to every segment joining a point on the original figure with its image.

39. Two triangles are considered similar if one set of the corresponding angles is congruent and one set of corresponding sides is proportional.

40. The area of a kite or a rhombus can be found by using the formula $A = (0.5)d_1 d_2$, where A is the area and d_1 and d_2 are the lengths of the diagonals.

41. If you can see your shadow, you can estimate the height of a nearby tall tree.

42. A glide reflection is a combination of a translation and a rotation.

43. Equilateral triangles, squares, and regular octagons can be used to create monohedral tessellations.

44. When using the coordinate plane to dilate a figure, any point can be used as the center of dilation.

In Exercises 45–49, select the correct answers.

45. An isosceles triangle has ? .

    A. two congruent base angles

    B. at least one altitude that bisects a side.

    C. an angle bisector that is also the altitude and median.

    D. is always an acute triangle

46. The area of a triangle is given by the formula ? , where A is the area, b is the length of the base, and h is the height.

    A. $A = bh$ **B.** $A = \frac{1}{2}bh$

    C. $A = \frac{2bh}{4}$ **D.** $A = b^2 h$

47. The ordered pair rule $(x, y) \rightarrow (y, x)$ is a _?_.

    A. reflection over the x-axis   **B.** reflection over the y-axis

    C. reflection over the line $y = x$ **D.** rotation 90° about the origin

48. The composition of two reflections over two intersecting lines is equivalent to _?_.

    A. a single reflection   **B.** a translation

    C. a rotation   **D.** no single transformation

49. The total surface area of a cone is equal to _?_, where r is the radius of the circular base and l is the slant height.

    A. $\pi r^2 + 2\pi r$ **B.** $\pi r l$

    C. $\pi r l + 2\pi r$ **D.** $\pi r l + \pi r^2$

50. Is $\angle THU \cong \angle GDU$?
Is $\angle HTU \cong \angle DGU$?
$p = $ _?_, $q = $ _?_ Ⓗ

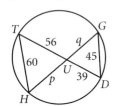

51. Why is $\triangle SUN \sim \triangle TAN$?
$r = $ _?_, $s = $ _?_

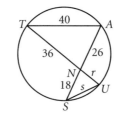

52. Create a flowchart proof to show that the diagonal of a rectangle divides the rectangle into two congruent triangles.

53. Copy the ball positions onto patty paper.

    a. At what point on the S cushion should a player aim so that the cue ball bounces off and strikes the 8 ball? Mark the point with the letter A.

    b. At what point on the W cushion should a player aim so that the cue ball bounces off and strikes the 8 ball? Mark the point with the letter B.

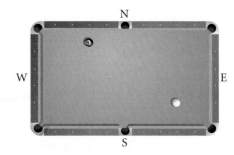

54. Find the area of the shaded region.

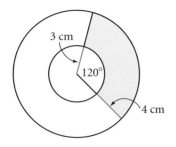

55. The cylindrical container below has an open top. Find the surface area of the container (inside and out) to the nearest square foot.

9 ft

5 ft

56. The side length of a regular pentagon is 6 cm, and the apothem measures about 4.1 cm. What is the approximate area of the pentagon?

57. Use the ordered pair rule, $(x, y) \rightarrow \left(\frac{1}{2}x, \frac{1}{2}y\right)$, to relocate the coordinates of the vertices of parallelogram $ABCD$. Call the new parallelogram $A'B'C'D'$. Is $A'B'C'D'$ similar to $ABCD$? If they are similar, what is the ratio of the perimeter of $ABCD$ to the perimeter of $A'B'C'D'$? What is the ratio of their areas?

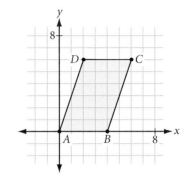

58. Points $A(-9, 5)$, $B(4, 13)$, and $C(1, -7)$ are connected to form a triangle. Find the area of $\triangle ABC$.

59. If the front tire of this motorcycle has a diameter of 50 cm (0.5 m), how many revolutions will it make if it is pushed 1 km to the nearest gas station? In other words, how many circumferences of the circle are there in 1000 meters?

 TAKE ANOTHER LOOK

1. Show how the Tangent Segments Conjecture follows logically from the Tangent Conjecture and the converse of the Angle Bisector Conjecture.

2. Investigate the quadrilateral formed by two tangent segments to a circle and the two radii to the points of tangency. State a conjecture. Explain why your conjecture is true, based on the properties of radii and tangents.

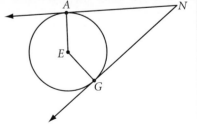

3. State the Cyclic Quadrilateral Conjecture in "if-then" form. Then state the converse of the conjecture in "if-then" form. Is the converse also true?

4. Recall that a quadrilateral inscribed in a circle is also called a cyclic quadrilateral. Which of these quadrilaterals are always cyclic: parallelograms, kites, isosceles trapezoids, rhombuses, rectangles, or squares? Which ones are never cyclic? Explain why each is or is not always cyclic.

5. A polygon inscribed in a circle is a cyclic polygon. Investigate cyclic *n*-gons where *n* is even. What do you notice about the sum of alternating angles? Make a conjecture. Here is a hint that helps to explain why.

Cyclic 4-gon   Cyclic 6-gon   Cyclic 8-gon

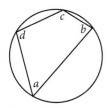
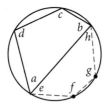

6. In Lesson 5.5 Properties of Special Parallelograms, you discovered how to use the parallel edges of your straightedge (the DESE tool) to construct a rhombus, the bisector of an angle, and the perpendicular bisector of a segment. Here is another DESE construction. Use a round object such as a lid from a plastic container to draw a circle on your paper. Use your DESE tool to locate the center of the circle by DESE construction. Explain your method.

7. In Lesson 9.6 you constructed a curly-4-gon with circles of radius 1 unit and found its perimeter. The construction of a curly-8-gon is shown below. Construct a curly-12-gon and calculate its perimeter if the circles have a radius of 1 unit. What is the perimeter of a curly-*n*-gon with radius of 1? Explain your method.

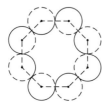

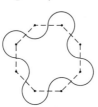

8. Use what you know about inscribed angles and exterior angles of a triangle to find the missing angle measures in each diagram. Examine these cases to find a relationship between the measure of the angle formed by two intersecting secants, $\angle ECA$, and the measures of the two intercepted arcs, $\overset{\frown}{NTS}$ and $\overset{\frown}{AE}$. Then complete the conjecture below and write a proof confirming your conjecture.

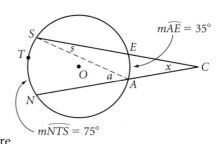

$m\overset{\frown}{AE} = 35°$

$m\overset{\frown}{NTS} = 75°$

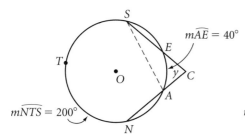

$m\overset{\frown}{AE} = 40°$

$m\overset{\frown}{NTS} = 200°$

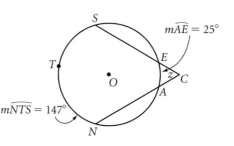

$m\overset{\frown}{AE} = 25°$

$m\overset{\frown}{NTS} = 147°$

Conjecture: The measure of an angle formed by two secants that intersect outside a circle is ?. (Intersecting Secants Conjecture)

The Pythagorean Theorem

M. C. Escher's *Waterfall* ©2014 The M. C. Escher Company—The Netherlands.
All rights reserved. www.mcescher.com

"But serving up an action, suggesting the dynamic in the static, has become a hobby of mine . . . . The "flowing" on that motionless plane holds my attention to such a degree that my preference is to try and make it into a cycle."

M. C. ESCHER

OBJECTIVES

In this chapter you will

- explore several proofs of the Pythagorean Theorem
- use the Pythagorean Theorem to calculate the distance between any two points
- use conjectures related to the Pythagorean Theorem to solve problems
- use coordinates to compute areas and perimeters of polygons
- derive the formula for the equation of a circle

The Pythagorean Theorem and Its Converse

hypotenuse

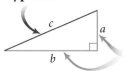

legs

In a right triangle, the side opposite the right angle is called the **hypotenuse**. The other two sides are called **legs**. In the figure at left, *a* and *b* represent the lengths of the legs, and *c* represents the length of the hypotenuse.

There is a special relationship between the lengths of the legs and the length of the hypotenuse. This relationship is known today as the **Pythagorean Theorem**.

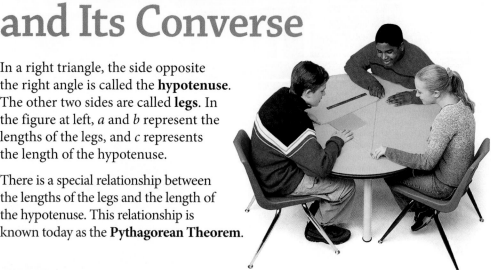

INVESTIGATION 1

YOU WILL NEED

- scissors
- a compass
- a straightedge
- the Dissection of Squares worksheet

The Three Sides of a Right Triangle

In earlier courses you discovered the Pythagorean theorem by demonstrating that the area of the square on the hypotenuse of a right triangle was equal to the sum of the areas of squares on the two legs. The puzzle in this investigation uses a **dissection,** which means you will cut apart one or more geometric figures and make the pieces fit into another figure.

→ History
CONNECTION

Pythagoras of Samos (ca. 569–475 B.C.E.) founded a mathematical society whose members proved what is now called the Pythagorean Theorem, although it was discovered and used 1000 years earlier by the Chinese and Babylonians.

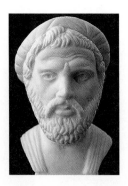

Step 1 Separate the four diagrams on the worksheet so each person in your group starts with a different right triangle. Each diagram includes a right triangle with a square constructed on each side of the triangle. Label the legs *a* and *b* and the hypotenuse *c*. What is the area of each square in terms of its side?

Step 2 Locate the center of the square on the longer leg by drawing its diagonals. Label the center *O*.

Step 3 Through point *O*, construct line *j* perpendicular to the hypotenuse and line *k* perpendicular to line *j*. Line *k* is parallel to the hypotenuse. Why? Lines *j* and *k* divide the square on the longer leg into four parts.

Step 4 Cut out the square on the shorter leg and the four parts of the square on the longer leg. Arrange them to exactly cover the square on the hypotenuse. Explain what this demonstrates.

Step 5 State the Pythagorean Theorem.

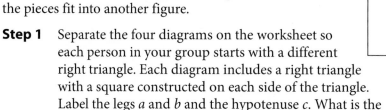

The Pythagoren Theorem   **C-88**

In a right triangle, the sum of the squares of the lengths of the legs equals ? .

A **theorem** is a conjecture that has been proved. A demonstration, like the one in the investigation, is the first step toward proving the Pythagorean Theorem.

There are more than 200 proofs of the Pythagorean Theorem. Elisha Scott Loomis's *Pythagorean Proposition*, published in 1927, contains original proofs by Pythagoras, Euclid, Leonardo da Vinci, and U.S. President James Garfield. Let's look at one proof.

DEVELOPING PROOF

Pythagorean Theorem

Cutting out the squares on the two legs of your right triangle and reassembling them on the square on the hypotenuse may have convinced you that the Pythagorean Theorem is true, but it may not help you explain why it is true. The following is one of many proofs of the famous theorem.

In your study of the similarity of triangles, you found that there are several ways you can prove similarity. In the triangle below left, there are three similar triangles. The three similar triangles are transformed as needed to highlight each triangle. Discuss why each of these triangles is similar. Which angles are congruent? How do the ratios of the sides compare?

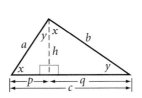 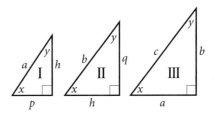

In your group discuss how you can use similarity to derive the Pythagorean theorem. Here are the first few steps to get you started:

Since $\triangle I \sim \triangle III$ then: $\dfrac{c}{a} = \dfrac{a}{p}$

Since $\triangle II \sim \triangle III$ then: $\dfrac{c}{b} = \dfrac{b}{q}$

Now you complete the proof. Make sure you begin your proof by describing why the three triangles are similar.

You just proved that if a triangle is a right triangle, then the square of the length of its hypotenuse is equal to the sum of the squares of the lengths of the two legs. What about the converse? If x, y, and z are the lengths of the three sides of a triangle and they satisfy the Pythagorean equation, $a^2 + b^2 = c^2$, must the triangle be a right triangle? Let's find out.

INVESTIGATION 2

YOU WILL NEED

- string
- a ruler
- paper clips
- a protractor

Is the Converse True?

Three positive integers that work in the Pythagorean equation are called **Pythagorean triples**. For example, 8-15-17 is a Pythagorean triple because $8^2 + 15^2 = 17^2$. Here are nine sets of Pythagorean triples.

3-4-5	5-12-13	7-24-25	8-15-17
6-8-10	10-24-26		16-30-34
9-12-15			
12-16-20			

Step 1 Select one set of Pythagorean triples from the list above. Mark off four points, A, B, C, and D, on a string to create three consecutive lengths from your set of triples.

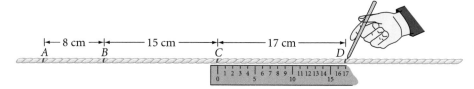

→ *History*
CONNECTION

Some historians believe Egyptian "rope stretchers" used the Converse of the Pythagorean Theorem to help reestablish land boundaries after the yearly flooding of the Nile and to help construct the pyramids. Some ancient tombs show workers carrying ropes tied with equally spaced knots.

Step 2 Loop three paper clips onto the string. Tie the ends together so that points A and D meet.

Step 3 Three group members should each pull a paper clip at point A, B, or C to stretch the string tight.

Step 4 With your protractor or the corner of a piece of paper, check the largest angle. What type of triangle is formed?

Step 5 Select another set of triples from the list. Repeat Steps 1–4 with your new lengths.

Step 6 Compare results in your group. State your results as your next conjecture.

Converse of the Pythagoren Theorem	C-89
If the lengths of the three sides of a triangle satisfy the Pythagorean equation, then the triangle ? .	

DEVELOPING PROOF

Converse of Pythagorean Theorem

Marking off three lengths that satisfy the Pythagorean relationship on string and pulling the string tight to form a triangle that appears to be a right triangle may have convinced you that the converse of the Pythagorean Theorem is true, but it may not help you explain why it is true. The following is one proof of the converse of this famous theorem. This proof of the Converse of the Pythagorean Theorem is interesting because it is a rare instance where the original theorem is used to prove the converse. Finish this proof as a group.

Conjecture: If the lengths of the three sides of a triangle work in the Pythagorean equation, then the triangle is a right triangle.

Given: a, b, c are the lengths of the sides of $\triangle ABC$ and $a^2 + b^2 = c^2$

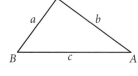

Show: $\triangle ABC$ is a right triangle

Plan: Use the think backward strategy repeatedly. To show that $\triangle ABC$ is a right triangle, you need to prove that $\angle C$ is a right angle. One way to do this is to show that $\angle C$ is congruent to another right angle. A familiar idea is to prove that both angles are corresponding parts of congruent triangles. So you can construct a right triangle, $\triangle DEF$, with right angle F, legs of lengths a and b, and hypotenuse of length x. Now show that $x = c$ to prove that the triangles are congruent.

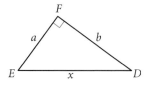

Let's look at a few examples to see how you can use the Pythagorean Theorem and its converse.

EXAMPLE A | How high up on the wall will a 20-foot ladder touch if the foot of the ladder is placed 5 feet from the wall?

Solution | The ladder is the hypotenuse of a right triangle, so $a^2 + b^2 = c^2$.

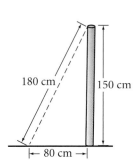

$(5)^2 + (h)^2 = (20)^2$	Substitute.
$25 + h^2 = 400$	Multiply.
$h^2 = 375$	Subtract 25 from both sides.
$h = \sqrt{375} \approx 19.4$	Take the square root of each side.

The top of the ladder will touch the wall about 19.4 feet up from the ground.

Notice that the exact answer in Example A is $\sqrt{375}$. However, this is a practical application, so you need to calculate the approximate answer.

EXAMPLE B | A steel pole 150 cm in length has been placed in the ground ready for cement to seal it in place. To check to see if it is perpendicular to the ground, the contractor has measured a distance of 180 cm from the top of the pole to 80 cm from the base of the pole on the ground. Is the pole perpendicular to the ground?

Solution | $80^2 + 150^2 = 28,900$

But $180^2 = 32,400$

Therefore $80^2 + 150^2 < 180^2$, so the triangle is not a right triangle and thus the pole is not perpendicular to the ground.

10.1 Exercises

In Exercises 1–12, find each missing length. All measurements are in centimeters. Use the symbol ≈ for approximate answers and round to the nearest tenth of a centimeter.

1.
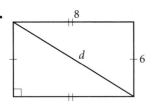

2.
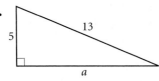

3.
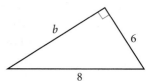

4.
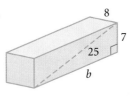

5.
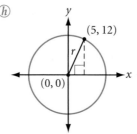

6. ⓗ

7.
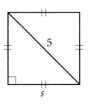

8.
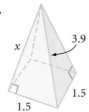

9. The base is a circle.

10.
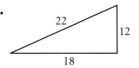

11. ⓗ
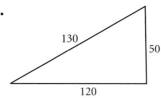

12. $H = 24$, $r = 5$, $K = $?
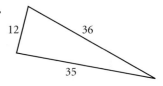

In Exercises 13–18, determine whether each triangle is a right triangle.

13.
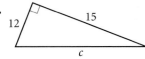

14.
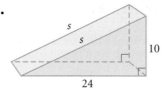

15.

16.
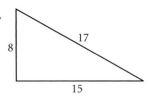

17.
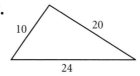

18. ⓗ

19. A baseball infield is a square, each side measuring 90 feet. To the nearest foot, what is the distance from home plate to second base?

20. The diagonal of a square measures 32 meters. What is the area of the square? ⓗ

21. What is the length of the diagonal of a square whose area is 64 cm²?

22. The lengths of the three sides of a right triangle are consecutive integers. Find them. ⓗ

23. A rectangular garden 6 meters wide has a diagonal measuring 10 meters. Find the perimeter of the garden.

24. Is a triangle with sides measuring 9 feet, 12 feet, and 18 feet a right triangle?

25. A window frame that seems rectangular has height 408 cm, length 306 cm, and one diagonal with length 525 cm. Is the window frame really rectangular? Explain.

26. One very famous proof of the Pythagorean Theorem is by the Hindu mathematician Bhaskara. It is often called the "Behold" proof because, as the story goes, Bhaskara drew the diagram on the right and offered no verbal argument other than to exclaim, "Behold!" Use algebra to fill in the steps, explaining why this diagram proves the Pythagorean Theorem. ⓗ

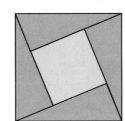

27. Is $\triangle ABC \cong \triangle XYZ$? Explain your reasoning.

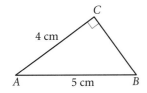 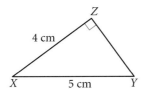

→ *History*
CONNECTION

Bhaskara (1114–1185, India) was one of the first mathematicians to gain a thorough understanding of number systems and how to solve equations, several centuries before European mathematicians. He wrote six books on mathematics and astronomy, and led the astronomical observatory at Ujjain.

Review

28. Explain why $m + n = 120°$.

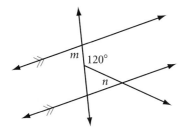

29. Calculate each lettered angle or arc measure. $\overline{EF}$ is a diameter; ℓ_1 and ℓ_2 are tangents. Explain how you determined the measures g and u.

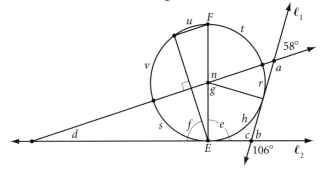

30. Identify the point of concurrency from the construction marks.

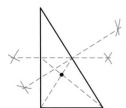

31. Two paths from C to T (traveling on the surface) are shown on the 8 cm by 8 cm by 4 cm prism below. M is the midpoint of edge $\overline{UA}$. Which is the shorter path from C to T: C-M-T or C-A-T? Explain. Ⓗ

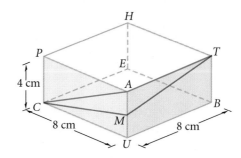

32. Line CF is tangent to circle D at C. The arc measure of $\overset{\frown}{CE}$ is a. Explain why $x = \left(\frac{1}{2}\right)a$. Ⓗ

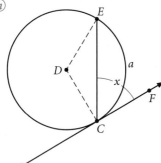

33. Sketch the solid shown, but with the two blue cubes removed and the red cube moved to cover the visible face of the green cube.

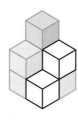

PERFORMANCE TASK

Pythagorean Theorem

In your group, discuss the reasoning below to prove the Pythagorean Theorem using another method.

You can arrange four copies of any right triangle into a square, as shown at right. To derive the Pythagorean Theorem you need to show that $a^2 + b^2 = c^2$.

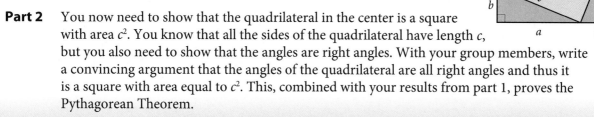

Part 1 The area of the entire square is $(a + b)^2$ and the area of each triangle is $\left(\frac{1}{2}\right)ab$. The area of the quadrilateral in the center is the area of the entire square minus the area of the four right triangles. Use algebra to derive an expression for the area of the quadrilateral in terms of a and b.

Part 2 You now need to show that the quadrilateral in the center is a square with area c^2. You know that all the sides of the quadrilateral have length c, but you also need to show that the angles are right angles. With your group members, write a convincing argument that the angles of the quadrilateral are all right angles and thus it is a square with area equal to c^2. This, combined with your results from part 1, proves the Pythagorean Theorem.

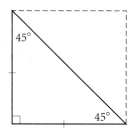
Two Special Right Triangles

In this lesson you will use the Pythagorean Theorem to discover some relationships between the sides of two special right triangles.

One of these special triangles is an isosceles right triangle, also called a 45°-45°-90° triangle. Each isosceles right triangle is half a square, so these triangles show up often in construction and engineering. Is there a relationship between the legs of the right triangle and the hypotenuse? In other words, if you know the length of the side, can you find the hypotenuse without using the Pythagorean Theorem? Let's investigate several triangles and make a conjecture.

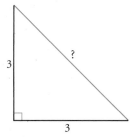

An isosceles right triangle

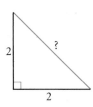

INVESTIGATION 1

Isosceles Right Triangles

In this investigation, you will discover a relationship between the length of the legs and the length of the hypotenuse in a 45°-45°-90° triangle.

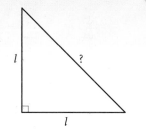

Step 1   Find the length of the hypotenuse of each isosceles right triangle above. Simplify each square root.

Step 2   Copy and complete this table. Draw additional triangles as needed.

Length of each leg	1	2	3	4	5	6	7	...	10	...	l
Length of hypotenuse											

Step 3   Discuss the results with your group. Do you see a pattern between the length of the legs and the length of the hypotenuse? State your observations as your next conjecture.

> **Isosceles Right Triangle Conjecture**    **C-90**
>
> In an isosceles right triangle, if the legs have length l, then the hypotenuse has length _?_ .

DEVELOPING PROOF

Another special right triangle is a 30°-60°-90° triangle, also called a 30°-60° right triangle, that is formed by bisecting any angle of an equilateral triangle. The 30°-60°-90° triangle also shows up often in construction and engineering because it is half of an equilateral triangle.

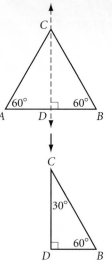

As a group, create a flowchart proof that proves the angle bisector through an angle in an equilateral triangle forms two congruent triangles. Then answer these questions:

1. Why must the angles in △BCD (or △ACD) be 30°, 60°, and 90°?

2. How does BD compare to AB? How does BD compare to BC?

3. In any 30°-60°-90° triangle, how does the length of the hypotenuse compare to the length of the shorter leg?

A 30°-60°-90° triangle

Let's use this relationship between the shorter leg and the hypotenuse of a 30°-60°-90° triangle and the Pythagorean Theorem to discover another relationship.

INVESTIGATION 2

30°-60°-90° Triangles

In this investigation you will discover a relationship between the lengths of the shorter and longer legs in a 30°-60°-90° triangle.

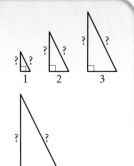

Step 1 Use the relationship from developing proof above to find the length of the hypotenuse of each 30°-60°-90° triangle above right. Then use the Pythagorean Theorem to calculate the length of the third side. Simplify each square root.

Step 2 Copy and complete this table. Draw additional triangles as needed.

Length of shorter leg	1	2	3	4	5	6	7	...	10	...	a
Length of hypotenuse											
Length of longer leg											

Step 3 Discuss the results with your group. Do you see a pattern between the length of the longer leg and the length of the shorter leg? State your observations as your next conjecture.

> **30°-60°-90° Triangle Conjecture**   C-91
>
> In a 30°-60°-90° triangle, if the shorter leg has length a, then the longer leg has length ? and the hypotenuse has length ?.

30°-60°-90° Triangle

Using the diagram on the right, use algebra to verify the 30°-60°-90° conjecture. Your proof should show that any number, even a non-integer, can be used for a. With your group, write an algebraic proof for this conjecture.

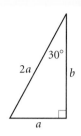

You can also demonstrate the 30°-60°-90° Triangle Conjecture for integer values on isometric dot paper.

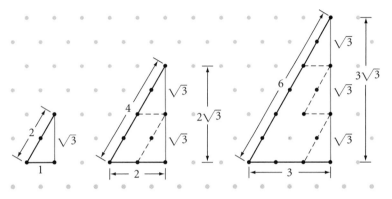

You will prove the Isosceles Right Triangle Conjecture and demonstrate it for integer values on square dot paper in the exercises.

10.2 Exercises

In Exercises 1–8, use your new conjectures to find the unknown lengths. All measurements are in centimeters.

YOU WILL NEED

Construction tools
for Exercises **20** and **21**

1. $a = \underline{\ ?\ }$

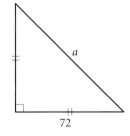

2. $b = \underline{\ ?\ }$ ⓗ

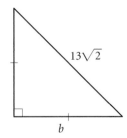

3. $a = \underline{\ ?\ }, b = \underline{\ ?\ }$

4. $c = \underline{\ ?\ }, d = \underline{\ ?\ }$ ⓗ

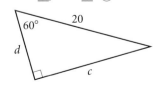

5. $e = \underline{\ ?\ }, f = \underline{\ ?\ }$

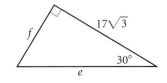

6. $k = \underline{\ ?\ }$

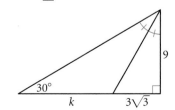
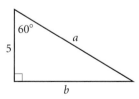

7. The solid is a cube.
$d = \underline{\ ?\ }$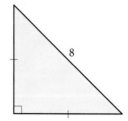

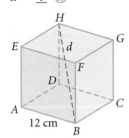

8. $g = \underline{\ ?\ }$, $h = \underline{\ ?\ }$

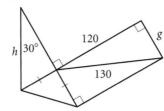
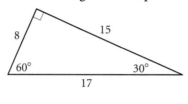

9. What is the area of the triangle?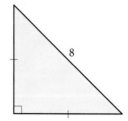

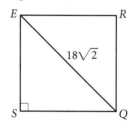

10. Find the coordinates of *P*.

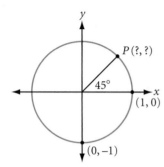

11. What's wrong with this picture?

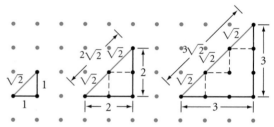

12. What is the perimeter of square *SQRE*?

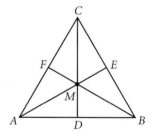

13. You can demonstrate the Isosceles Right Triangle Conjecture for integer values on square dot paper, as shown at right. Sketch and label a figure on square dot paper or graph paper to demonstrate that $\sqrt{32}$ is equivalent to $4\sqrt{2}$.

14. Sketch and label a figure to demonstrate that $\sqrt{45}$ is equivalent to $3\sqrt{5}$. (Use square dot paper or graph paper.)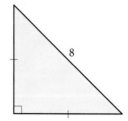

15. In equilateral triangle *ABC*, $\overline{AE}$, $\overline{BF}$, and $\overline{CD}$ are all angle bisectors, medians, and altitudes, simultaneously. These three segments divide the equilateral triangle into six overlapping 30°-60°-90° triangles and six smaller, non-overlapping 30°-60°-90° triangles.

   a. One of the overlapping triangles is △*CDB*. Name the other five triangles that are congruent to it.

   b. One of the non-overlapping triangles is △*MDA*. Name the other five triangles congruent to it.

16. Show that the Isosceles Right Triangle Conjecture holds true for any 45°-45°-90° triangle. Use the figure at right to represent the situation algebraically.

17. Find the area of an equilateral triangle whose sides measure 26 m.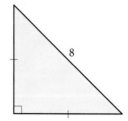

18. An equilateral triangle has an altitude that measures 26 m. Find the area of the triangle to the nearest square meter.

19. Sketch the largest 45°-45°-90° triangle that fits in a 30°-60°-90° triangle so that the right angles coincide. What is the ratio of the area of the 30°-60°-90° triangle to the area of the 45°-45°-90° triangle?

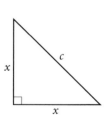

Review

20. Given the segment with length *a* below, construct segments with lengths $a\sqrt{2}$, $a\sqrt{3}$, and $a\sqrt{5}$. Use patty paper or a compass and a straightedge. ⓗ

•————————————•
    a

21. Draw a right triangle with sides of lengths 6 cm, 8 cm, and 10 cm. Locate the midpoint of each side. Construct a semicircle on each side with the midpoints of the sides as centers. Find the area of each semicircle. What relationship do you notice among the three areas?

22. The *Jiuzhang Suanshu* is an ancient Chinese mathematics text of 246 problems. Some solutions use the *gou gu*, the Chinese name for what we call the Pythagorean Theorem. The *gou gu* reads $(gou)^2 + (gu)^2 = (xian)^2$. Here is a *gou gu* problem translated from the ninth chapter of *Jiuzhang*.

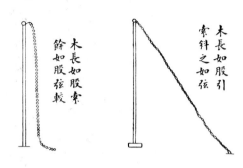

A rope hangs from the top of a pole with three *chih* of it lying on the ground. When it is tightly stretched so that its end just touches the ground, it is eight *chih* from the base of the pole. How long is the rope?

23. Explain why $m\angle 1 + m\angle 2 = 90°$. ⓗ

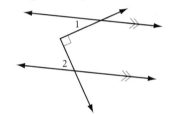

24. The lateral surface area of the cone below is unwrapped into a sector. What is the angle at the vertex of the sector?

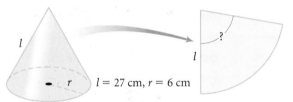

$l = 27$ cm, $r = 6$ cm

DEVELOPING MATHEMATICAL REASONING

Mudville Monsters

The 11 starting members of the Mudville Monsters football team and their coach, Osgood Gipper, have been invited to compete in the Smallville Punt, Pass, and Kick Competition. To get there, they must cross the deep Smallville River. The only way across is with a small boat owned by two very small Smallville football players. The boat holds just one Monster

visitor or the two Smallville players. The Smallville players agree to help the Mudville players across if the visitors agree to pay $5 each time the boat crosses the river. If the Monsters have a total of $100 among them, do they have enough money to get all players and the coach to the other side of the river?

Applications of the Pythagorean Theorem

You have learned that drawing a diagram will help you solve difficult problems. By now you know to look for many special relationships in your diagrams, such as congruent polygons, parallel lines, and right triangles. Now we can also use the Pythagorean Theorem as another special relationship. Let's apply these relationships to various scenarios.

A specially designed bat was made for Mr. Serra. What is the smallest box that could be used to ship the bat? What information would you need?

EXAMPLE | What is the longest stick that will fit inside a 24 in. by 30 in. by 18 in. box?

Solution | Draw a diagram.

You can lay a stick with length d diagonally at the bottom of the box. But you can position an even longer stick with length x along the diagonal of the box, as shown. How long is this stick?

Both d and x are the hypotenuses of right triangles, but finding d^2 will help you find x.

$$30^2 + 24^2 = d^2 \qquad\qquad d^2 + 18^2 = x^2$$
$$900 + 576 = d^2 \qquad\qquad 1476 + 18^2 = x^2$$
$$d^2 = 1476 \qquad\qquad 1476 + 324 = x^2$$
$$1800 = x^2$$
$$x \approx 42.4$$

The longest possible stick is about 42.4 in.

10.3 Exercises

1. Amir's sister is away at college, and he wants to mail her a 34 in. baseball bat. The packing service sells only one kind of box, which measures 24 in. by 20 in. by 12 in. Will the box be big enough?

2. A giant California redwood tree, 36 meters tall, cracked in a violent storm and fell as if hinged. The tip of the once beautiful tree hit the ground 24 meters from the base. Researcher Red Woods wishes to investigate the crack. How many meters up from the base of the tree does he have to climb? ⓗ

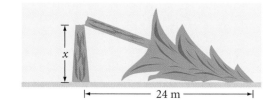

24 m

3. Meteorologist Paul Windward and geologist Rhaina Stone are rushing to a paleontology conference in Pecos Gulch. Paul lifts off in his balloon at noon from Lost Wages, heading east for Pecos Gulch Conference Center. With the wind blowing west to east, he averages a land speed of 30 km/h. This will allow him to arrive in 4 hours, just as the conference begins. Meanwhile, Rhaina is 160 km north of Lost Wages. At the moment of Paul's liftoff, Rhaina hops into an off-road vehicle and heads directly for the conference center. At what average speed must she travel to arrive at the same time Paul does? ⓗ

4. A 25-foot ladder is placed against a building. The bottom of the ladder is 7 feet from the building. If the top of the ladder slips down 4 feet, how many feet will the bottom slide out? (It is not 4 feet.) ⓗ

5. A regular hexagonal prism fits perfectly inside a cylindrical box with diameter 6 cm and height 10 cm. What is the surface area of the prism? What is the surface area of the cylinder? ⓗ

6. The front and back walls of an A-frame cabin are isosceles triangles, each with a base measuring 10 m and legs measuring 13 m. The entire front wall is made of glass 1 cm thick that costs $120/m². What did the glass for the front wall cost? ⓗ

7. What is the shortest distance from A to B on the surface of the cylinder? The right circular cylinder shown has a height of 12 cm and a circumference of 18 cm. Point A is on the top rim and point B is diametrically opposite on the bottom rim.

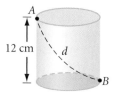

8. According to the Americans with Disabilities Act, the slope of a wheelchair ramp must be no greater than $\frac{1}{12}$. What is the length of ramp needed to gain a height of 4 feet? Read the Science Connection on the next page and then figure out how much constant force is required to go up the ramp if a person and a wheelchair together weigh 200 pounds.

For Exercises 9 and 10, refer to the Science Connection.

Science
CONNECTION

9. Compare what it would take to lift an object these three different ways.

   a. How much work, in foot-pounds, is necessary to lift 80 pounds straight up 2 feet?

   b. If a ramp 4 feet long is used to raise the 80 pounds up 2 feet, how much constant force, in pounds, will it take?

   c. If a ramp 8 feet long is used to raise the 80 pounds up 2 feet, how much constant force, in pounds, will it take?

It takes less effort to roll objects up an *inclined plane*, or ramp, than to lift them straight up. *Work* is a measure of continuous force applied over a distance, and you calculate it as a product of force and distance. For example, a force of 100 pounds is required to hold up a 100 pound object. The work required to lift it 2 feet is 200 foot-pounds. But if you distribute the work over the length of a 4 foot ramp, you can achieve 200 foot-pounds of work with only 50 pounds of force: 50 pounds times 4 feet equals 200 foot-pounds.

10. If you can exert only 70 pounds of force at any moment and you need to lift a 160-pound steel drum up 2 feet, what is the minimum length of ramp you should set up?

Review

11. Find the radius of circle Q.

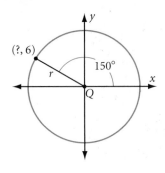

12. Find the length of $\overline{AC}$.

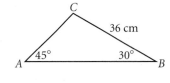

13. The two rays are tangent to the circle. What's wrong with this picture?

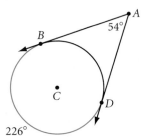

14. In the figure below, point A' is the image of point A after a reflection across $\overrightarrow{OT}$. What are the coordinates of A'?

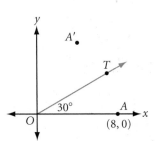

15. Which congruence shortcut can you use to show that $\triangle ABP \cong \triangle DCP$?

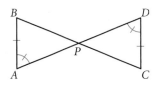

16. Identify the point of concurrency in $\triangle QUO$ from the construction marks.

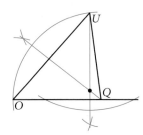

17. In parallelogram $QUID$, $m\angle Q = 2x + 5°$ and $m\angle I = 4x - 55°$. What is $m\angle U$?

18. In $\triangle PRO$, $m\angle P = 70°$ and $m\angle R = 45°$. Which side of the triangle is the shortest?

19. The figures below were created using the seven tangram pieces described in the Recreation Connection at right. If the area of the red square piece is 4 cm², what are the areas of the other six pieces? What are the dimensions of each of the seven pieces? What is the total area of the cat? How does the area of the cat compare to the areas of the square and rabbit? Explain.

→ *Recreation*
CONNECTION

The *qi qiao*, or tangram puzzle, originated in China and consists of seven pieces—five isosceles right triangles, a square, and a parallelogram. The puzzle involves rearranging the pieces into a square or hundreds of other shapes.

Square

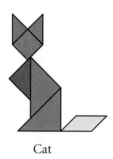

Cat

Rabbit

20. Make a set of your own seven tangram pieces and create the Swan and Horse with Rider, as shown below.

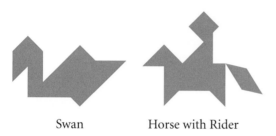

Swan   Horse with Rider

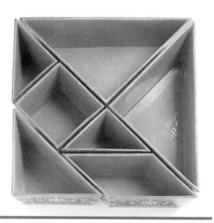

This set of enameled porcelain *qi qiao* bowls can be arranged to form a 37 cm by 37 cm square (as shown) or other tangram puzzles.

DEVELOPING MATHEMATICAL REASONING

Fold, Punch, and Snip

A square sheet of paper is folded vertically, a hole is punched out of the center, and then one of the corners is snipped off. When the paper is unfolded it will look like the figure at right.

Sketch what a square sheet of paper will look like when it is unfolded after the following sequence of folds, punches, and snips.

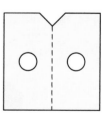

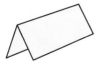

Fold once.

Fold twice.

Snip double-fold corner.

Punch opposite corner.

Distance in Coordinate Geometry

Isabella is standing on the corner of Seventh Street and 8th Avenue, and her sister Kayleigh is on the corner of Second Street and 3rd Avenue. To find her shortest sidewalk route to Kayleigh, Isabella can simply count blocks. But if Isabella wants to know her diagonal distance to Kayleigh, she would need the Pythagorean Theorem to measure across blocks.

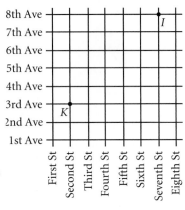

You can think of a coordinate plane as a grid of streets with two sets of parallel lines running perpendicular to each other. Every segment in the plane that is not in the *x*- or *y*-direction is the hypotenuse of a right triangle whose legs are in the *x*- and *y*-directions. So you can use the Pythagorean Theorem to find the distance between any two points on a coordinate plane.

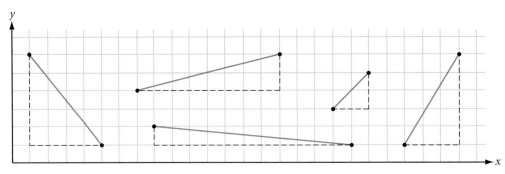

INVESTIGATION

YOU WILL NEED
• graph paper

The Distance Formula

In Steps 1 and 2, find the length of each segment by using the segment as the hypotenuse of a right triangle. Simply count the squares on the horizontal and vertical legs, then use the Pythagorean Theorem to find the length of the hypotenuse.

Step 1 Copy graphs a–d from the next page onto your own graph paper. Use each segment as the hypotenuse of a right triangle. Draw the legs along the grid lines. Find the length of each segment.

a.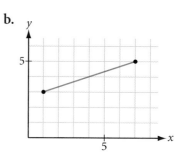

b.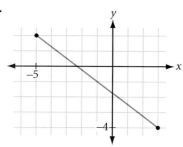

c.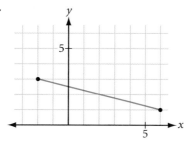

d.

Step 2 Graph each pair of points, then find the distances between them.

    a. $(-1, -2), (11, -7)$ **b.** $(-9, -6), (3, 10)$

What if the points are so far apart that it's not practical to plot them? For example, what is the distance between the points $A(15, 34)$ and $B(42, 70)$? A formula that uses the coordinates of the given points would be helpful. To find this formula, you first need to find the lengths of the legs in terms of the x- and y-coordinates. From your work with slope triangles, you know how to calculate horizontal and vertical distances.

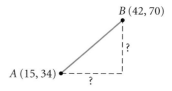

Step 3 Write an expression for the length of the horizontal leg using the x-coordinates.

Step 4 Write a similar expression for the length of the vertical leg using the y-coordinates.

Step 5 Use your expressions from Steps 3 and 4, and the Pythagorean Theorem, to find the distance between points $A(15, 34)$ and $B(42, 70)$.

Step 6 Generalize what you have learned about the distance between two points in a coordinate plane. Copy and complete the conjecture below.

Distance Formula

The distance between points $A(x_1, y_1)$ and $B(x_2, y_2)$ is given by
$(AB)^2 = \left(\underline{\ ?\ }\right)^2 + \left(\underline{\ ?\ }\right)^2$ or $AB = \sqrt{\left(\underline{\ ?\ }\right)^2 + \left(\underline{\ ?\ }\right)^2}$.

Let's look at an example to see how you can apply the distance formula.

EXAMPLE A | Is the quadrilateral with vertices $A(0, 2)$, $B(1, 5)$, $C(5, 3)$, $D(4, 0)$ a rectangle?

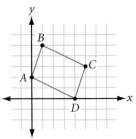

Solution | A rectangle must have four right angles and its opposite sides must be congruent and parallel. First we'll compare the sides of the quadrilateral using the distance formula.

$$(AB)^2 = (x_2 - x_1)^2 + (y_2 - y_1)^2 \quad \text{The distance formula.}$$

$$= (1 - 0)^2 + (5 - 2)^2 \quad \text{Substitute 0 for } x_1, 2 \text{ for } y_1, 1 \text{ for } x_2,$$
$$\text{and 5 for } y_2.$$

$$= 1^2 + 3^2 \quad \text{Subtract.}$$

$$(AB)^2 = 10 \quad \text{Square 1 and 3 and add.}$$

$$AB = \sqrt{10} \quad \text{Take the square root of both sides.}$$

Using the distance formula again for each segment, we find that $CD = \sqrt{10}$, $BC = 2\sqrt{5}$, and $AD = 2\sqrt{5}$. Since $AB = CD$ and $AD = BC$, we can conclude that the opposite sides of the quadrilateral are congruent.

To determine if the angles in the rectangle are right angles, let's look at the slopes of the sides of the quadrilateral. If the slopes are opposite reciprocals of each other, the segments are perpendicular and hence meet at a right angle.

$$\text{Slope of } \overline{AB} = \frac{5 - 2}{1 - 0} = \frac{3}{1} = 3$$

$$\text{Slope of } \overline{BC} = \frac{3 - 5}{5 - 1} = \frac{-2}{4} = -\frac{1}{2}$$

Since the slopes of $\overline{AB}$ and $\overline{BC}$ are not opposite reciprocals of each other, they are not perpendicular and hence are not right angles. Therefore, quadrilateral $ABCD$ is not a rectangle. Is the quadrilateral a parallelogram? How could you find out?

EXAMPLE B | What is the area and perimeter of $\triangle LMN$?

Solution | To find the perimeter of $\triangle LMN$, use the distance formula to find the length of each side of the triangle and find the sum.

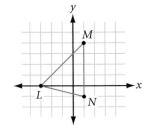

$$MN = \sqrt{(1 - 1)^2 + (-1 - 4)^2} = \sqrt{0 + (-5)^2} = \sqrt{25} = 5$$

$$LM = \sqrt{(1 - (-3))^2 + (4 - 0)^2} = \sqrt{4^2 + 4^2} = \sqrt{32} = 4\sqrt{2}$$

$$LN = \sqrt{(1 - (-3))^2 + (-1 - 0)^2} = \sqrt{4^2 + (-1)^2} = \sqrt{17}$$

Perimeter of $\triangle LMN = MN + LM + LN = 5 + 4\sqrt{2} + \sqrt{17} \approx 14.78$

To find the area of $\triangle LMN$, identify a base and height and use the formula for the area of a triangle. With $\overline{MN}$ the base, and the altitude $\overline{LD}$ the height, the area would be:

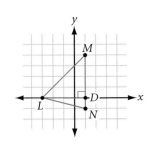

$$\text{Area} = \frac{1}{2}bh = \frac{1}{2}(5)(4) = 10$$

Exercises

In Exercises 1–3, find the distance between each pair of points.

1. (10, 20), (13, 16)

2. (15, 37), (42, 73)

3. (−19, −16), (−3, 14)

4. Look back at the diagram of Isabella's and Kayleigh's locations at the beginning of this lesson. Assume each block is approximately 50 meters long. What is the shortest distance, to the nearest meter, from Isabella to Kayleigh?

5. Find the perimeter of $\triangle ABC$ with vertices $A(2, 4)$, $B(8, 12)$, and $C(24, 0)$.

6. Find the perimeter and area of quadrilateral $ZOID$ given $Z(−6, 5)$, $O(−8, 3)$, $I(14, −3)$, and $D(−1, 5)$.

7. Determine whether $\triangle DEF$ with vertices $D(6, −6)$, $E(39, −12)$, and $F(24, 18)$ is scalene, isosceles, or equilateral.

For Exercises 8–11, graph each quadrilateral using the given vertices. Then use the distance formula and the slope formula to determine the most specific name for each quadrilateral: trapezoid, kite, rectangle, rhombus, square, parallelogram, or just quadrilateral. Find the area of each quadrilateral.

8. $A(6, 8)$, $B(9, 7)$, $C(7, 1)$, $D(4, 2)$

9. $E(1, −2)$, $F(5, −5)$, $G(2, −8)$, $H(−2, −5)$

10. $I(−4, 0)$, $J(−7, −1)$, $K(−8, 2)$, $L(−4, 5)$

11. $M(−3, 5)$, $N(−1, 1)$, $O(3, 3)$, $P(1, 7)$

12. Find the area of triangle TRY given $T(−8, −7)$, $R(−3, 5)$, and $Y(6, −7)$.

13. In Chapter 5 you proved that the midpoint on the hypotenuse of a right triangle is equally distant to the three vertices of the right triangle. Now try the proof using the distance formula.

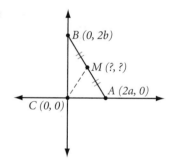

Given: Right $\triangle ABC$ with the coordinates of the vertices $A(2a, 0)$, $B(0, 2b)$, and $C(0, 0)$. (Since a and b are arbitrary, the coordinates of the three vertices are still arbitrary and thus the proof is valid for any right triangle.) M is the midpoint of the hypotenuse $\overline{AB}$.

Prove: $\overline{MB} \cong \overline{MA} \cong \overline{MC}$

DEVELOPING MATHEMATICAL REASONING

The Spider and the Fly

(attributed to the British puzzlist Henry E. Dudeney, 1857–1930)

In a rectangular room, measuring 30 ft by 12 ft by 12 ft, a spider is at point A on the middle of one of the end walls, 1 foot from the ceiling. A fly is at point B on the center of the opposite wall, 1 foot from the floor. What is the shortest distance that the spider must crawl to reach the fly, which remains stationary? The spider never drops or uses its web, but crawls fairly.

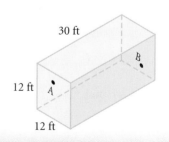

Circles in Coordinate Geometry

Video game companies are continuously improving the gaming experience through better graphics and innovative gaming devices. For new games, software engineers must create and improve their codes. With respect to mathematics, anytime a software engineer wants to create a circle, she must graph the circle on the screen using a coordinate grid. What equation would she use? Let's use what we know about coordinate geometry to derive the equation of a circle that she would use.

 INVESTIGATION

YOU WILL NEED

- graph paper
- compass
- geometry software
  optional

Equation of a Circle

In the last lesson you used the distance formula to find lengths of segments in a coordinate plane. The distance formula can also be used to find the equation of a circle. What is the equation of a circle with radius r and center (h, k)? Use graph paper and compass or geometry software to investigate and make a conjecture.

Step 1 Given its center and radius, graph each circle.
Circle A: center $= (1, -2)$, $r = 8$
Circle B: center $= (0, 2)$, $r = 6$

Step 2 On each circle, select any point and label it (x, y). Use the distance formula to write an equation for the distance from the center of the circle to (x, y).

Step 3 Graph another circle with a different center and radius from Step 1. Repeat Step 2. Compare your equations with your group members. What do you notice?

Step 4 Look for patterns, then copy and complete the conjecture.

> **Equation of a Circle**
>
> The equation of a circle with radius r and center (h, k) is:
> $(x - \underline{?})^2 + (y - \underline{?})^2 = \underline{?}$.

EXAMPLE A | Write an equation for the circle with center (5, 4) and radius 7 units.

Solution | Let (x, y) represent any point on the circle. The distance from (x, y) to the circle's center, (5, 4), is 7. Substitute this information in the distance formula.

$$(x - 5)^2 + (y - 4)^2 = 7^2$$

Substitute (x, y) for (x_2, y_2).   Substitute (5, 4) for (x_1, y_1).   Substitute 7 as the distance.

So, the equation is $(x - 5)^2 + (y - 4)^2 = 7^2$.

DEVELOPING PROOF

Equation of a Circle

As a group, discuss the conjecture you wrote in the investigation. How does the graphic on the right relate to your conjecture? Discuss how you could use the diagram to derive the equation of a circle. Then, derive the formula from the diagram. Explain each step.

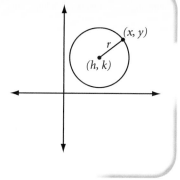

In Example A you found the equation of a circle when you were given the center and radius of the circle. How would you find the center and radius of a circle if you were given the equation of the circle?

EXAMPLE B | The equation $x^2 - 4x + y^2 + 2y = 20$ defines a circle. What are the coordinates of the center and radius of the circle?

Solution | In order to find the center and radius, we must rewrite the equation as the sum of two perfect squares equal to the radius squared. In order to do this, we must complete the square.

$$x^2 - 4x + y^2 + 2y = 20$$ Original equation.

$$x^2 - 4x + ? + y^2 + 2y + ? = 20 + ?$$ What numbers need to be added to make a perfect square?

$$x^2 - 4x + (-2)^2 + y^2 + 2y + (1)^2 = 20 + (-2)^2 + (1)^2$$ Add $(-2)^2$ and $(1)^2$ to each term to complete the square. You must add them to both sides to maintain equality.

$$(x - 2)^2 + (y + 1)^2 = 25$$ Factor into perfect squares.

Using the equation of a circle, the center is $(2, -1)$ and the radius is 5.

Exercises

1. Find the equation of the circle with center $(2, 0)$ and radius 5.

2. Find the radius and coordinates of the center of the circle $x^2 + (y - 1)^2 = 81$.

3. The center of a circle is $(3, -1)$. One point on the circle is $(6, 2)$. Find the equation of the circle. ⓗ

For Exercises 4–6, write the equation of the circle.

4.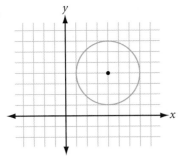

5.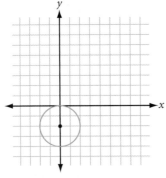

6.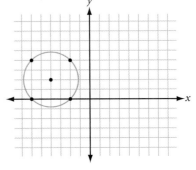

7. Which points are on the circle defined by the equation $(x - 2)^2 + y^2 = 9$? Explain how you know.

   a. $(-1, 0)$
   b. $(5, 0)$
   c. $(0, \sqrt{5})$
   d. $(3, \sqrt{5})$

For Exercises 8 and 9, find the coordinates of the center and the radius of the circle.

8. $x^2 + 10x + y^2 + 4y + 24 = 0$

9. $x^2 - 20x + y^2 - 8y = -100$

DEVELOPING MATHEMATICAL REASONING

Sam Loyd's Classic Dissection Puzzle

Sam Loyd (1842–1911) was the most prolific puzzle creator in the United States. One of his classic puzzles is dissecting two Greek crosses into four pieces and assembling them into one square. Since each Greek cross is made up of five squares then the area of the square must be ten square units. This means each side of the square is $\sqrt{10}$ units. This is a great clue. How can you draw a segment with a length of $\sqrt{10}$ units in the Greek cross?

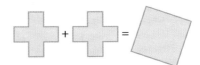

Circles and the Pythagorean Theorem

"You must do things you think you cannot do."

ELEANOR ROOSEVELT

In Chapter 9, you discovered a number of properties that involved right angles in and around circles. In this lesson you will use the conjectures you made, along with the Pythagorean Theorem, to solve some challenging problems. Let's review two conjectures that involve right angles and circles.

Tangent Conjecture: A tangent to a circle is perpendicular to the radius drawn to the point of tangency.

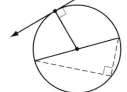

Angles Inscribed in a Semicircle Conjecture: Angles inscribed in a semicircle are right angles.

Here are two examples that use circle conjectures and dissections, special right triangles, and the Pythagorean Theorem.

EXAMPLE A

If $\overline{OC} \perp \overline{AB}$, $AB = 24$ cm, and $MC = 8$ cm, find the diameter of circle O.

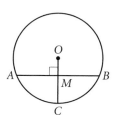

Solution

If $AB = 24$ cm, then $AM = 12$ cm. Let $x = OM$, so the radius of the circle is $x + 8$. Use the Pythagorean Theorem to solve for x.

$$(x + 8)^2 = x^2 + 12^2$$
$$x^2 + 16x + 64 = x^2 + 144$$
$$16x + 64 = 144$$
$$16x = 80$$
$$x = 5$$

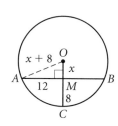

The diameter is $2(5 + 8)$, or 26 cm.

EXAMPLE B

$HA = 8\sqrt{3}$ cm. Find the shaded area. Round your answer to the nearest tenth.

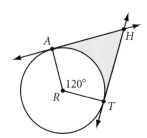

Solution | The auxiliary line $\overline{RH}$ forms two 30°-60°-90° triangles. Because longer leg $\overline{HA}$ is equal to $8\sqrt{3}$ cm, shorter leg $\overline{RA}$ is equal to 8 cm. As shown in the picture equation, half the shaded area is equal to the difference of the right triangle area and the circle sector area.

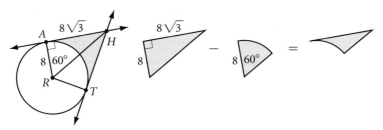

$$A_{\text{triangle}} = \frac{1}{2}(8)(8\sqrt{3}) = 32\sqrt{3} \text{ cm}^2$$

$$A_{\text{sector}} = \frac{60}{360}\pi(8^2) = \frac{1}{6}\pi \cdot 64 = \frac{32\pi}{3} \text{ cm}^2$$

$$A_{\text{shaded}} = 2\left(A_{\text{triangle}} - A_{\text{sector}}\right)$$

$$= 2\left(32\sqrt{3} - \frac{32\pi}{3}\right) = 2\left[32\left(\sqrt{3} - \frac{\pi}{3}\right)\right] = 64\left(\sqrt{3} - \frac{\pi}{3}\right) \text{ cm}^2$$

The shaded area is about 43.8 cm².

DEVELOPING PROOF

In Example B, the solution stated that auxiliary line $\overline{RH}$ forms two 30°-60°-90° triangles but didn't explain why. How do we know that is true? In your groups, prove that auxiliary line $\overline{RH}$ in Example B forms two 30°-60°-90° triangles.

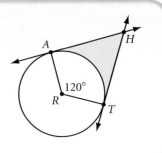

10.4 Exercises

In Exercises 1–8, find the area of the shaded region in each figure. Assume lines that appear tangent are tangent at the labeled points.

1.

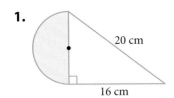

20 cm
16 cm

2. Square SQRE, with SQ = 4 m

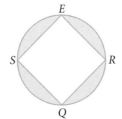

3. OD = 24 cm ⓗ

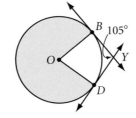

105°

4. TA = $12\sqrt{3}$ cm

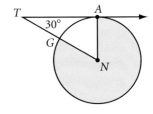

30°

5. $HT = 8\sqrt{3}$ m ⓗ

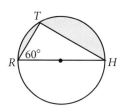

6. Kite $ABCD$, with $AB = 6$ cm and $BC = 8$ cm

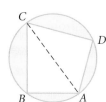

7. $HO = 8\sqrt{3}$ cm ⓗ

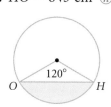

8. ⓗ

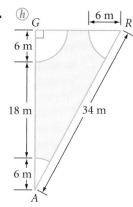

9. In her latest expedition, Ertha Diggs has uncovered a portion of circular, terra-cotta pipe that she believes is part of an early water drainage system. To find the diameter of the original pipe, she lays a meterstick across the portion and measures the length of the chord at 48 cm. The depth of the portion from the midpoint of the chord is 6 cm. What was the pipe's original diameter?

10. Use the Pythagorean Theorem to prove the Tangent Segments Conjecture: Tangent segments to a circle from a point outside the circle are congruent.

11. A 3 meter wide circular track is shown at right. The radius of the inner circle is 12 meters. What is the longest straight path that stays on the track? (In other words, find AB.) ⓗ

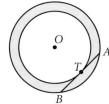

12. An annulus has a 36 cm chord of the outer circle that is also tangent to the inner concentric circle. Find the area of the annulus. ⓗ

13. The Gothic arch shown is based on the equilateral triangle. If the base of the arch measures 80 cm, what is the area of the shaded region? ⓗ

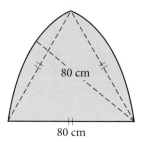

14. Each of three circles of radius 6 cm is tangent to the other two, and they are inscribed in a rectangle, as shown. What is the height of the rectangle? ⓗ

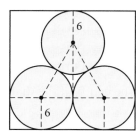

15. Sector *ARC* has a radius of 9 cm and an angle that measures 80°. When sector *ARC* is cut out and $\overline{AR}$ and $\overline{RC}$ are taped together, they form a cone. The length of $\overset{\frown}{AC}$ becomes the circumference of the base of the cone. What is the height of the cone? ⓗ

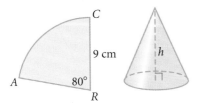
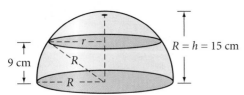

16. Will plans to use a circular cross-section of wood to make a square table. The cross-section has a circumference of 336 cm. To the nearest centimeter, what is the side length of the largest square that he can cut from it?

17. The hemisphere shown has a radius of 15 cm. A plane is passed through it 9 cm up from the base of the hemisphere creating a circular cross-section. Find the area of the circular cross-section. ⓗ

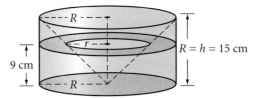

18. The cylinder shown has a radius and height of 15 cm. A cone with a radius and height of 15 cm is removed from the cylinder. A plane is passed through this new solid 9 cm up from the base creating an annulus (ring) cross section. What is the area of the annulus? ⓗ

Review

19. Find the equation of a circle with center (3, 3) and radius 6.

20. Prove that the quadrilateral *ROSM* with vertices $R(1, -7)$, $O(13, 2)$, $S(7, 10)$, and $M(-5, 1)$ is a rectangle.

21. Felice wants to determine the diameter of a large heating duct. She places a carpenter's square up to the surface of the cylinder, and the length of each tangent segment is 10 inches.

　a. What is the diameter? Explain your reasoning.

　b. Describe another way she can find the diameter of the duct.

22. Find the area of triangle *JEF* given $J(-18, -3)$, $E(5, -10)$, and $F(12, 13)$.

23. Here is another dissection proof of the Pythagorean Theorem in pictures. Explain how this proves the theorem.

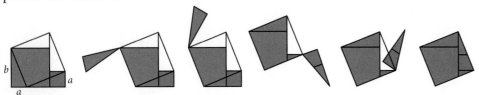

EXPLORATION

Sherlock Holmes and Forms of Valid Reasoning

"That's logical!" You've probably heard that expression many times. What do we mean when we say someone is thinking logically? One dictionary defines *logical* as "capable of reasoning or using reason in an orderly fashion that brings out fundamental points."

"Prove it!" That's another expression you've probably heard many times. It is an expression that is used by someone concerned with logical thinking. In daily life, proving something often means you can present some facts to support a point.

The fictional character Sherlock Holmes, created by Sir Arthur Conan Doyle, was known as the master of deductive reasoning. The reasoning about his sidekick Watson in the examples and exercises below is adapted from a Sherlock Holmes story, *The Adventure of the Dancing Men.*

When you apply deductive reasoning, you are "being logical" like detective Sherlock Holmes. The statements you take as true are called premises, and the statements that follow from them are conclusions.

When you translate a deductive argument into symbolic form, you use capital letters to stand for simple statements. When you write "If *P* then *Q*," you are writing a conditional statement. Here are two examples.

English argument	Symbolic translation
If Watson has chalk between his fingers, then he has been playing billiards. Watson has chalk between his fingers. Therefore Watson has been playing billiards.	*P*: Watson has chalk between his fingers. *Q*: Watson has been playing billiards. If *P* then *Q*. *P* ∴ *Q*
If △*ABC* is isosceles, then the base angles are congruent. Triangle *ABC* is isosceles. Therefore its base angles are congruent.	*P*: Triangle *ABC* is isosceles. *Q*: Triangle *ABC*'s base angles are congruent. If *P* then *Q*. *P* ∴ *Q*

The symbol ∴ means "therefore." So you can read the last two lines "*P*, ∴*Q*" as "*P*, therefore *Q*" or "*P* is true, so *Q* is true."

Both of these examples illustrate one of the well-accepted forms of valid reasoning. According to **Modus Ponens** (MP), if you accept "If *P* then *Q*" as true and you accept *P* as true, then you must logically accept *Q* as true.

In geometry—as in daily life—we often encounter "not" in a statement. "Not *P*" is the **negation** of statement *P*. If *P* is the statement "It is raining," then "not *P*," symbolized ∼*P*, is the statement "It is not raining" or "It is not the case that it is raining." To remove negation from a statement, you remove the not. The negation of the statement "It is not raining" is "It is raining." You can also negate a "not" by adding yet another "not." So you can also negate the statement "It is not raining" by saying "It is not the case that it is not raining." This property is called **double negation**.

According to ***Modus Tollens*** (MT), if you accept "If *P* then *Q*" as true and you accept ∼*Q* as true, then you must logically accept ∼*P* as true. Here are two examples.

English argument	Symbolic translation
If Watson wished to invest money with Thurston, then he would have had his checkbook with him. Watson did not have his checkbook with him. Therefore Watson did not wish to invest money with Thurston.	*P*: Watson wished to invest money with Thurston. *Q*: Watson had his checkbook with him. If *P* then *Q*. ∼*Q* ∴ ∼*P*
If $\overline{AC}$ is the longest side in △ABC, then ∠*B* is the largest angle in △ABC. ∠*B* is not the largest angle in △ABC. Therefore $\overline{AC}$ is not the longest side in △ABC.	*P*: $\overline{AC}$ is the longest side in △ABC. *Q*: ∠*B* is the largest angle in △ABC. If P then Q. ∼*Q* ∴∼*P*

Activity

It's Elementary!

In this activity you'll apply what you have learned about *Modus Ponens* (MP) and *Modus Tollens* (MT). You'll also get practice using the symbols of logic such as *P* and ∼*P* as statements and ∴ for "so" or "therefore." To shorten your work even further, you can symbolize the conditional "If *P* then *Q*" as *P* → *Q*. Then *Modus Ponens* and *Modus Tollens* written symbolically look like this:

Modus Ponens	*Modus Tollens*
P → *Q*	*R* → *S*
P	∼*S*
∴ *Q*	∴ ∼*R*

Step 1 Use logic symbols to translate parts a–e. Tell whether *Modus Ponens* or *Modus Tollens* is used to make the reasoning valid.

a. If Watson was playing billiards, then he was playing with Thurston. Watson was playing billiards. Therefore Watson was playing with Thurston.

b. Every cheerleader at Washington High School is in the 11th grade. Mark is a cheerleader at Washington High School. Therefore Mark is in the 11th grade.

c. If Carolyn studies, then she does well on tests. Carolyn did not do well on her tests, so she must not have studied.

d. If $\overline{ED}$ is a midsegment in $\triangle ABC$, then $\overline{ED}$ is parallel to a side of $\triangle ABC$. $\overline{ED}$ is a midsegment in $\triangle ABC$. Therefore $\overline{ED}$ is parallel to a side of $\triangle ABC$.

e. If $\overline{ED}$ is a midsegment in $\triangle ABC$, then $\overline{ED}$ is parallel to a side of $\triangle ABC$. $\overline{ED}$ is not parallel to a side of $\triangle ABC$. Therefore $\overline{ED}$ is a not a midsegment in $\triangle ABC$.

Step 2 Use logic symbols to translate parts a–e. If the two premises fit the valid reasoning pattern of *Modus Ponens* or *Modus Tollens*, state the conclusion symbolically and translate it into English. Tell whether *Modus Ponens* or *Modus Tollens* is used to make the reasoning valid. Otherwise write "no valid conclusion."

a. If Aurora passes her Spanish test, then she will graduate. Aurora passes the test.

b. The diagonals of *ABCD* are not congruent. If *ABCD* is a rectangle, then its diagonals are congruent.

c. If yesterday was Thursday, then there is no school tomorrow. There is no school tomorrow.

d. If you don't use Shining Smile toothpaste, then you won't be successful. You do not use Shining Smile toothpaste.

e. If squiggles are flitz, then ruggles are bodrum. Ruggles are not bodrum.

Step 3 Identify each symbolic argument as *Modus Ponens* or *Modus Tollens*. If the argument is not valid, write "no valid conclusion."

a. $P \to S$
  P
  $\therefore S$

b. $\sim T \to P$
  $\sim T$
  $\therefore P$

c. $R \to \sim Q$
  Q
  $\therefore \sim R$

d. $Q \to S$
  S
  $\therefore \sim Q$

e. $Q \to P$
  $\sim Q$
  $\therefore \sim P$

f. $\sim R \to S$
  $\sim S$
  $\therefore R$

g. $\sim P \to (R \to Q)$
  $\sim P$
  $\therefore (R \to Q)$

h. $(T \to \sim P) \to Q$
  $\sim Q$
  $\therefore \sim (T \to \sim P)$

i. $P \to (\sim R \to P)$
  $(\sim R \to P)$
  $\therefore P$

DEVELOPING MATHEMATICAL REASONING

The Spider and the Fly, revisited

A large empty glass flower vase is 12 inches tall with a circumference of 18 inches. On the exterior of the vase one inch from the top (at S) is a hungry spider. On the interior of the vase, one inch from the bottom (at *F*) and directly opposite the spider is a confused fly. What is the shortest distance, from S to F that the spider must crawl on the surfaces of the cylinder to reach the stationary fly?

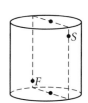

If 50 years from now you've forgotten everything else you learned in geometry, you'll probably still remember the Pythagorean Theorem. (Though let's hope you don't really forget everything else!) That's because it has practical applications in the mathematics and science that you encounter throughout your education.

It's one thing to remember the equation $a^2 + b^2 = c^2$. It's another to know what it means and to be able to apply it. Review your work from this chapter to be sure you understand how to use special triangle shortcuts, how to find the distance between two points in a coordinate plane in two-dimensions to identify polygons, and how to derive and apply the equation of a circle.

Exercises

For Exercises 1–4, measurements are given in centimeters.

1. $x = \underline{?}$

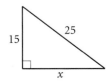

2. $AB = \underline{?}$

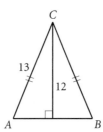

3. Is $\triangle ABC$ an acute, obtuse, or right triangle?

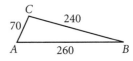

4. The solid is a rectangular prism. $AB = \underline{?}$

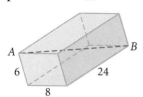

5. Find the coordinates of point U.

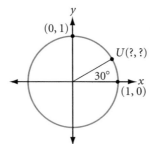

6. Find the coordinates of point V.

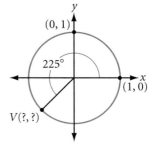

7. What is the area of the triangle?

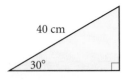

8. The area of this square is 144 cm². Find d.

9. What is the area of trapezoid $ABCD$?

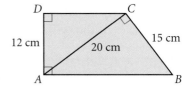

In Exercises 10–12, find the area of the shaded region.

10. The arc is a semicircle.

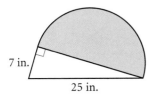

7 in.

25 in.

11. Rays *TA* and *TB* are tangent to circle *O* at *A* and *B* respectively, and $BT = 6\sqrt{3}$ cm.

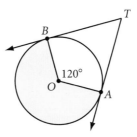

B

T

120°

O

A

12. The quadrilateral is a square, the arcs are portions of circles centered at *R* and *S*, and $QE = 2\sqrt{2}$ cm.

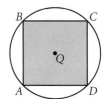

E

R

S

Q

13. The area of circle *Q* at right is 350 cm². Find the area of square *ABCD* to the nearest 0.1 cm².

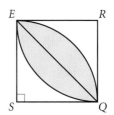

B   C

·Q

A   D

14. Determine whether △ABC with vertices *A*(3, 5), *B*(11, 3), and *C*(8, 8) is an equilateral, isosceles, or isosceles right triangle.

15. Sagebrush Sally leaves camp on her dirt bike, traveling east at 60 km/h with a full tank of gas. After 2 hours, she stops and does a little prospecting—with no luck. So she heads north for 2 hours at 45 km/h. She stops again, and this time hits pay dirt. Sally knows that she can travel at most 350 km on one tank of gas. Does she have enough fuel to get back to camp? If not, how close can she get?

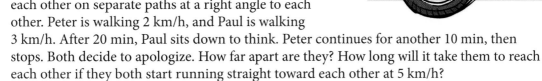

16. A parallelogram has sides measuring 8.5 cm and 12 cm, and a diagonal measuring 15 cm. Is the parallelogram a rectangle? How do you know? If not, is the 15 cm diagonal the longer or shorter diagonal?

17. After an argument, Peter and Paul walk away from each other on separate paths at a right angle to each other. Peter is walking 2 km/h, and Paul is walking 3 km/h. After 20 min, Paul sits down to think. Peter continues for another 10 min, then stops. Both decide to apologize. How far apart are they? How long will it take them to reach each other if they both start running straight toward each other at 5 km/h?

18. Will Flora's flute fit? Flora is away at camp and wants to mail her flute back home. The flute is 24 inches long. Will it fit diagonally within a box whose inside dimensions are 12 in. by 16 in. by 14 in.?

19. To the nearest foot, find the original height of a fallen flagpole that cracked and fell as if hinged, forming an angle of 45 degrees with the ground. The tip of the pole hit the ground 12 feet from its base.

20. You are standing 12 feet from a cylindrical corn-syrup storage tank. The distance from you to a point of tangency on the tank is 35 feet. What is the radius of the tank?

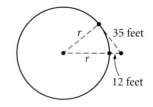

21. Prove or disprove that the point $(-3, 4)$ lies on the circle centered at the origin and containing the point $(5, 0)$.

22. A diver hooked to a 25 meter line is searching for the remains of a Spanish galleon in the Caribbean Sea. The sea is 20 meters deep and the bottom is flat. What is the area of circular region that the diver can explore?

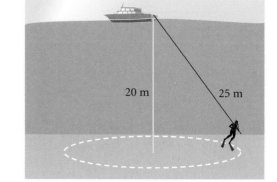

23. What are the lengths of the two legs of a 30°-60°-90° triangle if the length of the hypotenuse is $12\sqrt{3}$?

24. Find the side length of an equilateral triangle with an area of $36\sqrt{3}$ m².

25. Find the perimeter of an equilateral triangle with a height of $7\sqrt{3}$.

26. Here is another dissection proof of the Pythagorean Theorem in pictures. Explain how this proves the theorem.

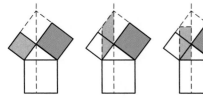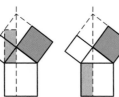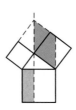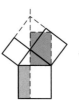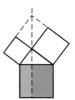

27. Which points are on the circle defined by $(x-1)^2 + (y+2)^2 = 10$? How do you know?

   a. $(5, 0)$
   b. $(0, 1)$
   c. $(0, -5)$
   d. $(4, -1)$

28. Find the area and circumference of the circle defined by $(x + 5)^2 + y^2 = 25$.

For Exercises 29–31 determine whether the quadrilateral is a square, parallelogram, rectangle, or not a special quadrilateral.

29. $C(-1, 3), D(5, 5), E(6, 2), F(0, 0)$

30. $J(-3, -1), K(-2, -3), L(-3, -5), M(-4, -3)$

31. $Q(-1, 0), R(1, 2), S(-1, 4), T(-3, 2)$

32. Find the area and perimeter of the quadrilateral in Exercise 30.

33. Find the center and radius of the circle defined by $x^2 + 10x + y^2 + 6y + 30 = 0$.

34. Al baked brownies for himself and his two sisters. He divided the square pan of brownies into three parts. He measured three 30° angles at one of the corners so that two pieces formed right triangles and the middle piece formed a kite. Did he divide the pan of brownies equally? Draw a sketch and explain your reasoning.

35. Find the equation of the circle that circumscribes a quadrilateral with vertices $(-4, 5)$, $(-2, 7)$, $(0, 5)$, and $(-2, 3)$.

36. Which area is greatest? One of the sketches below shows the greatest area that you can enclose in a right-angled corner with a rope of length s. Which one? Explain your reasoning.

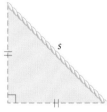

A triangle

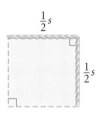

A square

A quarter-circle

37. A wire is attached to a block of wood at point A. The wire is pulled over a pulley as shown. How far will the block move if the wire is pulled 1.4 meters in the direction of the arrow?

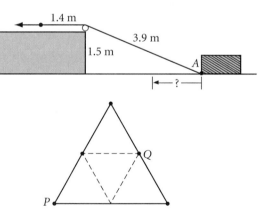

38. A net for a regular tetrahedron is shown at right with vertices P and Q identified. If the side of each equilateral triangle in the net is 6 cm, find:

a. Find the distance from P to Q on the net.

b. Find the distance from P to Q through space when the net is folded into a regular tetrahedron.

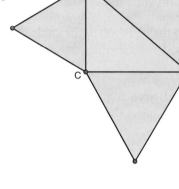

1. Use geometry software to demonstrate the Pythagorean Theorem. Does your demonstration still work if you use a shape other than a square—for example, an equilateral triangle or a semicircle?

2. Use the SSS Congruence Conjecture to verify the converse of the 30°-60°-90° Triangle Conjecture. That is, show that if a triangle has sides with lengths x, $x\sqrt{3}$, and $2x$, then it is a 30°-60°-90° triangle.

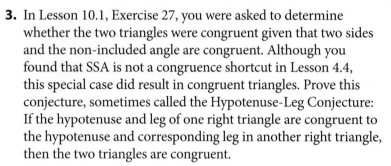

3. In Lesson 10.1, Exercise 27, you were asked to determine whether the two triangles were congruent given that two sides and the non-included angle are congruent. Although you found that SSA is not a congruence shortcut in Lesson 4.4, this special case did result in congruent triangles. Prove this conjecture, sometimes called the Hypotenuse-Leg Conjecture: If the hypotenuse and leg of one right triangle are congruent to the hypotenuse and corresponding leg in another right triangle, then the two triangles are congruent.

4. Starting with an isosceles right triangle, use geometry software or a compass and straightedge to start a right triangle like the one shown at right. Continue constructing right triangles on the hypotenuse of the previous triangle at least five more times. Calculate the length of each hypotenuse and leave them in radical form. What will happen in the long run?

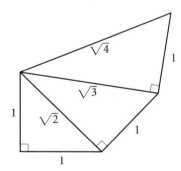

5. **INVESTIGATE–CONJECTURE–PROVE.** Dan has found the Pythagorean theorem to be such a very important property of right triangles and is wondering if there is a similar relationship with rectangles. Annie, with a twinkle in her eye, suggests to him that the sum of the squares of the four sides of a rectangle is always equal to the sum of the squares of the two diagonals. Is this true? How does she know so quickly? Prove it.

6. **INVESTIGATE–CONJECTURE–PROVE.** Dan was able to prove that the sum of the squares of the four sides of a rectangle is equal to the sum of the squares of the two diagonals. Then he thought, maybe it is true for any parallelogram. Is it? Either prove it is true or find a counterexample.

7. **INVESTIGATE–CONJECTURE–PROVE.** After seeing Dan's proof that for any parallelogram the sum of the squares of the four sides is equal to the sum of the squares of the two diagonals, Annie wondered if it was true for any convex quadrilateral. She has challenged Dan to prove it! Help Dan prove it or find a counterexample that proves it false.

Volume

"Perhaps all I pursue is astonishment and so I try to awaken only astonishment in my viewers. Sometimes "beauty" is a nasty business."

M. C. ESCHER

OBJECTIVES

In this chapter you will

- explore and define many three-dimensional solids
- visualize relationships between two-dimensional and three-dimensional objects
- discover formulas for finding the volumes of prisms, pyramids, cylinders, cones, and spheres
- learn how density is related to volume
- derive a formula for the surface area of a sphere
- learn about volume relationships in similar solids

The Geometry of Solids

Most of the geometric figures you have worked with so far have been flat plane figures with two dimensions—base and height. In this chapter you will work with solid figures with three dimensions—length, width, and height. Most real-world solids, like rocks and plants, are very irregular, but many others are geometric. Some real-world geometric solids occur in nature: viruses, oranges, crystals, the earth itself. Others are human-made: books, buildings, baseballs, soup cans, ice cream cones.

This amethyst crystal is an irregular solid, but parts of it have familiar shapes.

→ *Science*
CONNECTION

Three-dimensional geometry plays an important role in the structure of molecules. For example, when carbon atoms are arranged in a very rigid network, they form diamonds, one of the earth's hardest materials. But when carbon atoms are arranged in planes of hexagonal rings, they form graphite, a soft material used in pencil lead.

Carbon atoms can also bond into very large molecules. Named fullerenes, after U.S. engineer Buckminster Fuller (1895–1983), these carbon molecules have the same symmetry as a soccer ball, as shown below. They are popularly called buckyballs.

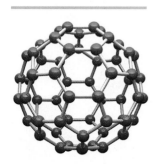

A solid formed by polygons that enclose a single region of space is called a **polyhedron**. The flat polygonal surfaces of a polyhedron are called its **faces**. Although a face of a polyhedron includes the polygon and its interior region, we identify the face by naming the polygon that encloses it. A segment where two faces intersect is called an **edge**. The point of intersection of three or more edges is called a **vertex** of the polyhedron.

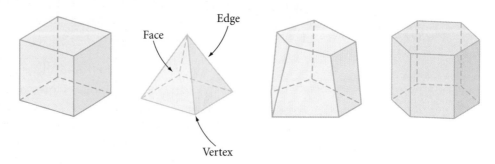

Just as a polygon is classified by its number of sides, a polyhedron is classified by its number of faces. The prefixes for polyhedrons are the same as they are for polygons with one exception: A polyhedron with four faces is called a **tetrahedron**. Here are some examples of polyhedrons.

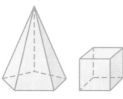

Hexahedrons

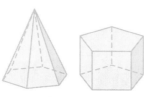

Heptahedrons

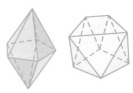

Decahedrons

If each face of a polyhedron is enclosed by a regular polygon, and each face is congruent to the other faces, and the faces meet at each vertex in exactly the same way, then the polyhedron is called a **regular polyhedron**. The regular polyhedron shown at right is called a regular dodecahedron because it has 12 faces.

Regular dodecahedron

A **prism** is a special type of polyhedron, with two faces called **bases**, that are congruent, parallel polygons. The other faces of the polyhedron, called **lateral faces**, are parallelograms that connect the corresponding sides of the bases.

The lateral faces meet to form the **lateral edges**. Each solid shown below is a prism.

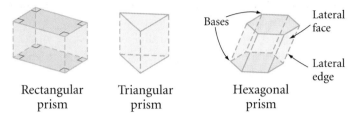

Rectangular prism   Triangular prism   Hexagonal prism

Prisms are classified by their bases. For example, a prism with triangular bases is a triangular prism, and a prism with hexagonal bases is a hexagonal prism.

A prism whose lateral faces are rectangles is called a **right prism**. Its lateral edges are perpendicular to its bases. A prism that is not a right prism is called an **oblique prism**. The **altitude** of a prism is any perpendicular segment from one base to the plane of the other base. The length of an altitude is the **height** of the prism.

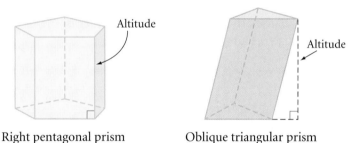

Right pentagonal prism   Oblique triangular prism

A **pyramid** is another special type of polyhedron. Pyramids have only one base. As in a prism, the other faces are called the lateral faces, and they meet to form the lateral edges. The common vertex of the lateral faces is the vertex of the pyramid.

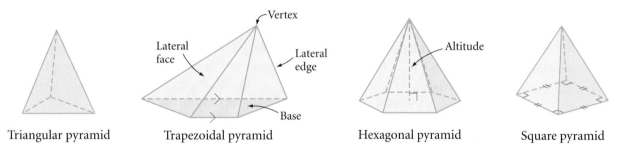

Triangular pyramid   Trapezoidal pyramid   Hexagonal pyramid   Square pyramid

Like prisms, pyramids are also classified by their bases. The pyramids of Egypt are square pyramids because they have square bases.

The altitude of the pyramid is the perpendicular segment from its vertex to the plane of its base. The length of the altitude is the height of the pyramid.

Polyhedrons are geometric solids with flat surfaces. There are also geometric solids that have curved surfaces.

One solid with a curved surface is a **cylinder**. Soup cans, drums, and plumbing pipes are shaped like cylinders. Like a prism, a cylinder has two bases that are both parallel and congruent. Instead of polygons, however, the bases of cylinders are circles and their interiors. The segment connecting the centers of the bases is called the **axis** of the cylinder. The **radius** of the cylinder is the radius of a base.

If the axis of a cylinder is perpendicular to the bases, then the cylinder is a **right cylinder**. A cylinder that is not a right cylinder is an **oblique cylinder**.

The altitude of a cylinder is any perpendicular segment from the plane of one base to the plane of the other. The height of a cylinder is the length of an altitude.

100 Cans **(1962 oil on canvas), by pop art artist Andy Warhol (1925–1987), repeatedly used the cylindrical shape of a soup can like the one shown to make an artistic statement with a popular image.**

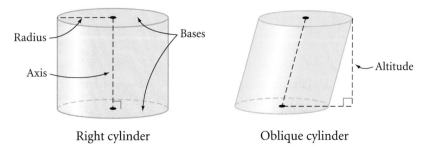

Right cylinder   Oblique cylinder

Another type of solid with a curved surface is a **cone**. Funnels and ice cream cones are shaped like cones. Like a pyramid, a cone has a base and a vertex.

The base of a cone is a circle and its interior. The radius of a cone is the radius of the base. The vertex of a cone is the point that is the greatest perpendicular distance from the base. The altitude of a cone is the perpendicular segment from the vertex to the plane of the base. The length of the altitude is the height of a cone. If the line segment connecting the vertex of a cone with the center of its base is perpendicular to the base, then the cone is a **right cone**.

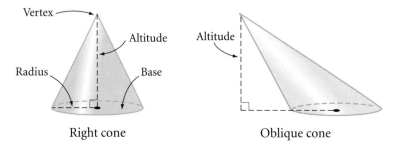

Right cone   Oblique cone

A third type of solid with a curved surface is a **sphere**. Basketballs, globes, and oranges are shaped like spheres. A sphere is the set of all points in space at a given distance from a given point. You can think of a sphere as a three-dimensional circle.

The given distance is called the **radius** of the sphere, and the given point is the **center** of the sphere. A **hemisphere** is half a sphere and its circular base. The circle that encloses the base of a hemisphere is called a **great circle** of the sphere. Every plane that passes through the center of a sphere determines a great circle. All the longitude lines on a globe of Earth are great circles. The equator is the only latitude line that is a great circle.

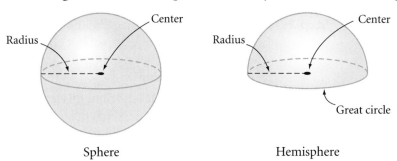

Sphere   Hemisphere

If every plane that intersects a sphere through its center is a great circle, what about planes that do not intersect at its center? Are they still circles? What about planes that intersect cubes? Will the intersection always be a square? Let's investigate.

INVESTIGATION 1

Slicing Solids

YOU WILL NEED

• Polyhedron models (*optional*)

Recall from Chapter 1 that when a solid is cut by a plane, the resulting two-dimensional figure is called a cross-section.

Step 1   Using polyhedron models or the diagrams of polyhedron in this lesson, investigate what types of cross-sections result from a plane intersecting with the following solids. Determine how many different types of two-dimensional figures can be formed, describe the intersection of the plane and the solid, and sketch the resulting figure. Consider only right solids.

   a. Cube
   b. Rectangular prism
   c. Triangular prism
   d. Cylinder
   e. Cone
   f. Sphere

Step 2   If you investigate oblique solids, will your results change? Why or why not? Investigate some of the solids from Step 1 as oblique solids to confirm or deny your conjecture.

Another way to create a solid is by rotating a two dimensional figure about an axis. Mechanical engineers often use this method to draw solids when they are creating their designs. Which of the solids discussed in this lesson can be created by rotation? What other types of solids can you create with rotations?

INVESTIGATION 2

Rotating Figures

YOU WILL NEED
- Heavy weight paper
- Scissors

Step 1 Construct and cut out a right triangle. Using the long leg as the axis, rotate the triangle around the axis. Visualize what shape it will create if the triangle left an "image" of itself at every point on the way around the axis. Describe the solid.

Step 2 Using the same triangle, use the short leg as the axis. Rotate the triangle and describe the solid it creates. How does this solid compare to the solid in Step 1? Are they congruent? Explain your reasoning.

Step 3 Which of the solids described in this lesson can be created by rotating a two dimensional figure? Sketch the original figure, describe the rotation, and sketch the resulting solid.

Step 4 Which solids were impossible to create in this way? Why?

Step 5 What other types of solids can you create by rotation? Create a solid using rotation and describe your method. Include sketches of your process.

11.1 Exercises

1. Complete this definition:

A pyramid is a ? with one ? face (called the base) and whose other faces (lateral faces) are ? formed by segments connecting the vertices of the base to a common point (the vertex) not on the base.

For Exercises 2–9, refer to the figures below. All measurements are in centimeters.

2. Name the bases of the prism.

3. Name all the lateral faces of the prism.

4. Name all the lateral edges of the prism.

5. What is the height of the prism?

6. Name the base of the pyramid.

7. Name the vertex of the pyramid.

8. Name all the lateral edges of the pyramid.

9. What is the height of the pyramid?

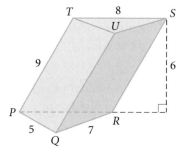

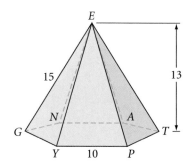

For Exercises 10–22, match each real object with a geometry term. You may use a geometry term more than once or not at all.

10. Tomb of Egyptian rulers

11. Honeycomb

A. Cylinder
B. Cone
C. Square prism
D. Square pyramid
E. Sphere
F. Triangular pyramid
G. Octagonal prism
H. Triangular prism
I. Trapezoidal prism
J. Rectangular prism
K. Heptagonal pyramid
L. Hexagonal prism
M. Hemisphere

12. Die

13. Stop sign

14. Holder for a scoop of ice cream

15. Wedge or doorstop

16. Moon

17. Can of tuna fish

18. Box of breakfast cereal

19. Book

20. Plastic bowl with lid

21. Pup tent

22. Ingot of silver

For Exercises 23–26, draw and label each solid. Use dashed lines to show the hidden edges. Identify which of these solids can be created by rotating a figure around an axis. Explain why some can be created using this method and why others cannot.

23. A triangular pyramid whose base is an equilateral triangular region (Use the proper marks to show that the base is equilateral.)

24. A hexahedron with two trapezoidal faces

25. A cylinder with a height that is twice the diameter of the base (Use x and $2x$ to indicate the height and the diameter.)

26. A right cone with a height that is half the diameter of the base

For Exercises 27–35, identify each statement as true or false. Sketch a counterexample for each false statement and explain why it is false.

27. A lateral face of a pyramid is always a triangular region.

28. A lateral edge of a pyramid is always perpendicular to the base.

29. Every cross-section of a prism cut parallel to the bases is congruent to the bases. ⓗ

30. When the lateral surface of a right cylinder is unwrapped and laid flat, it is a rectangle.

31. When the lateral surface of a right circular cone is unwrapped and laid flat, it is a triangle. ⓗ

32. Every cross-section of a cylinder, parallel to the base, is congruent to the base.

33. The length of a segment from the vertex of a cone to the circular base is the height of the cone.

34. The length of the axis of a right cylinder is the height of the cylinder.

35. All cross-sections of a sphere passing through the sphere's center are congruent.

36. In Investigation 2 you rotated a right triangle about its long leg and then its short leg. What solid would you create if you rotated the triangle about its hypotenuse? Sketch the resulting solid.

Review

37. For each net, decide whether it folds to make a box. If it does, copy the net and mark each pair of opposite faces with the same symbol.

a.    **b.**   **c.**   **d.**

38. The hemisphere shown has a radius of 25 cm. A plane is passed through it 7 cm up from the base of the hemisphere creating a circular cross-section. Find the area of the circular cross-section.

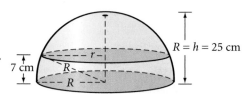

39. The cylinder shown has a radius and height of 25 cm. A cone with a radius and height of 25 cm is removed out of the cylinder. A plane is passed through this new solid 7 cm up from the base creating an annulus (ring) cross-section. What is the area of the annulus?

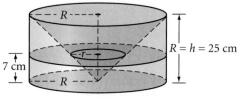

40. Trapezoid *ZOID* with vertices $Z(-2, 1)$, $O(3, 0)$, $I(3, 6)$, and $D(-2, 4)$ is transformed by the ordered pair rule $(x, y) \rightarrow (2x, 2y)$ to create the image $Z'O'I'D'$. What is the area of trapezoid $Z'O'I'D'$?

DEVELOPING MATHEMATICAL REASONING

Piet Hein's Puzzle

In 1936, while listening to a lecture on quantum physics, the Danish mathematician Piet Hein (1905–1996) devised the following visual thinking puzzle:

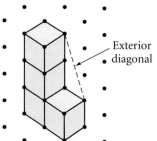

Exterior diagonal

> What are all the possible nonconvex solids that can be created by joining four or fewer cubes face-to-face?

A nonconvex polyhedron is a solid that has at least one diagonal that is exterior to the solid. For example, four cubes in a row, joined face-to-face, form a convex polyhedron. But four cubes joined face-to-face into an L-shape form a nonconvex polyhedron.

Use isometric dot paper to sketch the nonconvex solids that solve Piet Hein's puzzle.

Volume of Prisms and Cylinders

In real life you encounter many volume problems. For example, when you shop for groceries, it's a good idea to compare the volumes and the prices of different items to find the best buy. When you fill a car's gas tank or when you fit last night's leftovers into a freezer dish, you fill the volume of an empty container.

Many occupations also require familiarity with volume. An engineer must calculate the volume and the weight of sections of a bridge to avoid putting too much stress on any one section. Chemists, biologists, physicists, and geologists must all make careful volume measurements in their research. Carpenters, plumbers, and painters also know and use volume relationships. A chef must measure the correct volume of each ingredient in a cake to ensure a tasty success.

A father and son test the quality of the grain harvested on their family farm. The payment they receive from the processing plant is based on the volume of grain, not its weight.

Volume is the measure of the amount of space contained in a solid. You use cubic units to measure volume: cubic inches (in³), cubic feet (ft³), cubic yards (yd³), cubic centimeters (cm³), cubic meters (m³), and so on. The volume of an object is the number of unit cubes that completely fill the space within the object.

Length: 1 unit

Volume: 1 cubic unit

Volume: 20 cubic units

INVESTIGATION

The Volume Formula for Prisms and Cylinders

Step 1 Find the volume of each right rectangular prism below in cubic centimeters. That is, how many cubes measuring 1 cm on each edge will fit into each solid? Within your group, discuss different strategies for finding each volume. How could you find the volume of any right rectangular prism?

a.

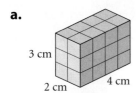

3 cm

2 cm   4 cm

b.

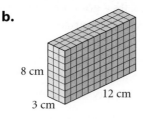

8 cm

3 cm   12 cm

c.

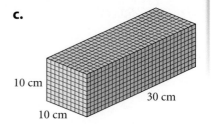

10 cm

10 cm   30 cm

Notice that the number of cubes resting on the base equals the number of square units in the area of the base. The number of layers of cubes equals the number of units in the height of the prism. In a sense, you can visualize a repeated vertical translation of the base. So you can use the area of the base and the height of the prism to calculate the volume.

Step 2 Complete the conjecture.

Rectangular Prism Volume Conjecture   `C-92a`

If B is the area of the base of a right rectangular prism and H is the height of the solid, then the formula for the volume is $V = \underline{?}$.

In Chapter 8, you discovered that you can reshape parallelograms, triangles, trapezoids, and circles into rectangles to find their area. You can use the same method to find the areas of bases that have these shapes. Again visualizing a repeated vertical translation of the base, you can multiply the area of the base by the height of the prism to find its volume. For example, to find the volume of a right triangular prism, find the area of the triangular base (the number of cubes resting on the base) and multiply it by the height (the number of layers of cubes).

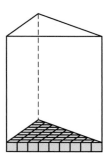

So, you can extend the Rectangular Prism Volume Conjecture to all right prisms and right cylinders.

Step 3 Complete the conjecture.

Right Prism-Cylinder Volume Conjecture   `C-92b`

If B is the area of the base of a right prism (or cylinder) and H is the height of the solid, then the formula for the volume is $V = \underline{?}$.

What about the volume of an oblique prism or cylinder? You can approximate the shape of this oblique rectangular prism with a staggered stack of three reams of 8.5 in. by 11 in. paper. If you nudge the individual pieces of paper into a slanted stack, then your approximation can be even better.

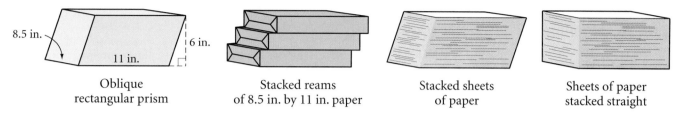

Oblique
rectangular prism

Stacked reams
of 8.5 in. by 11 in. paper

Stacked sheets
of paper

Sheets of paper
stacked straight

Rearranging the paper into a right rectangular prism changes the shape, but certainly the volume of paper hasn't changed. The area of the base, 8.5 in. by 11 in., didn't change and the height, 6 inches, didn't change, either.

In the same way, you can use crackers or coins to show that an oblique cylinder has the same volume as a right cylinder with the same base and height.

Step 4 Use the stacking model to extend the last conjecture to oblique prisms and cylinders. Complete the conjecture.

Oblique Prism-Cylinder Volume Conjecture　　　　C-92c

The volume of an oblique prism (or cylinder) is the same as the volume of a right prism (or cylinder) that has the same _?_ and the same _?_ .

Finally, you can combine the last three conjectures into one conjecture for finding the volume of any prism or cylinder, whether it's right or oblique.

Step 5 Copy and complete the conjecture.

Prism-Cylinder Volume Conjecture　　　　C-92

The volume of a prism or a cylinder is the _?_ multiplied by the _?_ .

If you successfully completed the investigation, you saw that the same volume formula applies to all prisms and cylinders, regardless of the shapes of their bases. To calculate the volume of a prism or cylinder, first calculate the area of the base using the formula appropriate to its shape. Then multiply the area of the base by the height of the solid. In oblique prisms and cylinders, the lateral edges are no longer at right angles to the bases, so you do *not* use the length of the lateral edge as the height.

EXAMPLE A | Find the volume of a right trapezoidal prism that has a height of 10 cm. The two bases of the trapezoid measure 4 cm and 8 cm, and its height is 5 cm.

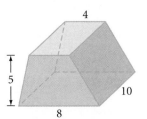

Solution | Find the area of the base.

$$B = \frac{1}{2}h(b_1 + b_2)$$ The base is a trapezoid, so use this formula to find the area of the base.

$$B = \frac{1}{2}(5)(4 + 8) = 30$$ Substitute the given values into the equation, then simplify.

Find the volume.

$$V = BH$$ The volume of a prism is equal to the area of its base multiplied by its height.

$$V = (30)(10) = 300$$ Substitute the calculated area and given height into the equation, then simplify.

The volume is 300 cm³.

EXAMPLE B | Find the volume of an oblique cylinder that has a base with a radius of 6 inches and a height of 7 inches.

Solution | Find the area of the base.

$$B = \pi r^2$$ The base is a circle, so use this formula to find the area of the base.

$$B = \pi(6)^2 = 36\pi$$ Substitute the given values into the equation, then simplify.

Find the volume.

$$V = BH$$ The volume of a prism is equal to the area of its base multiplied by its height.

$$V = (36\pi)(7) = 252\pi$$ Substitute the calculated area and given height into the equation, then simplify.

The volume is 252π in³, or about 791.68 in³.

11.2 Exercises

Find the volume of each solid in Exercises 1–6. All measurements are in centimeters.
Round approximate answers to the nearest hundredths.

1. Oblique rectangular prism

2. Right triangular prism ⓗ

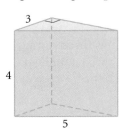

3. Right trapezoidal prism

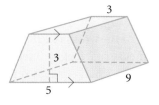

4. Right cylinder

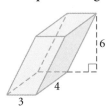

5. Right semicircular cylinder ⓗ

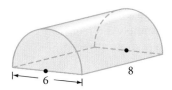

6. Right cylinder with a 90° slice removed ⓗ

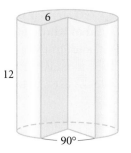

7. Use the information about the base and height of each solid to find the volume.
All measurements are given in centimeters.

Information about base of solid	Height of solid	Right triangular prism	Right rectangular prism	Right trapezoidal prism	Right cylinder
$b = 6$, $b_2 = 7$, $h = 8$, $r = 3$	$H = 20$	**a.** $V =$ ⓗ	**d.** $V =$	**g.** $V =$	**j.** $V =$
$b = 9$, $b_2 = 12$, $h = 12$, $r = 6$	$H = 20$	**b.** $V =$	**e.** $V =$	**h.** $V =$	**k.** $V =$
$b = 8$, $b_2 = 19$, $h = 18$, $r = 8$	$H = 23$	**c.** $V =$	**f.** $V =$	**i.** $V =$	**l.** $V =$

For Exercises 8–9, sketch and label each solid described, then find the volume.

8. An oblique trapezoidal prism. The trapezoidal base has a height of 4 in. and bases that measure 8 in. and 12 in. The height of the prism is 24 in.

9. A right circular cylinder with a height of T. The radius of the base is $\sqrt{Q}$. ⓗ

10. Sketch and label two different rectangular prisms, each with a volume of 288 cm³.

In Exercises 11–13, express the volume of each solid.

11. Right rectangular prism

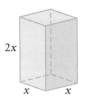

12. Oblique cylinder

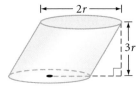

13. Right rectangular prism with a rectangular hole

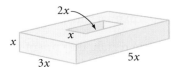

14. A cord of firewood is 128 cubic feet. Margaretta has three storage boxes for firewood that each measure 2 feet by 3 feet by 4 feet. Does she have enough space to order a full cord of firewood? A half cord? A quarter cord? Explain.

15. A contractor needs to build a ramp, as shown at right, from the street to the front of a garage door. How many cubic yards of fill will she need?

16. If an average rectangular block of limestone used to build the Great Pyramid of Khufu at Giza is approximately 2.5 feet by 3 feet by 4 feet, and limestone weighs approximately 170 pounds per cubic foot, what is the weight of one of the nearly 2,300,000 limestone blocks used to build the pyramid?

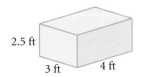

The Great Pyramid of Khufu at Giza, Egypt, was built around 2500 B.C.E.

17. Although the Exxon *Valdez* oil spill (estimated 11 million gallons of oil spilled) was one of the most notorious oil spills, it was small compared to the 200 million gallons of crude oil that were spilled during the BP Deepwater Horizon oil disaster in the Gulf of Mexico in 2010. A gallon occupies 0.13368 cubic foot. If the 200 million gallons could be placed in one cubic container, how tall, to the nearest foot, would the container be? Would you be able to see it from the space station?

18. When folded, a 12 ft by 12 ft section of the AIDS Memorial Quilt requires about 1 cubic foot of storage. In 1996, the quilt consisted of 32,000 3 ft by 6 ft panels. What was the volume of the folded quilt? If the storage facility had a floor area of 1,500 square feet, how high did the quilt panels need to be stacked?

The NAMES Project AIDS Memorial Quilt memorializes persons all around the world who have died of AIDS. In 1996, the 32,000 panels represented less than 10% of the AIDS deaths in the United States alone, yet the quilt could cover about 19 football fields.

Review

For Exercises 19 and 20, draw and label each solid. Use dashed lines to show the hidden edges. Determine whether or not the solids could be created using a rotation around an axis. Describe your reasoning.

19. An octahedron with all triangular faces and another octahedron with at least one nontriangular face

20. A cylinder with both radius and height r, a cone with both radius and height r resting flush on one base of the cylinder, and a hemisphere with radius r resting flush on the other base of the cylinder

For Exercises 21 and 22, identify each statement as true or false. Sketch a counterexample for each false statement and explain why it is false.

21. A prism always has an even number of vertices.

22. A section of a cube is either a square or a rectangle.

23. The solids in exercises 4, 5, and 6 can be created using a rotation. What two dimensional shape is rotated? Describe the rotation that is completed to create the solid.

24. Six points are equally spaced around a circular track with a 20 m radius. Ben runs around the track from one point, past the second, to the third. Al runs straight from the first point to the second, and then straight to the third. How much farther does Ben run than Al?

25. $\overrightarrow{AS}$ and $\overrightarrow{AT}$ are tangent to circle O at S and T, respectively. $m\angle SMO = 90°$, $m\angle SAT = 90°$, $SM = 6$. Find the exact value of PA. ⓗ

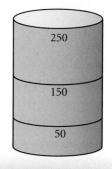

DEVELOPING MATHEMATICAL REASONING

Container Problem I

You have a small cylindrical measuring glass with a maximum capacity of 250 mL. All the marks have worn off except the 150 mL and 50 mL marks. You also have a large unmarked container. It is possible to fill the large container with exactly 350 mL. How? What is the fewest number of steps required to obtain 350 mL?

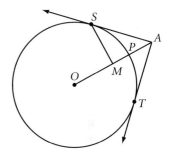

Volume of Pyramids and Cones

"If I had influence with the good fairy . . . I should ask that her gift to each child in the world be a sense of wonder so indestructible that it would last throughout life."

RACHEL CARSON

There is a simple relationship between the volumes of prisms and pyramids with congruent bases and the same height, and between cylinders and cones with congruent bases and the same height. You'll discover this relationship in the investigation.

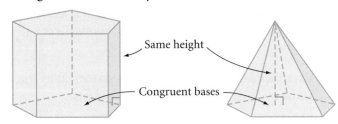

Same height

Congruent bases

Do they have the same volume?

INVESTIGATION

The Volume Formula for Pyramids and Cones

YOU WILL NEED

- container pairs of prisms and pyramids
- container pairs of cylinders and cones
- sand, rice, or water

Step 1 Choose a prism and a pyramid that have congruent bases and the same height.

Step 2 Fill the pyramid, then pour the contents into the prism. About what fraction of the prism is filled by the volume of one pyramid?

Step 3 Check your answer by repeating Step 2 until the prism is filled.

Step 4 Choose a cone and a cylinder that have congruent bases and the same height and repeat Steps 2 and 3.

Step 5 Compare your results with the results of others. Did you get similar results with both your pyramid-prism pair and the cone-cylinder pair? You should be ready to make a conjecture.

Pyramid-Cone Volume Conjecture	C-93

If B is the area of the base of a pyramid or a cone and H is the height of the solid, then the formula for the volume is $V = \underline{\ ?\ }$.

If you successfully completed the investigation, you probably noticed that the volume formula is the same for all pyramids and cones, regardless of the type of base they have. To calculate the volume of a pyramid or cone, first find the area of its base. Then find the product of the fraction you discovered in the investigation, the area of the base, and the height of the solid.

EXAMPLE A

Find the volume of a regular hexagonal pyramid with a height of 8 cm. Each side of its base is 6 cm.

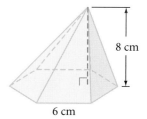

Solution

First, find the area of the base. To find the area of a regular hexagon, you need the apothem. By the 30°-60°-90° Triangle Conjecture, the apothem is $3\sqrt{3}$ cm.

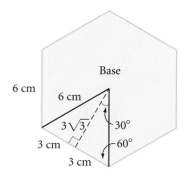

$B = \frac{1}{2}aP$ The area of a regular polygon is one-half the apothem times the perimeter.

$B = \frac{1}{2}(3\sqrt{3})(36)$ Substitute $3\sqrt{3}$ for a and 36 for P.

$B = 54\sqrt{3}$ Simplify.

The base has an area of $54\sqrt{3}$ cm². Now find the volume of the pyramid.

$V = \frac{1}{3}BH$ The volume of a pyramid is one-third the area of the base times the height.

$V = \frac{1}{3}(54\sqrt{3})(8)$ Substitute $54\sqrt{3}$ for B and 8 for H.

$V = 144\sqrt{3}$ Simplify.

The volume is $144\sqrt{3}$ cm³, or approximately 249.4 cm³.

EXAMPLE B

A cone has a base radius of 3 in. and a volume of 24π in³. Find the height.

Solution

Start with the volume formula and solve for H.

$V = \frac{1}{3}BH$ Volume formula for pyramids and cones.

$V = \frac{1}{3}(\pi r^2)H$ The base of a cone is a circle.

$24\pi = \frac{1}{3}(\pi \cdot 3^2)H$ Substitute 24π for the volume and 3 for the radius.

$24\pi = 3\pi H$ Simplify.

$8 = H$ Solve for H.

The height of the cone is 8 in.

Exercises

Find the volume of each solid named in Exercises 1–6. All measurements are in centimeters.

1. Square pyramid

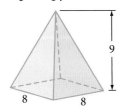

2. Cone

3. Trapezoidal pyramid ⓗ

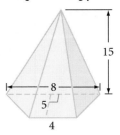

4. Triangular pyramid

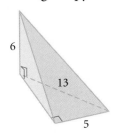

5. Semicircular cone

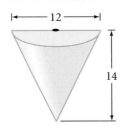

6. Cylinder with cone removed ⓗ

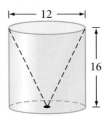

In Exercises 7–9, express the total volume of each solid. In Exercise 9, what percentage of the volume is filled with the liquid? All measurements are in centimeters.

7. Square pyramid

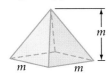

8. Cone

9. Cone

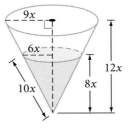

10. Use the information about the base and height of each solid to find the volume. All measurements are given in centimeters.

Information about base of solid	Height of solid	Triangular pyramid	Rectangular pyramid	Trapezoidal pyramid	Cone
$b = 6$, $b_2 = 7$, $h = 6$, $r = 3$	$H = 20$	**a.** $V =$ ⓗ	**d.** $V =$	**g.** $V =$	**j.** $V =$
$b = 9$, $b_2 = 22$, $h = 8$, $r = 6$	$H = 20$	**b.** $V =$	**e.** $V =$	**h.** $V =$	**k.** $V =$
$b = 13$, $b_2 = 29$, $h = 17$, $r = 8$	$H = 24$	**c.** $V =$	**f.** $V =$	**i.** $V =$	**l.** $V =$

11. Sketch and label a square pyramid with height H feet and each side of the base M feet. The altitude meets the square base at the intersection of the two diagonals. Find the volume in terms of H and M.

Mount Fuji is Japan's highest mountain. Legend claims that an earthquake created it.

12. Sketch and label two different circular cones, each with a volume of 2304π cm³.

13. Mount Fuji, the active volcano in Honshu, Japan, is 3776 m high and has a slope of approximately 30°. Mount Etna, in Sicily, is 3350 m high and approximately 50 km across the base. If you assume they both can be approximated by cones, which volcano is larger?

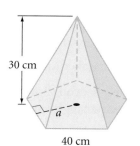

14. Bretislav has designed a crystal glass sculpture. Part of the piece is in the shape of a large regular pentagonal pyramid, shown at right. The apothem of the base measures 27.5 cm. How much will this part weigh if the glass he plans to use weighs 2.85 grams per cubic centimeter?

15. Jamala has designed a container that she claims will hold 50 in³. The net is shown at right. Check her calculations. What is the volume of the solid formed by this net? ⓗ

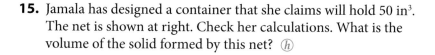

16. *Which is greater?* Which is greater, the volume of the solid formed by rotating the shaded figure at right about the x-axis or that formed by rotating about the y-axis? Explain.

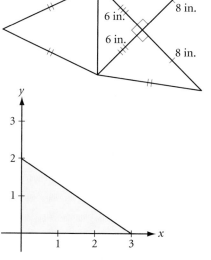

Review

17. Find the volume of the liquid in this right rectangular prism. All measurements are given in centimeters.

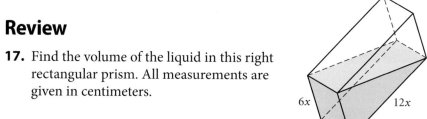

18. A swimming pool is in the shape of this prism. A cubic foot of water is about 7.5 gallons. How many gallons of water can the pool hold? If a pump is able to pump water into the pool at a rate of 15 gallons per minute, how long will it take to fill the pool? ⓗ

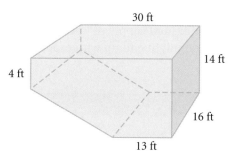

19. A landscape architect is building a stone retaining wall, as sketched at right. How many cubic feet of stone will she need?

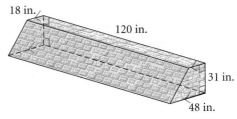

18 in. / 120 in. / 31 in. / 48 in.

20. As bad as tanker oil spills are, they are only about 12% of the 3.5 million tons of oil that enters the oceans each year. The rest comes from routine tanker operations, sewage treatment plants' runoff, natural sources, and offshore oil rigs. One month's maintenance and routine operation of a single supertanker produces up to 17,000 gallons of oil sludge that gets into the ocean! If a cylindrical barrel is about 1.6 feet in diameter and 2.8 feet tall, how many barrels are needed to hold 17,000 gallons of oil sludge? Recall that a cubic foot of water is about 7.5 gallons.

21. Find the surface area of each of the following polyhedrons. Give *exact* answers.

a. A regular tetrahedron with an edge of 4 cm

b. A regular hexahedron with an edge of 4 cm

c. A regular icosahedron with an edge of 4 cm

d. The dodecahedron shown at right, made of four congruent rectangles and eight congruent triangles

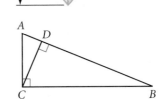

9 / 5 / 6

22. Given the triangle at right, reflect D over $\overline{AC}$ to D'. Then reflect D over $\overline{BC}$ to D''. Explain why D', C, D'' are collinear.

(triangle with vertices A, D, C, B)

23. In each diagram, $WXYZ$ is a parallelogram. Find the coordinates of Y.

a.
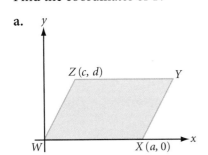

$Z(c, d)$ / Y / W / $X(a, 0)$

b.
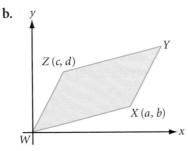

$Z(c, d)$ / Y / W / $X(a, b)$

c.
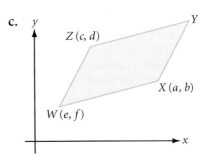

$Z(c, d)$ / Y / $W(e, f)$ / $X(a, b)$

DEVELOPING MATHEMATICAL REASONING

Container Problem II

You have an unmarked 9 liter container, an unmarked 4 liter container, and an unlimited supply of water. In table, symbol, or paragraph form, describe how you might end up with exactly 3 liters in one of the containers.

9 liters / 4 liters

LESSON
11.4

Applications of Volume

"If you have made mistakes . . . there is always another chance for you . . . for this thing we call "failure" is not the falling down, but the staying down."

MARY PICKFORD

Volume has applications in science, medicine, engineering, and construction. For example, a chemist needs to accurately measure the volume of reactive substances. A doctor may need to calculate the volume of a cancerous tumor based on a body scan. Engineers and construction personnel need to determine the volume of building supplies such as concrete or asphalt. The volume of the rooms in a completed building will ultimately determine the size of mechanical devices such as air conditioning units.

Sometimes, if you know the volume of a solid, you can calculate an unknown length of a base or the solid's height. Here are two examples.

EXAMPLE A

The volume of this right triangular prism is 1440 cm³. Find the height of the prism.

Solution

$V = BH$	Volume formula for prisms and cylinders.
$V = \left(\frac{1}{2}bh\right)H$	The base of the prism is a triangle.
$1440 = \frac{1}{2}(8)(15)H$	Substitute 1440 for the volume, 8 for the base of the triangle, and 15 for the height of the triangle.
$1440 = 60H$	Simplify.
$24 = H$	Solve for H.

The height of the prism is 24 cm.

EXAMPLE B

The volume of this sector of a right cylinder is 2814 m³. Find the radius of the base of the cylinder to the nearest m.

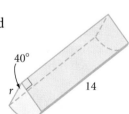

Solution

The volume is the area of the base times the height. To find the area of the sector, you first find what fraction the sector is of the whole circle: $\frac{40}{360} = \frac{1}{9}$.

$$V = BH$$
$$V = \left(\frac{1}{9}\pi r^2\right)H$$
$$2814 = \frac{1}{9}\pi r^2(14)$$
$$\frac{9 \cdot 2814}{14\pi} = r^2$$
$$575.8 \approx r^2$$
$$24 \approx r$$

The radius is about 24 m.

11.4 Exercises

YOU WILL NEED

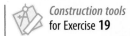
Construction tools
for Exercise **19**

1. If you cut a 1 inch square out of each corner of an 8.5 in. by 11 in. piece of paper and fold it into a box without a lid, what is the volume of the container?

2. The prism at right has equilateral triangle bases with side lengths of 4 cm. The height of the prism is 8 cm. Find the volume. ⓗ

3. A triangular pyramid has a volume of 180 cm³ and a height of 12 cm. Find the length of a side of the triangular base if the triangle's height from that side is 6 cm. ⓗ

4. A trapezoidal pyramid has a volume of 3168 cm³, and its height is 36 cm. The lengths of the two bases of the trapezoidal base are 20 cm and 28 cm. What is the height of the trapezoidal base? ⓗ

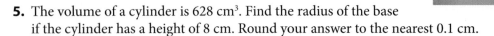

5. The volume of a cylinder is 628 cm³. Find the radius of the base if the cylinder has a height of 8 cm. Round your answer to the nearest 0.1 cm.

6. If you roll an 8.5 in. by 11 in. piece of paper into a cylinder by bringing the two longer sides together, you get a tall, thin cylinder. If you roll an 8.5 in. by 11 in. piece of paper into a cylinder by bringing the two shorter sides together, you get a short, fat cylinder. Which of the two cylinders has the greater volume? Explain.

7. Sylvia has just discovered that the valve on her cement truck failed during the night and that all the contents ran out to form a giant cone of hardened cement. To make an insurance claim, she needs to figure out how much cement is in the cone. The circumference of its base is 44 feet, and it is 5 feet high. Calculate the volume to the nearest cubic foot.

8. A sealed rectangular container 6 cm by 12 cm by 15 cm is sitting on its smallest face. It is filled with water up to 5 cm from the top. How many centimeters from the bottom will the water level reach if the container is placed on its largest face?

9. The solid shown to the right is a truncated cylinder. It is a cylinder that has been sliced on a slant by a plane and the top portion removed. The plane sliced the cylinder 48 meters and 36 meters up from the base. The circular base has a diameter of 40 meters. What is the volume of this truncated cylinder?

Use this information to solve Exercises 10–12: Water weighs about 63 pounds per cubic foot, and a cubic foot of water is about 7.5 gallons.

10. A king-size waterbed mattress measures 5.5 feet by 6.5 feet by 8 inches deep. To the nearest pound, how much does the water in this waterbed weigh? ⓗ

11. A child's wading pool has a diameter of 7 feet and is 8 inches deep. How many gallons of water can the pool hold? Round your answer to the nearest 0.1 gallon.

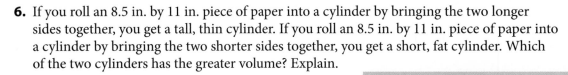

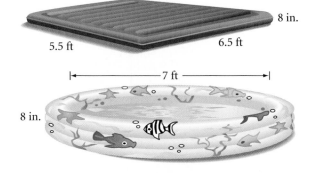

12. Madeleine's hot tub has the shape of a regular hexagonal prism. The chart on the hot-tub heater tells how long it takes to warm different amounts of water by 10°F. Help Madeleine determine how long it will take to raise the water temperature from 93°F to 103°F.

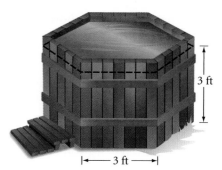
3 ft

3 ft

Minutes to Raise Temperature 10°F

Gallons	350	400	450	500	550	600	650	700
Minutes	9	10	11	12	14	15	16	18

13. A standard juice box holds 8 fluid ounces. A fluid ounce of liquid occupies 1.8 in³. Design a cylindrical can that will hold about the same volume as one juice box. What are some possible dimensions of the can?

14. *Which pan will give you a taller cake?* The directions on a cake mix box suggests using either a 9 in. round pan or an 8 in. square pan. Which pan will give you a taller cake? Explain.

15. An auto tunnel through a mountain is being planned. It will be in the shape of a semicircular cylinder with a radius of 10 m and a length of 2 km. How many cubic meters of dirt will need to be removed? If the bed of each dump truck has dimensions 2.2 m by 4.8 m by 1.8 m, how many loads will be required to carry away the dirt?

Review

16. In the figure at right, *ABCE* is a parallelogram and *BCDE* is a rectangle. Write a paragraph proof showing that △*ABD* is isosceles.

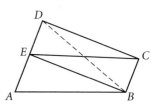

17. Find the height of this right square pyramid. Give your answer to the nearest 0.1 cm.

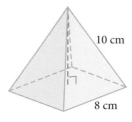

10 cm

8 cm

18. $\overleftrightarrow{EC}$ is tangent at *C*. $\overleftrightarrow{ED}$ is tangent at *D*. $m\widehat{BC} = 76°$. Find *x*.

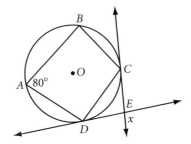

19. Use your geometry tools to construct an inscribed and circumscribed circle for an equilateral triangle.

20. A net for a cube is shown at right with two of the vertices *P* and *Q* shown. If the area of the net is 384 cm², find:

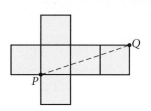

   a. Find the distance from *P* to *Q* on the net.

   b. Find the shortest distance through space from *P* to *Q* when the net is folded into a cube.

21. *M* is the midpoint of $\overline{AC}$ and $\overline{BD}$. For each statement, select always (A), sometimes (S), or never (N).

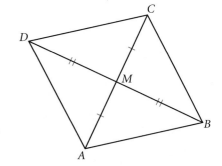

   a. *ABCD* is a parallelogram.

   b. *ABCD* is a rhombus.

   c. *ABCD* is a kite.

   d. $\triangle AMD \cong \triangle AMB$

   e. $\angle DAM \cong \angle BCM$

DEVELOPING MATHEMATICAL REASONING

Domino Puzzle I

The 28 dominoes of an entire double-six set have been arranged into a 7 × 8 rectangle. The outlines of the individual dominoes have been removed. Use your sequential reasoning and visual thinking skills to redraw the outlines of the individual dominoes. Pay particular attention to the arrangement of dots on the 2, 3, and 6. You might find it helpful to use patty paper or tracing paper to check on the orientation of the dominoes with two or three dots.

Polya's Problem

George Polya (1887–1985) was a mathematician who specialized in problem-solving methods. He taught mathematics and problem solving at Stanford University for many years, and wrote the book *How to Solve It.*

He posed this problem to his students: Into how many parts will five random planes divide space?

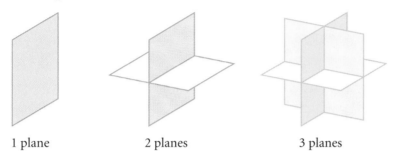

1 plane   2 planes   3 planes

Your task is to solve this problem. Here are some of Polya's problem-solving strategies to help you.

1. Understand the problem. Draw a figure or build a model. Can you restate the problem in your own words?

2. Break down the problem. Have you done any simpler problems that are like this one?

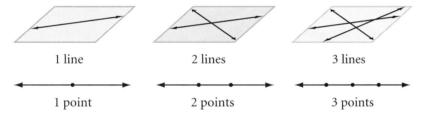

1 line   2 lines   3 lines

1 point   2 points   3 points

3. Check your answer. Can you find the answer in a different way to show that it is correct? (The answer, by the way, is not 32!)

Your solution should include all drawings and models you made or used, a description of the strategies you tried and how well each one worked, your answer, and why you think it's correct.

Displacement and Density

"Eureka! I have found it!"

ARCHIMEDES

What happens if you step into a bathtub that is filled to the brim? If you add a scoop of ice cream to a glass filled with root beer? In each case, you'll have a mess! The volume of the liquid that overflows in each case equals the volume of the solid below the liquid level. This volume is called an object's **displacement**.

EXAMPLE A

Mary Jo wants to find the volume of an irregularly shaped rock. She puts some water into a rectangular prism with a base that measures 10 cm by 15 cm. When the rock is put into the container, Mary Jo notices that the water level rises 2 cm because the rock displaces its volume of water. This new "slice" of water has a volume of (2)(10)(15), or 300 cm³. So the volume of the rock is 300 cm³.

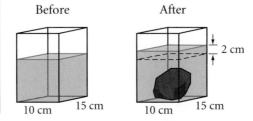

An important property of a material is its density. **Density** is the mass of matter in a given volume. You can find the mass of an object by weighing it. You calculate density by dividing the mass by the volume:

$$\text{density} = \frac{\text{mass}}{\text{volume}}$$

EXAMPLE B

A clump of metal with mass 351.4 grams is dropped into a cylindrical container, causing the water level to rise 1.1 cm. The radius of the base of the container is 3.0 cm. What is the density of the metal? Given the table, and assuming the metal is pure, what is the metal?

Metal	Density	Metal	Density
Aluminum	2.81 g/cm³	Nickel	8.89 g/cm³
Copper	8.97 g/cm³	Platinum	21.40 g/cm³
Gold	19.30 g/cm³	Potassium	0.86 g/cm³
Lead	11.30 g/cm³	Silver	10.50 g/cm³
Lithium	0.54 g/cm³	Sodium	0.97 g/cm³

Solution | First, find the volume of displaced water. Then divide the mass by the volume to get the density of the metal.

$$\text{volume} = \pi(3.0)^2(1.1) \qquad \text{density} \approx \frac{351.4}{31.1}$$
$$= (\pi)(9)(1.1) \qquad\qquad \approx 11.3$$
$$\approx 31.1$$

The density is 11.3 g/cm³. Therefore the metal is lead.

→ History
CONNECTION

Archimedes solved the problem of how to tell whether a crown was made of genuine gold by using displacement to calculate its density. Legend has it that the insight came to him while he was bathing. Thrilled by his discovery, Archimedes ran through the streets shouting "Eureka!" (Greek for "I have found it!") wearing just what he'd been wearing in the bathtub.

(11.5) Exercises

1. When you put a rock into a container of water, it raises the water level 3 cm. If the container is a rectangular prism whose base measures 15 cm by 15 cm, what is the volume of the rock?

2. You drop a solid glass ball into a cylinder with a radius of 6 cm, raising the water level 1 cm. What is the volume of the glass ball?

3. A fish tank 10 in. by 14 in. by 12 in. is the home of a large goldfish named Columbia. She is taken out when her owner cleans the tank, and the water level in the tank drops $\frac{1}{3}$ inch. What is Columbia's volume?

For Exercises 4–9, refer to the table on the first page of this lesson.

4. What is the mass of a solid block of aluminum if its dimensions are 4 cm by 8 cm by 20 cm?

5. Which has more mass: a solid cylinder of gold with a height of 5 cm and a diameter of 6 cm, or a solid cone of platinum with a height of 21 cm and a diameter of 8 cm?

→ Science
CONNECTION

Buoyancy is the tendency of an object to float in either a liquid or a gas. For an object to float on the surface of water, it must sink enough to displace the volume of water equal to its weight.

6. Chemist Dean Dalton is given a clump of metal and is told that it is sodium. He finds that the metal has mass 145.5 g. He places it into a nonreactive liquid in a square prism whose base measures 10 cm on each edge. If the metal is indeed sodium, how high should the liquid level rise? (h)

7. A square-prism container with a base 5 cm by 5 cm is partially filled with water. You drop a clump of metal with mass 525 g into the container, and the water level rises 2 cm. What is the density of the metal? Assuming the metal is pure, what is the metal?

8. *Is Lance a "sinker or a floater"?* Lance weighs 174 pounds and when he completely submerges himself in a 3 ft by 4 ft by 4 ft high tank the water level rises 3 inches. If the density of water is 62.4 lbs./ft.³ is Lance more dense ("sinker") or less dense ("floater") than the water?

9. Sherlock Holmes rushes home to his chemistry lab, takes a mysterious medallion from his case, and weighs it. "It has mass 3088 grams. Now let's check its volume." He pours water into a graduated glass container with a 10 cm by 10 cm square base, and records the water level, which is 53.0 cm. He places the medallion into the container and reads the new water level, 54.6 cm. He enjoys a few minutes of mental calculation, then turns to Dr. Watson. "This confirms my theory. Quick, Watson! Off to the train station."

"Holmes, you amaze me. Is it gold?" questions the good doctor.

"If it has a density of 19.3 grams per cubic centimeter, it is gold," smiles Mr. Holmes. "If it is gold, then Colonel Banderson is who he says he is. If it is a fake, then so is the Colonel."

"Well?" Watson queries.

Holmes smiles and says, "It's elementary, my dear Watson. Elementary geometry, that is."

What is the volume of the medallion? Is it gold? Is Colonel Banderson who he says he is?

Review

10. What is the volume of the slice removed from this right cylinder? Give your answer to the nearest cm³.

11. Ofelia has brought home a new aquarium shaped like the regular hexagonal prism shown at right. She isn't sure her desk is strong enough to hold it. The aquarium, without water, weighs 48 pounds. How much will it weigh when it is filled? (Water weighs 63 pounds per cubic foot.) If a small fish needs about 180 cubic inches of water to swim around in, about how many small fish can this aquarium house?

12. △ABC is equilateral. M is the centroid. AB = 6 Find the area of △CEA.

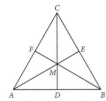

13. Give a paragraph or flowchart proof explaining why M is the midpoint of $\overline{PQ}$.

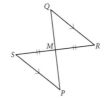

14. The three polygons are regular polygons. How many sides does the red polygon have?

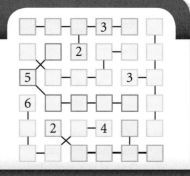

11.6

Volume of a Sphere

In this lesson you will develop a formula for the volume of a sphere. In the investigation you'll compare the volume of a right cylinder to the volume of a hemisphere.

INVESTIGATION

YOU WILL NEED

- cylinder and hemisphere with the same radius
- sand, rice, birdseed, or water

The Formula for the Volume of a Sphere

This investigation demonstrates the relationship between the volume of a hemisphere with radius r and the volume of a right cylinder with base radius r and height $2r$—that is, the smallest cylinder that encloses a given sphere.

Step 1 Fill the hemisphere.

Step 2 Carefully pour the contents of the hemisphere into the cylinder. What fraction of the cylinder does the hemisphere appear to fill?

Step 3 Fill the hemisphere again and pour the contents into the cylinder. What fraction of the cylinder do two hemispheres (one sphere) appear to fill?

Step 4 If the radius of the cylinder is r and its height is $2r$, then what is the volume of the cylinder in terms of r?

Step 5 The volume of the sphere is the fraction of the cylinder's volume that was filled by two hemispheres. What is the formula for the volume of a sphere? State it as your conjecture.

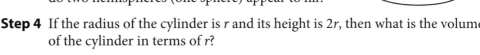

> **Sphere Volume Conjecture**   `C-94`
>
> The volume of a sphere with radius r is given by the formula _?_.

You just discovered a formula for finding the volume of a sphere given its radius. The investigation may have convinced you that the conjecture is true, but can you explain why it is true? To understand why your conjecture is true we will use a concept called **Cavalieri's Principle**, named after the Italian mathematician Bonaventura Cavalieri (1598–1647). Cavalieri's Principle says: *If two solids have the same cross sectional area whenever they are sliced at the same height, then the two solids must have the same volume.* With Cavalieri's Principle you can prove that the two solids shown below, a hemisphere and a cylinder with a cone removed, have the same volume.

You know how to find the volume of a cylinder and the volume of a cone. So you can find the volume of a cylinder with a cone removed from it. It turns out that such a solid, a "cylinder less cone," does have the same cross sectional area as a hemisphere whenever they are both sliced at the same height. The demonstration below will prove that for any given height, the area of a cross section of a hemisphere is always equal to the area of the cross section of a cylinder with cone removed. Thus by Cavalieri's Principle, the two solids have the same volume.

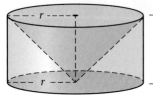

The hemisphere on the top left has radius r. The solid on the bottom left is a cylinder with height r and radius r, which has a cone of height r and radius r removed. In the proof we need to demonstrate that if these two solids are sliced at the same height, their cross-sectional areas are the same.

To demonstrate that these two solids have the same cross-sectional areas, we select an arbitrary height h and, with the help of algebra, find the cross-sectional area of each solid at height h.

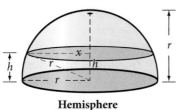

Hemisphere

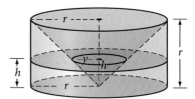

Cylinder with Cone Removed

The area of the circular cross-section is πx^2. But $x^2 + h^2 = r^2$ by the Pythagorean Theorem. Therefore $x^2 = r^2 - h^2$. Thus, the cross-sectional area is $\pi(r^2 - h^2)$.

The area of the annulus is $\pi r^2 - \pi y^2$. But since y and h are the legs of an isosceles right triangle, $y = h$. Therefore the area of the annulus is $\pi r^2 - \pi h^2$. By factoring this expression you get $\pi(r^2 - h^2)$.

Since both cross-sectional areas turned out to be the same, $\pi(r^2 - h^2)$, then the two solids must have the same volume by Cavalieri's Principle. With your group members, use the cross-sectional areas and your knowledge of volume to show that the two volumes are equal. Use the steps below as a guide to find the volume of the cylindrical solid.

$$\text{Volume}_{\text{cylinder}} = BH$$
$$= (?)(?)$$
$$= \underline{?}$$

$$\text{Volume}_{\text{cone}} = \left(\frac{1}{3}\right)BH$$
$$= \left(\frac{1}{3}\right)(?)(?)$$
$$= \underline{?}$$

By Cavalieri's Principle, the hemisphere must also have the same volume. Discuss with your group how you can use this proof to arrive at the formula for the volume of a sphere.

EXAMPLE A | As an exercise for her art class, Mona has cast a plaster cube 12 cm on each side. Her assignment is to carve the largest possible sphere from the cube. What percentage of the plaster will be carved away?

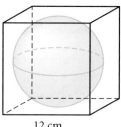

12 cm

Solution | The largest possible sphere will have a diameter of 12 cm, so its radius is 6 cm. Applying the formula for volume of a sphere, you get $V = \frac{4}{3}\pi r^3 = \frac{4}{3}\pi(6)^3 = \frac{4}{3}\pi \cdot 216 = 288\pi$, or about 905 cm³. The volume of the plaster cube is 12³, or 1728 cm³. You subtract the volume of the sphere from the volume of the cube to get the amount carved away, which is about 823 cm³. Therefore the percentage carved away is $\frac{823}{1728} \approx 48\%$.

EXAMPLE B | Find the volume of plastic (to the nearest cubic inch) needed for this hollow toy component. The outer-hemisphere diameter is 5.0 in. and the inner-hemisphere diameter is 4.0 in.

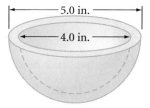

5.0 in.

4.0 in.

Solution | The formula for volume of a sphere is $V = \frac{4}{3}\pi r^3$, so the volume of a hemisphere is half of that, $V = \frac{2}{3}\pi r^3$. A radius is half a diameter.

Outer Hemisphere

$$V_o = \frac{2}{3}\pi r^3$$
$$= \frac{2}{3}\pi(2.5)^3$$
$$= \frac{2}{3}\pi \cdot 15.625$$
$$= \frac{31.25\pi}{3} \approx 32.7$$

Inner Hemisphere

$$V_i = \frac{2}{3}\pi r^3$$
$$= \frac{2}{3}\pi(2)^3$$
$$= \frac{2}{3}\pi \cdot 8$$
$$= \frac{16\pi}{3} \approx 16.8$$

Subtracting the volume of the inner hemisphere from the volume of the outer one, approximately 16 in³ of plastic are needed.

11.6 Exercises

YOU WILL NEED

Geometry software
for Exercise **20**

In Exercises 1–6, find the volume of each solid. All measurements are in centimeters.

1.

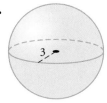

3

2.

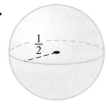

$\frac{1}{2}$

3.

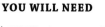

$\frac{3}{4}$

4. ⓗ

6

12

6

5.

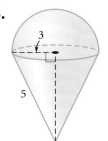

3

5

6. ⓗ

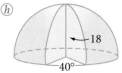

18

40°

7. What is the volume of the largest hemisphere that you could carve out of a wooden block whose edges measure 3 m by 7 m by 7 m?

8. Lickety Split ice cream comes in a cylindrical container with an inside diameter of 6 inches and a height of 10 inches. The company claims to give the customer 25 scoops of ice cream per container, each scoop being a sphere with a 3 inch diameter. How many scoops will each container really hold?

9. Find the volume of a spherical shell with an outer diameter of 8 meters and an inner diameter of 6 meters.

10. Which is greater, the volume of a hemisphere with radius 2 cm or the total volume of two cones with radius 2 cm and height 2 cm?

11. A sphere has a volume of 972π in³. Find its radius. ⓗ

12. A hemisphere has a volume of 18π in³. Find its radius.

13. The base of a hemisphere has an area of 256π cm². Find its volume.

14. If the diameter of a student's brain is about 12 centimeters, and you assume its shape is approximately a hemisphere, then what is the volume of the student's brain? If the typical student brain has a density of 1.04 g/cm³, how much does a typical student brain weigh?

15. A cylindrical glass 10 cm tall and 8 cm in diameter is filled to 1 cm from the top with water. If a golf ball 4 cm in diameter is placed into the glass, will the water overflow?

16. This underground gasoline storage tank is a right cylinder with a hemisphere at each end. How many gallons of gasoline will the tank hold? (1 gallon = 0.13368 cubic foot.) If the service station fills twenty 15 gallon tanks from the storage tank per day, how many days will it take to empty the storage tank?

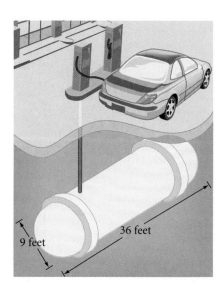

9 feet   36 feet

Review

17. Inspector Lestrade has sent a small piece of metal to the crime lab. The lab technician finds that its mass is 54.3 g. It appears to be lithium, sodium, or potassium, all highly reactive with water. Then the technician places the metal into a graduated glass cylinder of radius 4 cm that contains a nonreactive liquid. The metal causes the level of the liquid to rise 2.0 cm. Which metal is it? (Refer to the table on page 558.)

18. City law requires that any one-story commercial building supply a parking area equal in size to the floor area of the building. A-Round Architects has designed a cylindrical building with a 150 foot diameter. They plan to ring the building with parking. How far from the building should the parking lot extend? Round your answer to the nearest foot.

Parking

Building

19. Use the following characteristics to plot *A, B, C,* and *D* onto graph paper.

    A is (3, −5).

    C is the reflection of *A* over the *x*-axis.

    B is the rotation of *C* 180° around the origin.

    D is a transformation of *A* by the rule $(x, y) \rightarrow (x + 6, y + 10)$.

What kind of quadrilateral is *ABCD*? Give reasons for your answer.

20. Use geometry software to construct a circle. Choose a point *A* on the circle and a point *B* not on the circle, and construct the perpendicular bisector of $\overline{AB}$. Trace the perpendicular bisector as you animate *A* around the circle. Describe the locus of points traced.

21. Find *w, x,* and *y.*

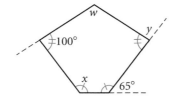

PERFORMANCE TASK

Will it all fit? A sphere of ice cream is placed onto your ice cream cone. Both have a diameter of 8 cm. The height of your cone is 12 cm. If you push the ice cream into the cone, will all of it fit? What diameters and cone heights can you find that will work?

Surface Area of a Sphere

Earth is so large that it is reasonable to use area formulas for plane figures—rectangles, triangles, and circles—to find the areas of most small land regions. But, to find Earth's entire surface area, you need a formula for the surface area of a sphere. Now that you know how to find the volume of a sphere, you can use that knowledge to arrive at the formula for the surface area of a sphere.

Earth rises over the Moon's horizon. From there, the Moon's surface seems flat.

INVESTIGATION

The Formula for the Surface Area of a Sphere

In this investigation you'll visualize a sphere's surface covered by tiny shapes that are nearly flat. So the surface area, S, of the sphere is the sum of the areas of all the "near polygons." If you imagine radii connecting each of the vertices of the "near polygons" to the center of the sphere, you are mentally dividing the volume of the sphere into many "near pyramids." Each of the "near polygons" is a base for a pyramid, and the radius, r, of the sphere is the height of the pyramid. So the volume, V, of the sphere is the sum of the volumes of all the pyramids. Now get ready for some algebra.

A horsefly's eyes resemble spheres covered by "near polygons."

Step 1 Divide the surface of the sphere into 1000 "near polygons" with areas $B_1, B_2, B_3, \ldots, B_{1000}$. Then you can write the surface area, S, of the sphere as the sum of the 1000 B's:

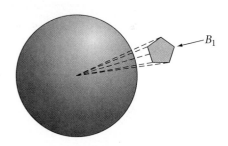

$$S = B_1 + B_2 + B_3 + \ldots + B_{1000}$$

Step 2 The volume of the pyramid with base B_1 is $\frac{1}{3}(B_1)(r)$, so the total volume of the sphere, V, is the sum of the volumes of the 1000 pyramids:

$$V = \frac{1}{3}B_1(r) + \frac{1}{3}B_2(r) + \ldots + \frac{1}{3}B_{1000}(r)$$

What common expression can you factor from each of the terms on the right side? Rewrite the last equation showing the results of your factoring.

Step 3 But the volume of the sphere is $V = \frac{4}{3}\pi r^3$. Rewrite your equation from Step 2 by substituting $\frac{4}{3}\pi r^3$ for V and substituting S for the sum of the areas of all the "near polygons."

Step 4 Solve the equation from Step 3 for the surface area, S. You now have a formula for finding the surface area of a sphere in terms of its radius. State this as your next conjecture and add it to your conjecture list.

> **Sphere Surface Area Conjecture** `C-95`
>
> The surface area, S, of a sphere with radius r is given by the formula __?__ .

EXAMPLE | Find the surface area of a sphere whose volume is $12{,}348\pi$ m³.

Solution | First, use the volume formula for a sphere to find its radius. Then use the radius to find the surface area.

Radius Calculation   Surface Area Calculation

$$V = \frac{4}{3}\pi r^3 \qquad\qquad S = 4\pi r^2$$

$$12{,}348\pi = \frac{4}{3}\pi r^3 \qquad\qquad = 4\pi(21)^2$$

$$\frac{3}{4} \cdot 12{,}348 = r^3 \qquad\qquad = 4\pi \cdot 441$$

$$9261 = r^3 \qquad\qquad S = 1764\pi \approx 5541.8$$

$$r = 21$$

The radius is 21 m and the surface area is 1764π m², or about 5541.8 m².

11.7 Exercises

For Exercises 1–3, find the volume and total surface area of each solid. All measurements are in centimeters.

1.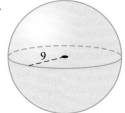

2.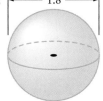

3. ⓗ

4. The shaded circle at right has area 40π cm². Find the surface area of the sphere. ⓗ

5. Find the volume of a sphere whose surface area is 64π cm².

6. Find the surface area of a sphere whose volume is 288π cm³.

7. If the radius of the base of a hemisphere (which is bounded by a great circle) is r, what is the area of the great circle? What is the total surface area of the hemisphere, including the base? How do they compare?

8. If Jose used 4 gallons of wood sealant to cover the hemispherical ceiling of his vacation home, how many gallons of wood sealant are needed to cover the floor?

9. Assume a Kickapoo wigwam is a semicylinder with a half-hemisphere on each end. The diameter of the semicylinder and each of the half-hemispheres is 3.6 meters. The total length is 7.6 meters. What is the volume of the wigwam and the surface area of its roof?

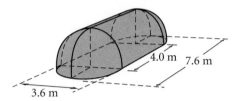

4.0 m 7.6 m

3.6 m

10. A farmer must periodically resurface the interior (wall, floor, and ceiling) of his silo to protect it from the acid created by the silage. The height of the silo to the top of the hemispherical dome is 50 ft, and the diameter is 18 ft.

  a. What is the approximate surface area that needs to be treated?

  b. If 1 gallon of resurfacing compound covers about 250 ft², how many gallons are needed?

  c. There is 0.8 bushel per ft³. Calculate the number of bushels of grain this silo will hold.

11. About 70% of Earth's surface is covered by water. If the diameter of Earth is about 12,750 km, find the area not covered by water to the nearest 100,000 km².

12. Earth has a thin outer layer called the *crust*, which averages about 24 km thick. Earth's diameter is about 12,750 km. What percentage of the volume of Earth is the crust?

Crust

Review

13. What is the ordered pair rule that would transform $\triangle ABC$ so that the image, $\triangle A'B'C'$, coincides with $\triangle DEF$?

14. Find the ratio of the area of the circle inscribed in an equilateral triangle to the area of the circumscribed circle.

15. Find the ratio of the area of the circle inscribed in a square to the area of the circumscribed circle.

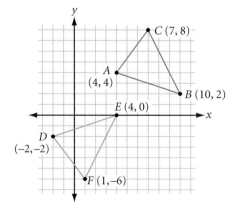

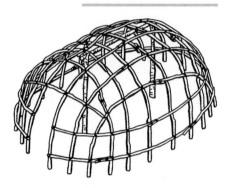

Cultural
CONNECTION

A wigwam is a domed structure used by Native American woodland tribes, such as the Kickapoo, Iroquois, and Cherokee. The wigwam has an oval floor pattern, and uses bent tree saplings tied together to support the framework.

C (7, 8)

A (4, 4)

B (10, 2)

E (4, 0)

D (−2, −2)

F (1, −6)

16. Find the ratio of the area of the circle inscribed in a regular hexagon to the area of the circumscribed circle.

17. Make a conjecture as to what happens to the ratio in Exercises 14–16 as the number of sides of the regular polygon increases. Make sketches to support your conjecture.

18. Prove the Rhombus Angles Conjecture: The diagonals of a rhombus bisect the angles of the rhombus.

Given: Rhombus *ABCD* with diagonal $\overline{BD}$

Show: $\overline{BD}$ bisects $\angle ABC$ and $\angle ADC$

Explain why the logic of this proof would also apply to the other diagonal, $\overline{AC}$.

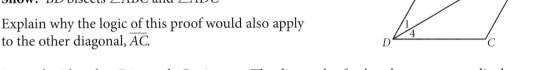

19. Prove the Rhombus Diagonals Conjecture: The diagonals of a rhombus are perpendicular bisectors of each other. Start with rhombus *ABCD* in the figure below and follow these steps.

a. Use the Rhombus Angles Conjecture to prove that $\triangle AEB \cong \triangle CEB$.

b. Use part a to prove that $\overline{BD}$ bisects $\overline{AC}$.

c. Use part a to prove that $\angle 3$ and $\angle 4$ are right angles.

d. You've proved most of the Rhombus Diagonals Conjecture. Explain what is missing and describe how you could complete the proof.

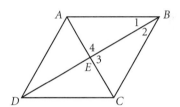

DEVELOPING MATHEMATICAL REASONING

Knight's Tour Semi-Magic Square Puzzle

If all the rows and columns add to the same sum, the magic sum, but the sums in the two main diagonals do not add to the magic sum, then that square arrangement of numbers is called a *semi-magic square*. To the right is a portion of a spectacular 8 × 8 semi-magic square, which some believe was created by the Swiss mathematician Leonard Euler (1707–1783). Not only is the entire 8 × 8 grid a semi-magic square but each corner 4 × 4 is also a semi-magic square. But that is just the start! When completed this semi-magic square is also a knight's tour. That is, it is possible to start at the 1, move to the 2, to the 3, and so on, all the way to the last number 64 by making the *L*-shaped move of the chess knight. Copy and complete this semi-magic square knight's tour puzzle.

1		31		33		63	
	51		3		19		
		49		15			
			45		61	36	13
		25				21	
28		8	41	24			
43	6	55			10		
			58		38		

LESSON

11.8

Similarity and Volume

The statues at right are giant versions of an Oscar, the Academy Awards statuette that is handed out each year for excellence in the motion-picture industry. Assume that a statue is similar to the actual Oscar, but six times as long in each dimension. If it costs $250 to gold-plate the surface of the actual Oscar, how much would it cost to gold-plate the statue? As you learned in Chapter 8, the surface area is not six times greater, but 6^2, or 36 times greater, so the cost would be $9,000!

How are their weights related? The actual Oscar weighs 8.5 pounds. If the statue were made of the same material as the actual Oscar, its weight would not be six times greater, or even 36 times greater. It would weigh 1836 pounds! In this lesson you will discover why.

Solids that have the same shape but not necessarily the same size are similar. All cubes are similar, but not all prisms are similar. All spheres are similar, but not all cylinders are similar. Two polyhedrons are similar if all their corresponding faces are similar and the lengths of their corresponding edges are proportional. Two right cylinders (or right cones) are similar if their radii and heights are proportional.

EXAMPLE A

Are these right rectangular prisms similar?

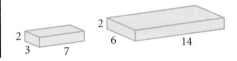

Solution

The two prisms are not similar because the corresponding edges are not proportional.

$$\frac{2}{2} \neq \frac{3}{6} = \frac{7}{14}$$

EXAMPLE B

Are these right circular cones similar?

Solution

The two cones are similar because the radii and heights are proportional.

$$\frac{8}{12} = \frac{14}{21}$$

INVESTIGATION

Volume Ratios

How does the ratio of lengths of corresponding edges of similar solids compare with the ratio of their volumes? Let's find out.

— Fish

— Snake

Step 1 Use blocks to build the "snake." Calculate its volume.

Step 2 Multiply each edge length by a scale factor of 2 and build an enlarged snake. Calculate its volume.

Step 3 What is the ratio of the lengths of corresponding edges of the larger snake to the smaller snake? What is the ratio of their volumes?

Step 4 Build the "fish" or design your own solid using nine cubes or less. Draw the fish or other solid on isometric dot paper. Calculate its volume.

Step 5 Multiply each edge length by a scale factor of 3 and draw the enlarged solid that would result. Calculate its volume.

Step 6 Calculate the ratio of edge lengths and the ratio of volumes of the two solids. How do your results compare with the ratios of the areas you discovered in Chapter 8?

Step 7 Discuss how you would calculate the volumes of the snake and your other solid if you multiplied the edges by a scale factor of 5. You should be ready to state a conjecture.

Proportional Volumes Conjecture   `C-96`

If corresponding edge lengths (or radii, or heights) of two similar solids compare in the ratio $\frac{m}{n}$, then their volumes compare in the ratio ? .

The reason behind the Proportional Volumes Conjecture is that volume is a three-dimensional measure. Because volume is related to the product of a two-dimensional base and height, when all three dimensions are doubled, the volume increases by a factor of eight.

Let's look at an application of both the Proportional Areas Conjecture and Proportional Volumes Conjecture.

EXAMPLE C

The diameter of a soccer ball is about 8.75 in. and the diameter of a tennis ball is about 2.5 in. How many times more surface material is needed to make the outside of a soccer ball than a tennis ball? How many times more air does a soccer ball hold than a tennis ball?

Solution

The ratio of the diameters is $\frac{8.75}{2.5}$, or $\frac{7}{2}$, so the ratio of the surface areas is $\left(\frac{7}{2}\right)^2$, or $\frac{49}{4}$, and the ratio of the volumes is $\left(\frac{7}{2}\right)^3$, or $\frac{343}{8}$. Therefore, the soccer ball requires $12\frac{1}{4}$ times as much material to make and holds $42\frac{7}{8}$ times as much air.

11.8 Exercises

YOU WILL NEED

Construction tools
for Exercises **19** and **20**

1. The pentagonal pyramids are similar.

$\frac{h}{H} = \frac{4}{7}$

volume of large pyramid = ?
volume of small pyramid = 320 cm³ ⓗ

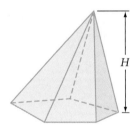
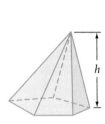

2. These right cones are similar.

$H = \underline{?}, h = \underline{?}$

volume of large cone = ?
volume of small cone = ?

$\frac{\text{volume of large cone}}{\text{volume of small cone}} = \underline{?}$

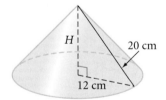

3 cm   20 cm   12 cm

3. These right trapezoidal prisms are similar.

volume of small prism = 324 cm³

$\frac{\text{area of base of small prism}}{\text{area of base of large prism}} = \frac{9}{25}$

$\frac{h}{H} = \underline{?}$

$\frac{\text{volume of large prism}}{\text{volume of small prism}} = \underline{?}$

volume of large prism = ? ⓗ

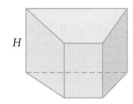

4. These right cylinders are similar.

volume of large cylinder = 4608π ft³

volume of small cylinder = ?

$\frac{\text{volume of large cylinder}}{\text{volume of small cylinder}} = \underline{?}$

$H = \underline{?}$

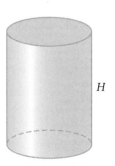

9   24

5. The ratio of the lengths of corresponding edges of two similar triangular prisms is $\frac{5}{3}$. What is the ratio of their volumes?

6. The ratio of the volumes of two similar pentagonal prisms is 8:125. What is the ratio of their heights?

7. The ratio of the weights of two spherical steel balls is $\frac{8}{27}$. What is the ratio of their diameters?

8. The energy (and cost) needed to operate an air conditioner is proportional to the volume of the space that is being cooled. It costs ZAP Electronics about $125 per day to run an air conditioner in their small rectangular warehouse. The company's large warehouse, a few blocks away, is 2.5 times as long, wide, and high as the small warehouse. Estimate the daily cost of cooling the large warehouse with the same model of air conditioner. ⓗ

This bronze sculpture named _The Thinker_ was one of many created by Auguste Rodin (1840–1917).

9. A sculptor creates a small bronze statue that weighs 38 lb. She plans to make a version that will be four times as large in each dimension. How much will this larger statue weigh if it is also bronze?

10. A tabloid magazine at a supermarket checkout exclaims, "Scientists Breed 4 Foot Tall Chicken." A photo shows a giant chicken that supposedly weighs 74 pounds and will solve the world's hunger problem. What do you think about this headline? Assuming an average chicken stands 14 inches tall and weighs 7 pounds, would a 4 foot chicken weigh 74 pounds? Is it possible for a chicken to be 4 feet tall? Explain your reasoning.

11. The goliath frog is the largest known frog—about 0.3 m long and 3.2 kg in weight. The Brazilian gold frog is one of the smallest known frogs—about 9.8 mm long. Approximate the weight of a Brazilian gold frog. What assumptions do you need to make? Explain your reasoning.

12. Orcas and dolphins both belong to the same family. Assume their bodies are similar. An orca is typically about 32 ft long, while a dolphin is about 8 ft long. What is the ratio of the surface area of the orca to that of the dolphin? What is the ratio of their volumes? Which animal has the greater surface area to volume ratio?

13. The black sphere at right has radius 9 inches. The red sphere inside has a radius of 6 inches. Imagine these spheres as two separate spheres. What is the ratio of the volume of the red sphere to the volume of the black sphere (without a section removed)? What is the ratio of the surface areas? Revisiting the picture at the right, what is the volume of the black part of the sphere if the red sphere takes up the space inside? Assume the black sphere is a complete sphere.

14. Imagine stretching all three dimensions of a 2 cm by 3 cm by 1 cm rectangular prism by multiplying them by scale factor x. Make a table of the surface area and volume of the prism for values of x from 1 to 5 and plot both sets of points on a graph. Write function $S(x)$ that gives the surface area of the prism as a function of x and function $V(x)$ that gives the volume of the prism as a function of x. How do their equations and graphs differ?

15. In the diagram at right, the second rectangular prism is a dilation of the first rectangular prism by scale factor r. Given that the ratio of the corresponding sides of the similar prisms is r, prove that the ratio of their volumes is r^3.

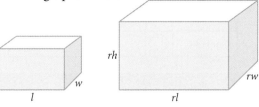

Review

16. A cone or pyramid that is sliced parallel to its base and has its top removed is called a **truncated** cone or pyramid, or a frustum. Find the volume of this truncated cone.

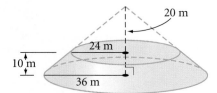

17. The large circles are tangent to the square and tangent to each other. The smaller circle is tangent to each larger circle. Find the radius of the smaller circle in terms of *s*, the length of each side of the square. ⓗ

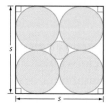

18. Triangle *PQR* has side lengths 18 cm, 24 cm, and 30 cm. Is △*PQR* a right triangle? Explain why or why not.

19. Use the triangular figure at right and its rotated image. ⓗ

a. Copy the figure and its image onto a piece of patty paper. Locate the center of rotation. Explain your method.

b. Copy the figure and its image onto a sheet of paper. Locate the center of rotation using a compass and straightedge. Explain your method.

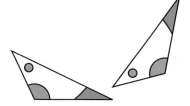

20. The Angle Bisector/Opposite Side Conjecture gives you a way to divide a segment into any ratio you wish. Follow the steps below to divide a segment into a 2:3 ratio.

a. Construct any segment *AB*. $A \overline{\qquad} B$

b. Construct a second segment. Call its length *x*. $\overline{\quad x \quad}$

c. Construct two more segments with lengths 2*x* and 3*x*. $\overline{\quad 2x \quad}$ $\overline{\quad\quad 3x \quad\quad}$

d. Construct a triangle with lengths 2*x*, 3*x*, and *AB*.

e. Explain what to do next and why it works.

DEVELOPING MATHEMATICAL REASONING

Color Code Puzzle II

Here is another Color Code Puzzle challenge. For a reminder of the rules, see the puzzle at the end of Lesson 7.5. The clues are included below. Good luck!

In the game below, a number of guesses have been made, with the clue for each guess shown to its right. From the given set of guesses and clues, determine the four-color arrangement.

Answer ⊘ ⊘ ⊘ ⊘

Guess #4	◯	◯	◯	◯	⊕⊕
Guess #3	◯	◯	◯	◯	⊕⊕⊖
Guess #2	◯	◯	◯	◯	⊖
Guess #1	◯	◯	◯	◯	◯

Clues

◯: Nothing is correct.

⊖: One color disc is correct but in the wrong position.

⊕: One color disc is correct and in the correct position.

EXPLORATION

Two More Forms of Valid Reasoning

In the Chapter 10 Exploration, Sherlock Holmes and Forms of Valid Reasoning, you learned about *Modus Ponens* and *Modus Tollens*. A third form of valid reasoning is called the Law of Syllogism.

According to the **Law of Syllogism** (LS), if you accept "If *P* then *Q*" as true and if you accept "If *Q* then *R*" as true, then you must logically accept "If *P* then *R*" as true.

Here is an example of the Law of Syllogism.

English statement	Symbolic translation
If I eat pizza after midnight, then I will have nightmares. If I have nightmares, then I will get very little sleep. Therefore, if I eat pizza after midnight, then I will get very little sleep.	*P*: I eat pizza after midnight. *Q*: I will have nightmares. *R*: I will get very little sleep. $P \rightarrow Q$ $Q \rightarrow R$ $\therefore P \rightarrow R$

To work on the next law, you need some new statement forms. Every conditional statement has three other conditionals associated with it. To get the converse of a statement, you switch the "if" and "then" parts. To get the **inverse**, you negate both parts. To get the **contrapositive**, you reverse and negate the two parts. These new forms may be true or false.

Statement	If two angles are vertical angles, then they are congruent.	$P \rightarrow Q$	true
Converse	If two angles are congruent, then they are vertical angles.	$Q \rightarrow P$	false
Inverse	If two angles are not vertical angles, then they are not congruent.	$\sim P \rightarrow \sim Q$	false
Contrapositive	If two angles are not congruent, then they are not vertical angles.	$\sim Q \rightarrow \sim P$	true

Notice that the original conditional statement and its contrapositive have the same truth value. This leads to a fourth form of valid reasoning. The **Law of Contrapositive** (LC) says that if a conditional statement is true, then its contrapositive is also true. Conversely, if the contrapositive is true, then the original conditional statement must also be true. This also means that if a conditional statement is false, so is its contrapositive.

Often, a logical argument contains multiple steps, applying the same rule more than once or applying more than one rule. Here is an example.

English statement	Symbolic translation
If the consecutive sides of a parallelogram are congruent, then it is a rhombus. If a parallelogram is a rhombus, then its diagonals are perpendicular bisectors of each other. The diagonals are not perpendicular bisectors of each other. Therefore the consecutive sides of the parallelogram are not congruent.	*P*: The consecutive sides of a parallelogram are congruent. *Q*: The parallelogram is a rhombus. *R*: The diagonals are perpendicular bisectors of each other. $P \rightarrow Q$ $Q \rightarrow R$ $\sim R$ $\therefore \sim P$

You can show that this argument is valid in three logical steps.

Step 1 $P \to Q$
   $Q \to R$
   $\therefore P \to R$ by the Law of Syllogism

Step 2 $P \to R$
   $\therefore \sim R \to \sim P$ by the Law of Contrapositive

Step 3 $\sim R \to \sim P$
   $\sim R$
   $\therefore \sim P$ by *Modus Ponens*

So far, you have learned four basic forms of valid reasoning.

Now let's apply them in symbolic proofs.

Four Forms of Valid Reasoning			
$P \to Q$	$P \to Q$	$P \to Q$	$P \to Q$
P	$\sim Q$	$Q \to R$	$\therefore \sim Q \to \sim P$
$\therefore Q$	$\therefore \sim P$	$\therefore P \to R$	
by MP	by MT	by LS	by LC

Activity

Symbolic Proofs

Step 1   Determine whether or not each logical argument is valid. If it is valid, state what reasoning form or forms it follows. If it is not valid, write "no valid conclusion."

a. $P \to \sim Q$
   Q
   $\therefore \sim P$

b. $\sim S \to P$
   $R \to \sim S$
   $\therefore R \to P$

c. $\sim Q \to \sim R$
   $\sim S$
   $\therefore \sim R$

d. $R \to P$
   $T \to \sim P$
   $\therefore R \to T$

e. $\sim P \to \sim R$
   R
   $\therefore P$

f. $P \to Q$
   $\sim R \to \sim Q$
   $\therefore P \to R$

Step 2   Translate parts a–c into symbols, and give the reasoning form(s) or state that the conclusion is not valid.

a. If I study all night, then I will miss my late-night talk show. If Jeannine comes over to study, then I study all night. Jeannine comes over to study. Therefore I will miss my late-night talk show.

b. If I don't earn money, then I can't buy a computer. If I don't get a job, then I don't earn money. I have a job. Therefore I can buy a computer.

c. If $\overline{EF}$ is not parallel to side $\overline{AB}$ in trapezoid $ABCD$, then $\overline{EF}$ is not a midsegment of trapezoid $ABCD$. If $\overline{EF}$ is parallel to side $\overline{AB}$, then $ABFE$ is a trapezoid. $\overline{EF}$ is a midsegment of trapezoid $ABCD$. Therefore $ABFE$ is a trapezoid.

Step 3   Show how you can use *Modus Ponens* and the Law of Contrapositive to make the same logical conclusions as *Modus Tollens*.

Tic-Tac-Square

This is one of many variations on tic-tac-toe. Instead of trying to get your X's or O's collinear, the object is to get your X's or O's arranged at the vertices of a square. There are many ways to get four X's or O's arranged at the vertices of a square. Two completed example games are shown below. Numbers are used to show the sequence of moves in each game.

Answer the questions about each of the four unfinished games. You can identify a possible move by the letter of the row and number of the column. For example, the top-right square in the grid is a5.

Example A

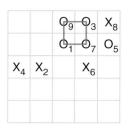

In this game, O went first and won.

Example B

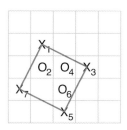

In this game, X went first and won.

1.

	1	2	3	4	5
a		X_6	O_5	X_8	
b		O_1	O_3	O_7	O_{13}
c		X_4	X_2	O_9	X_{14}
d	O_{17}	O_{11}	X_{10}	X_{12}	X_{18}
e		X_{16}			O_{15}

Where should O play to prevent X from winning?

2.

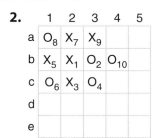

	1	2	3	4	5
a	O_8	X_7	X_9		
b	X_5	X_1	O_2	O_{10}	
c	O_6	X_3	O_4		
d					
e					

Explain why O's last move, b4, was a mistake

3.

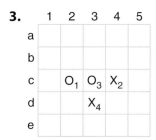

	1	2	3	4	5
a					
b					
c		O_1	O_3	X_2	
d			X_4		
e					

Where should O play O_5 and O_7 to guarantee a win on O_9?

4.

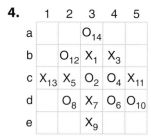

	1	2	3	4	5
a			O_{14}		
b		O_{12}	X_1	X_3	
c	X_{13}	X_5	O_2	O_4	X_{11}
d		O_8	X_7	O_6	O_{10}
e			X_9		

Which moves were forced? Who should win? Explain.

In this chapter you learned vocabulary to describe solids of geometry and explored their cross-sections. You created a few solids by rotating a two dimensional figure about an axis. You also discovered a number of formulas for finding volumes. It's as important to remember how you discovered these formulas as it is to remember the formulas themselves. For example, if you recall pouring the contents of a cone into a cylinder with the same base and height, you may recall that the volume of the cone is one-third the volume of the cylinder. Making connections will help too. Recall that prisms and cylinders share the same volume formula because their shapes—two congruent bases connected by lateral faces—are alike.

You should also be able to find the surface area of a sphere. The formula for the surface area of a sphere was intentionally not included in Chapter 8, where you first learned about surface area. Look back at the investigations in Lesson 8.5 and explain why the surface area formula requires that you know volume.

As you have seen, volume formulas can be applied to many practical problems. Volume also has many extensions such as calculating displacement and density. When finding the volumes of similar solids, the ratios of the volume are related to the ratios of their dimensions. Recall that as the dimensions increase, the volume increases by a cubed factor.

Exercises

1. How are a prism and a cylinder alike?

2. What does a cone have in common with a pyramid?

For Exercises 3–8, find the volume of each solid. Each quadrilateral is a rectangle. All solids are right (not oblique). All measurements are in centimeters.

3.

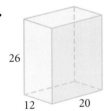

26
12   20

4.

21

|← 14 →|

5.

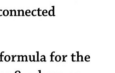

12
12
10
8
6

6.

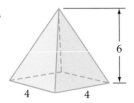

6
4   4

7.

12

|← 10 →|

8.

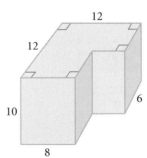

15

For Exercises 9–12, calculate each unknown length given the volume of the solid. All measurements are in centimeters.

9. Find *H*. *V* = 768 cm³

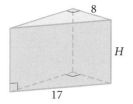

10. Find *h*. *V* = 896 cm³

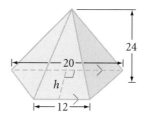

11. Find *r*. *V* = 1728π cm³

12. Find *r*. *V* = 256π cm³

13. For Exercises 11 and 12, sketch the geometric figure that could be used to create these solids of revolution. What is the amount of rotation that was used for each?

14. Find the volume of a rectangular prism whose dimensions are twice those of another rectangular prism that has a volume of 120 cm³.

15. Find the height of a cone with a volume of 138π cubic meters and a base area of 46π square meters.

16. Find the volume of a regular hexagonal prism that has a cylinder drilled from its center. Each side of the hexagonal base measures 8 cm. The height of the prism is 16 cm. The cylinder has a radius of 6 cm. Express your answer to the nearest cubic centimeter.

17. Two rectangular prisms have equal heights but unequal bases. Each dimension of the smaller solid's base is half each dimension of the larger solid's base. The volume of the larger solid is how many times as great as the volume of the smaller solid?

18. The "extra large" popcorn container is a right rectangular prism with dimensions 3 in. by 3 in. by 6 in. The "jumbo" is a cone with height 12 in. and diameter 8 in. The "colossal" is a right cylinder with diameter 10 in. and height 10 in.

  a. Find the volume of all three containers.

  b. The volume of the "colossal" is approximately how many times as great as that of the "extra large"?

19. Two solid cylinders are made of the same material. Cylinder A is six times as tall as cylinder B, but the diameter of cylinder B is four times the diameter of cylinder A. Which cylinder weighs more? How many times as much?

20. Rosa Avila is a plumbing contractor. She needs to deliver 200 lengths of steel pipe to a construction site. Each cylindrical steel pipe is 160 cm long, has an outer diameter of 6 cm, and has an inner diameter of 5 cm. Rosa needs to know whether her quarter-tonne truck can handle the weight of the pipes. To the nearest kilogram, what is the mass of these 200 pipes? How many loads will Rosa have to transport to deliver the 200 lengths of steel pipe? (Steel has a density of about 7.7 g/cm³. One tonne equals 1000 kg.)

21. A ball is placed snugly into the smallest possible box that will completely contain the ball. What percentage of the box is filled by the ball?

22. The blueprint for a cement slab floor is shown at right. How many cubic feet of cement are needed for ten identical floors that are each 4 inches thick?

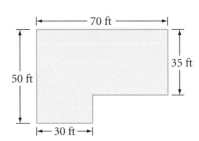

23. Will the sauce spill over? A prep chef has just made two dozen meatballs. Each meatball has a 2 inch diameter. Right now, before the meatballs are added, the sauce is 2 inches from the top of the 14 inch diameter pot. Will the sauce spill over when the chef adds the meatballs to the pot?

24. Is Inspector Clouseau the thief? To solve a crime, Betty Holmes, who claims to be Sherlock's distant cousin, and her friend Professor Hilton Gardens must determine the density of a metal art deco statue with mass 5560 g. She places it into a graduated glass prism filled with water and finds that the level rises 4 cm. Each edge of the glass prism's regular hexagonal base measures 5 cm. Professor Gardens calculates the statue's volume, then its density. Next, Betty Holmes checks the density table (see page 558) to determine if the statue is platinum. If so, it is the missing piece from her client's collection and Inspector Clouseau is the thief. If not, then the Baron is guilty of fraud. What is the statue made of?

25. Can you pick up a solid steel ball of radius 6 inches? Steel has a density of 0.28 pound per cubic inch. To the nearest pound, what is the weight of the ball?

26. To the nearest pound, what is the weight of a hollow steel ball with an outer diameter of 14 inches and a thickness of 2 inches?

27. A hollow steel ball has a diameter of 14 inches and weighs 327.36 pounds. Find the thickness of the ball.

28. A water barrel that is 1 m in diameter and 1.5 m long is partially filled. By tapping on its sides, you estimate that the water is 0.25 m deep at the deepest point. What is the volume of the water in cubic meters?

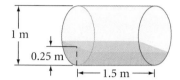

29. Find the volume of the solid formed by rotating the shaded figure about the *y*-axis.

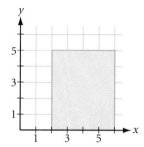

30. Paulie and Pamela are building separate rectangular box homes for their pet python Peter. Paulie uses one pint of paint to cover the surface of his box. Pamela is building her box for Peter with dimensions twice as great. How many pints of paint will Pamela need to paint her home for Peter? How many times as much volume does Pamela's pet python box hold? Can you say "pints of paint for Paulie and Pamela's pet python Peter" ten times without a mistake?

31. The ratio of the surface areas of two spheres is $\frac{25}{16}$. What is the ratio of their radii? What is the ratio of their volumes?

32. Greek mathematician Archimedes liked the design at right so much that he wanted it on his tombstone. In Chapter 8, you found the ratio of the area of the square, the area of the circle, and the area of the isosceles triangle in the figure at the right.

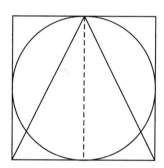

a. When each of the figures is rotated about the vertical line of symmetry, it generates a solid of revolution—a cylinder, a sphere, and a cone. Calculate their volumes. Copy and complete this statement of proportionality.

Volume of cylinder to Volume of sphere to Volume of cone is _?_ to _?_ to _?_.

b. What is so special about this design?

33. Many fanciful stories are about people who accidentally shrink to a fraction of their original height. If a person shrank to one-twentieth his original height, how would that change the amount of food he'd require, or the amount of material needed to clothe him, or the time he'd need to get to different places? Explain.

34. Would 15 pounds of 1 inch ice cubes melt faster than a 15 pound block of ice? Explain.

1. You may be familiar with the area model of the expression $(a + b)^2$, shown below. Draw or build a volume model of the expression $(a + b)^3$. How many distinct pieces does your model have? What's the volume of each type of piece? Use your model to write the expression $(a + b)^3$ in expanded form.

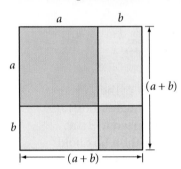 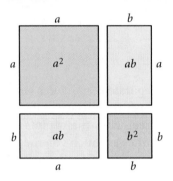

2. Use algebra to show that if you double all three dimensions of a prism, a cylinder, a pyramid, or a cone, the volume is increased eightfold, but the surface area is increased only four times.

3. Any sector of a circle can be rolled into a cone. Find a way to calculate the volume of a cone given the radius and central angle of the sector.

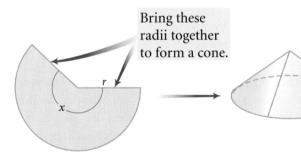

Bring these radii together to form a cone.

4. Build a model of three pyramids with equal volumes that you can assemble into a prism. It's easier to start with the prism and then separate it into the pyramids.

5. The five Platonic Solids are shown to the right. Deriving the formula for the volume of the hexahedron or cube is pretty straightforward ($V = s^3$, where s is the length of each edge), but what about the formula for the volume of a tetrahedron or the volume of an octahedron?

PLATONIC SOLIDS

Tetrahedron   Hexahedron   Octahedron   Dodecahedron   Icosahedron

a. Derive the volume formula for the regular octahedron where s is the length of each edge. (Hint: the octahedron is two square-based pyramids.)

b. Derive the volume formula for the regular tetrahedron, where s is the length of each edge. (Hint: each face is an equilateral triangle and the altitude of the pyramid intersects the centroid of the equilateral triangular base.)

6. Prove that the volume of a regular tetrahedron with edge length $2s$ is equal to the volume of four regular tetrahedrons with edge length of s and one regular octahedron with edge length s.

CHAPTER

12

Trigonometry

M. C. Escher's *Belvedere* ©2014 The M. C. Escher Company—
The Netherlands. All rights reserved. www.mcescher.com

"I wish I'd learn to draw a little better! What exertion and determination it takes to try and do it well. . . . It is really just a question of carrying on doggedly, with continuous and, if possible, pitiless self-criticism."

M. C. ESCHER

OBJECTIVES

In this chapter you will

- learn about the branch of mathematics called trigonometry
- use similarity to define three important ratios between the sides of a right triangle
- explain the relationship between the sine and cosine of complementary angles
- use trigonometry to solve problems involving right triangles
- discover how trigonometry extends beyond right triangles

Trigonometric Ratios

Trigonometry is the study of the relationships between the sides and the angles of triangles. In this lesson you will discover some of these relationships for right triangles.

When studying right triangles, early mathematicians discovered that whenever the ratio of the shorter leg's length to the longer leg's length was close to a specific fraction, the angle opposite the shorter leg was close to a specific measure. They found this (and its converse) to be true for all similar right triangles. For example, in every right triangle in which the ratio of the shorter leg's length to the longer leg's length is $\frac{3}{5}$, the angle opposite the shorter leg is almost exactly 31°.

→ **Astronomy**
CONNECTION

Trigonometry has origins in astronomy. The Greek astronomer Claudius Ptolemy (100–170 C.E.) used tables of chord ratios in his book known as *Almagest*. These chord ratios and their related angles were used to describe the motion of planets in what were thought to be circular orbits. This woodcut shows Ptolemy using astronomy tools.

 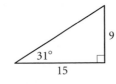 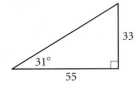

What early mathematicians discovered is supported by what you know about similar triangles. If two right triangles each have an acute angle of the same measure, then the triangles are similar by the AA Similarity Conjecture. And if the triangles are similar, then corresponding sides are proportional. For example, in the similar right triangles shown below, these proportions are true:

$$\frac{BC}{AB} = \frac{EF}{DE} = \frac{HI}{GH} = \frac{KL}{JK}$$

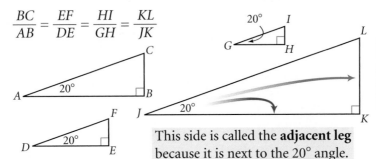

This side is called the **opposite leg** because it is across from the 20° angle.

This side is called the **adjacent leg** because it is next to the 20° angle.

The ratio of the length of the opposite leg to the length of the adjacent leg in a right triangle came to be called the **tangent** of the angle.

In Chapter 7, you used mirrors and shadows to measure heights indirectly. Trigonometry gives you another indirect measuring method.

EXAMPLE A

At a distance of 36 meters from a tree, the angle from the ground to the top of the tree is 31°. Find the height of the tree.

Solution

As you saw in the right triangles at the beginning of the lesson, the ratio of the length of the side opposite a 31° angle divided by the length of the side adjacent to a 31° angle is approximately $\frac{3}{5}$, or 0.6. You can set up a proportion using this tangent ratio.

$\dfrac{HT}{HA} \approx \tan 31°$ The definition of tangent.

$\dfrac{HT}{HA} \approx 0.6$ The tangent of 31° is approximately 0.6.

$\dfrac{HT}{36} \approx 0.6$ Substitute 36 for HA.

$HT \approx 36 \cdot 0.6$ Multiply both sides by 36 and simplify the left side.

$HT \approx 22$ Multiply.

The height of the tree is approximately 22 meters.

→ **History**

CONNECTION

Before calculators and computers, mathematicians had to use tables to find angle measures. This excerpt from a trigonometric table shows sine, cosine, and tangent ratios for angles measuring from 12.0° to 14.2°.

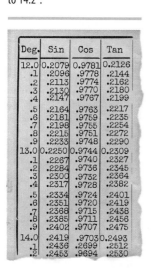

Deg.	Sin	Cos	Tan
12.0	0.2079	0.9781	0.2126
.1	.2096	.9778	.2144
.2	.2113	.9774	.2162
.3	.2130	.9770	.2180
.4	.2147	.9767	.2199
.5	.2164	.9763	.2217
.6	.2181	.9759	.2235
.7	.2198	.9755	.2254
.8	.2215	.9751	.2272
.9	.2233	.9748	.2290
13.0	0.2250	0.9744	0.2309
.1	.2267	.9740	.2327
.2	.2284	.9736	.2345
.3	.2300	.9732	.2364
.4	.2317	.9728	.2382
.5	.2334	.9724	.2401
.6	.2351	.9720	.2419
.7	.2368	.9715	.2438
.8	.2385	.9711	.2456
.9	.2402	.9707	.2475
14.0	.2419	.9703	0.2493
.1	.2436	.2699	.2512
.2	.2453	.9694	.2530

In order to solve problems like Example A, early mathematicians made tables that related ratios of side lengths to angle measures. They named six possible ratios. You will work with three.

Sine, abbreviated sin, is the ratio of the length of the opposite leg to the length of the hypotenuse.

Cosine, abbreviated cos, is the ratio of the length of the adjacent leg to the length of the hypotenuse.

Tangent, abbreviated tan, is the ratio of the length of the opposite leg to the length of the adjacent leg.

Trigonometric Ratios

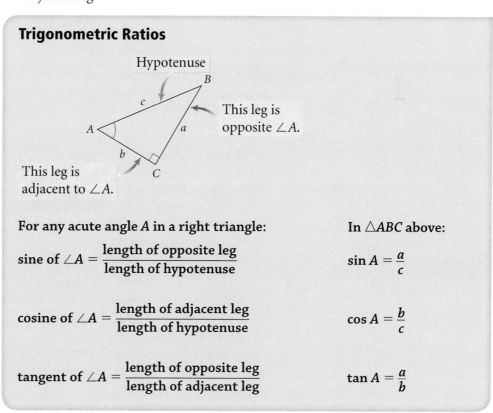

Hypotenuse

This leg is opposite $\angle A$.

This leg is adjacent to $\angle A$.

For any acute angle A in a right triangle:

$$\text{sine of } \angle A = \frac{\text{length of opposite leg}}{\text{length of hypotenuse}}$$

$$\text{cosine of } \angle A = \frac{\text{length of adjacent leg}}{\text{length of hypotenuse}}$$

$$\text{tangent of } \angle A = \frac{\text{length of opposite leg}}{\text{length of adjacent leg}}$$

In $\triangle ABC$ above:

$$\sin A = \frac{a}{c}$$

$$\cos A = \frac{b}{c}$$

$$\tan A = \frac{a}{b}$$

INVESTIGATION

YOU WILL NEED

● a protractor

● a ruler

● a scientific calculator

Trigonometric Tables

In this investigation you will make a small table of trigonometric ratios for angles measuring 20° and 70°.

Step 1 Use your protractor to make a large right triangle ABC with $m\angle A = 20°$, $m\angle B = 90°$, and $m\angle C = 70°$.

Step 2 Measure AB, AC, and BC to the nearest millimeter.

Step 3 Use your side lengths and the definitions of sine, cosine, and tangent to complete a table like this. Round your calculations to the nearest thousandth.

$m\angle A$	sin A	cos A	tan A		$m\angle C$	sin C	cos C	tan C
20°					70°			

Step 4 Share your results with your group. Calculate the average of each ratio within your group. Create a new table with your group's average values.

Step 5 Discuss your results. What observations can you make about the trigonometric ratios you found? What is the relationship between the values for 20° and the values for 70°? Explain why you think these relationships exist.

Today, trigonometric tables have been replaced by calculators that have sin, cos, and tan keys.

Step 6 Experiment with your calculator to determine how to find the sine, cosine, and tangent values of angles.

Step 7 Use your calculator to find sin 20°, cos 20°, tan 20°, sin 70°, cos 70°, and tan 70°. Check your group's table. How do the trigonometric ratios found by measuring sides compare with the trigonometric ratios you found on the calculator?

Step 8 Recall that the acute angles of a right triangle are complementary angles. Would the same relationship for the trigonometric ratios that you found in Step 7 exist with other complementary angles? Test your conjecture by repeating Step 7 with right triangles with the following acute angle measures:

$\triangle DEF$ with $m\angle D = 40°$ and $m\angle F = 50°$

$\triangle RST$ with $m\angle R = 30°$ and $m\angle T = 60°$

$\triangle XYZ$ with $m\angle X = 45°$ and $m\angle Z = 45°$

Did your results verify your conjecture? Explain why or why not.

Using your calculator, you can find the approximate lengths of the sides of a right triangle given the measures of any acute angle and any side.

EXAMPLE B

Find the length of the hypotenuse of a right triangle if an acute angle measures 20° and the leg opposite the angle measures 410 feet.

Solution

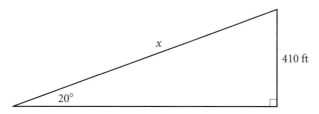

Sketch a diagram. The trigonometric ratio that relates the lengths of the opposite leg and the hypotenuse is the sine ratio.

$$\sin 20° = \frac{410}{x}$$ Substitute 20° for the measure of $\angle A$ and substitute 410 for the length of the opposite side. The length of the hypotenuse is unknown, so use x.

$$x \cdot \sin 20° = 410$$ Multiply both sides by x and simplify the right side.

$$x = \frac{410}{\sin 20°}$$ Divide both sides by $\sin 20°$ and simplify the left side.

From your table in the investigation, or from a calculator, you know that $\sin 20°$ is approximately 0.342.

$$x \approx \frac{410}{0.342}$$ Sin 20° is approximately 0.342.

$$x \approx 1199$$ Divide.

The length of the hypotenuse is approximately 1199 feet.

With the help of a calculator, it is also possible to determine the size of either acute angle in a right triangle if you know the length of any two sides of that triangle. For instance, if you know the ratio of the legs in a right triangle, you can find the measure of one acute angle by using the **inverse tangent**, or $\tan^{-1}$, function. Let's look at an example.

The inverse tangent of x is defined as the measure of the acute angle whose tangent is x. The tangent function and inverse tangent function undo each other. That is, $\tan^{-1}(\tan A) = A$ and $\tan(\tan^{-1} x) = x$.

EXAMPLE C

A right triangle has legs of length 8 inches and 15 inches. Find the measure of the angle opposite the 8-inch leg.

Solution

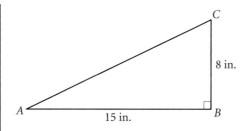

Sketch a diagram. In this sketch the angle opposite the 8 inch leg is $\angle A$. The trigonometric ratio that relates the lengths of the opposite leg and the adjacent leg is the tangent ratio.

$$\tan A = \frac{8}{15}$$

Substitute 8 for the length of the opposite leg and substitute 15 for the length of the adjacent leg.

$$\tan^{-1}(\tan A) = \tan^{-1}\left(\frac{8}{15}\right)$$

Take the inverse tangent of both sides.

$$A = \tan^{-1}\left(\frac{8}{15}\right)$$

The tangent function and inverse tangent function undo each other.

$$A \approx 28$$

Use your calculator to evaluate $\tan^{-1}\left(\frac{8}{15}\right)$.

The measure of the angle opposite the 8 inch leg is approximately 28°.

> To find the angle that has a specific tangent value, use the tan⁻¹ feature on your calculator.

You can also use inverse sine, or sin⁻¹, and inverse cosine, or cos⁻¹, to find angle measures.

12.1 Exercises

YOU WILL NEED

A calculator
for Exercises **1–7**
and **11–23**

Construction tools
for Exercise **25**

For Exercises 1–3, use a calculator to find each trigonometric ratio accurate to the nearest ten thousandth.

1. sin 37°   **2.** cos 29°   **3.** tan 8°

4. Use your calculator to determine which value is greater in each pair.

   a. sin 36° or cos 54°   **b.** cos 89° or sin 1°   **c.** sin 48° or 2(sin 24°)(cos 24°)

For Exercises 5–7, solve for x. Express each answer accurate to the nearest hundredth of a unit.

5. $\sin 40° = \frac{x}{18}$ **6.** $\cos 52° = \frac{19}{x}$ **7.** $\tan 29° = \frac{x}{112}$

For Exercises 8–10, find each trigonometric ratio.

8. $\sin A = \underline{\ ?\ }$
   $\cos A = \underline{\ ?\ }$
   $\tan A = \underline{\ ?\ }$ ⓗ

9. $\sin \theta = \underline{\ ?\ }$
   $\cos \theta = \underline{\ ?\ }$
   $\tan \theta = \underline{\ ?\ }$

10. $\sin A = \underline{\ ?\ }$ $\sin B = \underline{\ ?\ }$
    $\cos A = \underline{\ ?\ }$ $\cos B = \underline{\ ?\ }$
    $\tan A = \underline{\ ?\ }$ $\tan B = \underline{\ ?\ }$

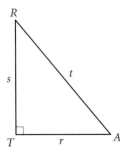

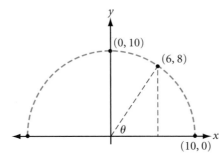

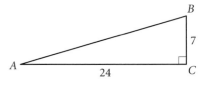

For Exercises 11–14, find the measure of each angle accurate to the nearest degree.

11. sin A = 0.5 ⓗ   **12.** cos B = 0.6

13. tan C = 0.5773   **14.** $\tan x = \frac{48}{106}$

For Exercises 15–21, find the values of *a*–*g* accurate to the nearest whole unit.

15. ⓗ

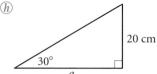

20 cm

30°

a

16.

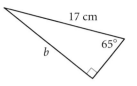

17 cm

65°

b

17.

c

70°

36 yd

18.

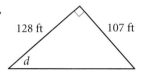

128 ft   107 ft

d

19.

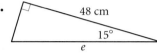

48 cm

15°

e

20.

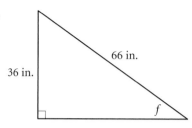

66 in.

36 in.

f

21.

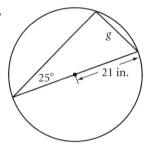

g

25°   21 in.

22. Find the perimeter of this quadrilateral. ⓗ

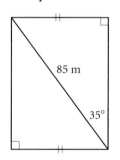

85 m

35°

23. Find *x*.

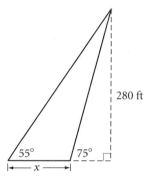

280 ft

55°   75°

x

Review

24. If point *B* is reflected across $\overleftrightarrow{AO}$, what are the coordinates of its image *B'*?

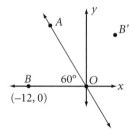

A

B'

B   60°   *O*

(−12, 0)

y

x

25. Copy $\overline{AB}$ and point *G* onto your paper. Construct △*ABC* given side *AB* and the triangle's centroid *G*.

G•

A •————————• *B*

26. Which is the better buy—a pizza with a 16 inch diameter for $12.50 or a pizza with a 20 inch diameter for $20.00?

27. Which is the better buy—ice cream in a cylindrical container with a base diameter of 6 inches and a height of 8 inches for $3.98 or ice cream in a box (square prism) with a base edge of 6 inches and a height of 8 inches for $4.98?

28. A diameter of a circle is cut at right angles by a chord into a 12 cm segment and a 4 cm segment. How long is the chord? ⓗ

Problem Solving with Right Triangles

Right triangle trigonometry is often used indirectly to find the height of a tall object. To solve a problem of this type, measure the angle from the horizontal to your line of sight when you look at the top or bottom of the object.

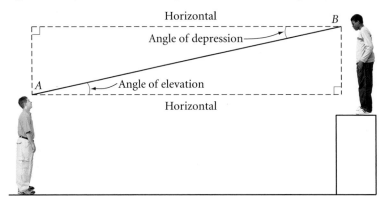

Horizontal
Angle of depression
B
A
Angle of elevation
Horizontal

If you look up, you measure the **angle of elevation**. If you look down, you measure the **angle of depression**.

EXAMPLE

The angle of elevation from a sailboat to the top of a 121 foot lighthouse on the shore measures 16°. How far is the sailboat from the lighthouse?

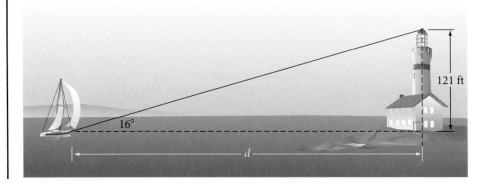

121 ft

16°

d

Solution

Distance means the shortest distance, which is the horizontal distance. The height of the lighthouse is opposite the 16° angle. The unknown distance is the adjacent side. Set up a tangent ratio.

$$\tan 16° = \frac{121}{d}$$
$$d(\tan 16°) = 121$$
$$d = \frac{121}{\tan 16°}$$
$$d \approx 422$$

The sailboat is approximately 422 feet from the lighthouse.

12.2 Exercises

YOU WILL NEED

 A calculator
for Exercises **1–19**

 Geometry
software
for Exercise **24**

For Exercises 1–9, find each length or angle measure accurate to the nearest whole unit.

1. $a \approx$?

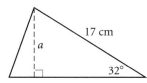

17 cm
a
32°

2. $x \approx$?

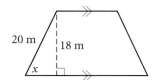

20 m   18 m
x

3. $r \approx$?

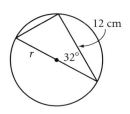

12 cm
r 32°

4. $e \approx$?

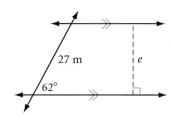

27 m e
62°

5. $d_1 \approx$? ⓗ

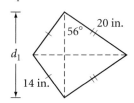

56°   20 in.
d_1
14 in.

6. $f \approx$?

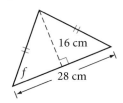

16 cm
f 28 cm

7. $\theta \approx$?

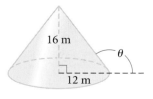

16 m
θ
12 m

8. $\beta \approx$? ⓗ

10 ft
β
8 ft   15 ft

9. $h \approx$?

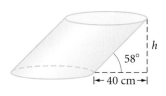

h
58°
40 cm

→ Science
CONNECTION

When there are no visible
landmarks, sailors at sea depend
on the location of stars or the
Sun for navigation. For example,
in the Northern Hemisphere,
Polaris (the North Star), stays
approximately at the same angle
above the horizon for a given
latitude. If Polaris appears higher
overhead or closer to the horizon,
sailors can tell that their course
is taking them north or south
respectively.

10. According to a Chinese legend from the Han dynasty (206 B.C.E.–220 C.E.), General Han Xin flew a kite over the palace of his enemy to determine the distance between his troops and the palace. If the general let out 800 meters of string and the kite was flying at a 35° angle of elevation, how far away was the palace from General Han Xin's position?

11. Benny is flying a kite directly over his friend Frank, who is 125 meters away. When he holds the kite string down to the ground, the string makes a 39° angle with the level ground. How high is Benny's kite?

12. The angle of elevation from a ship to the top of a 42 meter lighthouse on the shore measures 33°. How far is the ship from the lighthouse? (Assume the horizontal line of sight meets the bottom of the lighthouse.)

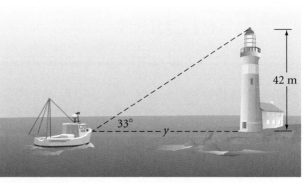

13. A salvage ship's sonar locates wreckage at a 12° angle of depression. A diver is lowered 40 meters to the ocean floor. How far does the diver need to walk along the ocean floor to the wreckage?

14. A ship's officer sees a lighthouse at a 42° angle to the path of the ship. After the ship travels 1800 m, the lighthouse is at a 90° angle to the ship's path. What is the distance between the ship and the lighthouse at this second sighting? Ⓗ

15. A meteorologist shines a spotlight vertically onto the bottom of a cloud formation. He then places an angle-measuring device 165 meters from the spotlight and measures an 84° angle of elevation from the ground to the spot of light on the clouds. How high are the clouds?

The distance from the ground to a cloud formation is called the cloud *ceiling*.

16. Meteorologist Wendy Stevens uses a theodolite (an angle-measuring device) on a 1 meter tall tripod to find the height of a weather balloon. She views the balloon at a 44° angle of elevation. A radio signal from the balloon tells her that it is 1400 meters from her theodolite.

a. How high is the balloon? Ⓗ

b. How far is she from the point directly below the balloon?

c. If Wendy's theodolite were on the ground rather than on a tripod, would your answers change? Explain your reasoning.

Review

For Exercises 17–19, find the measure of each angle to the nearest degree.

17. sin *D* = 0.7071

18. tan *E* = 1.7321

19. cos *F* = 0.5

20. *a* = _?_ , *b* = _?_ Ⓗ

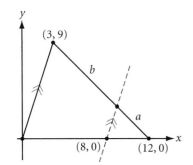

21. Find *x* and *y*.

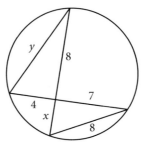

22. Will it sink or float? A 3 cm by 5 cm by 6 cm block of wood is dropped into a cylindrical container of water with radius 5 cm. The level of the water rises 0.8 cm. Does the block sink or float? Explain how you know.

23. Scalene triangle ABC has altitudes $\overline{AX}$, $\overline{BY}$, and $\overline{CZ}$. If $AB > BC > AC$, write an inequality that relates the heights.

24. GUESS-N-CHECK In the diagram at right, $\overrightarrow{PT}$ and $\overrightarrow{PS}$ are tangent to circle O at points T and S, respectively. As point P moves to the right along $\overrightarrow{AB}$, describe what happens to each of these measures or ratios. First, try this as a visual thinking experiment and make your conjectures for *a–f*. Finally create the figure with geometry software and test your conjectures. How good were your visualizations?

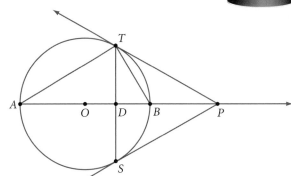

    a. $m\angle TPS$ **b.** OD

    c. $m\angle ATB$ **d.** Area of $\triangle ATB$

    e. $\dfrac{AP}{BP}$ **f.** $\dfrac{AD}{BD}$

25. Points S and Q, shown at right, are consecutive vertices of square $SQRE$. Find coordinates for the other two vertices, R and E. There are two possible answers. Try to find both.

26. The two diagonals of trapezoid $PART$ intersect at Y dividing the trapezoid into four triangles. If the bases of the trapezoid $\overline{PA}$ and $\overline{RT}$ are 65 cm and 117 cm respectively, and the height of $\triangle TRY$ is 45 cm, find the shaded area.

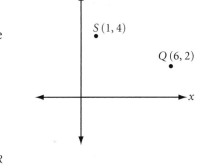

DEVELOPING MATHEMATICAL REASONING

Bagels Puzzle III

One variation for the game of Bagels is to play with four-digit numbers instead of three-digit numbers. Try your hand, or rather your mental abilities, on these.

    bagels: no digit is correct
    pico: one digit is correct but in the wrong position
    fermi: one digit is correct and in the correct position

Game 1:	1234	*pico*	**Game 2:**	1234	*pico pico pico*
	5678	*fermi*		5678	*fermi*
	9073	*pico fermi*		5123	*pico pico pico*
	9602	*pico pico*		2371	*fermi fermi pico*
	4098	*fermi pico pico*		????	
	????				

EXPLORATION

Indirect Measurement

How would you measure the height of your
school building? In Chapter 7, you used shadows,
mirrors, and similar triangles to measure the height
of tall objects that you couldn't measure directly. Right
triangle trigonometry gives you yet another method
of indirect measurement.

In this exploration you will use two or three
different methods of indirect measurement.
Then you will compare your results from
each method.

Activity

Using a Clinometer

In this activity you will use a **clinometer**—
a protractor-like tool used to measure
angles. You probably will want to make
your clinometer in advance, based on one
of the designs below. Practice using it before
starting the activity.

- a measuring tape or
  metersticks
- a clinometer (use the
  Making a Clinometer
  worksheet or make one
  of your own design)
- a mirror

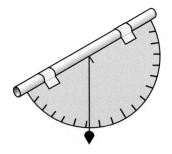

Clinometer 1

Clinometer 2

Step 1 Locate a tall object that would be difficult to measure directly, such as
a school building. Start a table like this one.

Name of object	Viewing angle	Height of observer's eye	Distance from observer to object	Calculated height of object

Step 2 Use your clinometer to measure the viewing angle from the horizontal to
the top of the object.

Step 3 Measure the observer's eye height. Measure the distance from the observer
to the base of the object.

Step 4 Calculate the approximate height of the object.

Step 5 Use either the shadow method or the mirror method or both to measure
the height of the same object. How do your results compare? If you got
different results, explain what part of each process could contribute to the
differences.

Step 6 Repeat Steps 1–5 for another tall object. If you measure the height of the
same object as another group, compare your results when you finish.

594 CHAPTER 12 Trigonometry

The Law of Sines

So far you have used trigonometry only to solve problems with right triangles. But you can use trigonometry with any triangle. For example, if you know the measures of two angles and one side of a triangle, you can find the other two sides with a trigonometric property called the **Law of Sines**. The Law of Sines is related to the area of a triangle. Let's first see how trigonometry can help you find area.

"To think and to be fully alive are the same."

HANNAH ARENDT

EXAMPLE A

Find the area of △ABC.

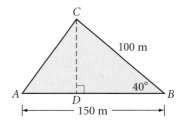

Solution

Consider $\overline{AB}$ as the base and use trigonometry to find the height, CD.

$\sin 40° = \dfrac{CD}{100}$ In △BCD, CD is the length of the opposite side and 100 is the length of the hypotenuse.

$100 \cdot \sin 40° = CD$ Multiply both sides by 100 and simplify the right side.

Now find the area.

$A = 0.5bh$ Area formula for a triangle.

$A = 0.5(AB)(CD)$ Substitute AB for the length of the base and CD for the height.

$A = 0.5(150)(100 \cdot \sin 40°)$ Substitute 150 for AB and substitute the expression $(100 \cdot \sin 40°)$ for CD.

$A \approx 4821$ Evaluate.

The area is approximately 4821 m².

In the next investigation, you will find a general formula for the area of a triangle given the lengths of two sides and the measure of the included angle.

 # INVESTIGATION 1

Area of a Triangle

Step 1   Find the area of each triangle. Use Example A as a guide.

a.

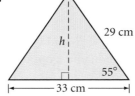

b.

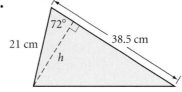

c.

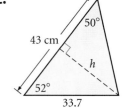

Step 2 Generalize Step 1 to find the area of this triangle in terms of a, b, and $\angle C$. State your general formula as your next conjecture.

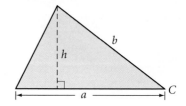

SAS Triangle Area Conjecture   C-97

The area of a triangle is given by the formula $A = \underline{\ ?\ }$, where a and b are the lengths of two sides and C is the angle between them.

Now use what you've learned about finding the area of a triangle to derive the property called the Law of Sines.

INVESTIGATION 2

The Law of Sines

Consider $\triangle ABC$ with height h.

Step 1 Find h in terms of a and the sine of an angle.

Step 2 Find h in terms of b and the sine of an angle.

Step 3 Use algebra to show

$$\frac{\sin A}{a} = \frac{\sin B}{b}$$

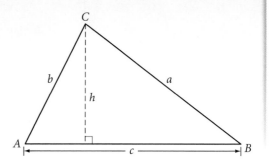

Now consider the same $\triangle ABC$ using a different height, k.

Step 4 Find k in terms of c and the sine of an angle.

Step 5 Find k in terms of b and the sine of an angle.

Step 6 Use algebra to show

$$\frac{\sin B}{b} = \frac{\sin C}{c}$$

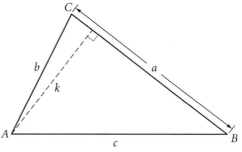

Step 7 Combine Steps 3 and 6. Complete this conjecture.

Law of Sines   C-98

For a triangle with angles A, B, and C and sides of lengths a, b, and c (a opposite A, b opposite B, and c opposite C),

$$\frac{\sin A}{?} = \frac{?}{b} = \frac{?}{?}$$

Did you notice that you used deductive reasoning rather than inductive reasoning to discover the Law of Sines?

You can use the Law of Sines to find the lengths of a triangle's sides when you know one side's length and two angles' measures.

EXAMPLE B

Find the length of side $\overline{AC}$ in $\triangle ABC$.

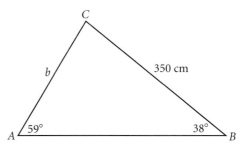

Solution

Start with the Law of Sines, and solve for b.

$$\frac{\sin A}{a} = \frac{\sin B}{b}$$ The Law of Sines.

$$b \sin A = a \sin B$$ Multiply both sides by ab and simplify.

$$b = \frac{a \sin B}{\sin A}$$ Divide both sides by $\sin A$ and simplify the left side.

$$b = \frac{(350)(\sin 38°)}{\sin 59°}$$ Substitute 350 for a, 38° for B, and 59° for A.

$$b \approx 251$$ Multiply and divide.

The length of side $\overline{AC}$ is approximately 251 cm.

You can also use the Law of Sines to find the measure of a missing angle, but only if you know whether the angle is acute or obtuse. Recall from Chapter 4 that SSA failed as a congruence shortcut. For example, if you know in $\triangle ABC$ that $BC = 160$ cm, $AC = 260$ cm, and $m\angle A = 36°$, you would not be able to find $m\angle B$. There are two possible measures for $\angle B$, one acute and one obtuse.

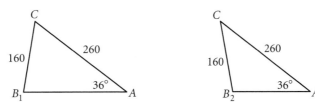

Because you've defined trigonometric ratios only for acute angles, you'll be asked to find only acute angle measures.

EXAMPLE C

Find the measure of angle B in $\triangle ABC$.

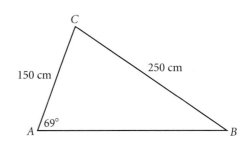

Solution | Start with the Law of Sines, and solve for B.

$$\frac{\sin A}{a} = \frac{\sin B}{b}$$ The Law of Sines.

$$\sin B = \frac{b \sin A}{a}$$ Solve for sin B.

$$\sin B = \frac{(150)(\sin 69°)}{250}$$ Substitute known values.

$$B = \sin^{-1}\frac{(150)(\sin 69°)}{250}$$ Take the inverse sine of both sides.

$$B \approx 34$$ Use your calculator to evaluate.

The measure of ∠B is approximately 34°.

(12.3) Exercises

YOU WILL NEED

A calculator
for Exercises **1–15**

Construction tools
for Exercise **18**

In Exercises 1–4, find the area of each polygon to the nearest square centimeter.

1.

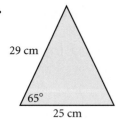
29 cm
65°
25 cm

2.

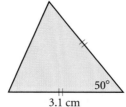
50°
3.1 cm

3. Ⓗ

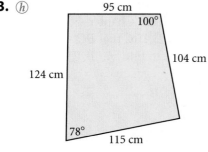
95 cm
100°
104 cm
124 cm
78°
115 cm

4. Ⓗ

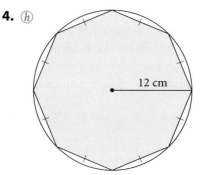
12 cm

In Exercises 5–7, find each length to the nearest centimeter.

5. $w \approx \underline{\ ?\ }$ Ⓗ

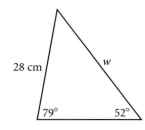
28 cm
w
79°   52°

6. $x \approx \underline{\ ?\ }$

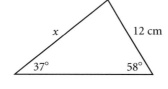
x   12 cm
37°   58°

7. $y \approx \underline{\ ?\ }$

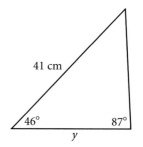
41 cm
46°   87°
y

For Exercises 8–10, each triangle is an acute triangle. Find each angle measure to the nearest degree.

8. $m\angle A \approx$?

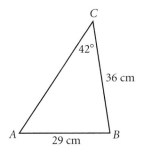

9. $m\angle B \approx$?

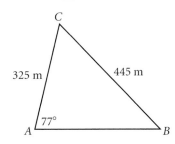

10. $m\angle C \approx$?

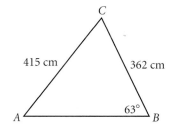

11. Alphonse (point *A*) is over a 2500 meter landing strip in a hot-air balloon. At one end of the strip, Beatrice (point *B*) sees Alphonse with an angle of elevation measuring 39°. At the other end of the strip, Collette (point *C*) sees Alphonse with an angle of elevation measuring 62°.

a. What is the distance between Alphonse and Beatrice?

b. What is the distance between Alphonse and Collette?

c. How high up is Alphonse?

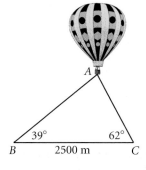

12. Archaeologists have started uncovering remains of James Fort (also known as Jamestown Fort) in Virginia. The fort was in the shape of an isosceles triangle. Unfortunately, one corner has disappeared into the James River. If the remaining complete wall measures 300 feet and the remaining corners measure 46.5° and 87°, how long were the two incomplete walls? What was the approximate area of the original fort?

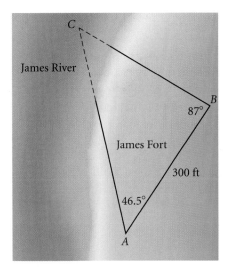

> **History CONNECTION**
>
> For over 200 years, people believed that the entire site of James Fort was washed into the James River. Archaeologists have uncovered over 250 feet of the fort's wall, as well as hundreds of thousands of artifacts dating to the early 1600s.

13. A tree grows vertically on a hillside. The hill is at a 16° angle to the horizontal. The tree casts an 18 meter shadow up the hill when the angle of elevation of the sun measures 68°. How tall is the tree? ⓗ

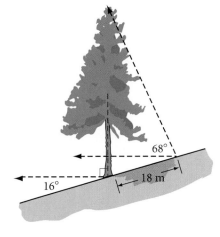

Review

14. Each step of El Castillo is 30 cm deep by 26 cm high. How tall is the pyramid, not counting the platform at the top? What is the angle of ascent?

15. Find the volume of this cone.

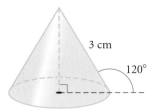

3 cm

120°

16. Use the circle diagram below and write a paragraph proof to show that $\triangle ABE$ is isosceles.

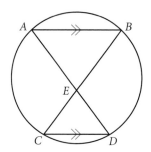

→ History
CONNECTION

One of the most impressive Mayan pyramids is El Castillo in Chichén Itzá, Mexico. Built in approximately 800 C.E., it has 91 steps on each of its four sides, or 364 steps in all. The top platform adds a level, so the pyramid has 365 levels to represent the number of days in the Mayan year.

17. According to legend, Galileo (1564–1642, Italy) used the Leaning Tower of Pisa to conduct his experiments in gravity. Assume that when he dropped objects from the top of the 55 meter tower (this is the measured length, not the height, of the tower), they landed 4.8 meters from the tower's base. What was the angle that the tower was leaning from the vertical?

18. Put two points on patty paper. Assume these points are opposite vertices of a square. Find the two missing vertices. Explain your reasoning.

PERFORMANCE TASK

Consider a circle O with chord $\overline{AP}$ and radius r. Describe what happens to the area of $\triangle OAP$ as P moves around the circle from A back to A. For what value of $m\angle P$ is the area of $\triangle OAP$ greatest? Explain how you know.

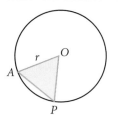

The Law of Cosines

You've solved a variety of problems with the Pythagorean Theorem. It is perhaps your most important geometry conjecture. In Chapter 10, you found that the distance formula is really just the Pythagorean Theorem. You even used the Pythagorean Theorem to derive the equation of a circle.

The Pythagorean Theorem is very powerful, but its use is still limited to right triangles. Recall from Chapter 10 that the Pythagorean Theorem does not work for acute triangles or obtuse triangles. You might ask, "What happens to the Pythagorean equation for acute triangles or obtuse triangles?"

If the legs of a right triangle are brought closer together so that the right angle becomes an acute angle, you'll find that $c^2 < a^2 + b^2$. In order to make this inequality into an equality, you would have to subtract something from $a^2 + b^2$.

$$c^2 = a^2 + b^2 - something$$

If the legs are widened to form an obtuse angle, you'll find that $c^2 > a^2 + b^2$. Here, you'd have to add something to make an equality.

$$c^2 = a^2 + b^2 + something$$

Mathematicians found that the "something" was $2ab \cos C$. The Pythagorean Theorem generalizes to all triangles with a property called the **Law of Cosines**.

→ **History**

CONNECTION

Many, if not most, geometric discoveries were made inductively and then proved deductively. Occasionally geometric properties are discovered deductively. That is surely how the law of sines and the law of cosines were discovered!

$ab \cos C$

Law of Cosines	*C-99*

For any triangle with sides of lengths a, b, and c, and with C the angle opposite the side with length c,

$$c^2 = a^2 + b^2 - 2ab \cos C$$

For obtuse angles, the expression $2ab \cos C$ is negative, so subtracting it adds a positive quantity.

DEVELOPING PROOF

With your group members study and discuss the diagram to the right to derive the Law of Cosines ($c^2 = a^2 + b^2 - 2ab \cos C$.)

Consider acute $\triangle ABC$ with altitude $\overline{AD}$, as shown at right. You can define the lengths of the sides opposite angles A, B, and C as a, b, and c, respectively, the height as h, and the length of $\overline{CD}$ as x. The length of $\overline{BD}$ is the difference between the lengths of $\overline{BC}$ and $\overline{CD}$, or $a - x$. Use the following as a guide.

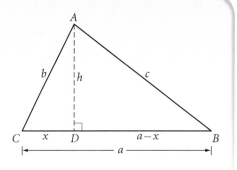

a. Use the Pythagorean Theorem and the sides of $\triangle CDA$ to write an equation with x, h, and b. (Label this equation 1.)

b. Use the Pythagorean Theorem and the sides of $\triangle BDA$ to write an equation with $(a - x)$, h, and c. Expand the expression $(a - x)^2$. (Label this equation 2.)

c. Use equation 1 and equation 2 to write another equation without an h in it. (Label this equation 3.)

d. Now your task is to get rid of the x in equation 3. Hint: Cos $C = \frac{x}{b}$. Complete the derivation of the Law of Cosines.

While this derivation of the Law of Cosines is for an acute triangle, it also works for obtuse triangles. Deriving the Law of Cosines for an obtuse triangle is left as a Take Another Look activity.

You can use the Law of Cosines when you are given three side lengths or two side lengths and the angle measure between them (SSS or SAS).

EXAMPLE A

Find the length of side $\overline{ST}$ in triangle SRT.

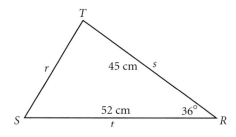

Solution

To find r, use the Law of Cosines:

$$c^2 = a^2 + b^2 - 2ab \cos C \qquad \text{The Law of Cosines.}$$

Using the variables in this problem, the Law of Cosines becomes

$r^2 = s^2 + t^2 - 2st \cos R$ Substitute r for c, s for a, t for b, and R for C.

$r^2 = 45^2 + 52^2 - 2(45)(52)(\cos 36°)$ Substitute 45 for s, 52 for t, and 36° for R.

$r = \sqrt{45^2 + 52^2 - 2(45)(52)(\cos 36°)}$ Take the positive square root of both sides.

$r \approx 31$ Evaluate.

The length of side $\overline{ST}$ is about 31 cm.

EXAMPLE B

What is the measure of the largest angle of a triangle with sides of 175 cm, 225 cm, and 250 cm?

Solution

First we draw and label a triangle with the given information. In $\triangle QED$, $\angle Q$ is the largest angle because it is opposite the largest side. Use the Law of Cosines and solve for Q.

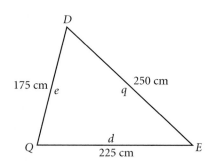

$$q^2 = e^2 + d^2 - 2ed \cos Q$$ The Law of Cosines with respect to $\angle Q$.

$$\cos Q = \frac{q^2 - e^2 - d^2}{-2ed}$$ Solve for cos Q.

$$\cos Q = \frac{250^2 - 175^2 - 225^2}{-2(175)(225)}$$ Substitute known values.

$$Q = \cos^{-1}\left[\frac{250^2 - 175^2 - 225^2}{-2(175)(225)}\right]$$ Take the inverse cosine of both sides.

$$Q \approx 76$$ Evaluate.

The measure of $\angle Q$ is about 76°.

12.4 Exercises

YOU WILL NEED

🖩 *A calculator*
for Exercises **1–13**

In Exercises 1–3, find each length to the nearest centimeter.

1. $w \approx$? ⓗ

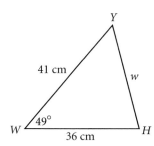

2. $y \approx$?

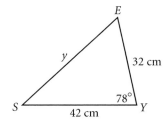

3. $x \approx$?

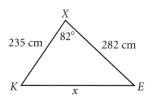

In Exercises 4–6, each triangle is an acute triangle. Find each angle measure to the nearest degree.

4. $m\angle A \approx$? ⓗ

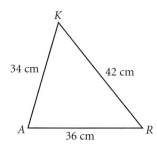

5. $m\angle B \approx$?

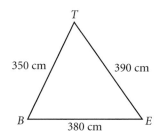

6. $m\angle C \approx$?

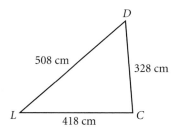

7. Two 24 centimeter radii of a circle form a central angle measuring 126°. What is the length of the chord connecting the two radii?

8. Find the measure of the smallest angle in a triangle whose side lengths are 4 m, 7 m, and 8 m. ⓗ

9. Two sides of a parallelogram measure 15 cm and 20 cm, and one of the diagonals measures 19 cm. What are the measures of the angles of the parallelogram to the nearest degree?

10. Captain Malloy is flying a passenger jet. He is heading east at 720 km/h when he sees an electrical storm straight ahead. He turns the jet 20° to the north to avoid the storm and continues in this direction for 1 h. Then he makes a second turn, back toward his original flight path. Eighty minutes after his second turn, he makes a third turn and is back on course. By avoiding the storm, how much time did Captain Malloy lose from his original flight plan? ⓗ

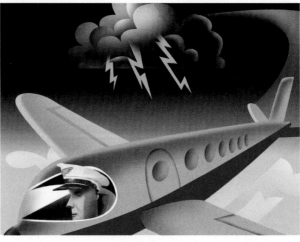

Review

11. Ertha Diggs uncovers the remains of a square-based Egyptian pyramid. The base is intact and measures 130 meters on each side. The top of the pyramid has eroded away, but what remains of each face of the pyramid forms a 65° angle with the ground. What was the original height of the pyramid? ⓗ

12. A lighthouse keeper 55 meters above sea level spots a distress signal from a sailboat. The angle of depression to the sailboat measures 21°. How far away is the sailboat from the base of the lighthouse?

13. A painting company has a general safety rule to place ladders at an angle measuring between 55° and 75° from the level ground. Regina places the foot of her 25 ft ladder 6 ft from the base of a wall. What is the angle of the ladder? Is the ladder placed safely? If not, how far from the base of the wall should she place the ladder?

14. Show that $\dfrac{\sin A}{\cos A} = \tan A$.

15. *TRAP* is an isosceles trapezoid with $TP = PA = RA$ and $TR = 2PA$. M is the midpoint of the base $\overline{TR}$. Show that $\overline{PM}$ and $\overline{MA}$ divide the trapezoid into three equilateral triangles. ⓗ

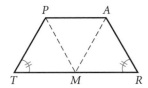

16. *TRAP* is an isosceles trapezoid. ⓗ

    a. Find PR in terms of x.

    b. Write a paragraph proof to show that $m\angle TPR = 90°$.

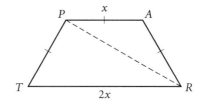

17. Which of these figures, the cone or the square pyramid, has the greater

    a. base perimeter?

    b. volume?

    c. surface area?

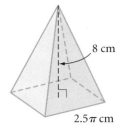

18. What single transformation is equivalent to the composition of transformations in each of the following?

    a. A reflection over the line $x = -2$ followed by a reflection over the line $x = 3$

    b. A reflection over the x-axis followed by a reflection over the y-axis

Problem Solving with Trigonometry

"One ship drives east and another drives west With the self-same winds that blow, 'Tis the set of the sails and not the gales Which tells us the way to go."

ELLA WHEELER WILCOX

There are many practical applications of trigonometry. Some of them involve vectors. Vectors, represented by an arrow, describe quantities like velocity, acceleration, and force. The length and direction of the arrow represent the speed and direction of an object. In the following example, you will learn how to use the Law of Sines or Law of Cosines and a parallelogram to determine the resulting speed and direction of an object when two different forces act upon it.

EXAMPLE

Poland's world champion rower Monika Kowalska is in a stream flowing north to south at 3 km/h. She is rowing northeast at a rate of 4.5 km/h. At what speed is she moving? In which direction (bearing) is she actually moving?

Solution

First, sketch and label the vector parallelogram. The resultant vector, *r*, divides the parallelogram into two congruent triangles. In each triangle you know the lengths of two sides and the measure of the included angle. Use the Law of Cosines to find the length of the resultant vector or the speed that it represents.

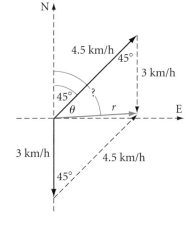

$$r^2 = 4.5^2 + 3^2 - 2(4.5)(3)(\cos 45°)$$

$$r \approx 3.2$$

Monika is moving at a speed of approximately 3.2 km/h.

To find Monika's bearing (an angle measured clockwise from north), you need to find θ, and add its measure to 45°. Use the Law of Sines.

$$\frac{\sin \theta}{3} = \frac{\sin 45°}{3.2}$$

$$\sin \theta = \frac{3 \cdot \sin 45°}{3.2}$$

$$\theta = \sin^{-1}\left(\frac{3 \cdot \sin 45°}{3.2}\right) \approx 42°$$

Add 42° and 45° to find that Monika is moving at a bearing of 87°.

12.5 Exercises

1. The steps to the front entrance of a public building rise a total of 1 m. A portion of the steps will be replaced by a wheelchair ramp. By a city ordinance, the angle of inclination for a ramp cannot measure greater than 4.5°. What is the minimum distance from the entrance that the ramp must begin?

2. Giovanni is flying his Cessna airplane on a heading as shown. His instrument panel shows an air speed of 130 mi/h. (Air speed is the speed in still air without wind.) However, there is a 20 mi/h crosswind. What is the resulting speed of the plane? ⓗ

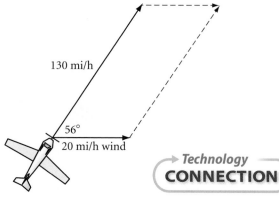

130 mi/h

56°

20 mi/h wind

3. A lighthouse is east of a Coast Guard patrol boat. The Coast Guard station is 20 km north of the lighthouse. The radar officer aboard the boat measures the angle between the lighthouse and the station to be 23°. How far is the boat from the station?

Technology CONNECTION

Used for centuries in Egypt to lift water from the Nile River, the Archimedean screw is thought to have been invented by Archimedes in the third century B.C.E., when he sailed to Egypt. It is also called an Archimedes Snail because of its spiral channels that resemble a snail shell. Once powered by people or animals, the device is now modernized to shift grain in mills and powders in factories.

4. The Archimedean screw is a water-raising device that consists of a wooden screw enclosed within a cylinder. When the cylinder is turned, the screw raises water. The screw is very efficient at an angle measuring 25°. If a screw needs to raise water 2.5 meters, how long should its cylinder be?

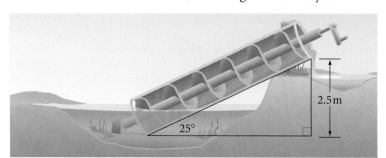

2.5 m

25°

5. Annie and Sashi are backpacking in the Sierra Nevada. They walk 8 km from their base camp at a bearing of 42°. After lunch, they change direction to a bearing of 137° and walk another 5 km. ⓗ

   a. How far are Annie and Sashi from their base camp?

   b. At what bearing must Sashi and Annie travel to return to their base camp?

6. During a strong wind, the top of a tree cracks and bends over, touching the ground as if the trunk were hinged. The tip of the tree touches the ground 20 feet 6 inches from the base of the tree and forms a 38° angle with the ground. What was the tree's original height?

7. A surveyor at point *A* needs to calculate the distance to an island's dock, point *C*. He walks 150 meters up the shoreline to point *B* such that $\overline{AB} \perp \overline{AC}$. Angle *ABC* measures 58°. What is the distance between *A* and *C*?

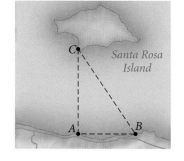

Santa Rosa Island

C

A   B

8. A pocket of matrix opal is known to be 24 meters beneath point *A* on Alan Ranch. A mining company has acquired rights to mine beneath Alan Ranch, but not the right to bring equipment onto the property. So the mining company cannot dig straight down. Brian Ranch has given permission to dig on its property at point *B*, 8 meters from point *A*. At what angle to the level ground must the mining crew dig to reach the opal? What distance must they dig?

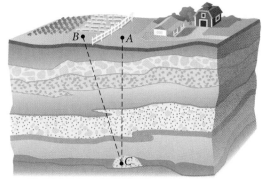

9. Todd's friend Olivia is flying her plane at an elevation of 6.3 km. From the ground, Todd sees the plane moving directly toward him from the west at a 49° angle of elevation. Three minutes later he turns and sees the plane moving away from him to the east at a 65° angle of elevation. How fast is Olivia flying in kilometers per hour? ⓗ

10. Draw a regular decagon with side length 6 cm. Divide the decagon into ten congruent isosceles triangles.

   a. Find the length of the apothem, and then use the Regular Polygon Area Conjecture to find the area of the decagon.

   b. Find the lengths of the legs of the isosceles triangles, and then use the SAS Triangle Area Conjecture to find the area of each isosceles triangle. Multiply to find the area of the decagon.

   c. Compare your answers from parts a and b.

11. Find the volume of this right regular pentagonal prism. ⓗ

7 cm

3 cm

12. A friend claims to have found the formula $A = \frac{ns^2}{4 \tan \theta}$, in a box of old math books in his grandpa's attic. It appears to be a formula for the area of a regular polygon where *n* is the number of sides, *s* is the length of each side, and $\theta = \frac{360}{2n}$. Is this formula correct? Explain.

13. A water pipe for a farm's irrigation system must go through a small hill. Farmer Golden attaches a 14.5 meter rope to the pipe's entry point and an 11.2 meter rope to the exit point. When he pulls the ropes taut, their ends meet at a 58° angle. What is the length of pipe needed to go through the hill? At what angle with respect to the first rope should the pipe be laid so that it comes out of the hill at the correct exit point? ⓗ

Review

14. Find the volume of the largest cube that can fit into a sphere with a radius of 12 cm.

15. How does the area of a triangle change if its vertices are transformed by the rule $(x, y) \rightarrow (-3x, -3y)$? Give an example to support your answer.

16. What's wrong with this picture?

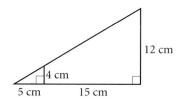

12 cm

4 cm

5 cm   15 cm

17. GUESS-N-CHECK As P moves to the right on line ℓ_1, describe what happens to each of the following values. First, try this as a "mental experiment." Take a guess, then create the diagram with your geometry software and see how good you were at visualization.

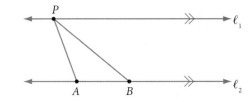

  a. PA

  b. $\angle APB$

  c. Area of $\triangle APB$

  d. Perimeter of $\triangle APB$

18. What single transformation is equivalent to the composition of each pair of transformations below?

  a. A reflection across the line $y = x$ followed by a counterclockwise 270° rotation about the origin

  b. A rotation 180° about the origin followed by a reflection across the x-axis

19. The design for the rise of a 15 stone semicircular arch is 24 ft and the total height is to be 27 ft. What will be the dimensions of each of the congruent isosceles trapezoidal voussoirs? Find the lengths x, y, and z, and the angle measures a and b.

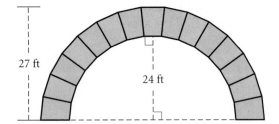

DEVELOPING MATHEMATICAL REASONING

Domino Puzzle II

The 28 dominoes of an entire double-six set have been arranged into a 7 × 8 rectangle. The outlines of 27 of the individual dominoes have been removed. The dots have been replaced by their numerals. The 5-3 domino has been correctly placed to get you started. Use your sequential reasoning and visual thinking skills to redraw the outlines of the remaining 27 dominoes.

1	6	2	4	0	3	2	0
1	5	3	1	5	1	0	4
6	0	3	4	3	6	3	5
2	4	2	2	0	4	5	2
1	0	5	0	0	6	5	3
4	5	3	6	2	3	4	6
6	1	2	1	5	1	4	6

0	0

0	1	1	1

0	2	1	2	2	2

0	3	1	3	2	3	3	3

0	4	1	4	2	4	3	4	4	4

0	5	1	5	2	5	3	5	4	5	5	5

0	6	1	6	2	6	3	6	4	6	5	6	6	6

EXPLORATION

Three Types of Proofs

In previous explorations, you learned four forms of valid reasoning: *Modus Ponens* (MP), *Modus Tollens* (MT), the Law of Syllogism (LS), and the Law of Contrapositive (LC). You can use these forms of reasoning to make logical arguments, or proofs. In this exploration you will learn the three basic types of proofs: direct proofs, conditional proofs, and indirect proofs.

In a **direct proof**, the given information or premises are stated, then valid forms of reasoning are used to arrive directly at a conclusion. Here is a direct proof given in two-column form. In a **directed two-column proof**, each statement in the argument is written in the left column, and the reason for each statement is written directly across in the right column.

Direct Proof

Premises: $P \to Q$

$R \to P$

$\sim Q$

Conclusion: $\sim R$

1. $P \to Q$	1. Premise
2. $\sim Q$	2. Premise
3. $\sim P$	3. From lines 1 and 2, using MT
4. $R \to P$	4. Premise
5. $\therefore \sim R$	5. From lines 3 and 4, using MT

A **conditional proof** is used to prove that a $P \to Q$ statement follows from a set of premises. In a conditional proof, the first part of the conditional statement, called the **antecedent**, is assumed to be true. Then logical reasoning is used to demonstrate that the second part, called the **consequent**, must also be true. If this process is successful, it's demonstrated that *if* P *is true, then* Q *must be true*. In other words, a conditional proof shows that the antecedent implies the consequent. Here is an example.

Conditional Proof

Premises: $P \to R$

$S \to \sim R$

Conclusion: $P \to \sim S$

1. P	1. Assume the antecedent
2. $P \to R$	2. Premise
3. R	3. From lines 1 and 2, using MP
4. $S \to \sim R$	4. Premise
5. $\sim S$	5. From lines 3 and 4, using MT

Assuming P is true, the truth of $\sim S$ is established.

$\therefore P \to \sim S$

An **indirect proof** is a clever approach to proving something. To prove indirectly that a statement is true, you begin by assuming it is *not* true. Then you show that this assumption leads to a contradiction. For example, if you are given a set of premises and are asked to show that some conclusion P is true, begin by assuming that the opposite of P, namely ~P, is true. Then show that this assumption leads to a contradiction of an earlier statement. If ~P leads to a contradiction, it must be false and P must be true. Here is an example.

Indirect Proof

Premises: $R \rightarrow S$

$\sim R \rightarrow \sim P$

P

Conclusion: S

1. ~S	1. Assume the opposite of the conclusion
2. $R \rightarrow S$	2. Premise
3. ~R	3. From lines 1 and 2, using MT
4. $\sim R \rightarrow \sim P$	4. Premise
5. ~P	5. From lines 3 and 4, using MP
6. P	6. Premise

But lines 5 and 6 contradict each other. It's impossible for both P and ~P to be true.

Therefore, ~S, the original assumption, is false. If ~S is false, then S is true.

∴ S

Many logical arguments can be proved using more than one type of proof. For instance, you can prove the argument in the example above by using a direct proof. (Try it!) With practice you will be able to tell which method will work best for a particular argument.

Activity

Prove It!

Step 1 Copy the direct proof below, including the list of premises and the conclusion. Provide each missing reason.

Premises: $P \rightarrow Q$

$Q \rightarrow \sim R$

R

Conclusion: $\sim P$

1. $Q \rightarrow \sim R$	1. ?
2. R	2. ?
3. $\sim Q$	3. ?
4. $P \rightarrow Q$	4. ?
5. ∴ $\sim P$	5. ?

Step 2 Copy the conditional proof below, including the list of premises and the conclusion. Provide each missing statement or reason.

Premises: $\sim R \to \sim Q$

$T \to \sim R$

$S \to T$

Conclusion: $S \to \sim Q$

1. S	1. ?
2. $S \to T$	2. ?
3. T	3. From lines 1 and 2, using ?
4. $T \to \sim R$	4. ?
5. $\sim R$	5. ?
6. ?	6. ?
7. ?	7. ?

Assuming S is true, the truth of $\sim Q$ is established.

$\therefore$?

Step 3 Copy the indirect proof below, including the list of premises and the conclusion. Provide each missing statement or reason.

Premises: $P \to (Q \to R)$

$Q \to \sim R$

Q

Conclusion: $\sim P$

1. P	1. Assume the ? of the ?
2. $P \to (Q \to R)$	2. ?
3. $Q \to R$	3. ?
4. Q	4. ?
5. R	5. ?
6. ?	6. ?
7. ?	7. From lines ? and ?, using ?

But lines ? and ? contradict each other.

Therefore, P, the assumption, is false.

$\therefore \sim P$

Step 4 Provide the steps and reasons to prove each logical argument. You will need to decide whether to use a direct, a conditional, or an indirect proof.

a. Premises: $P \to Q$

$Q \to \sim R$

$T \to R$

Conclusion: $T \to \sim P$

b. Premises: $(R \to S) \to P$

$T \to Q$

$\sim T \to \sim P$

$\sim Q$

Conclusion: $\sim (R \to S)$

c. Premises: $S \to Q$

$P \to S$

$\sim R \to P$

$\sim Q$

Conclusion: R

d. Premises: $P \to Q$

$\sim P \to S$

$R \to \sim S$

$\sim Q$

Conclusion: $\sim R$

Step 5 Translate each argument into symbolic terms, then prove it is valid.

a. If all wealthy people are happy, then money can buy happiness. If money can buy happiness, then true love doesn't exist. But true love exists. Therefore, not all wealthy people are happy.

b. If Clark is performing at the theater today, then everyone at the theater has a good time. If everyone at the theater has a good time, then Lois is not sad. Lois is sad. Therefore, Clark is not performing at the theater today.

c. If Evette is innocent, then Alfa is telling the truth. If Romeo is telling the truth, then Alfa is not telling the truth. If Romeo is not telling the truth, then he has something to gain. Romeo has nothing to gain. Therefore, if Romeo has nothing to gain, then Evette is not innocent.

DEVELOPING MATHEMATICAL REASONING

Rope Tricks

Each rope will be cut 50 times as shown (parallel cuts). For each rope, how many pieces will result?

1.

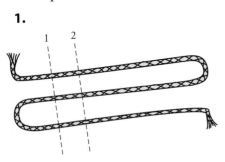

2.

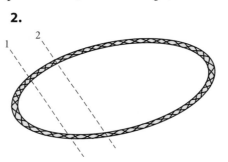

3.

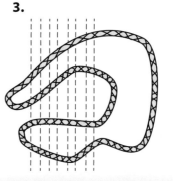

Trigonometry was first developed by astronomers who wanted to map the stars. Obviously, it is hard to directly measure the distances between stars and planets. That created a need for new methods of indirect measurement. As you've seen, you can solve many indirect measurement problems by using triangles. Using sine, cosine, and tangent ratios, you can find unknown lengths and angle measures if you know just a few measures in a right triangle. You can extend these methods to any triangle using the Law of Sines or the Law of Cosines.

What's the least you need to know about a right triangle in order to find all its measures? What parts of a nonright triangle do you need to know in order to find the other parts? Describe a situation in which an angle of elevation or depression can help you find an unknown height.

Exercises

YOU WILL NEED

A calculator
for Exercises **1–3, 9–30**

For Exercises 1–3, use a calculator to find each trigonometric ratio accurate to four decimal places.

1. $\sin 57°$

2. $\cos 9°$

3. $\tan 88°$

For Exercises 4–6, find each trigonometric ratio.

4. $\sin A = \underline{\ ?\ }$
$\cos A = \underline{\ ?\ }$
$\tan A = \underline{\ ?\ }$

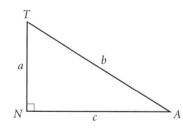

5. $\sin B = \underline{\ ?\ }$
$\cos B = \underline{\ ?\ }$
$\tan B = \underline{\ ?\ }$

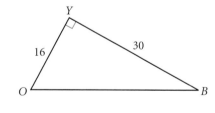

6. $\sin \theta = \underline{\ ?\ }$
$\cos \theta = \underline{\ ?\ }$
$\tan \theta = \underline{\ ?\ }$

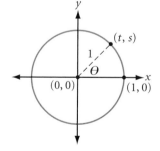

7. You learned the Law of Sines as

$$\frac{\sin A}{a} = \frac{\sin B}{b} = \frac{\sin C}{c}$$

Use algebra to show that

$$\frac{a}{\sin A} = \frac{b}{\sin B} = \frac{c}{\sin C}$$

8. The Law of Cosines is generally stated using $\angle C$.

$$c^2 = a^2 + b^2 - 2ab \cos C$$

State the Law of Cosines in two different ways, using $\angle A$ and $\angle B$.

For Exercises 9–11, find the measure of each acute angle to the nearest degree.

9. $\sin A = 0.5447$

10. $\cos B = 0.0696$

11. $\tan C = 2.9043$

12. shaded area ≈ ?

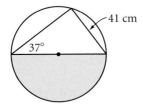
41 cm
37°

13. volume ≈ ?

h
112°
18 cm

14. According to the Americans with Disabilities Act, enacted in 1990, the slope of a wheelchair ramp must be less than $\frac{1}{12}$ and there must be a minimum 5 ft by 5 ft landing for every 2.5 ft of rise. These dimensions were chosen to accommodate handicapped people who face physical barriers in public buildings and at work. An architect has submitted the orthographic plan shown at right. Does the plan meet the requirements of the act? What will be the ramp's angle of ascent?

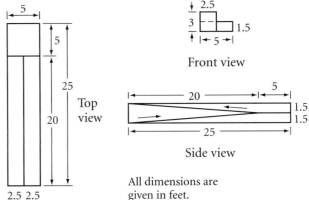

Top view

Front view

Side view

All dimensions are given in feet.

15. A lighthouse is east of a sailboat. The sailboat's dock is 30 km north of the lighthouse. The captain measures the angle between the lighthouse and the dock and finds it to be 35°. How far is the sailboat from the dock?

16. An air traffic controller must calculate the angle of descent (the angle of depression) for an incoming jet. The jet's crew reports that their land distance is 44 km from the base of the control tower and that the plane is flying at an altitude of 5.6 km. Find the measure of the angle of descent.

17. A new house is 32 feet wide. The rafters will rise at a 36° angle and meet above the center line of the house. Each rafter also needs to overhang the side of the house by 2 feet. How long should the carpenter make each rafter?

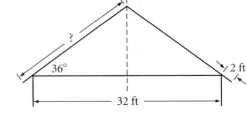
?
36°
2 ft
32 ft

18. During a flood relief effort, a Coast Guard patrol boat spots a helicopter dropping a package near the Florida shoreline. Officer Duncan measures the angle of elevation to the helicopter to be 15° and the distance to the helicopter to be 6800 m. How far is the patrol boat from the point where the package will land?

19. At an air show, Amelia sees a jet heading south away from her at a 42° angle of elevation. Twenty seconds later the jet is still moving away from her, heading south at a 15° angle of elevation. If the jet's elevation is constantly 6.3 km, how fast is it flying in kilometers per hour?

For Exercises 20–25, find each measure to the nearest unit or to the nearest square unit.

20. area = ?

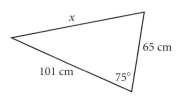

21. w = ?

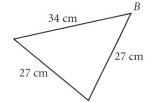

22. △ABC is acute.
 m∠A = ?

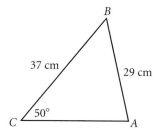

23. x = ?

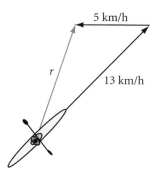

24. m∠B = ?

25. area = ?

26. Find the length of the apothem of a regular pentagon with a side measuring 36 cm.

27. Find the area of a triangle formed by two 12 cm radii and a 16 cm chord in a circle.

28. A circle is circumscribed about a regular octagon with a perimeter of 48 cm. Find the diameter of the circle.

29. A 16 cm chord is drawn in a circle of diameter 24 cm. Find the area of the segment of the circle.

30. Leslie is paddling his kayak at a bearing of 45°. In still water his speed would be 13 km/h but there is a 5 km/h current moving west. What is the resulting speed and direction of Leslie's kayak?

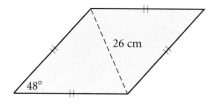

31. The cube has a volume of 64 cm³. Points L, O, and C are the midpoints of three edges of the cube. Find the following:

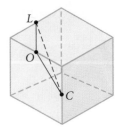

   a. the distance from L to O to C

   b. the shortest distance, the distance through space, from L to C

   c. the measure of $\angle LOC$

Mixed Review

For Exercises 32–44, identify each statement as true or false. For each false statement, explain why it is false and sketch a counterexample.

32. An octahedron is a prism that has an octagonal base.

33. If the four angles of one quadrilateral are congruent to the four corresponding angles of another quadrilateral, then the two quadrilaterals are similar.

34. The three medians of a triangle meet at the centroid.

35. To use the Law of Cosines, you must know three side lengths or two side lengths and the measure of the included angle.

36. If the ratio of corresponding sides of two similar polygons is $\frac{m}{n}$, then the ratio of their areas is $\frac{m}{n}$.

37. The measure of an angle inscribed in a semicircle is always 90°.

38. If $\angle T$ is an acute angle in a right triangle, then

$$\text{tangent of } \angle T = \frac{\text{length of leg adjacent to } \angle T}{\text{length of leg opposite } \angle T}$$

39. If C^2 is the area of the base of a pyramid and C is the height of the pyramid, then the volume of the pyramid is $\frac{1}{3}C^3$.

40. If two different lines intersect at a point, then the sum of the measures of at least one pair of vertical angles will be equal to or greater than 180°.

41. If a line cuts two sides of a triangle proportionally, then it is parallel to the third side.

42. If two sides of a triangle measure 6 cm and 8 cm and the angle between the two sides measures 60°, then the area of the triangle is $12\sqrt{3}$ cm².

43. A nonvertical line ℓ_1 has slope m and is perpendicular to line ℓ_2. The slope of ℓ_2 is also m.

44. If two sides of one triangle are proportional to two sides of another triangle, then the two triangles are similar.

For Exercises 45–56, select the correct answer.

45. The diagonals of a parallelogram
  i. are perpendicular to each other.
  ii. bisect each other.
  iii. form four congruent triangles.
  A. i only   **B.** ii only   **C.** iii only   **D.** i and ii

46. What is the formula for the volume of a sphere?

  A. $V = 4\pi r^2$ **B.** $V = \pi r^2 h$ **C.** $V = \frac{4}{3}\pi r^3$ **D.** $V = \frac{1}{3}\pi r^2 h$

47. For the triangle at right, what is the measure of $\angle L$ to the nearest degree?
  A. 34°   **B.** 44°
  C. 52°   **D.** cannot be determined

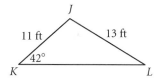

48. The diagonals of a rhombus
  i. are perpendicular to each other.
  ii. bisect each other.
  iii. form four congruent triangles.
  A. i only   **B.** iii only   **C.** i and ii   **D.** all of the above

49. The ratio of the surface areas of two similar solids is $\frac{4}{9}$. What is the ratio of the volumes of the solids?

  A. $\frac{2}{3}$ **B.** $\frac{8}{27}$ **C.** $\frac{64}{729}$ **D.** $\frac{16}{81}$

50. A cylinder has height T and base area K. What is the volume of the cylinder?

  A. $V = \pi K^2 T$ **B.** $V = KT$ **C.** $V = 2\pi KT$ **D.** $V = \frac{1}{3}KT$

51. Which of the following is not a similarity shortcut?
  A. SSA   **B.** SSS   **C.** AA   **D.** SAS

52. If a triangle has sides of lengths a, b, and c, and C is the angle opposite the side of length c, which of these statements must be true?

  A. $a^2 = b^2 + c^2 - 2ab \cos C$ **B.** $c^2 = a^2 + b^2 - 2ab \cos C$
  C. $c^2 = a^2 + b^2 + 2ab \cos C$ **D.** $a^2 = b^2 + c^2$

53. In the drawing at right, $\overline{WX} \parallel \overline{YZ} \parallel \overline{BC}$. What is the value of m?
  A. 6 ft   **B.** 8 ft
  C. 12 ft   **D.** 16 ft

54. When a rock is added to a container of water, it raises the water level by 4 cm. If the container is a rectangular prism with a base that measures 8 cm by 9 cm, what is the volume of the rock?

A. 4 cm^3 B. 32 cm^3

C. 36 cm^3 D. 288 cm^3

55. Which law could you use to find the value of v?

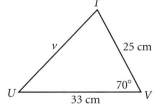

A. Law of Supply and Demand   B. Law of Syllogism

C. Law of Cosines   D. Law of Sines

56. A 32 foot telephone pole casts a 12 foot shadow at the same time a boy nearby casts a 1.75 foot shadow. How tall is the boy?

A. 4 ft 8 in.   B. 4 ft 6 in.   C. 5 ft 8 in.   D. 6 ft

Exercises 57–59 are portions of cones. Find the volume of each solid.

57.

58.

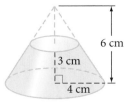

59.

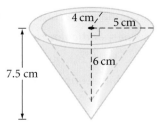

60. Each person at a family reunion hugs everyone else exactly once. There were 528 hugs. How many people were at the reunion?

61. Triangle TRI with vertices $T(-7, 0)$, $R(-5, 3)$, and $I(-1, 0)$ is translated by the rule $(x, y) \rightarrow (x + 2, y - 1)$. Then its image is translated by the rule $(x, y) \rightarrow (x - 1, y - 2)$. What single translation is equivalent to the composition of these two translations?

62. $\triangle LMN \sim \triangle PQR$. Find w, x, and y.

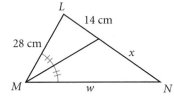

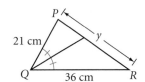

63. Find x.

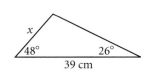

64. The diameter of a circle has endpoints $(5, -2)$ and $(5, 4)$. Find the equation of the circle.

65. Archaeologist Ertha Diggs uses a clinometer to find the height of an ancient temple. She views the top of the temple with a 37° angle of elevation. She is standing 130 meters from the center of the temple's base, and her eye is 1.5 meters above the ground. How tall is the temple?

66. In the diagram below, the length of $\overset{\frown}{HK}$ is 20π ft. Find the radius of the circle.

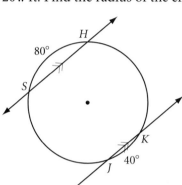

67. The shaded area is 10π cm². Find r.

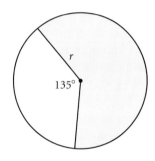

68. Triangle ABC is isosceles with $\overline{AB}$ congruent to $\overline{BC}$. Point D is on $\overline{AC}$ such that $\overline{BD}$ is perpendicular to $\overline{AC}$. Make a sketch and answer these questions.

  a. $m\angle ABC = \underline{\ ?\ } \; m\angle ABD$

  b. What can you conclude about $\overline{BD}$?

69. $\triangle ABC$ with vertices $A(10, 4)$, $B(3, 4)$, and $C(7, 8)$, is reflected across the line $y = x$ to create the image $\triangle A'B'C'$. What is the area of $\triangle A'B'C'$?

TAKE ANOTHER LOOK

1. Pick any measure of $\angle A$ and find the value of the expression $(\sin A)^2 + (\cos A)^2$. Repeat for other measures of $\angle A$ and make a conjecture. Then write ratios for $\sin A$ and $\cos A$, using the diagram at right, and substitute these ratios into the expression above. Simplify, using algebra and the Pythagorean Theorem, to prove your conjecture.

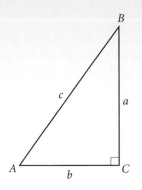

2. Recall that SSA does not determine a triangle. For that reason, you've been asked to find only acute angles using the Law of Sines. Take another look at a pair of triangles, $\triangle AB_1C$ and $\triangle AB_2C$, determined by SSA. How is $\angle CB_1A$ related to $\angle CB_2A$? Find $m\angle CB_1A$ and $m\angle CB_2A$. Find the sine of each angle. Find the sines of another pair of angles that are related in the same way, then complete this conjecture: For any angle θ, $\sin \theta = \sin(\underline{\ ?\ })$.

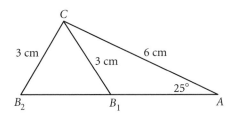

3. Draw several triangles ABC where $\angle C$ is obtuse. Measure the sides a and b and angle C. Use the Law of Cosines to calculate the length of side c, then measure side c and compare these two values. Does the Law of Cosines work for obtuse angles? What happens to the value of the term $-2ab \cos C$ when $\angle C$ is obtuse?

4. Derive the Law of Cosines for an obtuse triangle, using the diagram at right.

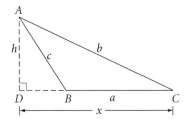

5. Is there a relationship between the measure of the central angle of a sector of a circle and the angle at the vertex of the right cone formed when rolled up? Explain your reasoning.

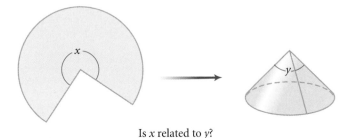

Is x related to y?

Geometry as a Mathematical System

> *"This search for new possibilities, this discovery of new jigsaw puzzle pieces, which in the first place surprises and astonishes the designer himself, is a game that through the years has always fascinated and enthralled me anew."*
>
> M. C. ESCHER

M. C. Escher's *Another World (Other World)* ©2014 The M. C. Escher Company—
The Netherlands. All rights reserved. www.mcescher.com

OBJECTIVES

In this chapter you will

- look at geometry as a mathematical system
- see how some conjectures are logically related to each other
- review a number of proof strategies, such as working backward and analyzing diagrams

The Premises of Geometry

*"Geometry is the art
of correct reasoning
on incorrect figures."*

GEORGE POLYA

Greek mathematician Thales of Miletus (ca. 625–547 B.C.E.) made his geometry ideas convincing by supporting his discoveries with logical reasoning. Other Greek mathematicians, including Thales' most famous student, Pythagoras, began linking chains of logical reasoning. The tradition continued with Plato. Euclid, in his famous work about geometry and number theory, *Elements*, established a single chain of deductive arguments for most of the geometry known then.

As you learned in previous chapters, for thousands of years Babylonian, Egyptian, Chinese, and other mathematicians discovered many geometry principles and developed procedures for doing practical geometry.

By 600 B.C.E., a prosperous new civilization had begun to grow in the trading towns along the coast of Asia Minor (present-day Turkey) and later in Greece, Sicily, and Italy. People had free time to discuss and debate issues of government and law. They began to insist on reasons to support statements made in debate. Mathematicians began to use logical reasoning to deduce mathematical ideas.

This map of the ancient Greek world shows Sicily, Italy, Greece, and Asia Minor along the north coast of the Mediterranean Sea. The map was drawn by Homann Heirs in 1741.

You have learned that Euclid used geometric constructions to study properties of lines and shapes. Euclid also created a **deductive system**—a set of **premises**, or accepted facts, and a set of logical rules—to organize geometry properties. He started from a collection of simple and useful statements he called **postulates**. He then systematically demonstrated how each geometry discovery followed logically from his postulates and his previously proved conjectures, or **theorems**.

Up to now, you have been discovering geometry properties inductively, the way many mathematicians have over the centuries. You have studied geometric figures and have made conjectures about them. Then, to explain your conjectures, you turned to deductive reasoning. You used informal proofs to explain why a conjecture was true. However, you did not prove every conjecture. In fact, you sometimes made critical assumptions or relied on unproved conjectures in your proofs. A conclusion in a proof is true if and only if your premises are true and all your arguments are valid. Faulty assumptions can lead to the wrong conclusion. Have all your assumptions been reliable?

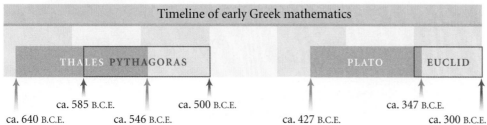

Timeline of early Greek mathematics

THALES PYTHAGORAS   PLATO   EUCLID

ca. 585 B.C.E.   ca. 500 B.C.E.   ca. 347 B.C.E.

ca. 640 B.C.E.   ca. 546 B.C.E.   ca. 427 B.C.E.   ca. 300 B.C.E.

Inductive reasoning process

Deductive reasoning process

In this chapter you will look at geometry as Euclid did. You will start with premises: definitions, properties, and postulates. From these premises you will systematically prove your earlier conjectures. Proved conjectures will become theorems, which you can use to prove other conjectures, turning them into theorems, as well. You will build a logical framework using your most important ideas and conjectures from geometry.

> ### Premises for Logical Arguments in Geometry
>
> 1. Definitions and undefined terms
> 2. Properties of arithmetic, equality, and congruence
> 3. Postulates of geometry
> 4. Previously proved geometry conjectures (theorems)

You are already familiar with the first type of premise on the list: the undefined terms—point, line, and plane. In addition, you have a list of basic definitions in your notebook.

You used the second set of premises, properties of arithmetic and equality, in your algebra course.

These Mayan stone carvings, found in Qurigua, Guatemala, show the glyphs, or symbols, used in the Mayan number system.

Properties of Arithmetic

For any numbers a, b, and c:

Commutative property of addition
$a + b = b + a$

Commutative property of multiplication
$ab = ba$

Associative property of addition
$(a + b) + c = a + (b + c)$

Associative property of multiplication
$(ab)c = a(bc)$

Distributive property of multiplication over addition
$a(b + c) = ab + ac$

Properties of Equality

For any numbers a, b, c, and d:

Reflexive property
$a = a$ (Any number is equal to itself.)

Transitive property
If $a = b$ and $b = c$, then $a = c$. (This property often takes the form of the **substitution property**, which says that if $b = c$, you can substitute c for b.)

Symmetric property
If $a = b$, then $b = a$.

Addition property
If $a = b$, then $a + c = b + c$.
(Also, if $a = b$ and $c = d$, then $a + c = b + d$.)

Subtraction property
If $a = b$, then $a - c = b - c$.
(Also, if $a = b$ and $c = d$, then $a - c = b - d$.)

Multiplication property
If $a = b$, then $ac = bc$.
(Also, if $a = b$ and $c = d$, then $ac = bd$.)

Division property
If $a = b$, then $\frac{a}{c} = \frac{b}{c}$ provided $c \neq 0$.
(Also, if $a = b$ and $c = d$, then $\frac{a}{c} = \frac{b}{d}$ provided that $c \neq 0$ and $d \neq 0$.)

Square root property
If $a^2 = b$, then $a = \pm\sqrt{b}$.

Zero product property
If $ab = 0$, then $a = 0$ or $b = 0$ or both a and $b = 0$.

You have used these properties to solve algebraic equations. The process of solving an equation is really an algebraic proof that your solution is valid. To arrive at a correct solution, you must support each step by a property. The addition property of equality, for example, permits you to add the same number to both sides of an equation to get an equivalent equation.

EXAMPLE | Solve for x: $5x - 12 = 3(x + 2)$

Solution |

$5x - 12 = 3(x + 2)$ Given.

$5x - 12 = 3x + 6$ Distributive property of multiplication over addition.

$5x = 3x + 18$ Addition property of equality.

$2x = 18$ Subtraction property of equality.

$x = 9$ Division property of equality.

Why are the properties of arithmetic and equality important in geometry? The lengths of segments and the measures of angles involve numbers, so you will often need to use these properties in geometry proofs. And just as you use equality to express a relationship between numbers, you use congruence to express a relationship between geometric figures.

Definition of Congruence

If $AB = CD$, then $\overline{AB} \cong \overline{CD}$, and conversely, if $\overline{AB} \cong \overline{CD}$, then $AB = CD$.
If $m\angle A = m\angle B$, then $\angle A \cong \angle B$, and conversely, if $\angle A \cong \angle B$, then $m\angle A = m\angle B$.

Congruence is defined by equality, so you can extend the properties of equality to a reflexive property of congruence, a transitive property of congruence, and a symmetric property of congruence. This is left for you to do in the exercises.

The third set of premises is specific to geometry. These premises are traditionally called postulates. Postulates should be very basic. Like undefined terms, they should be useful and easy for everyone to agree on, with little debate.

As you've performed basic geometric constructions in this class, you've observed some of these "obvious truths." Whenever you draw a figure or use an auxiliary line, you are using these postulates.

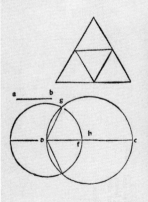

A page from a Latin translation of Euclid's *Elements*. What conjectures might he be discussing on this page?

Postulates of Geometry

Line Postulate You can construct exactly one line through any two points. In other words, two points determine a line.

Line Intersection Postulate The intersection of two distinct lines is exactly one point.

Euclid wrote 13 books covering, among other topics, plane geometry and solid geometry. He started with definitions, postulates, and "common notions" about the properties of equality. He then wrote hundreds of propositions, which we would call conjectures, and used constructions based on the definitions and postulates to show that they were valid. The statements that we call postulates were actually Euclid's postulates, plus a few of his propositions.

Segment Duplication Postulate You can construct a segment congruent to another segment.

Angle Duplication Postulate You can construct an angle congruent to another angle.

Midpoint Postulate You can construct exactly one midpoint on any line segment.

Angle Bisector Postulate You can construct exactly one angle bisector in any angle.

Parallel Postulate Through a point not on a given line, you can construct exactly one line parallel to the given line.

Perpendicular Postulate Through a point not on a given line, you can construct exactly one line perpendicular to the given line.

Segment Addition Postulate If point B is on $\overline{AC}$ and between points A and C, then $AB + BC = AC$.

Angle Addition Postulate If point D lies in the interior of $\angle ABC$, then $m\angle ABD + m\angle DBC = m\angle ABC$.

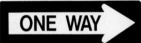

There are certain rules that everyone needs to agree on so we can drive safely! What are the "road rules" of geometry?

Linear Pair Postulate If two angles are a linear pair, then they are supplementary.

Corresponding Angles Postulate If two parallel lines are cut by a transversal, then the corresponding angles are congruent. Conversely, if two coplanar lines are cut by a transversal forming congruent corresponding angles, then the lines are parallel.

SSS Congruence Postulate If the three sides of one triangle are congruent to three sides of another triangle, then the two triangles are congruent.

SAS Congruence Postulate If two sides and the included angle in one triangle are congruent to two sides and the included angle in another triangle, then the two triangles are congruent.

ASA Congruence Postulate If two angles and the included side in one triangle are congruent to two angles and the included side in another triangle, then the two triangles are congruent.

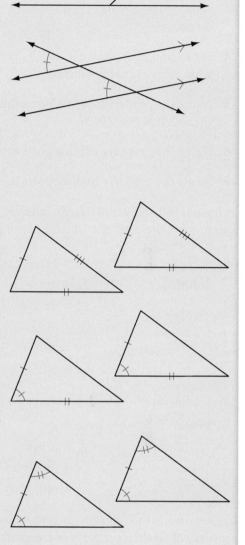

To build a logical framework for the geometry you have learned, you will start with the premises of geometry. In the exercises, you will see how these premises are the foundations for some of your previous assumptions and conjectures. You will also use these postulates and properties to see how some geometry statements are logical consequences of others.

13.1 Exercises

1. What is the difference between a postulate and a theorem?

2. Euclid might have stated the addition property of equality (translated from the Greek) in this way: "If equals are added to equals, the results are equal." State the subtraction, multiplication, and division properties of equality as Euclid might have stated them. (You may write them in English—extra credit for the original Greek!)

3. Add the reflexive property of congruence, the transitive property of congruence, and the symmetric property of congruence to your notebook. Include a diagram for each property. Illustrate one property with congruent triangles, another property with congruent segments, and another property with congruent angles. (These properties may seem ridiculously obvious. This is exactly why they are accepted as premises, which require no proof!)

4. When you state $AC = AC$, what property are you using? When you state $\overline{AC} \cong \overline{AC}$, what property are you using? ⓗ

5. Name the property that supports this statement: If $\angle ACE \cong \angle BDF$ and $\angle BDF \cong \angle HKM$, then $\angle ACE \cong \angle HKM$.

6. Name the property that supports this statement: If $x + 120 = 180$, then $x = 60$.

7. Name the property that supports this statement: If $2(x + 14) = 36$, then $x + 14 = 18$.

In Exercises 8 and 9, provide the missing property of equality or arithmetic as a reason for each step to solve the algebraic equation or to prove the algebraic argument.

8. Solve for x: $\quad 7x - 22 = 4(x + 2)$

Solution: $\quad 7x - 22 = 4(x + 2) \qquad$ Given.

$\quad\quad\quad\quad\quad 7x - 22 = 4x + 8 \qquad$ _?_ property of multiplication over addition.

$\quad\quad\quad\quad\quad 3x - 22 = 8 \qquad\quad$ _?_ property of equality.

$\quad\quad\quad\quad\quad\quad\quad 3x = 30 \qquad\quad$ _?_ property of equality.

$\quad\quad\quad\quad\quad\quad\quad\ x = 10 \qquad\quad$ _?_ property of equality.

9. **Conjecture:** $\quad$ If $\frac{x}{m} - c = d$, then $x = m(c + d)$, provided that $m \neq 0$. ⓗ

Proof: $\quad\quad \frac{x}{m} - c = d \qquad\quad$ _?_

$\quad\quad\quad\quad\ \frac{x}{m} = d + c \qquad\quad$ _?_

$\quad\quad\quad\quad\ x = m(d + c) \qquad$ _?_

$\quad\quad\quad\quad\ x = m(c + d) \qquad$ _?_

In Exercises 10–17, identify each statement as true or false. Then state which definition, property of algebra, property of congruence, or postulate supports your answer.

10. If M is the midpoint of $\overline{AB}$, then $AM = BM$.

11. If M is the midpoint of $\overline{CD}$ and N is the midpoint of $\overline{CD}$, then M and N are the same point. ⓗ

12. If $\overrightarrow{AB}$ bisects $\angle CAD$, then $\angle CAB \cong \angle DAB$.

13. If $\overrightarrow{AB}$ bisects $\angle CAD$ and $\overrightarrow{AF}$ bisects $\angle CAD$, then $\overrightarrow{AB}$ and $\overrightarrow{AF}$ are the same ray.

14. Lines ℓ and m can intersect at different points A and B.

15. If line ℓ passes through points A and B and line m passes through points A and B, lines ℓ and m do not have to be the same line.

16. If point P is in the interior of $\angle RAT$, then $m\angle RAP + m\angle PAT = m\angle RAT$.

17. If point M is on $\overline{AC}$ and between points A and C, then $AM + MC = AC$.

18. Copy and complete this flowchart proof. For each reason, state the definition, the property of algebra, or the property of congruence that supports the statement.

Given: $\overline{AO}$ and $\overline{BO}$ are radii

Show: $\triangle AOB$ is isosceles

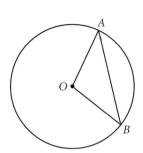

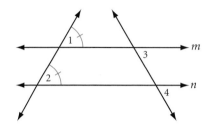

For Exercises 19–21, copy and complete each flowchart proof.

19. Given: $\angle 1 \cong \angle 2$

Show: $\angle 3 \cong \angle 4$

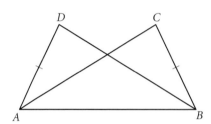

20. Given: $\overline{AC} \cong \overline{BD}$, $\overline{AD} \cong \overline{BC}$

Show: $\angle D \cong \angle C$

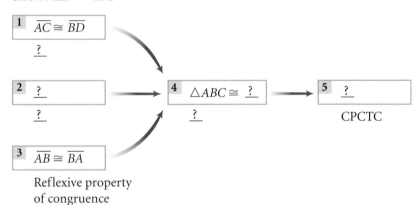

21. Given: Isosceles triangle ABC with $\overline{AB} \cong \overline{BC}$

Show: $\angle A \cong \angle C$

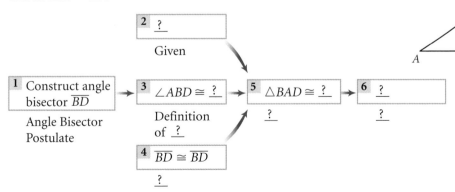

22. The Declaration of Independence states, "We hold these truths to be self-evident . . . ," then goes on to list four postulates of good government. Look up the Declaration of Independence and list the four self-evident truths that were the original premises of the United States government.

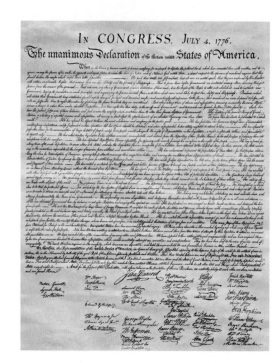

23. You have probably noticed that the sum of two odd integers is always an even integer. The rule $2n$ generates even integers and the rule $2n - 1$ generates odd integers. Let $2n - 1$ and $2m - 1$ represent any two odd integers, and prove that the sum of two odd integers is always an even integer.

24. Let $2n - 1$ and $2m - 1$ represent any two odd integers, and prove that the product of any two odd integers is always an odd integer.

25. Show that the sum of any three consecutive integers is always divisible by 3. ⓗ

Review

26. Shannon and Erin are hiking up a mountain. Of course, they are packing the clinometer they made in geometry class. At point A along a flat portion of the trail, Erin sights the mountain peak straight ahead at an angle of elevation of 22°. The level trail continues 220 m straight to the base of the mountain at point B. At that point, Shannon measures the angle of elevation to be 38°. From B the trail follows a ridge straight up the mountain to the peak. At point B, how far are they from the mountain peak?

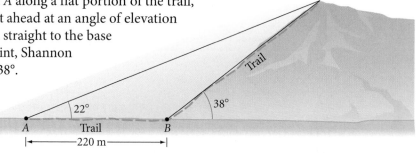

27.

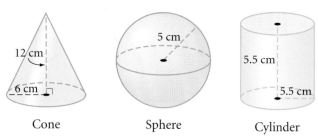

Cone   Sphere   Cylinder

Arrange the names of the solids in order, greatest to least.

Volume: ?   ?   ?

Surface area: ?   ?   ?

Length of the longest rod that will fit inside: ?   ?   ?

28. Two communication towers stand 64 ft apart. One is 80 ft high and the other is 48 ft high. Each has a guy wire from its top anchored to the base of the other tower. At what height do the two guy wires cross?

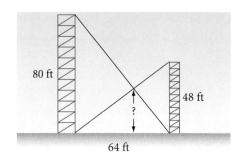

In Exercises 29 and 30, all length measurements are given in meters.

29. What's wrong with this picture?

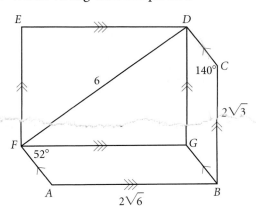

30. Find angle measures *x* and *y*, and length *a*.

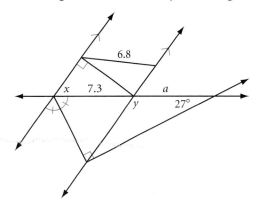

31. Each arc is a quarter of a circle with its center at a vertex of the square.

Given: Each square has side length 1 unit   **Find:** The shaded area

a.

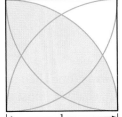

b.

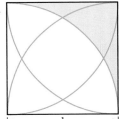

c.

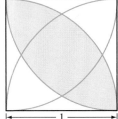

DEVELOPING MATHEMATICAL REASONING

Net Puzzle

The clear cube shown has the letters *DOT* printed on one face. When a light is shined on that face, the image of *DOT* appears on the opposite face. The image of *DOT* on the opposite face is then painted. Copy the net of the cube and sketch the painted image of the word, *DOT*, on the correct square and in the correct position.

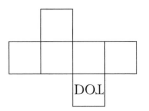

Planning a Geometry Proof

*"What is now proved was
once only imagined."*

WILLIAM BLAKE

A proof in geometry consists of a sequence of statements, starting with a given set of premises and leading to a valid conclusion. Each statement follows from one or more of the previous statements and is supported by a reason. A reason for a statement must come from the set of premises that you learned about in Lesson 13.1.

In earlier chapters you informally proved many conjectures. Now you can formally prove them, using the premises of geometry. In this lesson you will identify for yourself what is given and what you must show, in order to prove a conjecture. You will also create your own labeled diagrams.

As you have seen, you can state many geometry conjectures as conditional statements. For example, you can write the conjecture "Vertical angles are congruent" as a conditional statement: "If two angles are vertical angles, then they are congruent." To prove that a conditional statement is true, you assume that the first part of the conditional is true, then logically demonstrate the truth of the conditional's second part. In other words, you demonstrate that the first part implies the second part. The first part is what you assume to be true in the proof; it is the *given* information. The second part is the part you logically demonstrate in the proof; it is what you want to *show*.

Given

> Two angles are vertical angles

Show

> They are congruent

Next, draw and label a diagram that illustrates the given information. Then use the labels in the diagram to restate graphically what is given and what you must show.

Once you've created a diagram to illustrate your conjecture and you know where to start and where to go, make a plan using the reasoning strategies you've been developing. Use your plan to write the proof. Here's the complete process.

> ### Writing a Proof
>
> **Task 1** From the conditional statement, identify what is given and what you must show.
>
> **Task 2** Draw and label a diagram to illustrate the given information.
>
> **Task 3** Restate what is given and what you must show in terms of your diagram.
>
> **Task 4** Plan a proof using your reasoning strategies. Organize your reasoning mentally or on paper.
>
> **Task 5** From your plan, write a proof.

In Chapter 2, you proved the Vertical Angles Conjecture using conjectures that have now become postulates.

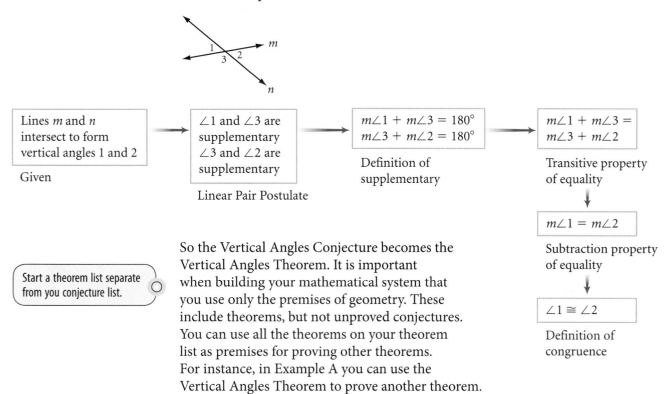

Lines m and n intersect to form vertical angles 1 and 2

Given

→ ∠1 and ∠3 are supplementary
∠3 and ∠2 are supplementary

Linear Pair Postulate

→ $m\angle 1 + m\angle 3 = 180°$
$m\angle 3 + m\angle 2 = 180°$

Definition of supplementary

→ $m\angle 1 + m\angle 3 = m\angle 3 + m\angle 2$

Transitive property of equality

↓

$m\angle 1 = m\angle 2$

Subtraction property of equality

↓

$\angle 1 \cong \angle 2$

Definition of congruence

Start a theorem list separate from you conjecture list.

So the Vertical Angles Conjecture becomes the Vertical Angles Theorem. It is important when building your mathematical system that you use only the premises of geometry. These include theorems, but not unproved conjectures. You can use all the theorems on your theorem list as premises for proving other theorems. For instance, in Example A you can use the Vertical Angles Theorem to prove another theorem.

You may have noticed that in the previous lesson we stated the Corresponding Angles Conjecture as a postulate, but not the Alternate Interior Angles Conjecture or the Alternate Exterior Angles Conjecture. In this first example you will see how to use the five tasks of the proof process to prove the Alternate Interior Angles Conjecture.

EXAMPLE A | Prove the Alternate Interior Angles Conjecture: If two parallel lines are cut by a transversal, then the alternate interior angles are congruent.

Solution | **Task 1: Identify what is given and what you must show.**

Given: Two parallel lines are cut by a transversal
Show: Alternate interior angles formed by the lines are congruent

Task 2: Draw and label a diagram.

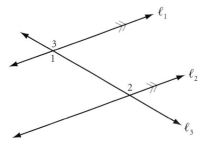

Task 3: Restate what is given and what you must show in terms of the diagram.

Given: Parallel lines ℓ_1 and ℓ_2 cut by transversal ℓ_3 to form alternate interior angles $\angle 1$ and $\angle 2$

Show: $\angle 1 \cong \angle 2$

Task 4: Plan a proof. Organize your reasoning mentally or on paper.

Plan:

I need to show that $\angle 1 \cong \angle 2$. Looking over the postulates and theorems, the ones that look useful are the Corresponding Angles Postulate and the Vertical Angles Theorem. From the Corresponding Angles Postulate, I know that $\angle 2 \cong \angle 3$ and from the Vertical Angles Theorem, $\angle 1 \cong \angle 3$. If $\angle 2 \cong \angle 3$ and $\angle 1 \cong \angle 3$, then by substitution $\angle 1 \cong \angle 2$.

Task 5: Create a proof from your plan.

Flowchart Proof

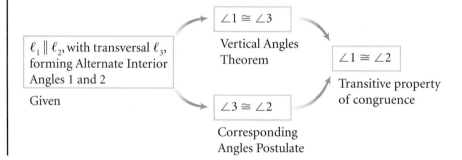

So, the Alternate Interior Angles Conjecture becomes the Alternate Interior Angles Theorem. Add this theorem to your theorem list.

In Chapter 4, you informally proved the Triangle Sum Conjecture. The proof is short, but clever too, because it required the construction of an auxiliary line. All the steps in the proof use properties that we now designate as postulates. Example B shows the flowchart proof. For example, the Parallel Postulate guarantees that it will always be possible to construct an auxiliary line through a vertex, parallel to the opposite side.

EXAMPLE B | Prove the Triangle Sum Conjecture: The sum of the measures of the angles of a triangle is 180°.

Solution | **Given:** $\angle 1$, $\angle 2$, and $\angle 3$ are the three angles of $\triangle ABC$

Show: $m\angle 1 + m\angle 2 + m\angle 3 = 180°$

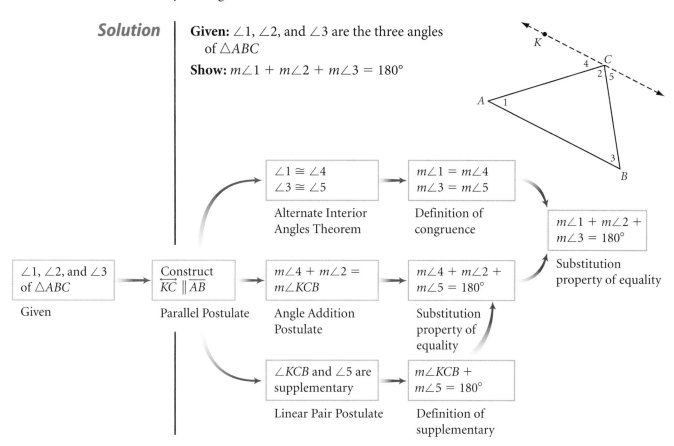

So, the Triangle Sum Conjecture becomes the Triangle Sum Theorem. Add it to your theorem list. Notice that each reason we now use in a proof is a postulate, theorem, definition, or property.

To make sure a particular theorem has been properly proved, you can also check the "logical family tree" of the theorem. When you create a family tree for a theorem, you trace it back to all the postulates that the theorem relied on. You don't need to list all the definitions and properties of equality and congruence; list only the theorems and postulates used in the proof. For the theorems that were used in the proof, which postulates and theorems were used in *their* proofs, and so on. In Chapter 4, you informally proved the Third Angle Conjecture. Let's look again at the proof.

Third Angle Conjecture: If two angles of one triangle are congruent to two angles of a second triangle, then the third pair of angles are congruent.

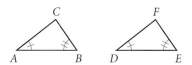

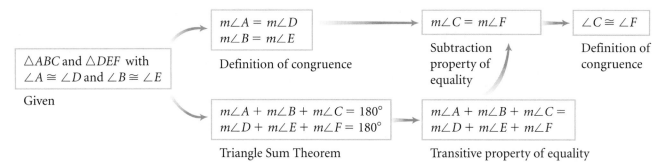

m∠A = m∠D
m∠B = m∠E

Definition of congruence

m∠C = m∠F

Subtraction property of equality

∠C ≅ ∠F

Definition of congruence

△ABC and △DEF with ∠A ≅ ∠D and ∠B ≅ ∠E

Given

m∠A + m∠B + m∠C = 180°
m∠D + m∠E + m∠F = 180°

Triangle Sum Theorem

m∠A + m∠B + m∠C = m∠D + m∠E + m∠F

Transitive property of equality

What does the logical family tree of the Third Angle Theorem look like?

You start by putting the Third Angle Theorem in a box. Find all the postulates and theorems used in the proof. The only postulate or theorem used was the Triangle Sum Theorem. Put that box above it.

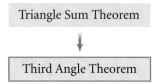

Triangle Sum Theorem

Third Angle Theorem

Next, locate all the theorems and postulates used to prove the Triangle Sum Theorem. Place them in boxes above the Triangle Sum Theorem. Connect the boxes with arrows showing the logical connection. Now the family tree looks like this:

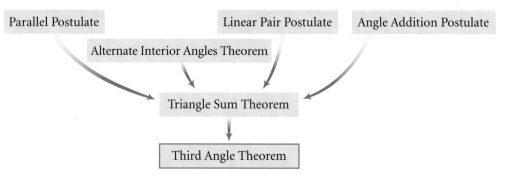

Parallel Postulate

Linear Pair Postulate

Angle Addition Postulate

Alternate Interior Angles Theorem

Triangle Sum Theorem

Third Angle Theorem

To prove the Alternate Interior Angles Theorem, we used the Corresponding Angles Postulate and the Vertical Angles Theorem, and to prove the Vertical Angles Theorem, we used the Linear Pair Postulate. The Linear Pair Postulate is already in the family tree, but move it up so it's above both the Triangle Sum Theorem and the Vertical Angles Theorem. The completed family tree looks like this:

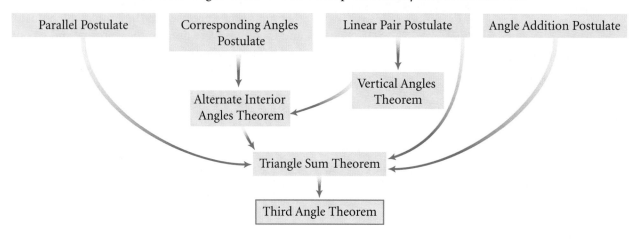

Parallel Postulate

Corresponding Angles Postulate

Linear Pair Postulate

Angle Addition Postulate

Vertical Angles Theorem

Alternate Interior Angles Theorem

Triangle Sum Theorem

Third Angle Theorem

The family tree shows that, ultimately, the Third Angle Theorem relies on the Parallel Postulate, the Corresponding Angles Postulate, the Linear Pair Postulate, and the Angle Addition Postulate. You might notice that the family tree of a theorem looks similar to a flowchart proof. The difference is that the family tree focuses on the premises and traces them back to the postulates.

Notice how the Third Angle Theorem follows directly from the Triangle Sum Theorem without using any other theorems or postulates. A theorem that is the immediate consequence of another proven theorem is called a **corollary**. So, the Third Angle Theorem is a corollary of the Triangle Sum Theorem.

13.2 Exercises

1. Which postulate(s) does the Vertical Angles Theorem rely on?

2. Which postulate(s) does the Triangle Sum Theorem rely on?

3. If you need a parallel line in a proof, which postulate allows you to construct it?

4. If you need a perpendicular line in a proof, which postulate allows you to construct it?

In Exercises 5–14, write a paragraph proof or a flowchart proof of the conjecture. Once you have completed their proofs, add the statements to your theorem list.

5. If two angles are both congruent and supplementary, then each is a right angle. (Congruent and Supplementary Theorem)

6. Supplements of congruent angles are congruent. (Supplements of Congruent Angles Theorem)

7. All right angles are congruent. (Right Angles are Congruent Theorem)

8. If two lines are cut by a transversal forming congruent alternate interior angles, then the lines are parallel. (Converse of the Alternate Interior Angles Theorem)

9. If two parallel lines are cut by a transversal, then the alternate exterior angles are congruent. (Alternate Exterior Angles Theorem)

10. If two lines are cut by a transversal forming congruent alternate exterior angles, then the lines are parallel. (Converse of the Alternate Exterior Angles Theorem)

11. If two parallel lines are cut by a transversal, then the interior angles on the same side of the transversal are supplementary. (Interior Supplements Theorem)

12. If two lines are cut by a transversal forming interior angles on the same side of the transversal that are supplementary, then the lines are parallel. (Converse of the Interior Supplements Theorem)

13. If two lines in the same plane are parallel to a third line, then they are parallel to each other. (Parallel Transitivity Theorem)

14. If two lines in the same plane are perpendicular to a third line, then they are parallel to each other. (Perpendicular to Parallel Theorem)

15. Prove that the acute angles in a right triangle are complementary. Explain why this is a corollary of the Triangle Sum Theorem.

16. Draw a family tree of the Converse of the Alternate Exterior Angles Theorem.

Review

17. Suppose the top of a pyramid with volume 1107 cm³ is sliced off and discarded, resulting in a truncated pyramid. If the cut was parallel to the base and two-thirds of the distance to the vertex, what is the volume of the truncated pyramid?

18. Abraham is building a dog house for his terrier. His plan is shown at right.

    He will cut a door and a window later. After he builds the frame for the structure, can he complete it using one piece of 4 foot by 8 foot plywood? If the answer is yes, show how he should cut the plywood. If no, explain why not.

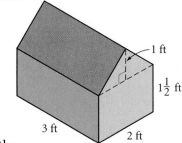

1 ft

$1\frac{1}{2}$ ft

3 ft

2 ft

19. A triangle has vertices $A(7, -4)$, $B(3, -2)$, and $C(4, 1)$. Find the coordinates of the vertices after a dilation with center $(8, 2)$ and scale factor 2. Write the ordered pair rule for the dilation: $(x, y) \rightarrow (\underline{?}, \underline{?})$. ⓗ

DEVELOPING MATHEMATICAL REASONING

Mental Blocks

In the top figure at right, every cube is lettered exactly alike. Copy and complete the two-dimensional representation of one of the cubes to show how the letters are arranged on the six faces.

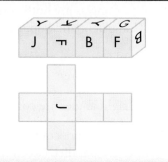

LESSON
13.3

Triangle Proofs

*"The most violent
element in our society
is ignorance."*

EMMA GOLDMAN

Now that the theorems from the previous lesson have been proved, make sure you have added them to your theorem list. They will be useful to you in proving future theorems.

Triangle congruence is so useful in proving other theorems that we will focus next on triangle proofs. You may have noticed that in Lesson 13.1, three of the four triangle congruence conjectures were stated as postulates (the SSS Congruence Postulate, the SAS Congruence Postulate, and the ASA Congruence Postulate). The SAA Conjecture was not stated as a postulate. In Lesson 4.5, you used the ASA Conjecture (now the ASA Postulate) to explain the SAA Conjecture. The family tree for SAA congruence looks like this:

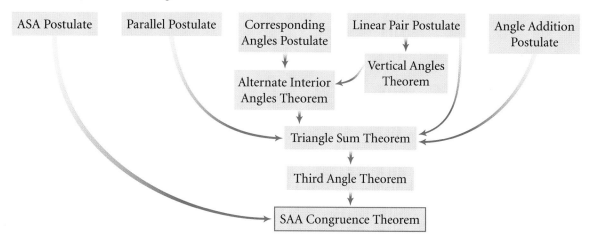

So the SAA Conjecture becomes the SAA Theorem. Add this theorem to your theorem list. This theorem will be useful in some of the proofs in this lesson.

Let's use the five-task proof process and triangle congruence to prove the Angle Bisector Conjecture.

EXAMPLE

Prove the Angle Bisector Conjecture: Any point on the bisector of an angle is equidistant from the sides of the angle.

Solution

Given: Any point on the bisector of an angle

Show: The point is equidistant from the sides of the angle

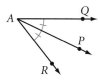

Given: $\overrightarrow{AP}$ bisects $\angle QAR$

Show: P is equally distant from sides $\overrightarrow{AQ}$ and $\overrightarrow{AR}$

Plan: The distance from a point to a line is measured along the perpendicular from the point to the line. So begin by constructing $\overline{PB} \perp \overrightarrow{AQ}$ and $\overline{PC} \perp \overrightarrow{AR}$ (the Perpendicular Postulate). You can show that $\overline{PB} \cong \overline{PC}$ if they are corresponding parts of congruent triangles. $\overline{AP} \cong \overline{AP}$ by the identity property of congruence, and $\angle QAP \cong \angle RAP$ by the definition of an angle bisector. $\angle ABP$ and $\angle ACP$ are right angles and thus they are congruent.

So $\triangle ABP \cong \triangle ACP$ by the SAA Theorem. If the triangles are congruent, then $\overline{PB} \cong \overline{PC}$ by CPCTC.

Based on this plan, you can write a flowchart proof.

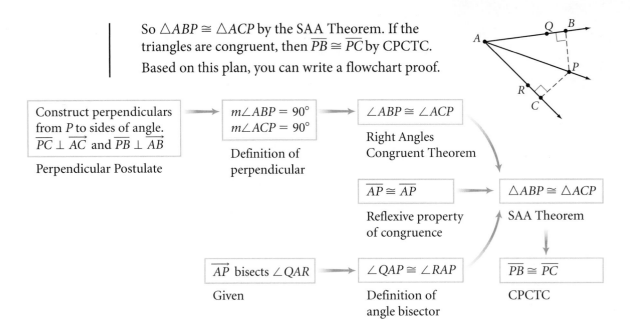

Thus the Angle Bisector Conjecture becomes the Angle Bisector Theorem.

As our own proofs build on each other, flowcharts can become too large and awkward. You can also use a two-column format for writing proofs. A **directed two-column proof** is identical to a flowchart or paragraph proof, except that the statements are listed in the first column, each supported by a reason (a postulate, definition, property, or theorem) in the second column.

Here is the same proof from the example above, following the same plan, presented as a directed two-column proof. Arrows link the steps.

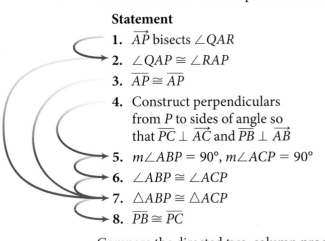

Statement	Reason
1. $\overrightarrow{AP}$ bisects $\angle QAR$	1. Given
2. $\angle QAP \cong \angle RAP$	2. Definition of angle bisector
3. $\overline{AP} \cong \overline{AP}$	3. Reflexive property of congruence
4. Construct perpendiculars from P to sides of angle so that $\overrightarrow{PC} \perp \overrightarrow{AC}$ and $\overrightarrow{PB} \perp \overrightarrow{AB}$	4. Perpendicular Postulate
5. $m\angle ABP = 90°$, $m\angle ACP = 90°$	5. Definition of perpendicular
6. $\angle ABP \cong \angle ACP$	6. Right Angles Congruent Theorem
7. $\triangle ABP \cong \triangle ACP$	7. SAA Theorem
8. $\overline{PB} \cong \overline{PC}$	8. CPCTC

Compare the directed two-column proof you just saw with the flowchart proof in the Example. What similarities do you see? What are the advantages of each format?

No matter what format you choose, your proof should be clear and easy for someone to follow.

13.3 Exercises

In Exercises 1–12, write a proof of the conjecture. Once you have completed the proofs, add the theorems to your list.

YOU WILL NEED

Geometry software for Exercise **22**

Construction tools for Exercise **19**

1. If a point is on the perpendicular bisector of a segment, then it is equally distant from the endpoints of the segment. (Perpendicular Bisector Theorem)

2. If a point is equally distant from the endpoints of a segment, then it is on the perpendicular bisector of the segment. (Converse of the Perpendicular Bisector Theorem) *(h)*

3. If a triangle is isosceles, then the base angles are congruent. (Isosceles Triangle Theorem)

4. If two angles of a triangle are congruent, then the triangle is isosceles. (Converse of the Isosceles Triangle Theorem)

5. If a point is equally distant from the sides of an angle, then it is on the bisector of the angle. (Converse of the Angle Bisector Theorem) *(h)*

6. The three perpendicular bisectors of the sides of a triangle are concurrent. (Perpendicular Bisector Concurrency Theorem)

7. The three angle bisectors of the angles of a triangle are concurrent. (Angle Bisector Concurrency Theorem)

8. The measure of an exterior angle of a triangle is equal to the sum of the measures of the two remote interior angles. (Triangle Exterior Angle Theorem)

9. The sum of the measures of the four angles of a quadrilateral is 360°. (Quadrilateral Sum Theorem)

10. In an isosceles triangle, the medians to the congruent sides are congruent. (Medians to the Congruent Sides Theorem)

11. In an isosceles triangle, the angle bisectors to the congruent sides are congruent. (Angle Bisectors to the Congruent Sides Theorem)

12. In an isosceles triangle, the altitudes to the congruent sides are congruent. (Altitudes to the Congruent Sides Theorem)

Review

For Exercises 13 and 14 all measurements are in centimeters.

13. Find x and y.

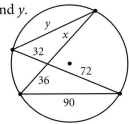

14. Find x and y. ⓗ

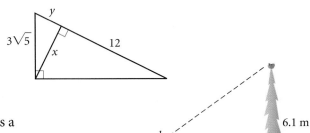

15. Two bird nests, 3.6 m and 6.1 m high, are on trees across a pond from each other, at points P and Q. The distance between the nests is too wide to measure directly (and there is a pond between the trees). A birdwatcher at point R can sight each nest along a dry path. $RP = 16.7$ m and $RQ = 27.4$ m. $\angle QPR$ is a right angle. What is the distance d between the nests?

16. Apply the glide reflection rule twice to find the first and second images of the point $A(-2, 9)$. ⓗ

Glide reflection rule: A reflection across the line $x + y = 5$ and a translation $(x, y) \rightarrow (x + 4, y - 4)$.

17. Explain why $\angle 1 \cong \angle 2$.

Given:

    B, G, F, E are collinear

    $m\angle DFE = 90°$

    $BC = FC$

    $\overline{AF} \parallel \overline{BC}$

    $\overline{BE} \parallel \overline{CD}$

    $\overline{AB} \parallel \overline{FC} \parallel \overline{ED}$

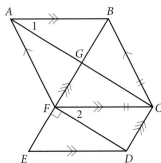

18. Each arc is a quarter of a circle with its center at a vertex of the square.

  Given: The square has side length 1 unit   **Find:** The shaded area

  a. Shaded area = ?   **b.** Shaded area = ?   **c.** Shaded area = ?

19. Given an arc of a circle on patty paper but not the whole circle or the center, fold the paper to construct a tangent at the midpoint of the arc.

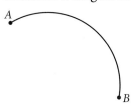

20. Find $m\angle BAC$ in this right rectangular prism.

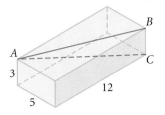

21. Choose **A** if the value of the expression is greater in Figure A.

Choose **B** if the value of the expression is greater in Figure B.

Choose **C** if the values are equal for both figures.

Choose **D** if it cannot be determined which value is greater.

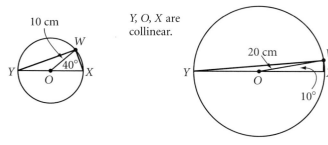

Figure A   Figure B

a. Perimeter of $\triangle WXY$

b. Area of $\triangle XOW$

22. Use geometry software to construct a circle. For part a, label any three points on the circle and construct tangents at those three points to form a circumscribed triangle. Connect the points of tangency to form an inscribed triangle. Repeat constructions for part b with four points and circumscribed and inscribed quadrilaterals.

a. Drag the points and observe the angle measures of each triangle. What relationship do you notice between x, a, and c? Is the same true for y and z?

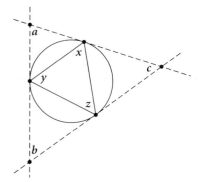

b. What is the relationship between the angle measures of a circumscribed quadrilateral and the inscribed quadrilateral formed by connecting the points of tangency?

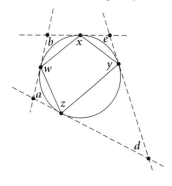

DEVELOPING MATHEMATICAL REASONING

Fantasy Functions

If $a \circ b = a^b$ then $3 \circ 2 = 3^2 = 9$,

and   if $a \triangle b = a^2 + b^2$ then $5 \triangle 2 = 5^2 + 2^2 = 29$.

If $8 \triangle x = 17 \circ 2$, find x.

Quadrilateral Proofs

"All geometric reasoning is, in the last result, circular."

BERTRAND RUSSELL

In Chapter 5, you discovered and informally proved several quadrilateral properties. As reasons for the statements in some of these proofs, you used conjectures that are now postulates or that you have proved as theorems. So those steps in the proofs are valid. Occasionally, however, you may have used unproven conjectures as reasons. In this lesson you will write formal proofs of some of these quadrilateral conjectures, using only definitions, postulates, and theorems. After you have proved the theorems, you'll create a family tree tracing them back to postulates and properties.

You can prove many quadrilateral theorems by using triangle theorems. For example, you can prove some parallelogram properties by using the fact that a diagonal divides a parallelogram into two congruent triangles. In the example below, we'll prove this fact as a lemma. Recall that a lemma is an auxiliary theorem used specifically to prove other theorems.

EXAMPLE | **Prove:** A diagonal of a parallelogram divides the parallelogram into two congruent triangles.

Solution | **Given:** Parallelogram $ABCD$ with diagonal $\overline{AC}$

Show: $\triangle ABC \cong \triangle CDA$

Directed Two-Column Proof

Statement	Reason
1. $ABCD$ is a parallelogram	1. Given
2. $\overline{AB} \parallel \overline{DC}$ and $\overline{AD} \parallel \overline{BC}$	2. Definition of parallelogram
3. $\angle CAB \cong \angle ACD$ and $\angle BCA \cong \angle DAC$	3. Alternate Interior Angles Theorem
4. $\overline{AC} \cong \overline{AC}$	4. Reflexive property of congruence
5. $\triangle ABC \cong \triangle CDA$	5. ASA Congruence Postulate

We'll call the lemma proved in the example the Parallelogram Diagonal Lemma. You can now add it to your theorem list and use it to prove other parallelogram conjectures.

DEVELOPING PROOF

Work with your group to prove three of your previous conjectures about parallelograms. Remember to draw a diagram, restate what is given and what you must show in terms of your diagram, and then make a plan before you prove each conjecture.

Proof 1: The Opposite Sides Conjecture states that the opposite sides of a parallelogram are congruent.

Proof 2: The Opposite Angles Conjecture states that the opposite angles of a parallelogram are congruent.

Proof 3: State the converse of the Opposite Sides Conjecture. Then write a proof of this conjecture.

After you have successfully proved the parallelogram conjectures above, you can call them theorems and add them to your theorem list.

Create a family tree that shows the relationship among the three theorems you just proved and traces each theorem back to the postulates of geometry.

13.4 Exercises

YOU WILL NEED

 *Geometry software* for Exercise **18**

In Exercises 1–12, write a directed two-column proof or a flowchart proof of the conjecture. Once you have completed the proofs, add the theorems to your list.

1. If the opposite angles of a quadrilateral are congruent, then the quadrilateral is a parallelogram. (Converse of the Opposite Angles Theorem) *(h)*

2. If one pair of opposite sides of a quadrilateral are parallel and congruent, then the quadrilateral is a parallelogram. (Opposite Sides Parallel and Congruent Theorem)

3. Each diagonal of a rhombus bisects two opposite angles. (Rhombus Angles Theorem)

4. The consecutive angles of a parallelogram are supplementary. (Parallelogram Consecutive Angles Theorem)

5. If a quadrilateral has four congruent sides, then it is a rhombus. (Four Congruent Sides Rhombus Theorem)

6. If a quadrilateral has four congruent angles, then it is a rectangle. (Four Congruent Angles Rectangle Theorem)

7. The diagonals of a rectangle are congruent. (Rectangle Diagonals Theorem)

8. If the diagonals of a parallelogram are congruent, then the parallelogram is a rectangle. (Converse of the Rectangle Diagonals Theorem)

9. The base angles of an isosceles trapezoid are congruent. (Isosceles Trapezoid Theorem)

10. The diagonals of an isosceles trapezoid are congruent. (Isosceles Trapezoid Diagonals Theorem)

11. If a diagonal of a parallelogram bisects two opposite angles, then the parallelogram is a rhombus. (Converse of the Rhombus Angles Theorem)

12. If two parallel lines are intersected by a second pair of parallel lines that are the same distance apart as the first pair, then the parallelogram formed is a rhombus. (Double-Edged Straightedge Theorem)

13. Create a family tree for the Parallelogram Consecutive Angles Theorem.

14. Create a family tree for the Double-Edged Straightedge Theorem.

Review

15. Yan uses a 40 ft rope to tie his horse to the corner of the barn to which a fence is attached. How many square feet of grazing, to the nearest square foot, does the horse have?

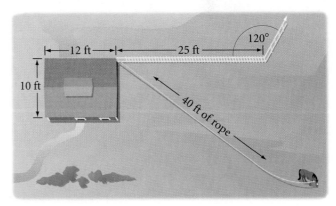

16. Complete the following chart with the symmetries and names of each type of special quadrilateral: parallelogram, rhombus, rectangle, square, kite, trapezoid, and isosceles trapezoid.

Name	Lines of symmetry	Rotational symmetry
	none	
trapezoid		
	1 diagonal	
		4-fold
	2 ⊥ bisectors of sides	
rhombus		
		none

17. Consider the rectangular prisms in Figure A and Figure B.
Choose **A** if the value of the expression is greater in Figure A.
Choose **B** if the value of the expression is greater in Figure B.
Choose **C** if the values are equal in both rectangular prisms.
Choose **D** if it cannot be determined which value is greater.

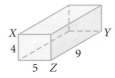 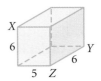

Figure A   Figure B

a. Volume
b. Surface area
c. XY
d. Measure of $\angle XYZ$
e. Shortest path from X to Y along the surface of the prism

18. **INVESTIGATE—CONJECTURE—PROVE** Construct one segment AC that bisects a second segment BD. Connect the four endpoints creating quadrilateral $ABCD$. Label the intersection of the two diagonals M (where $BM = MD$). Use the measurement tools in your geometry software to compare the two triangles created by diagonal AC in quadrilateral $ABCD$. Drag the vertices of the quadrilateral. Complete the conjecture: *If a diagonal d_1 in a quadrilateral bisects the other diagonal then diagonal d_1 creates two triangles that are* _____. Prove this conjecture. ⓗ

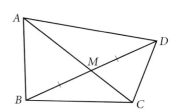

Indirect Proof

In the proofs you have written so far, you have shown *directly*, through a sequence of statements and reasons, that a given conjecture is true. In this lesson you will write a different type of proof, called an indirect proof. In an **indirect proof**, you show something is true by eliminating all the other possibilities. You have probably used this type of reasoning when taking multiple-choice tests. If you are unsure of an answer, you can try to eliminate choices until you are left with only one possibility.

This mystery story gives an example of an indirect proof.

Detective Sheerluck Holmes and three other people are alone on a tropical island. One morning, Sheerluck entertains the others by playing show tunes on his ukulele. Later that day, he discovers that his precious ukulele has been smashed to bits. Who could have committed such an antimusical act? Sheerluck eliminates himself as a suspect because he knows he didn't do it. He eliminates his girlfriend as a suspect because she has been with him all day. Colonel Moran recently injured both arms and therefore could not have smashed the ukulele with such force. There is only one other person on the island who could have committed the crime. So Sheerluck concludes that the fourth person, Sir Charles Mortimer, is the guilty one.

For a given mathematical statement, there are two possibilities: either the statement is true or it is not true. To prove indirectly that a statement is true, you start by assuming it is not true. You then use logical reasoning to show that this assumption leads to a contradiction. If an assumption leads to a contradiction, it must be false. Therefore, you can eliminate the possibility that the statement is not true. This leaves only one possibility—namely, that the statement is true!

"How often have I said to you that when you have eliminated the impossible, whatever remains, however improbable, must be the truth?"

SHERLOCK HOLMES IN *THE SIGN OF THE FOUR* BY SIR ARTHUR CONAN DOYLE

EXAMPLE A

Conjecture: If $m\angle N \neq m\angle O$ in $\triangle NOT$, then $NT \neq OT$.
Given: $\triangle NOT$ with $m\angle N \neq m\angle O$
Show: $NT \neq OT$

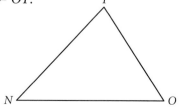

Solution

To prove indirectly that the statement $NT \neq OT$ is true, start by assuming that it is *not* true. That is, assume $NT = OT$. Then show that this assumption leads to a contradiction.

Paragraph Proof

Assume $NT = OT$. If $NT = OT$, then $m\angle N = m\angle O$ by the Isosceles Triangle Theorem. But this contradicts the given fact that $m\angle N \neq m\angle O$. Therefore, the assumption $NT = OT$ is false and so $NT \neq OT$ is true.

Here is another example of an indirect proof.

EXAMPLE B

Conjecture: The diagonals of a trapezoid do not bisect each other.

Given: Trapezoid *ZOID* with parallel bases $\overline{ZO}$ and $\overline{ID}$ and diagonals $\overline{DO}$ and $\overline{IZ}$ intersecting at point *Y*

Show: The diagonals of trapezoid *ZOID* do not bisect each other; that is, $DY \neq OY$ and $ZY \neq IY$

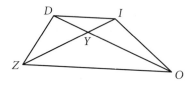

Solution

Paragraph Proof

Assume that one of the diagonals of trapezoid *ZOID*, say $\overline{ZI}$, does bisect the other. Then $\overline{DY} \cong \overline{OY}$. Also, by the Alternate Interior Angles Theorem, $\angle DIY \cong \angle OZY$, and $\angle IDY \cong \angle YOZ$. Therefore, $\triangle DYI \cong \triangle OYZ$ by the SAA Theorem. By CPCTC, $\overline{ZO} \cong \overline{ID}$. It is given that $\overline{ZO} \parallel \overline{ID}$. In Lesson 13.4, you proved that if one pair of opposite sides of a quadrilateral are parallel and congruent, then the quadrilateral is a parallelogram. So, *ZOID* is a parallelogram. Thus, *ZOID* has two pairs of opposite sides parallel. But because it is a trapezoid, it has exactly one pair of parallel sides. This is contradictory. Similarly, you can show that the assumption that $\overline{OD}$ bisects $\overline{ZI}$ leads to a contradiction. So the assumption that the diagonals of a trapezoid bisect each other is false and the conjecture is true.

In developing proof you'll write an indirect proof of the Tangent Conjecture from Chapter 9.

DEVELOPING PROOF

Tangent Conjecture

Copy the information and diagram below, then work with your group to complete an indirect proof of the Tangent Conjecture.

Conjecture: A tangent is perpendicular to the radius drawn to the point of tangency.

Given: Circle *O* with tangent $\overleftrightarrow{AT}$ and radius $\overline{AO}$

Show: $\overline{AO} \perp \overleftrightarrow{AT}$

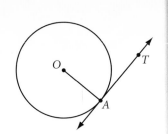

Consider the following statements as you plan your proof.

a. Assume $\overline{AO}$ is *not* perpendicular to $\overleftrightarrow{AT}$. Construct a perpendicular from point *O* to $\overleftrightarrow{AT}$ and label the intersection point *B* ($\overline{OB} \perp \overleftrightarrow{AT}$). Which postulate allows you to do this?

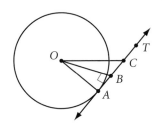

b. Select a point C on $\overleftrightarrow{AT}$, on the other side of B from A, such that $\overline{BC} \cong \overline{AB}$. Which postulate allows you to do this?

c. Next, construct $\overline{OC}$. Which postulate allows you to do this? $\angle ABO \cong \angle CBO$. Why?

d. $\overline{OB} \cong \overline{OB}$. What property of congruence tells you this? Therefore, $\triangle ABO \cong \triangle CBO$. Which congruence shortcut tells you the triangles are congruent? If $\triangle ABO \cong \triangle CBO$, then $\overline{AO} \cong \overline{CO}$. Why?

e. C must be a point on the circle (because a circle is the set of *all* points in the plane at a given distance from the center, and points A and C are both the same distance from the center). Therefore, $\overleftrightarrow{AT}$ intersects the circle in *two* points (A and C) and thus, $\overleftrightarrow{AT}$ is not a tangent. But this leads to a contradiction. Why?

Discuss the statements with your group. What was the contradiction? What does it prove? Now write a complete indirect proof of the Tangent Conjecture.

Plan and write an indirect proof of the converse of the Tangent Conjecture: A line that is perpendicular to a radius at its endpoint on the circle is tangent to the circle.

Add the Tangent Conjecture and the Converse of the Tangent Theorem to your list of theorems.

⏚ 13.5 Exercises

For Exercises 1 and 2, the correct answer is one of the choices listed. Determine the correct answer by indirect reasoning, explaining how you eliminated each incorrect choice.

1. Which is the capital of Mali?
   A. Paris   **B.** Tucson   **C.** London   **D.** Bamako

2. Which Italian scientist used a new invention called the telescope to discover the moons of Jupiter?
   A. Sir Edmund Halley   **B.** Julius Caesar   **C.** Galileo Galilei   **D.** Madonna

3. Is the proof in Example A claiming that if two angles of a triangle are not congruent, then the triangle is not isosceles? Explain.

4. Is the proof in Example B claiming that if one diagonal of a quadrilateral bisects the other, then the quadrilateral is not a trapezoid? Explain.

5. Fill in the blanks in the indirect proof below.

Conjecture: No triangle has two right angles.

Given: $\triangle ABC$

Show: No two angles are right angles

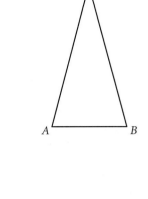

Directed Two-Column Proof

Statement	Reason
1. Assume $\triangle ABC$ has two right angles (Assume $m\angle A = 90°$ and $m\angle B = 90°$ and $0° < m\angle C < 180°$.)	**1.** _?_
2. $m\angle A + m\angle B + m\angle C = 180°$	**2.** _?_
3. $90° + 90° + m\angle C = 180°$	**3.** _?_
4. $m\angle C = $ _?_	**4.** _?_

But if $m\angle C = 0$, then the two sides $\overline{AC}$ and $\overline{BC}$ coincide, and thus there is no angle at C. This contradicts the given information. So the assumption is false. Therefore, no triangle has two right angles.

6. Write an indirect proof of the conjecture below.

Conjecture: No trapezoid is equiangular.

Given: Trapezoid $ZOID$ with bases $\overline{ZO}$ and $\overline{ID}$

Show: $ZOID$ is not equiangular

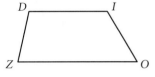

7. Write an indirect proof of the conjecture below.

Conjecture: In a scalene triangle, the median cannot be the altitude.

Given: Scalene triangle ABC with median $\overline{CD}$

Show: Median $\overline{CD}$ is not the altitude to $\overline{AB}$

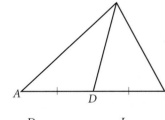

8. Write an indirect proof of the conjecture below.

Conjecture: The bases of a trapezoid have unequal lengths.

Given: Trapezoid $ZOID$ with parallel bases and $\overline{ZO}$ and $\overline{ID}$

Show: $ZO \neq ID$

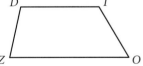

9. Write the "given" and the "show," and then plan and write the proof of the Perpendicular Bisector of a Chord Conjecture: The perpendicular bisector of a chord passes through the center of the circle. When you have finished your proof, add this to your list of theorems.

Review

10. Find *a*, *b*, and *c*.

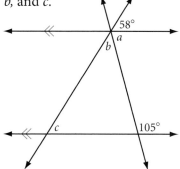

11. A clear plastic container is in the shape of a right cone atop a right cylinder, and their bases coincide. Find the volume of the container.

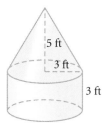

12. Each arc is a quarter of a circle with its center at a vertex of the square.

Given: The square has side length 1 unit   **Find:** The shaded area

a. Shaded area = ?

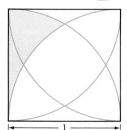

b. Shaded area = ?

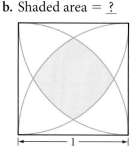

13. For each statement, select always (A), sometimes (S), or never (N).

a. An angle inscribed in a semicircle is a right angle.

b. An angle inscribed in a major arc is obtuse.

c. An arc measure equals the measure of its central angle.

d. The measure of an angle formed by two intersecting chords equals the measure of its intercepted arc.

e. The measure of the angle formed by two tangents to a circle equals the supplement of the central angle of the minor intercepted arc.

DEVELOPING MATHEMATICAL REASONING

Logical Liars

Five students have just completed a logic contest. To confuse the school's reporter, Lois Lang, each student agreed to make one true and one false statement to her when she interviewed them. Lois was clever enough to figure out the winner. Are you? Here are the students' statements.

Frances:	Kai was second. I was fourth.
Leyton:	I was third. Charles was last.
Denise:	Kai won. I was second.
Kai:	Leyton had the best score. I came in last.
Charles:	I came in second. Kai was third.

Circle Proofs

In Chapter 9, you completed the proof of the three cases of the Inscribed Angle Conjecture: The measure of an inscribed angle in a circle equals half the measure of its intercepted arc. There was a lot of algebra in the proof. You may not have noticed that the Angle Addition Postulate was used, as well as a property that we called *arc addition*. Arc Addition is a postulate that you need to add to your list.

Arc Addition Postulate

If point B is on $\overarc{AC}$ and between points A and C, then $m\overarc{AB} + m\overarc{BC} = m\overarc{AC}$.

Is the proof of the Inscribed Angle Conjecture now completely supported by the premises of geometry? Can you call it a theorem? To answer these questions, trace the family tree.

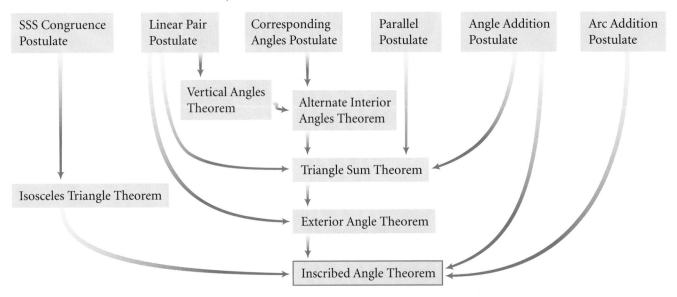

So, the Inscribed Angle Conjecture is completely supported by premises of geometry; therefore you can call it a theorem and add it to your theorem list.

A double rainbow creates arcs in the sky over Stonehenge near Wiltshire, England. Built from bluestone and sandstone from 3000 to 1500 B.C.E., Stonehenge itself is laid out in the shape of a major arc.

In the exercises, you will create proofs or family trees for many of your earlier discoveries about circles.

13.6 Exercises

YOU WILL NEED

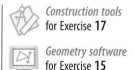

Construction tools
for Exercise **17**

Geometry software
for Exercise **15**

In Exercises 1–7, set up and write a proof of each conjecture. Once you have completed the proofs, add the theorems to your list.

1. Inscribed angles that intercept the same or congruent arcs are congruent. (Inscribed Angles Intercepting Arcs Theorem)

2. The opposite angles of an inscribed quadrilateral are supplementary. (Cyclic Quadrilateral Theorem)

3. Parallel lines intercept congruent arcs on a circle. (Parallel Secants Congruent Arcs Theorem)

4. If a parallelogram is inscribed within a circle, then the parallelogram is a rectangle. (Parallelogram Inscribed in a Circle Theorem)

5. Tangent segments from a point to a circle are congruent. (Tangent Segments Theorem)

6. The measure of an angle formed by two intersecting chords is half the sum of the measures of the two intercepted arcs. (Intersecting Chords Theorem)

7. Write and prove a theorem about the arcs intercepted by secants intersecting outside a circle, and the angle formed by the secants. (Intersecting Secants Theorem)

8. Prove the Angles Inscribed in a Semicircle Conjecture: An angle inscribed in a semicircle is a right angle. Explain why this is a corollary of the Inscribed Angle Theorem.

9. Create a family tree for the Tangent Segments Theorem.

10. Create a family tree for the Parallelogram Inscribed in a Circle Theorem.

Review

11. Find the coordinates of A and P to the nearest tenth.

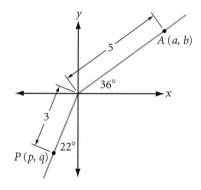

12. **Given:** $AX = 6$, $XB = 2$, $BC = 4$, $ZC = 3$
Find: $BY = \underline{\:?\:}$, $YC = \underline{\:?\:}$, $AZ = \underline{\:?\:}$

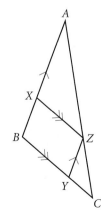

13. List the five segments in order from shortest to longest.

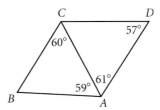

14. $\overline{AB}$ is a common external tangent. Find the length of $\overline{AB}$ (to a tenth of a unit).

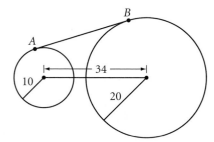

15. P is any point inside an equilateral triangle. Is there a relationship between the height of the equilateral triangle h and the sum $a + b + c$? Use geometry software to explore the relationship and make a conjecture. Then write a proof of your conjecture. ⓗ

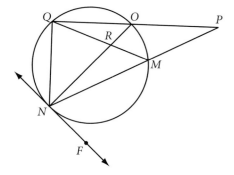

16. In the figure at right, $m\widehat{NQ} = 94°$, $m\widehat{OM} = 40°$, $\overleftrightarrow{NF}$ is a tangent. Find each measure or conclude that it "cannot be determined."

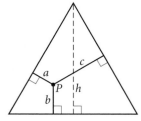

   a. $m\angle P$ **b.** $m\angle QON$

   c. $m\angle QRN$ **d.** $m\angle QMP$

   e. $m\angle ONF$ **f.** $m\angle \widehat{MN}$

17. Use a compass and straightedge to construct the two tangents to a circle from a point outside the circle. ⓗ

DEVELOPING MATHEMATICAL REASONING

Seeing Spots

The arrangement of green and yellow spots at right may appear to be random, but there is a pattern. Each row is generated by the row immediately above it. Find the pattern and add several rows to the arrangement. Do you think a row could ever consist of all yellow spots? All green spots? Could there ever be a row with one green spot? Does a row ever repeat itself? You should be able to do these "in your head."

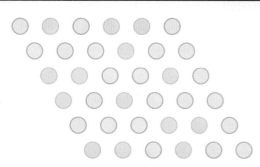

Similarity Proofs

To prove conjectures involving similarity, we need to extend the properties of equality and congruence to similarity.

Properties of Similarity

Reflexive property of similarity

Any figure is similar to itself.

Symmetric property of similarity

If Figure A is similar to Figure B, then Figure B is similar to Figure A.

Transitive property of similarity

If Figure A is similar to Figure B and Figure B is similar to Figure C, then Figure A is similar to Figure C.

The AA Similarity Conjecture is actually a similarity postulate.

AA Similarity Postulate

If two angles of one triangle are congruent to two angles of another triangle, then the two triangles are similar.

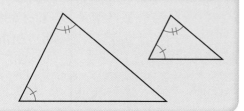

In Chapter 7, you also discovered the SAS and SSS shortcuts for showing that two triangles are similar. In the example that follows, you will see how to use the AA Similarity Postulate to prove the SAS Similarity Conjecture, making it the SAS Similarity Theorem.

EXAMPLE

Prove the SAS Similarity Conjecture: If two sides of one triangle are proportional to two sides of another triangle and the included angles are congruent, then the two triangles are similar.

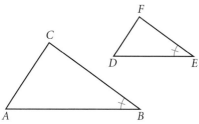

Solution

Given: $\triangle ABC$ and $\triangle DEF$ such that $\frac{AB}{DE} = \frac{BC}{EF}$ and $\angle B \cong \angle E$

Show: $\triangle ABC \sim \triangle DEF$

Plan: The only shortcut for showing that two triangles are similar is the AA Similarity Postulate, so you need to find another pair of congruent angles. One way of getting two congruent angles is to find two congruent triangles. You can draw a triangle within $\triangle ABC$ that is congruent to $\triangle DEF$. The Segment Duplication Postulate allows you to locate a point P on $\overline{AB}$ such that $PB = DE$. The Parallel Postulate allows you to construct a line $\overleftrightarrow{PQ}$ parallel to $\overline{AC}$. Then $\angle A \cong \angle QPB$ by the Corresponding Angles Postulate.

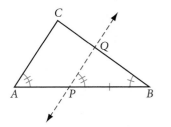
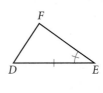

Now, if you can show that $\triangle PBQ \cong \triangle DEF$, then you will have two congruent pairs of angles to prove $\triangle ABC \sim \triangle DEF$. So, how do you show that $\triangle PBQ \cong \triangle DEF$? If you can get $\triangle ABC \sim \triangle PBQ$, then $\frac{AB}{PB} = \frac{BC}{BQ}$. It is given that $\frac{AB}{DE} = \frac{BC}{EF}$, and you constructed $PB = DE$. With some algebra and substitution, you can get $EF = BQ$. Then the two triangles will be congruent by the SAS Congruence Postulate.

Here is the directed two-column proof.

Statement	**Reason**
1. Locate P such that $PB = DE$	1. Segment Duplication Postulate
2. Construct $\overline{PQ} \parallel \overline{AC}$	2. Parallel Postulate
3. $\angle A \cong \angle QPB$	3. Corresponding Angles Postulate
4. $\angle B \cong \angle B$	4. Reflexive property of congruence
5. $\triangle ABC \sim \triangle PBQ$	5. AA Similarity Postulate
6. $\frac{AB}{PB} = \frac{BC}{BQ}$	6. Corresponding sides of similar triangles are proportional (CSSTP)
7. $\frac{AB}{DE} = \frac{BC}{BQ}$	7. Substitution
8. $\frac{AB}{DE} = \frac{BC}{EF}$	8. Given
9. $\frac{BC}{BQ} = \frac{BC}{EF}$	9. Transitive property of equality
10. $BQ = EF$	10. Algebra operations
11. $\angle B \cong \angle E$	11. Given
12. $\triangle PBQ \cong \triangle DEF$	12. SAS Congruence Postulate
13. $\angle QPB \cong \angle D$	13. CPCTC
14. $\angle A \cong \angle D$	14. Substitution
15. $\triangle ABC \sim \triangle DEF$	15. AA Similarity Postulate

This proves the SAS Similarity Conjecture.

The proof in the example above may seem complicated, but it relies on triangle congruence and triangle similarity postulates. Reading the plan again can help you follow the steps in the proof.

You can now call the SAS Similarity Conjecture the SAS Similarity Theorem and add it to your theorem list.

In the following developing proof activity you will use the SAS Similarity Theorem to prove the SSS Similarity Conjecture.

SSS Similarity Conjecture

Similarity proofs can be challenging. Consider the statements below and work with your group to prove the SSS Similarity Conjecture: If the three sides of one triangle are proportional to the three sides of another triangle, then the two triangles are similar.

Identify the given and show.

Restate what is given and what you must show in terms of this diagram.

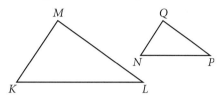

Plan your proof. (*Hint:* Use an auxiliary line like the one in the example.)

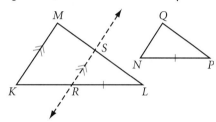

Copy the first ten statements and provide the reasons. Then write the remaining steps and reasons necessary to complete the proof.

Statement	Reason
1. Locate R such that $RL = NP$	**1.** ? Postulate
2. Construct $\overleftrightarrow{RS} \parallel \overline{KM}$	**2.** ? Postulate
3. $\angle SRL \cong \angle K$	**3.** ? Postulate
4. $\angle RSL \cong \angle M$	**4.** ? Postulate
5. $\triangle KLM \sim \triangle RLS$	**5.** ?
6. $\dfrac{KL}{RL} = \dfrac{LM}{LS} = \dfrac{MK}{SR}$	**6.** ?
7. $\dfrac{KL}{NP} = \dfrac{LM}{LS}$	**7.** ?
8. $\dfrac{KL}{NP} = \dfrac{LM}{PQ}$	**8.** ?
9. $\dfrac{KL}{NP} = \dfrac{MK}{SR}$	**9.** ?
10. $\dfrac{KL}{NP} = \dfrac{MK}{QN}$	**10.** ?
$\vdots$	$\vdots$

Draw arrows to show the flow of logic in your directed two-column proof.

When you have completed the proof, you can call the SSS Similarity Conjecture the SSS Similarity Theorem and add it to your theorem list.

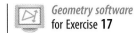
In Exercises 1 and 2, write a proof and draw the family tree of each theorem. If the family tree is completely supported by theorems and postulates, add the theorem to your list.

1. If two triangles are similar, then corresponding altitudes are proportional to the corresponding sides. (Corresponding Altitudes Theorem)

2. If two triangles are similar, then corresponding medians are proportional to the corresponding sides. (Corresponding Medians Theorem)

In Exercises 3–10, write a proof of the conjecture. Once you have completed the proofs, add the theorems to your list. As always, you may use theorems that have been proved in previous exercises in your proofs.

3. If two triangles are similar, then corresponding angle bisectors are proportional to the corresponding sides. (Corresponding Angle Bisectors Theorem)

4. If a line passes through two sides of a triangle parallel to the third side, then it divides the two sides proportionally. (Parallel/Proportionality Theorem) ⓗ

5. If a line passes through two sides of a triangle dividing them proportionally, then it is parallel to the third side. (Converse of the Parallel/Proportionality Theorem) ⓗ

6. If you drop an altitude from the vertex of a right angle to its hypotenuse, then it divides the right triangle into two right triangles that are similar to each other and to the original right triangle. (Three Similar Right Triangles Theorem) ⓗ

7. The length of the altitude to the hypotenuse of a right triangle is the geometric mean of the lengths of the two segments on the hypotenuse. (Altitude to the Hypotenuse Theorem) ⓗ

8. The Pythagorean Theorem ⓗ

9. Converse of the Pythagorean Theorem ⓗ

10. If the hypotenuse and one leg of a right triangle are congruent to the hypotenuse and one leg of another right triangle, then the two right triangles are congruent. (Hypotenuse-Leg Theorem) ⓗ

11. Create a family tree for the Parallel/Proportionality Theorem.

12. Create a family tree for the SSS Similarity Theorem.

13. Create a family tree for the Pythagorean Theorem.

This monument in Wellington, New Zealand, was designed by Maori architect Rewi Thompson. How would you describe the shape of the monument? How might the artist have used geometry in planning the construction?

Review

14. A circle with a 9.6 cm diameter has two parallel chords with lengths 5.2 cm and 8.2 cm. How far apart are the chords? Find two possible answers.

15. Choose **A** if the value is greater in the regular hexagon.

Choose **B** if the value is greater in the regular pentagon.

Choose **C** if the values are equal in both figures.

Choose **D** if it cannot be determined which value is greater.

10 cm

12 cm

Regular hexagon   Regular pentagon

a. Perimeter   **b.** Apothem   **c.** Area

d. Sum of interior angles   **e.** Sum of exterior angles

16. Cut out a small nonsymmetric concave quadrilateral. Number the vertices. Use your cut-out as a template to create a tessellation. Trace about 10 images that fit together to cover part of the plane. Number the vertices of each image to match the numbers on your cut-out.

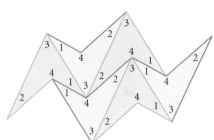

a. Draw two different translation vectors that transform your tessellation onto itself. How do these two vectors relate to your original quadrilateral?

b. Pick a quadrilateral in your tessellation. What transformation will transform the quadrilateral you picked onto an adjacent quadrilateral? With that transformation, what happens to the rest of the tessellation?

17. The diagram at right shows a scalene triangle with angle bisector $\overline{CG}$, and perpendicular bisector $\overline{GE}$ of side $\overline{AB}$. Study the diagram.

a. According to the diagram, which triangles are congruent?

b. You can use congruent triangles to prove that $\triangle ABC$ is isosceles. How?

c. Given a scalene triangle, you proved that it is isosceles. What's wrong with this proof?

d. Use geometry software to re-create the construction. What does the sketch tell you about what's wrong?

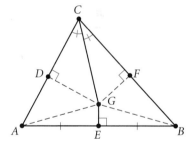

18. Dakota Davis is at an archaeological dig where he has uncovered a stone voussoir that resembles an isosceles trapezoidal prism. He assumes this stone is one of a number of identical voissoirs for a semicircular arch. Dakota measures the sides and angles of the trapezoidal face. The stone voissoir has bases that measure 40.0 cm and 50.0 cm, congruent legs that measure 48.0 cm each with angles of 84° and 96°. Help Dakota determine the rise and span of the arch to the nearest tenth of a centimeter when it was standing. What was the total height of the arch? Explain your method. *(h)*

Coordinate Proof

You can prove conjectures involving midpoints, slope, and distance using analytic geometry. When you do this, you create a **coordinate proof**. Coordinate proofs rely on the premises of geometry and these three properties from algebra.

> ## Coordinate Midpoint Property
>
> If (x_1, y_1) and (x_2, y_2) are the coordinates of the endpoints of a segment, then the coordinates of the midpoint are $\left(\frac{x_1 + x_2}{2}, \frac{y_1 + y_2}{2}\right)$.

> ## Parallel Slope Property
>
> In a coordinate plane, two distinct lines are parallel if and only if their slopes are equal.

> ## Perpendicular Slope Property
>
> In a coordinate plane, two nonvertical lines are perpendicular if and only if their slopes are opposite reciprocals of each other.

For coordinate proofs, you also use the coordinate version of the Pythagorean Theorem, the distance formula.

> ## Distance Formula
>
> The distance between points $A(x_1, y_1)$ and $B(x_2, y_2)$ is given by
> $$AB^2 = (x_2 - x_1)^2 + (y_2 - y_1)^2 \text{ or } AB = \sqrt{(x_2 - x_1)^2 + (y_2 - y_1)^2}.$$

The process you use in a coordinate proof contains the same five tasks that you learned in Lesson 13.2. However, in Task 2, you draw and label a diagram on a coordinate plane. Locate the vertices and other points of your diagram so that they reflect the given information, yet their coordinates do not restrict the generality of your diagram. In other words, do not assume any extra properties for your figure, besides the ones given in its definition.

EXAMPLE A | Write a coordinate proof of the Square Diagonals Conjecture: The diagonals of a square are congruent and are perpendicular bisectors of each other.

Solution | **Task 1: Identify what is given and what you must show.**

Given: A square with both diagonals

Show: The diagonals are congruent and are perpendicular bisectors of each other

Task 2: Draw and label a diagram on the coordinate plane.

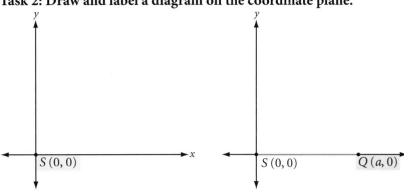

1. Placing one vertex at the origin will simplify later calculations because it is easy to work with zeros.

2. Placing the second vertex on the x-axis also simplifies calculations because the y-coordinate is zero. To remain general, call the x-coordinate a.

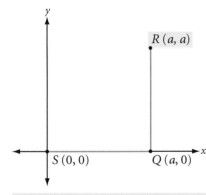

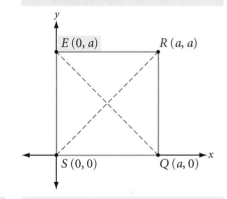

3. $\overline{RQ}$ needs to be vertical to form a right angle with $\overline{SQ}$, which is horizontal. $\overline{RQ}$ also needs to be the same length. So, R is placed a units vertically above Q.

4. The last vertex is placed a units above S.

You can check that SQRE fits the definition of a square—an equiangular, equilateral parallelogram.

Slope of $SQ = \dfrac{0-0}{a-0} = \dfrac{0}{a} = 0$

$SQ = \sqrt{(a-0)^2 + (0-0)^2} = \sqrt{a^2} = a$

Slope of $\overline{QR} = \dfrac{a-0}{a-a} = \dfrac{a}{0}$ (undefined)

$QR = \sqrt{(a-a)^2 + (a-0)^2} = \sqrt{a^2} = a$

Slope of $\overline{RE} = \dfrac{a-a}{0-a} = \dfrac{0}{-a} = 0$

$RE = \sqrt{(0-a)^2 + (a-a)^2} = \sqrt{a^2} = a$

Slope of $\overline{ES} = \dfrac{0-a}{0-0} = \dfrac{-a}{0}$ (undefined)

$ES = \sqrt{(0-0)^2 + (0-a)^2} = \sqrt{a^2} = a$

Opposite sides have the same slope and are therefore parallel, so $SQRE$ is a parallelogram. Also, from the slopes, $\overline{SQ}$ and $\overline{RE}$ are horizontal and $\overline{QR}$ and $\overline{ES}$ are vertical, so all angles are right angles and the parallelogram is equiangular. Lastly, all the sides have the same length, so the parallelogram is equilateral. $SQRE$ is an equiangular, equilateral parallelogram and is a square by definition.

Task 3: Restate what is given and what you must show in terms of the diagram.

Given: Square $SQRE$ with diagonals $\overline{SR}$ and $\overline{QE}$

Show: $\overline{SR} \cong \overline{QE}$, $\overline{SR}$ and $\overline{QE}$ bisect each other, and $\overline{SR} \perp \overline{QE}$

Task 4: Plan a proof. Organize your reasoning mentally or on paper.

To show that $\overline{SR} \cong \overline{QE}$, you must show that both segments have the same length. To show that $\overline{SR}$ and $\overline{QE}$ bisect each other, you must show that the segments share the same midpoint. To show that $\overline{SR} \perp \overline{QE}$, you must show that the segments have opposite reciprocal slopes. Because you know the coordinates of the endpoints of both $\overline{SR}$ and $\overline{QE}$, you can use the distance formula, the coordinate midpoint property, and the definition of slope to do the necessary calculations, and to show that the perpendicular slope property is satisfied.

Task 5: Create a proof from your plan.

Use the distance formula to find SR and QE.

$$SR = \sqrt{(a-0)^2 + (a-0)^2} = \sqrt{2a^2} = a\sqrt{2}$$

$$QE = \sqrt{(a-0)^2 + (0-a)^2} = \sqrt{2a^2} = a\sqrt{2}$$

So, by the definition of congruence, $\overline{SR} \cong \overline{QE}$ because both segments have the same length.

Use the coordinate midpoint property to find the midpoints of $\overline{SR}$ and $\overline{QE}$.

Midpoint of $\overline{SR} = \left(\dfrac{0+a}{2}, \dfrac{0+a}{2}\right) = (0.5a, 0.5a)$

Midpoint of $\overline{QE} = \left(\dfrac{0+a}{2}, \dfrac{a+0}{2}\right) = (0.5a, 0.5a)$

So, $\overline{SR}$ and $\overline{QE}$ bisect each other because both segments have the same midpoint.

Finally, compare the slopes of $\overline{SR}$ and $\overline{QE}$.

Slope of $\overline{SR} = \dfrac{a-0}{a-0} = 1$

Slope of $\overline{QE} = \dfrac{a-0}{0-a} = -1$

So, $\overline{SR} \perp \overline{QE}$ by the perpendicular slope property because the segments have opposite reciprocal slopes.

Therefore, the diagonals of a square are congruent and are perpendicular bisectors of each other.

Add the Square Diagonals Theorem to your list.

Here's another example. See if you can recognize how the five tasks result in this proof.

EXAMPLE B Write a coordinate proof of this conditional statement: If the diagonals of a quadrilateral bisect each other, then the quadrilateral is a parallelogram.

Solution **Given:** Quadrilateral $ABCD$ with diagonals $\overline{AC}$ and $\overline{BD}$ that bisect each other (common midpoint M)

Show: $ABCD$ is a parallelogram

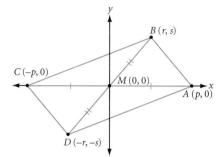

Proof

Slope of $\overline{AB} = \dfrac{s-0}{r-p} = \dfrac{s}{r-p}$

Slope of $\overline{BC} = \dfrac{0-s}{-p-r} = \dfrac{-(s)}{-(p+r)} = \dfrac{s}{p+r}$

Slope of $\overline{CD} = \dfrac{-s-0}{-r-(-p)} = \dfrac{-(s)}{-(r-p)} = \dfrac{s}{r-p}$

Slope of $\overline{DA} = \dfrac{0-(-s)}{p-(-r)} = \dfrac{s}{p+r}$

Opposite sides $\overline{AB}$ and $\overline{CD}$ have equal slopes, $\frac{s}{r-p}$. Opposite sides $\overline{BC}$ and $\overline{DA}$ have equal slopes, $\frac{s}{p+r}$. So, each pair is parallel by the parallel slope property. Therefore, quadrilateral $ABCD$ is a parallelogram by definition. Add this theorem to your list.

It is clear from these examples that creating a diagram on a coordinate plane is a significant challenge in a coordinate proof. The first seven exercises will give you some more practice creating these diagrams.

Exercises

In Exercises 1–3, each diagram shows a convenient general position of a polygon on a coordinate plane. Find the missing coordinates.

1. Triangle ABC is isosceles.

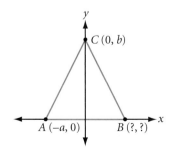

2. Quadrilateral $ABCD$ is a parallelogram.

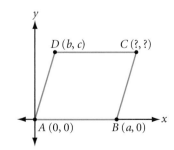

3. Quadrilateral $ABCD$ is a rhombus.

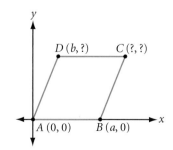

In Exercises 4–7, draw each figure on a coordinate plane. Assign general coordinates to each point of the figure. Then use the coordinate midpoint property, parallel slope property, perpendicular slope property, and/or the distance formula to check that the coordinates you have assigned meet the definition of the figure.

4. Rectangle *RECT*

5. Triangle *TRI* with its three midsegments

6. Isosceles trapezoid *TRAP*

7. Equilateral triangle *EQU*

In Exercises 8–13, write a coordinate proof of each conjecture. If it cannot be proven, write "cannot be proven."

8. The diagonals of a rectangle are congruent.

9. The midsegment of a triangle is parallel to the third side and half the length of the third side.

10. The midsegment of a trapezoid is parallel to the bases.

11. If only one diagonal of a quadrilateral is the perpendicular bisector of the other diagonal, then the quadrilateral is a kite.

12. The figure formed by connecting the midpoints of the sides of a quadrilateral is a parallelogram.

13. The quadrilateral formed by connecting the midpoint of the base to the midpoint of each leg in an isosceles triangle is a rhombus.

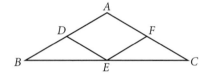

DEVELOPING MATHEMATICAL REASONING

A Precarious Proof

You have all the money you need.

Let h = the money you have.
Let n = the money you need.

Most people think that the money they have is some amount less than the money they need. Stated mathematically, $h = n - p$ for some positive p.

If $h = n - p$, then

$$h(h - n) = (n - p)(h - n)$$
$$h^2 - hn = hn - n^2 - hp + np$$
$$h^2 - hn + hp = hn - n^2 + np$$
$$h(h - n + p) = n(h - n + p)$$

Therefore $h = n$.

So the money you have is equal to the money you need!

Is there a flaw in this proof?

EXPLORATION

Midpoint Quadrilaterals

In Chapter 5 you discovered that when you connect consecutive midpoints of a quadrilateral the quadrilateral formed is a parallelogram. You proved this discovery using the Triangle Midsegment Conjecture. For example, connecting the midpoints *E, F, G, H* in quadrilateral *ABCD* gives you quadrilateral *EFGH*. When you drew the two diagonals $\overline{AC}$ and $\overline{BD}$ you recognized that the pairs of opposite sides of *EFGH* were parallel to the diagonals and thus *EFGH* was a parallelogram. This was also true for concave quadrilaterals. This property was first discovered and proved by the French mathematician, Pierre Varignon (1654–1722) and is called Varignon's Theorem.

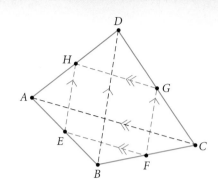

In this series of explorations you will investigate other "midpoint quadrilaterals." These investigations can be performed with compass and straightedge or patty paper, but with geometry software you are able to manipulate the figures and look for what remains constant. For each exploration, investigate, create a conjecture, and prove it if it is true or explain why it is false.

1. Construct one segment *AC* perpendicular to a second segment *BD*. Connect the four endpoints creating quadrilateral *ABCD*. Locate the midpoints of the four sides of *ABCD*. Connect the midpoints to create another quadrilateral *PQRS*. Grab and drag the vertices of *ABCD*. What do you notice? Make a conjecture about quadrilateral *PQRS* and prove it.

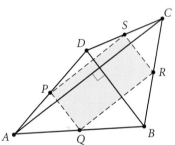

2. Construct a rhombus and connect the consecutive midpoints to form a parallelogram. Drag a vertex or a side and observe what happens. Is it any special type of parallelogram? If so, prove it. If not, explain why not.

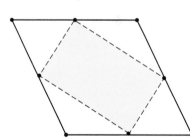

3. Construct a square and connect the consecutive midpoints to form a parallelogram. Drag a vertex or a side and observe what happens. Is it any special type of parallelogram? If so, prove it. If not, explain why not.

4. Construct a kite and connect the consecutive midpoints to form a parallelogram. Drag a vertex or a side and observe what happens. Is it any special type of parallelogram? If so, prove it. If not, explain why not.

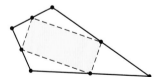

5. Construct a rectangle and connect the consecutive midpoints to form a parallelogram. Drag a vertex or a side and observe what happens. Is it any special type of parallelogram? If so, prove it. If not, explain why not.

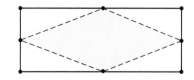

LESSON

13.8

From Conjecture to Proof

During your study of geometry you have investigated geometric relationships inductively and then proved your conjectures with deductive reasoning. In this lesson you will use all the material you have learned this year on these final performance tasks. Use your reasoning skills to perform investigations, make your own conjectures, and prove your conjectures. Although these geometric situations can be explored with just compass and straightedge or patty paper, they are probably best explored using geometry software.

Capstone Performance Tasks

INVESTIGATE–CONJECTURE–PROVE For each task, use geometry software to investigate the construction. State a conjecture about your results and write a proof to confirm your conjecture.

YOU WILL NEED

Geometry software
for Exercises 1–9

1. Construct a rectangle. Select a random point in the interior of the rectangle and draw segments to each of the four vertices. Drag the random point and observe the areas of the four triangles. Do you notice anything?

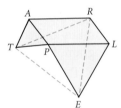

2. Construct a parallelogram *PARL*. Construct equilateral triangles △*PAT* and △*PLE* on consecutive sides to the exterior of the parallelogram. Construct △*TRE*. What do you notice about △*TRE*? Drag the vertices of the parallelogram and observe.

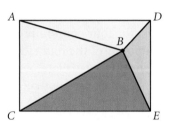

3. A trapezoid with vertices *T*(−6, −4), *R*(6, 0), *A*(2, 4), and *P*(−4, 2), has the midsegment and the segment connecting the midpoints of the parallel sides constructed. What are the coordinates of their intersection? What do you observe? Is this true for all trapezoids?

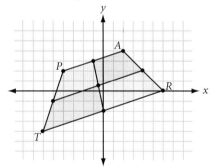

4. Two segments are constructed from each vertex of a pair of opposite angles of a parallelogram to the midpoints of the opposite sides. The vertices of the parallelogram are *P*(−4, −4), *A*(8, −4), *R*(4, 4), and *E*(−8, 4). What do you observe about the quadrilateral formed by the four segments? Is this true for all parallelograms?

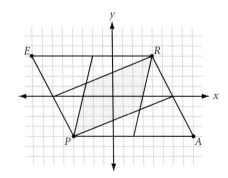

5. Construct a rectangle. Bisect each of the four right angles. Drag the vertices of the rectangle and observe the quadrilateral formed by the intersection of the four angle bisectors. What do you notice?

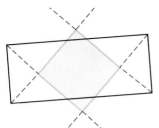

6. Construct a rectangle. Construct one diagonal. Construct the centroid of each of the two triangles formed by the diagonal. Construct the second diagonal of the rectangle. Construct the centroid of each of the two triangles formed by this second diagonal. What do you notice about the polygon formed by the four centroids? ⓗ

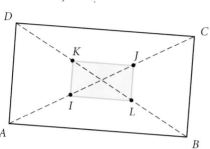

7. Construct a parallelogram. Construct one diagonal. Construct the centroid of each of the two triangles formed by the diagonal. Construct the second diagonal of the parallelogram. Construct the centroid of each of the two triangles formed by this second diagonal. What do you notice about the polygon formed by the four centroids? ⓗ

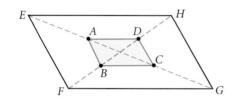

8. Construct an isosceles trapezoid. Construct one diagonal. Construct the centroid of each of the two triangles formed by the diagonal. Construct the second diagonal of the isosceles trapezoid. Construct the centroid of each of the two triangles formed by this second diagonal. What do you notice about the polygon formed by the four centroids? ⓗ

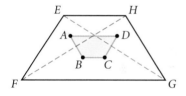

9. Construct a kite. Construct one diagonal. Construct the centroid of each of the two triangles formed by the diagonal. Construct the second diagonal of the kite. Construct the centroid of each of the two triangles formed by this second diagonal. What do you notice about the polygon formed by the four centroids? ⓗ

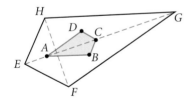

In this course you have discovered geometry properties and made conjectures based on inductive reasoning. You have also used deductive reasoning to explain why some of your conjectures were true. In this chapter you have focused on geometry as a deductive system. You learned about the premises of geometry. Starting fresh with these premises, you built a system of theorems.

By discovering geometry and then examining it as a mathematical system, you have been following in the footsteps of mathematicians throughout history. Your discoveries gave you an understanding of how geometry works. Proofs gave you the tools for taking apart your discoveries and understanding why they work.

Exercises

YOU WILL NEED

  Geometry software for Exercises **28–33**

In Exercises 1–7, identify each statement as true or false. For each false statement, sketch a counterexample or explain why it is false.

1. If one pair of sides of a quadrilateral are parallel and the other pair of sides are congruent, then the quadrilateral is a parallelogram.

2. If consecutive angles of a quadrilateral are supplementary, then the quadrilateral is a parallelogram.

3. If the diagonals of a quadrilateral are congruent, then the quadrilateral is a rectangle.

4. Two exterior angles of an obtuse triangle are obtuse.

5. The opposite angles of a quadrilateral inscribed within a circle are congruent.

6. The diagonals of a trapezoid bisect each other.

7. The midpoint of the hypotenuse of a right triangle is equidistant from all three vertices.

In Exercises 8–13, identify each statement as true or false. If true, prove it. If false, give a counterexample or explain why it is false.

8. If the diagonals of a parallelogram bisect the angles, then the parallelogram is a square.

9. The angle bisectors of one pair of base angles of an isosceles trapezoid are perpendicular.

10. The perpendicular bisectors to the congruent sides of an isosceles trapezoid are perpendicular.

11. The segment joining the feet of the altitudes on the two congruent sides of an isosceles triangle is parallel to the third side.

12. The diagonals of a rhombus are perpendicular.

13. The bisectors of a pair of opposite angles of a parallelogram are parallel.

In Exercises 14–18, complete each statement.

14. A tangent is _?_ to the radius drawn to the point of tangency.

15. Tangent segments from a point to a circle are _?_.

16. The perpendicular bisector of a chord passes through _?_.

17. The three midsegments of a triangle divide the triangle into _?_.

18. A lemma is _?_.

19. Restate this conjecture as a conditional: The segment joining the midpoints of the diagonals of a trapezoid is parallel to the bases.

20. Sometimes a proof requires a construction. If you need an angle bisector in a proof, which postulate allows you to construct one?

21. If an altitude is needed in a proof, which postulate allows you to construct one?

22. Describe the procedure for an indirect proof.

In Exercises 23–27, devise a plan and write a proof of each conjecture.

23. Refer to the figure at right.
   Given: Circle O with chords $\overline{PN}, \overline{ET}, \overline{NA}, \overline{TP}, \overline{AE}$
   Show: $m\angle P + m\angle E + m\angle N + m\angle T + m\angle A = 180°$

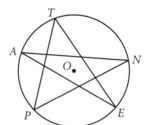

24. If a triangle is a right triangle, then it has at least one angle whose measure is less than or equal to 45°.

25. Prove the Triangle Midsegment Conjecture.

26. Prove the Trapezoid Midsegment Conjecture.

27. If two chords intersect in a circle, the product of the segment lengths on one chord is equal to the product of the segment lengths on the other chord.

28. **INVESTIGATE-CONJECTURE-PROVE** Construct squares $ABFG$ and $CDEF$ on the sides of equilateral $\triangle BCF$. Construct segments BG, GE, and EC. What type of quadrilateral does $BGEC$ appear to be? State a conjecture and prove it. ⓗ

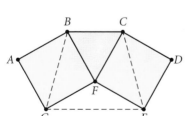

29. **INVESTIGATE-CONJECTURE-PROVE** Place points P and A on your paper. Construct a point A' such that A is the midpoint of $\overline{PA'}$. Place a point B on your paper. Construct a point B' such that B is the midpoint of $\overline{PB'}$. Compare the distances AB and $A'B'$. What do you notice about the segments? Make a conjecture. Test it with a third point C. Are you convinced? Prove it.

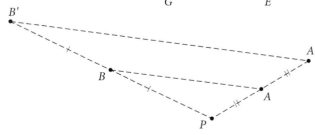

30. **INVESTIGATE–CONJECTURE–PROVE** Using the parallel edges of your ruler draw a pair of parallel lines. Draw three segments so that each segment has an endpoint on each of the parallel lines. Find the midpoints of these three segments. What do you observe? Do the midpoints appear to be collinear? Explain why. Does the line through the midpoints appear to be parallel to the two parallel lines? Explain why.

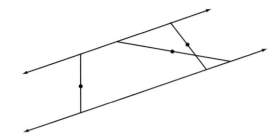

31. **INVESTIGATE–CONJECTURE–PROVE** Draw a line AE and a point P not on the line. Draw three lines through P that pass through $\overline{AE}$ and label their point of intersection B, C, and D. Find the midpoints K, L, and M of segments PB, PC, and PD respectively. What do you observe? Do the midpoints K, L, and M appear to be collinear? Explain why you think that. Does the line through the midpoints appear to be parallel to $\overline{AE}$? Prove your conjecture.

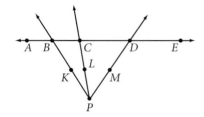

32. **INVESTIGATE–CONJECTURE–PROVE** Construct an isosceles trapezoid and connect the consecutive midpoints to form a parallelogram. Drag a vertex or a side and observe what happens. Is it any special type of parallelogram? If so, prove it. If not, explain why not.

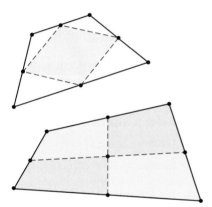

33. **INVESTIGATE–CONJECTURE–PROVE** Construct a quadrilateral and locate the midpoints of its four sides. Construct segments connecting the midpoints of the opposite sides. Construct the point of intersection of the two segments. Drag a vertex or a side of the quadrilateral and observe the lengths of the two segments that meet at the intersection. Make a conjecture and prove it.

Hints for Selected Exercises

...there are no answers to the problems of life in the back of the book.

SØREN KIERKEGAARD

You will find hints below for exercises that are marked with an ⓗ in the text. Instead of turning to a hint before you've tried to solve a problem on your own, make a serious effort to solve the problem without help. But if you need additional help to solve a problem, this is the place to look.

0

LESSON 0.1, PAGE 5

7. Here's the title of the sculpture.
Early morning calm
knotweed stalks
pushed into lake bottom
made complete by their own reflection

Derwent Water, Cumbria, February 20 and March 8–9, 1988

LESSON 0.2, PAGE 8

3. Design 1 Use one-half of the Astrid four times. **Design 2** Draw a triangle whose sides are the same length. Connect the midpoints of the sides with line segments and leave the middle triangle empty. Repeat the process on the three other triangles. Then repeat the rule again.

Design 3 Draw a 6-sided figure whose sides are the same length. Mark the point on each side that is one-third of the length of the side. Connect the points and repeat the process.

LESSON 0.3, PAGE 11

2. Use isometric dot paper, or draw a regular hexagon with sides of length 2. Each vertex of the hexagon will be the center of a circle with radius 1. Fit the seventh small circle inside the other six. The large circle has the same center as the seventh small circle, but with radius 3.

LESSON 0.6, PAGE 20

5. Draw two identical squares, one rotated $\frac{1}{8}$ turn, or 45°, from the other. Where is the center of each arc located?

1

LESSON 1.2, PAGES 37–41

12. Find $m\angle CQA$ and $m\angle BQA$ and subtract.

27. Don't forget that at half past the hour, the hour hand will be halfway between the 3 and the 4.

37. A $\frac{1}{4}$ rotation $= \frac{1}{4} \cdot 360°$. Subtract the sum of 15° and 21° from that result.

LESSON 1.3, PAGES 47–49

18. Do not limit your thinking to just two dimensions.

27. The measure of the incoming angle equals the measure of the outgoing angle (just as in pool).

28. Start with point C and use trial and error.

LESSON 1.4, PAGES 52–54

15. The order of the letters matters.

20. Look back at the investigation.

27. Only one of these is impossible.

LESSON 1.5, PAGES 58–59

14. There are four possible locations for point R. The slope of $\overline{CL}$ is $\frac{1}{5}$, so the slope of the perpendicular segment is $\frac{-5}{1}$ or $\frac{5}{-1}$.

22. Locate the midpoint of each rod. Draw the segment that contains all the midpoints.

LESSON 1.6, PAGES 62–64

20. Draw your diagram on patty paper or tracing paper. Test your diagram by folding your paper along the line of reflection to see whether the two halves coincide. Your diagram should have only one pair of parallel sides.

LESSON 1.8, PAGES 74–76

8. The biggest face is 3 m by 4 m. Your diagram will look similar to the diagram for Step 4 on page 72, except that the shortest segment will be vertical.

9. How many boxes are in each layer? How many layers are in the solid?

23. Do not limit your thinking to two dimensions. This situation can be modeled by using three pencils to represent the three lines.

5. Try a vertical number line. Look closely at the last few days.

6. The vertical distance from the top of the pole to the lowest point of the cable is 15 feet. Compare that distance with the length of the cable.

7. Draw a diagram. Draw two points, A and B, on your paper. Locate a point that appears to be equally spaced from points A and B. The midpoint of $\overline{AB}$ is only one such point; find others. Connect the points into a line. For points in space, picture a plane between the two points.

15. Copy trapezoid ABCD onto patty paper or tracing paper. Rotate the tracing paper 90°, or $\frac{1}{4}$ turn, counterclockwise. Point A on the tracing paper should coincide with point A on the diagram in the book.

27. The number of hexagons is increasing by one each time, but the perimeter is increasing by four.

1. Conjectures are statements that generalize from a number of instances to "all." Therefore, Stony is saying, "All ? ."

4. Change all fractions to the same denominator.

7. $1 + 1 = 2, 1 + 2 = 3, 2 + 3 = 5, 3 + 5 = 8, \ldots$

8. $1^2, 2^2, 3^2, 4^2, \ldots$

17. Substitute 1 for n and evaluate the expression to find the first term. Substitute 2 for n to find the second term, and so on.

21. For example, "I learned by trial and error that you turn wood screws clockwise to screw them into wood and counterclockwise to remove them."

22. Factor into length times width. See table below.

24. Compare how many 1's there are in the numbers that are multiplied with the middle digit of the answer; then compare both quantities with the row number.

28. Imagine folding the square up and "wrapping" the two rectangles and the other triangle around the square.

29. Turn your book so that the red line is vertical. Imagine rotating the figure so that the part jutting out is facing back to the right.

47. Remember that a kite is a quadrilateral with two pairs of consecutive, congruent sides. One of the diagonals does bisect the angles of the kite, the other does not.

4. Compare this exercise with the Investigation Party Handshakes and with Exercise 3. What change can you make to each of those functions to fit this pattern?

5. This is like Exercise 4 except that you add the number of sides to the number of diagonals.

6. In other words, each time a new line is drawn, it passes through all the others. This also gives the maximum number of intersections.

8. Let a point represent each team, and let the segments connecting the points represent *one* game played between them.

13. What happens if points A and B are on the same side of point E?

19. See table below.

22. Cut out a rectangle like the one shown and tape it to your pencil. Rotate your pencil to see what shape the rotating rectangle forms.

4. Use the ordered pair rule to rewrite the coordinates of quadrilateral PQRS.

7. Notice that in addition to taking the opposite of x, the x- and y-coordinates are reversed.

22. (*Lesson 2.2*)

Term number	1	2	3	4	5	6	7	...	10
Number of dots in array	2	6	12	20	30	42	56	...	110
Number of dots factored	1 · 2	2 · 3	3 · 4	4 · 5	5 · ?			...	

20. (*Lesson 2.3*)

Term number	1	2	3	4	5	n
Number of circles in array	2	9	20	35	54	
Number of circles factored	2 · 1	3 · 3	4 · 5	5 · ?		

10. Is the original figure congruent to the image? What type of transformation does this imply?

13. Compare the coordinates of the original figure to the image. How do they change?

16. Which coordinates stay the same? Which change?

19. Use patty paper to determine what type of transformation is used to create the image.

22. Compare the coordinates of the original figure to the image. How do they change?

LESSON 2.4, PAGES 121–124

9. What is the smallest possible size for an obtuse angle?

21. The number of rows increases by two, and the number of columns increases by one.

LESSON 2.5, PAGES 134–137

4. Here is how to begin:
$a = 60°$ because of the Vertical Angles Conjecture.
$b = 120°$ because of the Linear Pair Conjecture.

26. Refer to Lesson 2.3, Exercise 5, but subtract the number of couples from each term because the couples don't shake hands.

28. Refer to Lesson 2.3, Exercise 4 and use trial and error.

LESSON 2.6, PAGES 141–144

4.

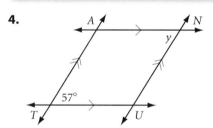

6.

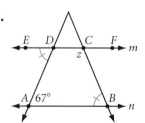

$\angle DAB$ and $\angle EDA$ are congruent by the Alternate Interior Angles Conjecture. So are $\angle CBA$ and $\angle BCF$.

7. Measures a, b, c, and d are all related by parallel lines. Measures e, f, g, h, i, j, k, and s are also all related by parallel lines.

17. Squares, rectangles, rhombuses, and kites are eliminated because they have reflectional symmetry.

20. You can add the first two function rules to find the third function rule.

21. Graph the original triangle and the new triangle on separate graphs. Cut one out and lay it on top of the other to see whether they are congruent.

LESSON 3.1, PAGES 152–154

2. Copy the first segment onto a ray. Copy the second segment immediately after the first.

11. You duplicated a triangle in Exercise 7. You can think of the quadrilateral as two triangles stuck together (they meet at the diagonal).

14. Fold the paper so that the two congruent sides of the triangle coincide.

17. It might be helpful to use pieces of dry spaghetti or to draw segments on patty paper and physically arrange them into a triangle.

LESSON 3.2, PAGES 157–159

2. Bisect, then bisect again.

3. Construct one pair of intersecting arcs, then change your compass setting to construct a second pair of intersecting arcs on the same side of the line segment as the first pair.

4. Bisect $\overline{CD}$ to get the length $\frac{1}{2}CD$. Subtract this length from $2AB$.

5. The average is the sum of the two lengths divided by the number of segments (two). Construct a segment of length $AB + CD$. Bisect the segment to get the average length. Or, take half of each, then add them.

9. Construct the median from the vertex to the midpoint.

17. Construct the perpendicular lines from each vertex of the triangle to the line of reflection to determine the distance from the vertices to the line of reflection.

24. It might be helpful to draw the 70° angle on patty paper, slide it to the appropriate position, and then draw the triangle on the patty paper.

LESSON 3.3, PAGES 162–164

5. Construct the perpendicular through point B to $\overrightarrow{TO}$. The altitude from point T is perpendicular to $\overrightarrow{BO}$.

6. Does your method from Investigation 1 still work? Can you modify it?

7. Construct right angles at Q and R.

12. Bisect $\overline{PR}$ to find the length of one side of the square.

14. The complement of ∠A and ∠A adjacent to each other make a right angle. So construct a perpendicular at point A.

16. Draw segments between corresponding vertices.

17. This will take two reflections. Start by drawing segment BE and finding the perpendicular bisector.

18. Look at two columns as a "group."
1st rectangle is 2 groups of 1
2nd rectangle is 3 groups of 3
3rd rectangle is 4 groups of 5
4th rectangle is 5 groups of 7
. . .
nth rectangle is $n + 1$ groups of $2n - 1$

22. Each central angle of a regular pentagon measures $\frac{360°}{5}$, or 72°. Construct a circle, measure off the five central angles, and then connect the points where the sides of the central angles intersect the circle.

LESSON 3.4, PAGES 166–169

19. Construct the angle bisector of ∠ABE.

25. Each central angle of a regular octagon measures $\frac{360°}{8}$, or 45°. Construct a circle, measure off the eight central angles, and then connect the points where the sides of the central angles intersect the circle.

26. Construct two lines perpendicular to each other, and then bisect all four right angles.

29. For the second triangle, it might be helpful to draw the 60° angle on patty paper and slide it to the appropriate position.

LESSON 3.5, PAGES 171–173

1. Plants in rows get equal space for better growth and it is easier to pick produce when ripe.

LESSON 3.6, PAGES 175–177

5. Duplicate ∠A and $\overline{AB}$ on one side of ∠A. Open the compass to length BC. If you put the compass point at point B, you'll find two possible locations to mark arcs for point C.

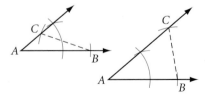

6. $y - x$ is the sum of the two equal sides. Find this length and bisect it to get the length of the other two legs of your triangle.

10.

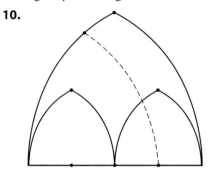

11. Construct a circle and locate 12 equally spaced points on it.

16. Start by drawing $\overline{AC}$ and labeling the endpoints. Extend the segment into a ray through point C. Draw two corresponding 110° angles with vertices at points A and C. Use the same process with $\overline{CE}$ to draw another corresponding 110° angle at point E as shown below, and finish by extending the line to find point R.

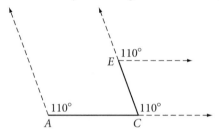

LESSON 3.8, PAGES 187–189

5. Find the incenter.

6. Find the circumcenter.

7. Draw a slightly larger circle on patty paper and try to fit it inside the triangle.

8. Draw a slightly smaller circle on patty paper and try to fit it outside the triangle.

19. Start by finding points whose coordinates add to 9, such as (3, 6) and (7, 2). Try writing an equation and graphing it.

20. One way is to construct the incenter by bisecting the two given angles. Then find two points with your compass on the unfinished sides, equidistant from the incenter and in the same direction (both closer to the missing point.) Now find a point equidistant from those two points with your compass. Draw the missing angle bisector through that point and the incenter.

24. The diagonal YE is a line of symmetry for the kite, and thus it divides the kite into two congruent triangles.

LESSON 3.9, PAGES 192–194

2. If $CM = 16$, then $UM = \frac{1}{2}(16) = 8$. If $TS = 21$, then $SM = \frac{1}{3}(21) = 7$.

8. A quadrilateral can be divided into two triangles in two different ways. How can you use the centroids of these triangles to find the centroid of the quadrilateral?

15. Construct the altitudes for the two other vertices. From the point where the two altitudes meet, construct a line perpendicular to the southern boundary of the triangle.

LESSON 4.1, PAGES 207–209

6. The total measure of the three angles is $3 \cdot 360°$ minus the sum of the interior angles of the triangle.

7. The sum of a linear pair of angles is 180°. So the total measure of the three angles is $3 \cdot 180°$ minus the sum of the interior angles of the triangle.

8. You can find a by looking at the large triangle that has 40° and 71° as its other measures. To find c, you first need to find the measure of the unmarked angle that is in the same triangle as a and b.

11. Draw a line and duplicate $\angle L$. Because the measures of the other two angles are equal, you can bisect the angle that is supplementary to $\angle L$ to get the other angles.

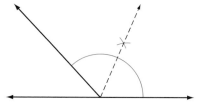

12. First, construct $\angle E$.

17. $m\angle A + m\angle B + x = 180°$ and $m\angle D + m\angle E + y = 180°$. Then use substitution to prove $x = y$.

LESSON 4.2, PAGES 214–216

1. $m\angle H + m\angle O = 180° - 22°$ and $m\angle H = m\angle O$.

10. Notice that $d = e$ and $d + e + e + 66° = 180°$. Next, find the alternate interior angle to c.

11. Notice that all the triangles are isosceles!

16. The sides do not have to be congruent.

17. Make $GK < MP$. **19.** Find the slopes.

25. Move each point right 5 units and down 3 units.

LESSON 4.3, PAGES 223–225

6. Use the Side-Angle Inequality Conjecture to find an inequality of sides for each triangle, then combine the inequalities.

12. Any side must be smaller than the sum of the other two sides. What must it be larger than?

16. All corresponding sides and angles are congruent. Can you see why? Remember to order the points correctly in stating the answer.

21. Try using the Triangle Sum Conjecture.

24. Label base angles of the isosceles triangles with x, y, and z. Use the Triangle Sum and Triangle Exterior Angle Conjectures to write equations relating these three variables.

LESSON 4.4, PAGES 230–232

4. Rotate one triangle 180°.

5. The shared side is congruent to itself.

11. Explain why the board secured across the back of the shelves on the right is a better shelving system than the one on the left.

12. Match congruent sides.

15. Take a closer look. Are corresponding parts congruent?

18. $UN = YA = 4, RA = US = 3, m\angle A = m\angle U = 90°$

20. Use the coordinate grid to create two right triangles. The two sides (vertical and horizontal) and the right angle between them in one triangle are congruent to the corresponding two sides and right angle between them in the other triangle.

24. Plot the triangles on a coordinate grid.

LESSON 4.5, PAGES 235–238

6. Flip one triangle over.

16. Because $\overline{BL} \parallel \overline{CK}$, you can show that various pairs of angles are congruent; but can you show any sides congruent?

22. The sides do not have to be congruent.

LESSON 4.6, PAGES 240–242

1. Don't forget to mark the shared segment as congruent to itself.

2. Use $\triangle CRN$ and $\triangle WON$.

4. Use $\triangle ATI$ and $\triangle GTS$.

5. Draw auxiliary line $\overline{FV}$.

7. Draw auxiliary line $\overline{UT}$.

10. Count the lengths of the horizontal and vertical segments, and label the right angles congruent.

12.

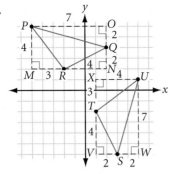

18. Make the included angles different.

22. Start with smaller grids. Copy and complete the table. Look for patterns.

Side Length	1	2	3	4	5	...	n	...	15
Elbows ⌐	4	4							
T's ⊤	0	4							
Crosses ✚	0	1							

LESSON 4.7, PAGES 245–248

8. Don't forget about the shared side and the Side-Angle Inequality Conjecture.

10. When you look at the larger triangles, ignore the marks for $\overline{OS} \cong \overline{RS}$. When you look at the smaller triangles, ignore the right-angle mark and the given statement $\overline{PO} \cong \overline{PR}$.

11. First, mark the vertical angles. In $\triangle ADM$, the side is included between the two angles. In $\triangle CRM$, the side is not included between the two angles.

14. Review incenter, circumcenter, orthocenter, and centroid.

16. You might use sugar cubes.

LESSON 4.8, PAGES 252–254

1. $AB + BC + AC = 48$
$AD = \frac{1}{2}AB$

10. $SL = LN = NS$ and $SI = LE = NT$. If you subtract equal lengths from equal lengths, then $IL = NE = TS$. If $\triangle SNL$ is equilateral, then it is equiangular, so $\angle S \cong \angle N \cong \angle L$. Now complete the explanation.

11. Use the vertex angle bisector as your auxiliary line segment.

14. At 3:15 the hands have not yet crossed each other. At 3:20 the hands have already crossed each other, because the minute hand is on the 4, but the hour hand is only one-third of its way from the 3 toward the 4. So, the hands overlap sometime between 3:15 and 3:20.

---

15. Make a table and look for a pattern.

19. Cycloheptane has seven carbons. How many H's branch off each C?

LESSON 5.1, PAGES 264–266

2. All angles are equal in measure.

6. $d + 44° + 30° = 180°$

7. $3g + 117° + 108° = 540°$

13. $(n - 2) \cdot 180° = 2700°$

14. $\frac{(n - 2) \cdot 180°}{n} = 156°$

17. Use the Triangle Sum Conjecture and angle addition. What does $i + j + k + l$ equal?

LESSON 5.2, PAGES 269–272

3. $24° = \frac{360°}{n}$

7. First, find the measure of an angle of the equiangular heptagon. Then find c by the Linear Pair Conjecture.

12. An obtuse angle measures greater than 90°, and the sum of exterior angles of a polygon is always 360°.

17. Look at $\triangle RAC$ and $\triangle DCA$.

18. Draw auxiliary line $\overline{AT}$.

LESSON 5.3, PAGES 278–281

7.

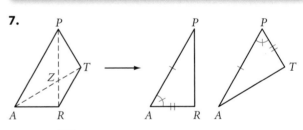

10. Add $\overline{YE}$ to the diagram in Exercise 9. You can show that the resulting triangles are congruent, and use this to show that $\overline{YE}$ is bisected and that the angles formed at the intersection of the diagonals are right angles. Or, you can show that B and Y lie on the perpendicular bisector of $\overline{YE}$ because they both are equidistant from the endpoints of $\overline{YE}$.

15. Construct $\angle I$ and $\angle W$ at the ends of $\overline{WI}$. Construct $\overline{IS}$. Construct a line through point S parallel to $\overline{WI}$.

19. Look at $\triangle AFG$ and $\triangle BEH$.

LESSON 5.4, PAGES 284–287

4. $VN = \frac{1}{2}VF$ and $NI = \frac{1}{2}EI$

8. With the midpoint of the longer diagonal as center and using the length of half the shorter diagonal as radius, construct a circle.

9. $PR = a$. Therefore, $MA = a$. Solve for the x-coordinate of M: $\underline{?} + a = b$. The height of M is equal to the height of A.

LESSON 5.5, PAGES 292–294

1. Consider the parallelogram below.

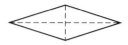

12. $\angle P$ and $\angle PAR$ are supplementary.

17. The diagonals of a square are equal in length and are perpendicular bisectors of each other.

18. Construct $\angle B$, then bisect it. Mark off the length of diagonal $\overline{BK}$ on the angle bisector. Then construct the perpendicular bisector of $\overline{BK}$.

20. Start by showing that two congruent segments that bisect each other form four congruent segments. To prove that the quadrilateral connecting the endpoints is a rectangle, use SAS to find two congruent pairs of triangles. Then show that the angle at each vertex of the quadrilateral is made up of the same two congruent angles. To show that the opposite sides are parallel, use the Converse of the AIA Conjecture.

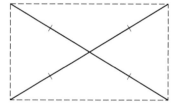

LESSON 5.6, PAGES 301–303

4. Use what is given, the *AIA* Conjecture and that fact that auxiliary line $\overline{PO}$ is shared by both triangles, to show that $\triangle SOP \cong \triangle APO$ by SAS. Then use CPCTP and the Converse of the AIA Conjecture to show that $\overline{PA} \parallel \overline{SO}$.

6. Look at $\triangle YIO$ and $\triangle OGY$.

7. Break up the rectangle into four triangles ($\triangle EAR$, etc.), and show that they are congruent triangles.

10. Calculate the measures of the angles of the regular polygons. Remember that there are 360° around any point.

13. The container is $\frac{8}{12} = \frac{2}{3}$ full. It will be $\frac{2}{3}$ full no matter which face it rests on.

LESSON 5.7, PAGES 307–310

2. $PO = \frac{1}{2}RA$

4. Use the Three Midsegments Conjecture.

11. Draw a diagonal of the original quadrilateral. Note that it's parallel to two other segments.

14. Show that $\overline{CP} \cong \overline{PD}$. Construct $\overline{PQ}$ parallel to $\overline{BC}$. Your task is to prove that $\triangle CPN \cong \triangle PDQ$.

15. Shade the resulting quadrilateral in a different color. Compare the angles.

16. Draw segments connecting the three midpoints. Seem familiar? Think Three Midsegments Conjecture.

LESSON 6.2, PAGES 325–327

7. Connect a pair of corresponding points with a segment. Construct two perpendiculars to the segment with half the distance between the two given figures between them.

15. Find the midpoint of the segment connecting the two points. Connect the midpoint to one of the endpoints with a curve. Copy the curve onto patty paper and rotate it about the midpoint.

EXPLORATION, PAGES 331–332

3. Reflect point B or C across the road.

LESSON 6.4, PAGES 350–351

9. If you are still unsure, use patty paper to trace the steps in the "Pegasus" example.

10. Work backward. Reflect a point of the 8-ball over the S cushion. Then reflect this image over the N cushion. Aim at this second image.

LESSON 6.6, PAGES 359–360

6. If you are still unsure, use patty paper to trace the steps in either Escher example.

LESSON 7.1, PAGES 378–381

12. All the corresponding angles are congruent. (Why?) Are all these ratios equal? $\frac{150}{165} = \underline{?}$, $\frac{120}{128} = \underline{?}$, $\frac{140}{154} = \underline{?}$, $\frac{180}{192} = \underline{?}$

17. Because the segments are parallel, $\angle B \cong \angle AED$ and $\angle C \cong \angle ADE$.

LESSON 7.2, PAGES 384–386

3. It helps to rotate △*ARK* so that you can see which sides correspond.

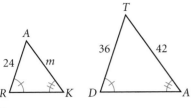

7.

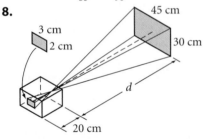

12. Draw a perpendicular segment from each point to the *x*-axis. Then use similar triangles.

LESSON 7.3, PAGES 388–390

3. Use the Pythagorean Theorem to first find the height of the flagpole.

7. Because △*PRE* ~ △*POC*, then $\frac{PR}{RE} = \frac{PO}{OC}$. Let $x = PR$. Then $\frac{x}{60} = \frac{x + 45}{90}$.

8.

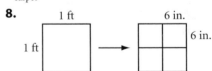

10. Draw the large and two small triangles separately to label and see them more clearly.

11.

13. The golden ratio is $\frac{2}{\sqrt{5} - 1}$. Let $AB = 2$ units. How would you construct the length $\sqrt{5}$? How would you construct the length $\sqrt{5} - 1$?

LESSON 7.4, PAGES 394–395

3. $\frac{CL}{ES} = \frac{CS}{EP}$ **9.** $\frac{12}{15} = \frac{x}{10 - x}$

11. You don't know the length of the third side, but you do know the ratio of its two parts is $\frac{2}{3}$.

12. Use the AA Similarity Conjecture for this proof. One pair of corresponding angles will be a nonbisected pair. The other pair of corresponding angles will consist of one-half of each bisected angle.

LESSON 7.5, PAGES 400–403

1. $\frac{4}{4 + 12} = \frac{a}{20}$

3. $\frac{60}{40} = \frac{c + 60}{70}$

6. $\frac{15}{36} \stackrel{?}{=} \frac{25}{55}$

8

LESSON 8.1, PAGES 413–414

15. The area of the triangle can be calculated in three different ways, but each should give the same area: $\frac{1}{2}(5)y = \frac{1}{2}(15)x = \frac{1}{2}(6)(9)$

LESSON 8.2, PAGES 416–418

6. Total cost is \$20/yd² = \$20/9 ft²; $A_{\text{carpet}} = 17 \cdot 27 - (6 \cdot 10 + 7 \cdot 9)$ ft²

8.

LESSON 8.3, PAGES 422–424

19. Divide the octagon into eight congruent triangles. Start by finding the area of the triangles.

20. Find the area of the large hexagon and subtract from it the area of the small hexagon. Because they are regular hexagons, the distance from the center to each vertex equals the length of each side.

LESSON 8.4, PAGES 426–428

6. The shaded area is equal to the area of the whole circle less the area of the smaller circle.

12. $10\pi = \frac{x}{360} \cdot \pi(10^2 - 8^2)$

15. What is the radius of each of the circles?

16. $A = \frac{1}{2}(b_1 + b_2)h$. Because the length of the midsegment is $\frac{1}{2}(b_1 + b_2)$, the formula can be rewritten $A = \text{midsegment} \cdot \text{height}$.

LESSON 8.5, PAGES 436–438

7. Use the formula for finding the area of a regular hexagon to find the area of each base. To find the area of the six lateral faces, imagine unfolding the six rectangles into one rectangle. The lateral area of this unfolded rectangle is the height times the perimeter.

9.

Top and bottom   Outer surface   Inner surface

LESSON 8.6, PAGES 441–443

1. $\left(\frac{6}{12}\right)^2 = \dfrac{\text{Area of } \triangle MSE}{72}$

3. If $\frac{\text{Area of } ZOID}{\text{Area of } TRAP} = \frac{16}{25}$, then the ratio of the lengths of corresponding sides is $\frac{4}{5}$.

7.

Area $= 6m^2$ Area $= 6n^2$

21. What kind of triangle is this?

TAKE ANOTHER LOOK, PAGES 449–450

12.

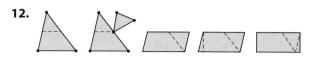

13.

LESSON 9.1, PAGES 455–457

2. $x + x + 70° = 180°$

5. $CP = PA = AO = OR$, $CT = TD = DS = SR$

8. From the Tangent Conjecture, you know that the tangent is perpendicular to the radius at the point of tangency.

15. Draw a diameter. Then bisect it repeatedly to find the centers of the circles.

16. Look at the angles in the quadrilateral formed.

21. Find and compare the radii.

LESSON 9.2, PAGES 461–464

9. $x + x + x + 72° = 360°$

21. Calculate the slope and midpoint of $\overline{AB}$. Recall that slopes of perpendicular lines are opposite reciprocals.

23. Draw the triangle formed by the three light switches. The center of the circumscribed circle would be equidistant from the three points.

LESSON 9.3, PAGES 468–470

3. $c + 120° = 2(95°)$

4. Draw in the radius to the tangent to form a right triangle.

14. The measure of each of the five angles is half the measure of its intercepted arc. But the five arcs add up to the complete circle.

15. $a = \frac{1}{2}(70°)$, $b = \frac{1}{2}(80°)$, $y = a + b$

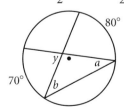

20. Draw the altitude to the point where the side of the triangle (extended if necessary) intersects the circle.

21. One possible location for the camera to get all students in the photo

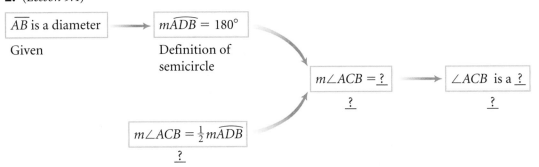

Students lined up for the photo

25. Start with an equilateral triangle whose vertices are the centers of the three congruent circles. Then locate the center of the triangle to find the center of the larger circle.

LESSON 9.4, PAGES 473–475

1. See flowchart below.   **2.** See flowchart below.

3. Note that $m\widehat{YLI} + m\widehat{YCI} = 360°$.

4. $\angle 1 \cong \angle 2$ by AIA, and $\angle 1$ and $\angle 2$ are inscribed angles.

5. Apply the Cyclic Quadrilateral Conjecture.

7. Draw four radii and use the Parallel Lines Intercepted Arcs Conjecture.

9. What type of triangle is $\triangle OAB$? What can you say about $\angle OBC$? How is $\overline{AB}$ related to any of the numbered angles? Use the Isosceles Triangle Conjecture, the Triangle Sum Conjecture, the Tangent Conjecture, and use the Substitution Property more than once.

20. Show that right triangles inside congruent isosceles triangles are congruent.

LESSON 9.5, PAGES 478–480

9. The diameter of the circle is 6 cm.

11. $\text{speed} = \dfrac{\text{distance}}{\text{time}} = \dfrac{\text{circumference}}{12 \text{ hours}}$

$= \dfrac{2\pi(2000 + 6400) \text{ km}}{12 \text{ hours}}$

17. Use the Inscribed Angle Conjecture and the Triangle Exterior Angle Conjecture.

22. Think about the pair of angles that form a linear pair and the isosceles triangle.

23. The center $(6, 3)$ is transformed to $(2, 1)$. Four points on the circle $(6, 0)$, $(9, 3)$, $(6, 6)$, and $(3, 3)$ are transformed to $(2, 0)$, $(3, 1)$, $(2, 2)$, and $(1, 1)$.

LESSON 9.6, PAGES 483–487

3. $\dfrac{210}{360}(24\pi)$

8. $m\widehat{AR} + 70° + m\widehat{EC} + 146° = 360°$,

$\dfrac{m\widehat{AR}}{360°}(2\pi r) = 40\pi$

9. The length of one lap is equal to $(2 \cdot 100) + (2 \cdot 20\pi)$. The total distance covered in 6 minutes is 4 laps.

11. $\dfrac{1}{9}(2\pi r) = 12$ meters

16. Since a semicircle equals π radians, $180° = \pi$ radians. Set up a proportion to find 1 radian.

---

1. (*Lesson 9.4*)

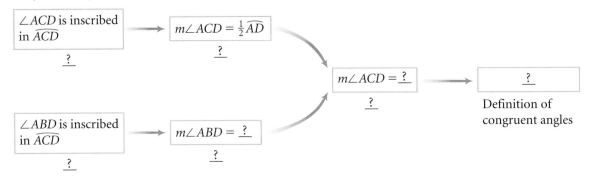

2. (*Lesson 9.4*)

Hints for Selected Exercises

20. Let z represent the measure of the exterior angle of $\triangle PBA$ formed by $\overline{BA}$ and tangent $\overrightarrow{PB}$.

21. The midsegment of a trapezoid is parallel to the bases, and the median to the base of an isosceles triangle is also the altitude.

22. It is not 180°. What fraction of a complete cycle has the minute hand moved since 10:00? Hasn't the little hand moved that same fraction of the way from 10:00 to 11:00?

26. Make an orderly list. Here is a beginning:
$\overline{RA}$ to $\overline{AL}$ to $\overline{LG}$
$\overline{RA}$ to $\overline{AN}$ to $\overline{NG}$

LESSON 10.1, PAGES 502–504

6. $6^2 + 6^2 = c^2$

11. The radius of the circle is the hypotenuse of the right triangle.

18. $a^2 + b^2$ must exactly equal c^2.

20. Let s represent the length of the side of the square. Then $s^2 + s^2 = 32^2$.

22. Three consecutive integers can be written algebraically as n, $n + 1$, and $n + 2$.

26. Show that the area of the entire square (c^2) is equal to the sum of the areas of the four right triangles and the area of the smaller square.

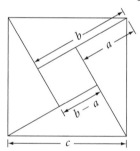

31. You could use the Pythagorean Theorem, but what if you just draw the prism unfolded?

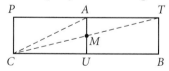

32. Because a radius is perpendicular to a tangent, $m\angle DCF = 90°$. Because all radii in a circle are congruent, $\triangle DCE$ is isosceles.

LESSON 10.2, PAGES 507–509

2. $b = $ hypotenuse $\div \sqrt{2}$

4. $d = \frac{1}{2} \cdot 20, c = d \cdot \sqrt{3}$

7. Draw diagonal $\overline{DB}$ to form a right triangle on the base of the cube and another right triangle in the interior of the cube.

9. Divide by $\sqrt{2}$ for the length of the leg.

14.

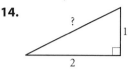

17. Draw an altitude of the equilateral triangle to form two 30°-60°-90° triangles.

20. Construct an isosceles right triangle with legs of length a; construct an equilateral triangle with sides of length $2a$ and construct an altitude; and construct a right triangle with legs of lengths $a\sqrt{2}$ and $a\sqrt{3}$.

23. Make the rays that form the right angle into lines, or draw an auxiliary line parallel to the other parallel lines through the vertex of the right angle.

LESSON 10.3, PAGES 510–513

2. The length of the hypotenuse is $(36 - x)$. Solve for x.

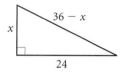

3. average speed $= \dfrac{d}{4 \text{ hours}}$

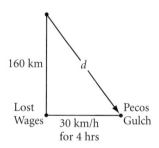

4. This is a two-step problem, so draw two right triangles. Find h, the height of the first triangle. The height of the second is 4 ft less than the height of the first. Then find x.

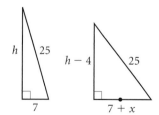

5. Find the apothem of the hexagon.

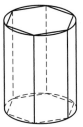

6.

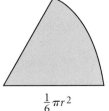 

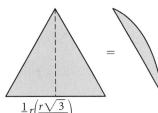

COORDINATE GEOMETRY 10, PAGE 520

3. Use the distance formula to find the length of the radius.

LESSON 10.4, PAGES 522–524

3. Find $m\angle DOB$ using the Quadrilateral Sum Conjecture.

5. $\triangle HRT$ is a 30°-60°-90° triangle with longer leg $8\sqrt{3}$ cm; so shorter leg RT is 8 cm long and hypotenuse HT is 16 cm long. The shaded area is the difference of the semicircle area and right triangle area.

7. From the center of the circle, drop a perpendicular to chord $\overline{HO}$, forming two 30°-60°-90° triangles with longer legs $4\sqrt{3}$.

8. Find the area of the right triangle. To find the area of the sectors, what do the angles in a triangle add up to?

11. When $\overline{OT}$ and $\overline{OA}$ are drawn, they form a right triangle, with $OA = 15$ (length of hypotenuse) and $OT = 12$ (length of leg).

12. Draw the radius $\overline{OB}$ of the larger circle and the radius $\overline{OT}$ of the smaller circle. Because $\overline{AB}$ is tangent to the smaller circle, $\triangle OTB$ is a right triangle. By the Pythagorean Theorem, $OT^2 + 18^2 = OB^2$, or $OB^2 - OT^2 = 18^2$. But the area of the annulus is $\pi OB^2 - \pi OT^2$, or $\pi(OB^2 - OT^2)$.

13. See picture equations below.

14. The triangle formed by the centers of the three circles is an equilateral triangle with height $6\sqrt{3}$.

15. The arc length of $\overarc{AC}$ is $\frac{80}{360}[2\pi(9)] = 4\pi$. Therefore, the circumference of the base of the cone is 4π. From this you can determine the radius of the base. The radius of the sector (9) becomes the slant height (the distance from the tip of the cone to the circumference of the base). The radius of the base, the slant height, and the height of the cone form a right triangle.

17. The height of the sphere is equal to the radius of the sphere. This gives you a right triangle with legs r and 9 cm and a hypotenuse of 15 cm.

18. Use similar triangles with legs r and R to solve for r.

11

LESSON 11.1, PAGES 538–540

29. Think of a prism as a stack of thin copies of the bases.

---

13. (*Lesson 10.4*)

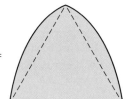

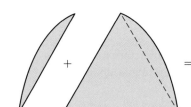

$\frac{1}{6}\pi r^2 \quad - \quad \frac{1}{2}r\left(\frac{r\sqrt{3}}{2}\right)$

31.

LESSON 11.2, PAGES 545–547

2. What is the shape of the base and how do you find its area? Use the Pythagorean Theorem to find the missing length.

5. You have only $\frac{1}{2}$ of a cylinder.

$$B = \frac{1}{2}\pi r^2$$

6. $\frac{90}{360}$, or $\frac{1}{4}$, of the cylinder is removed. Therefore, you need to find $\frac{3}{4}$ of the volume of the whole cylinder.

7a. What is the difference between this prism and the one in Exercise 2? Does it make a difference in the formula for the volume?

9. Cutie pie!

25. *SOTA* is a square, so the diagonals, $\overline{ST}$ and $\overline{OA}$, are congruent and are perpendicular bisectors of each other, and $SM = OM = 6$. Use right triangle *SMO* to find *OS*, which also equals *OP*. Find *PA* with the equation $PA = OA - OP$.

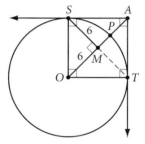

LESSON 11.3, PAGES 550–552

3. $V = \frac{1}{3}BH = \frac{1}{3}\left[\frac{b_1 + b_2}{2} \cdot h\right]H$

6. $V = V_{\text{cylinder}} - V_{\text{cone}}$
$$= BH - \frac{1}{3}BH$$

10a. What is *B*, the area of the triangular base?

15.

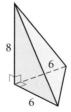

18. The swimming pool is a pentagonal prism resting on one of its lateral faces. The area of the pentagonal base can be found by dividing it into a rectangular region and a trapezoidal region.

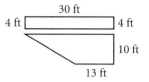

LESSON 11.4, PAGES 554–556

2. The base of the prism looks like this.

3. Substituting the given values into $V = \frac{1}{3}BH$ gives $180 = \frac{1}{3}B(12)$. Solve for *B*. Then substitute this value and the given value for *h* into $B = \frac{1}{2}bh$ and solve for *b*.

4. $V = \frac{1}{3}BH$; $3168 = \frac{1}{3}\left[\frac{1}{2}(20 + 28)h\right](36)$

10. First, change 8 inches to $\frac{2}{3}$ foot.

LESSON 11.5, PAGES 559–560

6. $0.97 = \dfrac{145.5}{V_{\text{displacement}}}$ and $V_{\text{displacement}} = (10)(10)H$

LESSON 11.6, PAGES 563–565

4. $V_{\text{capsule}} = 2 \cdot V_{\text{hemisphere}} + V_{\text{cylinder}} =$
$$2\left[\frac{2}{3}\pi(6)^3\right] + [\pi(6)^2(12)]$$

6. $\frac{40}{360}$, or $\frac{1}{9}$, of the hemisphere is missing. What fraction is still there?

11. $972\pi = \frac{4}{3}\pi r^3$

LESSON 11.7, PAGES 567–569

3. The surface area is the curved hemisphere *and* the circular bottom.

4. The surface area of a sphere is how many times the area of a circle with the same radius?

Hints for Selected Exercises

1. $\left(\frac{4}{7}\right)^3 = \dfrac{320}{\text{Volume of large pyramid}}$

3. $\left(\frac{h}{H}\right)^2 = \frac{9}{25}$; $\dfrac{\text{Volume of large prism}}{\text{Volume of small prism}} = \left(\frac{h}{H}\right)^3$

8. Volume of large warehouse = $2.5^3 \cdot$ (Volume of small warehouse)

17. Copy the diagram on your own paper, and connect the centers of two large circles and the center of the small circle to form a 45°-45°-90° triangle. Each radius of the larger circles will be $\frac{s}{4}$. Use the properties of special right triangles and algebra to find the radius of the smaller circle.

19. During a rotation, each vertex of the triangle will trace the path of a circle. So, if you connect any vertex of the original figure to its corresponding vertex in the image, you will get a chord. Now recall that the perpendicular bisector of a chord passes through the center of a circle.

8. The length of the side opposite $\angle A$ is s; the length of the side adjacent to $\angle A$ is r; the length of the hypotenuse is t.

11. Use your calculator to find $\sin^{-1}(0.5)$.

15. $\tan 30° = \dfrac{20}{a}$

22. Use $\sin 35° = \dfrac{b}{85}$ to find the length of the base, and then use $\cos 35° = \dfrac{h}{85}$ to find the height.

28. First, find the length of the radius of the circle and the length of the segment between the chord and the center of the circle. Use the Pythagorean Theorem to find the length of half of the chord.

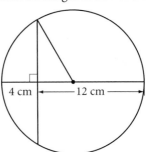

5. $\dfrac{\frac{1}{2}d_1}{20} = \cos 56°$

8. First find the length of the diagonal of the base. Then, $\tan \beta = \frac{10}{17}$

14.

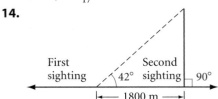

16a. $\sin 44° = \dfrac{h}{1400}$, where h is the height of the balloon *above* Wendy's sextant.

20. $a + b = \sqrt{(12-3)^2 + (0-9)^2}$. Once you have solved for $a + b$, then $\frac{4}{12} = \frac{a}{a+b}$.

3. Sketch a diagonal connecting the vertices of the unmeasured angles. Then find the area of the two triangles.

4. Divide the octagon into eight isosceles triangles. Then use trigonometry to find the area of each triangle.

5. $\dfrac{\sin 52°}{28°} = \dfrac{\sin 79°}{w}$

13. $\sin 16° = \dfrac{a}{18}$

$\cos 16° = \dfrac{b}{18}$

$\tan 68° = \dfrac{c}{b}$

1. $w^2 = 36^2 + 41^2 - 2(36)(41)\cos 49°$

4. $42^2 = 34^2 + 36^2 - 2(34)(36)\cos A$

8. The smallest angle is opposite the shortest side.

10. One approach divides the triangle into two right triangles, where $x = a + b$. When you have the straight-line distance, compare that time against the detour.

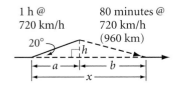

11.

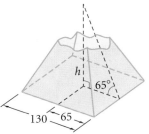

15. Mark all congruent segments and angles on your drawing. Which triangles are congruent?

16. The midpoint of the base can be used to create three equilateral triangles.

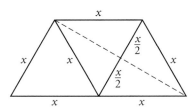

LESSON 12.5, PAGES 606–608

2.

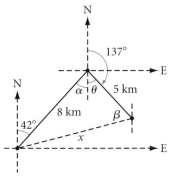

5. To find the angle between the 8 km side and the 5 km side, first find θ, and then find a.

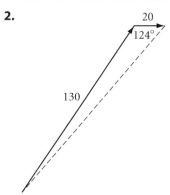

9.

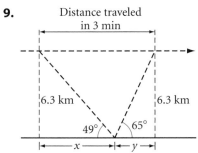

11. To find the area of the base, divide the pentagon into five congruent isosceles triangles and use either method from Exercise 10.

13.

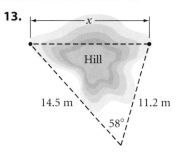

⑬

LESSON 13.1, PAGES 627–631

4. It's also called the identity property.

9. ？, ？, multiplication property of equality, ？

11. The Midpoint Postulate says that a segment has exactly one midpoint.

25. Two consecutive integers can be written as n and $n + 1$.

LESSON 13.2, PAGES 637–638

19.

LESSON 13.3, PAGES 641–643

2. Draw an auxiliary line from the point to the midpoint of the segment.

5. Draw an auxiliary line that creates two isosceles triangles. Use isosceles triangle properties and angle subtraction.

14. Use similarity of triangles to set up two proportions.

16. Graph point A and the line. Fold the graph paper along the line to see where point A reflects.

LESSON 13.4, PAGES 645–646

1. Use the Quadrilateral Sum Theorem.

18. Construct the altitudes of triangles ABC and ADC to the shared base $\overline{AC}$. What can you conclude about the triangles FBM and GDM?

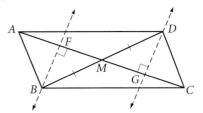

LESSON 13.6, PAGES 653–654

15. Divide the triangle into three triangles with common vertex P.

17. Draw a segment from the point to the center of the circle. Using this segment as a diameter, draw a circle. How does this help you find the points of tangency?

LESSON 13.7, PAGES 658–659

4.

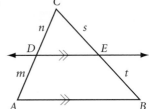

$$\frac{m+n}{n} = \frac{t+s}{s}$$
$$\frac{m}{n} + \frac{n}{n} = \frac{t}{s} + \frac{s}{s}$$
$$\frac{m}{n} + 1 = \frac{t}{s} + 1$$
$$\therefore \frac{m}{n} = \frac{t}{s}$$

5. Try revising the steps of the proof for the Parallel Proportionality Theorem.

6. In $\triangle ATH$, let $m\angle A = a$, $m\angle T = t$, then $a + t = 90$. In $\triangle LTH$, $m\angle T = t$, $m\angle H = h$, then $h + t = 90$. Therefore, $h + t = a + t$ and so $h = a$. Therefore, $\triangle ATH \sim \triangle HTL$ by AA. In like manner you can demonstrate that $\triangle ATH \sim \triangle AHL$, and thus by the transitive property of similarity all three are similar.

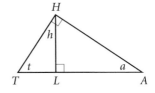

7. If a is the geometric mean of b and c, then $\frac{b}{a} = \frac{a}{c}$, or $a^2 = bc$.

8. Construct $\overline{AD}$ so that it's perpendicular to $\overline{AB}$ and intersects $\overleftrightarrow{BC}$ at point D.

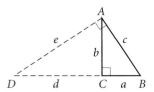

Use the Three Similar Right Triangles Theorem to write proportions and solve.

Construct right triangle DEF with legs of lengths a and b and hypotenuse of length x.

Then $x^2 = a^2 + b^2$ by the Pythagorean Theorem.

It is given that $c^2 = a^2 + b^2$. Therefore, $x^2 = c^2$, or $x = c$.

If $x = c$, then $\triangle DEF \cong \triangle ABC$.

10. See Exercise 27 in Lesson 10.1.

18. The span is not twice the rise (almost but not quite).

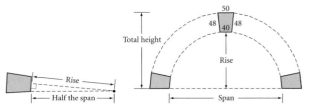

LESSON 13.8, PAGES 666–667

6. How does the area of the polygon formed compare to the area of the original rectangle?

7. How do the sides of the polygon formed compare to the sides of the original parallelogram?

8. Construct the midsegments of the trapezoids.

9. Construct the diagonals of the polygon formed.

Answers for Chapter Reviews

CHAPTER REVIEW 0

1. Possible answer: Islamic, Hindu, Celtic

2. The basket has 4-fold rotational symmetry because it looks the same after you rotate it 90° (a fourth of a circle), 180° (two-fourths of a circle), 270° (three-fourths of a circle), and 360° (one full circle).

3. Compass: A geometry tool used to construct circles.

Straightedge: A geometry tool used to construct straight lines.

4. Possible answer:

5.

Dodecagon   Regular Hexagon

Square   Equilateral Triangle

6. Possible answers: hexagon: honeycomb, snowflake; pentagon: starfish, flower

7. Answers will vary. Should be some form of an interweaving design.

8. Wheel A has four lines of reflectional symmetry; Wheel C has five lines of reflectional symmetry. Wheels B and D do not have reflectional symmetry.

9. Wheels B and D have only rotational symmetry. Wheels A and B have 4-fold, Wheel C has 5-fold, and Wheel D has 3-fold rotational symmetry.

10, 11. Drawing should contain concentric circles and symmetry in some of the rings.

12. The mandala should contain all the required elements.

13a. The flag of Puerto Rico is not symmetric because of the star and the colors.

13b. The flag of Kenya does not have rotational symmetry because of the spearheads.

13c. Possible answers:

Japan   Nigeria

CHAPTER REVIEW 1

1. True   **2.** False; it is written as $\overrightarrow{QP}$.

3. True

4. False; the vertex is point D.

5. True   **6.** True

7. False; its measure is less than 90°.

8. False; two possible counterexamples:

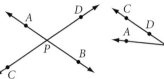
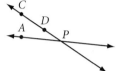

$\angle APD$ and $\angle APC$ $\angle APD$ and $\angle APC$
are a linear pair.   are the same angle.

9. True   **10.** True

11. False; they are supplementary.

12. True   **13.** True

14. True

15. False; it has five diagonals.

16. True   **17.** F

18. G   **19.** L

20. J   **21.** C

22. I   **23.** No match

24. A   **25.** No match

26.

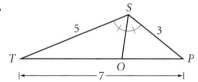

27.

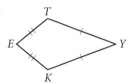

28.

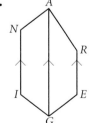

29.
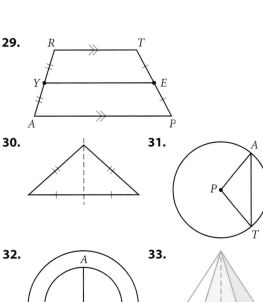

30. 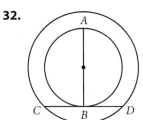 **31.**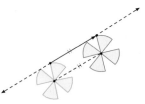

32. 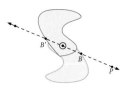 **33.**

34.
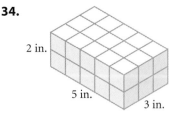
2 in.
5 in.
3 in.

35.
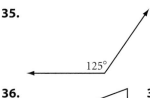
125°

36.
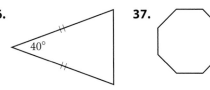
40°

37.

38. 114° **39.** $AB = 16$ cm
40. 96° **41.** 30°
42. (2, 3)
43.

44. Carefully trace the image on the other side of the line of reflection. A reflection is a rigid transformation that produces a mirror image, so the figures are congruent.

45. Copy the figure on a piece of patty paper. Construct a parallel line through another point on the figure. Duplicate the translation vector on that line. Place a second patty paper on top of the first and make a copy of the figure and the translation vectors. Using the translation vector as a guide, translate the second copy. A translation is a rigid transformation that preserves size and shape, so the image is congruent to the original.

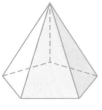

46. Draw the 180° angle on the original figure. Mark the intersection of the figure and the initial side of the angle. Using a patty paper copy of the figure, place a pencil point at the center and rotate the figure so that the intersection coincides with the terminal side of the 180° angle. Copy the figure. A rotation is a rigid transformation that preserves size and shape, so the image is congruent to the original.

47. One line of reflection. There are no other lines of reflection in which the original figure coincides with the image.

②

CHAPTER REVIEW

1a. False **1b.** False
1c. False **1d.** False
1e. Paradox
2. Poor inductive reasoning, but Diana was probably just being funny.
3. Answers will vary. **4.** Answers will vary.
5. 19, −30 **6.** S, 36
7. She could try eating one food at a time; inductive.
8.   **9.**

10. 900 **11.** 930

12. nth term $= -3n + 5$; 20th term $= -55$

13. nth term $= \dfrac{n(n+1)}{2}$; 20th term $= 210$

14. n^2, $30^2 = 900$

15. $\dfrac{n(n+1)}{2}$, $\dfrac{100(101)}{2} = 5050$

16. $\dfrac{n(n-1)}{2} = 741$; therefore, $n = 39$

17. $\dfrac{n(n-1)}{2} = 2926$; therefore, $n = 77$

18. $n - 2$, $54 - 2 = 52$

19a. Possible answers: $\angle EFC$ and $\angle AFG$, $\angle AFE$ and $\angle CFG$, $\angle FGD$ and $\angle BGH$, or $\angle BGF$ and $\angle HGD$

19b. Possible answers: $\angle AFE$ and $\angle EFC$, $\angle AFG$ and $\angle CFG$, $\angle BGF$ and $\angle FGD$, or $\angle BGH$ and $\angle HGD$ (there are four other pairs)

19c. Possible answers: $\angle EFC$ and $\angle FGD$, $\angle AFE$ and $\angle BGF$, $\angle CFG$ and $\angle DGH$, or $\angle AFG$ and $\angle BGH$

19d. Possible answers: $\angle AFG$ and $\angle FGD$ or $\angle CFG$ and $\angle BGF$

20. Possible answers: $\angle GFC$ by the Vertical Angles Conjecture, $\angle BGF$ by the Corresponding Angles Conjecture, and $\angle DGH$, using the Alternate Exterior Angles Conjecture

21. True. Converse: "If two polygons have the same number of sides, then the two polygons are congruent"; false. Counterexamples may vary; you might draw a concave quadrilateral and a convex quadrilateral.

22.

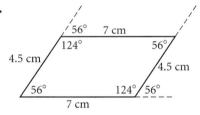

23. $\overleftrightarrow{PV} \parallel \overleftrightarrow{RX}$ and $\overleftrightarrow{SU} \parallel \overleftrightarrow{VX}$; explanations will vary.

24. The bisected angle measures 50° because of AIA. So each half measures 25°. The bisector is a transversal, so the measure of the other acute angle in the triangle is also 25° by AIA. However, this angle forms a linear pair with the angle measuring 165°, and $25° + 165° \neq 180°$, which contradicts the Linear Pair Conjecture.

25. $a = 38°$, $b = 38°$, $c = 142°$, $d = 38°$, $e = 50°$, $f = 65°$, $g = 106°$, $h = 74°$.
The angle with measure e forms a linear pair with an angle with measure 130° because of the Corresponding Angles Conjecture. So e measures 50° because of the Linear Pair Conjecture. The angle with measure f is half of the angle with measure 130°, so $f = 65°$. The angle with measure g is congruent to the angle with measure 106° by the Corresponding Angles Conjecture, so $g = 106°$.

26a.

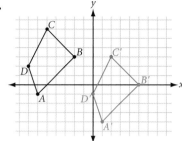

26b. Translation by vector $\langle 7, -4 \rangle$. The vertices of quadrilateral $A'B'C'D'$ are the same as the vertices of quadrilateral $EFGH$.

26c. Quadrilateral $A'B'C'D' \cong$ quadrilateral $EFGH$; quadrilateral $A'B'C'D' \cong$ quadrilateral $ABCD$.

26d. They are congruent.

27a.

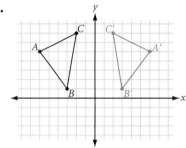

27b. Reflection across the y-axis. The vertices of $\triangle A'B'C'$ are the same as the vertices $\triangle DEF$.

27c. $\triangle A'B'C' \cong \triangle DEF$; $\triangle A'B'C' \cong \triangle ABC$

27d. They are congruent.

28a.

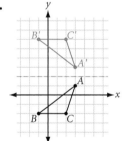

28b. $A'(3,3)$, $B'(-1,6)$, $C'(2,6)$

28c. $(x, y) \rightarrow (x, -y + 4)$

28d.

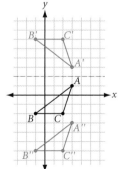

28e. $A''(3, -3)$, $B''(-1, -6)$, $C''(2, -6)$

28f. $(x, y) \rightarrow (x, y - 4)$

CHAPTER REVIEW

1. False; a geometric construction uses a straightedge and a compass.

2. False; a diagonal connects two non-consecutive vertices.

3. True　　　　　　**4.** True

5. False

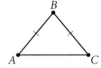

6. False; the lines can't be a given distance from a segment because the segment has finite length and the lines are infinite.

7. False

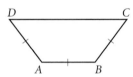

8. True　　　　　　**9.** True

10. False; the orthocenter does not always lie inside the triangle.

11. A　　**12.** B or K　　**13.** I　　**14.** H

15. G　　**16.** D　　**17.** J　　**18.** C

19.　　　　　　　　**20.**

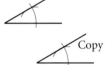

21.　　　　　　　　**22.**

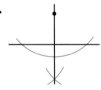

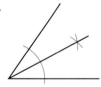

23. Construct a 90° angle and bisect it twice.

24.　　　　　　　　**25.** Incenter

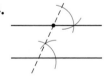

26. Dakota Davis should locate the circumcenter of the triangular region formed by the three stones, which is the location equidistant from the stones.

27.

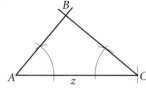

28.

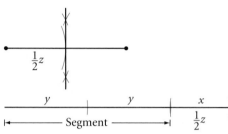

29.

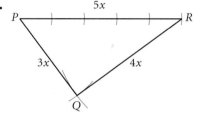

30. $m\angle A = m\angle D$. You must first find $\angle B$.
$m\angle B = 180° - 2(m\angle A)$.

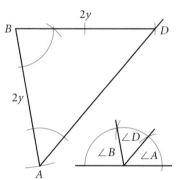

31.

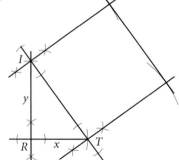

Answers for Chapter Reviews

32. Draw segment *RN*. Find perpendicular bisector of $\overline{RN}$. Reflect △*RSM* over the bisector to create △*R'S'M'*. Find angle bisector of ∠*AR'S'*. Reflect △*R'S'M'* over the angle bisector. Reflect the image over $\overline{NA}$.

33. D **34.** A **35.** C **36.** B

37. False; an isosceles triangle has two congruent sides.

38. True

39. False; any non-acute triangle is a counterexample.

40. False; possible explanation: The orthocenter is the point of intersection of the three altitudes.

41. True

42. False; any linear pair of angles is a counterexample.

43. False; each side is adjacent to one congruent side and one noncongruent side, so two consecutive sides may not be congruent.

44. False

45. False; the measure of an arc is equal to the measure of its central angle.

46. False; *TD* = 2*DR*

47. False; a radius is not a chord.

48. True

49. False; inductive reasoning is the process of observing data, recognizing patterns, and making generalizations about those patterns.

50. Paradox

51a. ∠2 and ∠6 or ∠3 and ∠5

51b. ∠1 and ∠5 **51c.** 138°

52. 55

53. Possible answer:

54a. Yes

54b. If the month has 31 days, then the month is October.

54c. No

55.

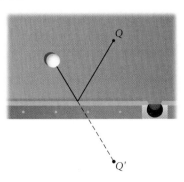

56. 2600

57.

58.

59.

60. *a* = 38°, *b* = 38°, *c* = 142°, *d* = 38°, *e* = 50°, *f* = 65°, *g* = 106°, *h* = 74°.
Possible explanation: The angle with measure *c* is congruent to an angle with measure 142° because of the Corresponding Angles Conjecture, so *c* = 142°. The angle with measure 130° is congruent to the bisected angle by the Corresponding Angles Conjecture. The angle with measure *f* has half the measure of the bisected angle, so *f* = 65°.

61. Triangles will vary. Check that the triangle is scalene and that at least two angle bisectors have been constructed.

62. *m*∠*FAD* = 30° so *m*∠*ADC* = 30°, but its vertical angle has measure 26°. This is a contradiction.

63. Minimum: 101 regions by 100 parallel lines; maximum: 5051 regions by 100 intersecting, noncurrent lines

64a. The circles are congruent. Both circles have a radius of 5.

64b. (*x*, *y*) → (*x* − 6, *y* + 10)

64c. The circles are congruent.

65. Quadrilateral *A'B'C'D'* is a parallelogram. There are no congruent sides or angles. $\overline{A'B'}$ and $\overline{C'D'}$ are three times the lengths of $\overline{AB}$ and $\overline{CD}$. $\overline{B'C'}$ and $\overline{A'D'}$ are half the length of $\overline{BC}$ and $\overline{CD}$. The transformation is not a rigid transformation.

66. *m*∠*FAB* = 30°. Step 1 located the point equidistant from points *A* and *B*. Connecting point *C* to both points *A* and *B* would have constructed an equilateral triangle, which means *m*∠*CAB* = 60°. Steps 2 and 3 bisect ∠*CAB*, so *m*∠*FAB* = 30°.

1a. True   **1b.** True

1c. False   **1d.** False

1e. Both

2. The Triangle Sum Conjecture states that the sum of the measures of the angles in every triangle is 180°. Possible answers: It applies to all triangles; many other conjectures rely on it.

3. The angle bisector of the vertex angle is also the median and the altitude.

4. The distance between A and B is along the segment connecting them. The distance from A to C to B can't be shorter than the distance from A to B. Therefore, $AC + CB > AB$. Points A, B, and C form a triangle. Therefore, the sum of the lengths of any two sides is greater than the length of the third side.

5. SSS, SAS, ASA, or SAA

6. In some cases, two different triangles can be constructed using the same two sides and non-included angle.

7. 1

8. Annie is correct. Given $\triangle NOT$.
$\angle N + \angle O + \angle T = 180°$ by the Triangle Sum Conjecture. So $2y + 2x + 2z = 180°$, or $y + x + z = 90°$. Subtracting z from each side gives $y + x = 90° - z$. If the bisectors met at right angles, then $y + x = 90°$ in $\triangle TPN$.

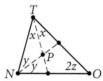

9. Cannot be determined

10. ZAP by SAA   **11.** OSU by SSS

12. Cannot be determined

13. APR by SAS   **14.** NGI by SAS

15. Cannot be determined

16. DCE by SAA or ASA

17. RBO or OBR by SAS

18. $\triangle AMD \cong \triangle UMT$ by SAS; $\overline{UT}$ by CPCTC

19. Cannot be determined

20. Cannot be determined

21. $\triangle TRI \cong \triangle ALS$ by SAA; $\overline{AL}$ by CPCTC

22. $\triangle SVE \cong \triangle NIK$ by SSS; $\overline{KV}$ by overlapping segments property

23. Cannot be determined

24. Cannot be determined

25. $\triangle LAZ \cong \triangle IAR$ by ASA, $\triangle LRI \cong \triangle IZL$ by ASA, and $\triangle LRD \cong \triangle IZD$ by ASA

26. Yes; $\triangle PTS \cong \triangle TPO$ by ASA or SAA

27. $\triangle ANG$ is isosceles, so $\angle A \cong \angle G$. However, the sum of $m\angle A + m\angle N + m\angle G = 188°$. The measures of the three angles of a triangle must sum to 180°.

28. $\triangle ROW \cong \triangle NOG$ by ASA, implying that $\overline{OW} \cong \overline{OG}$. However, the two segments shown are not equal in measure.

29. $a = g < e = d = b = f < c$. Thus, c is the longest segment, and a and g are the shortest.

30. $x = 20°$

31. Yes. $\triangle TRE \cong \triangle SAE$ by SAA, so sides are congruent by CPCTC.

32. Yes. $\triangle FRM \cong \triangle RFA$ by SAA. $\angle RFM \cong \angle FRA$ by CPCTC. Because base angles are congruent, $\triangle FRD$ is isosceles.

33. $x = 48°$

34. The legs form two triangles that are congruent by SAS. Because alternate interior angles are congruent by CPCTC, the seat must be parallel to the floor.

35. Construct $\angle P$ and $\angle A$ to be adjacent. The angle that forms a linear pair with the conjunction of $\angle P$ and $\angle A$ is $\angle L$. Construct $\angle A$. Mark off the length AL on one ray. Construct $\angle L$. Extend the unconnected sides of the angles until they meet. Label the point of intersection P.

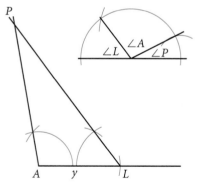

36. Construct $\angle P$. Mark off the length PB on one ray. From point B, mark off the two segments that intersect the other ray of $\angle P$ at distance x.

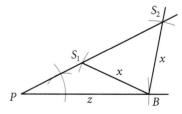

37. See flowchart below.

38. Possible method: Construct an equilateral triangle and bisect one angle to obtain 30°. Adjacent to that angle, construct a right angle and bisect it to obtain 45°.

39. *d, a = b, c, e, f*

40. True. The diagonals divide the quadrilateral into two triangles. In each triangle, the sum of the two lengths of any two sides of the triangle (sides of the parallelogram) are greater than the length of the third side (the diagonal).

41. True. In the figure, $\overrightarrow{BD}$ is the angle bisector of ∠*CBA*. By definition of an angle bisector ∠2 ≅ ∠5. $\overleftrightarrow{DE}$ is constructed so that $\overleftrightarrow{DE} \parallel \overleftrightarrow{CB}$. ∠1 ≅ ∠5 by AIA. If ∠1 ≅ ∠5 and ∠2 ≅ ∠5, then ∠1 ≅ ∠2. If ∠1 ≅ ∠2, then $\overline{BE} \cong \overline{DE}$ and △*BDE* is an isosceles triangle.

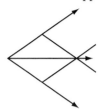

CHAPTER REVIEW

1a. True   **1b.** True

1c. False   **1d.** False

1e. Both

2. 360° divided by the number of sides

3. Sample answers: Using an interior angle, set interior angle measure formula equal to the angle and solve for *n*. Using an exterior angle, divide into 360°. Or find the interior angle measure and go from there.

4. Trace both sides of the ruler as shown below.

5. Make a rhombus using the double-edged straightedge, and draw a diagonal connecting the angle vertex to the opposite vertex.

6. Sample answer: Measure the diagonals with string to see if they are congruent and bisect each other.

7. Possible answer: Draw a third point and connect it with each of the two points to form two sides of a triangle. Find the midpoints of the two sides and connect them to construct the midsegment. The distance between the two points is twice the length of the midsegment.

8. *x* = 10°, *y* = 40°   **9.** *x* = 60 cm

10. *a* = 116°, *c* = 64°   **11.** 100

12. *x* = 38 cm

13. *y* = 34 cm, *z* = 51 cm

37. (*Chapter 4 Review*)

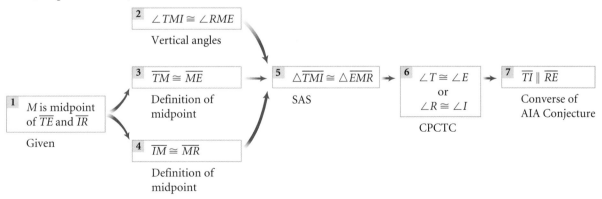

14. See table below. **15.** $a = 72°$, $b = 108°$

16. $a = 120°$, $b = 60°$, $c = 60°$, $d = 120°$, $e = 60°$, $f = 30°$, $g = 108°$, $m = 24°$, $p = 84°$; Possible explanation: Because $c = 60°$, the angle that forms a linear pair with e and its congruent adjacent angle measures 60°. So $60° + 2e = 180°$, and $e = 60°$. The triangle containing f has a 60° angle. The other angle is a right angle because it forms a linear pair with a right angle. So $f = 30°$ by the Triangle Sum Conjecture. Because g is an interior angle in an equiangular pentagon, divide 540° by 5 to get $g = 108°$.

17. 15 stones **18.** $(1, 0)$

19. When the swing is motionless, the seat, the bar at the top, and the chains form a rectangle. When you swing left to right, the rectangle changes to a parallelogram. The opposite sides stay equal in length, so they stay parallel. The seat and the bar at the top are also parallel to the ground.

20. $a = 60°$, $b = 120°$

21.
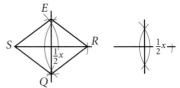

22. Possible answers:
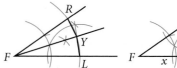

23.
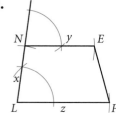

24. Possible answers:
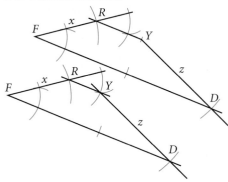

25. 20 sides **26.** 12 cm

---

14. (*Chapter 5 Review*)

	Kite	Isosceles Trapezoid	Parallelogram	Rhombus	Rectangle	Square
Opposite sides are parallel	No	No	Yes	Yes	Yes	Yes
Opposite sides are congruent	No	No	Yes	Yes	Yes	Yes
Opposite angles are congruent	No	No	Yes	Yes	Yes	Yes
Diagonals bisect each other	No	No	Yes	Yes	Yes	Yes
Diagonals are perpendicular	Yes	No	No	Yes	No	Yes
Diagonals are congruent	No	Yes	No	No	Yes	Yes
Exactly one line of symmetry	Yes	Yes	No	No	No	No
Exactly two lines of symmetry	No	No	No	Yes	Yes	No

27. See flowchart below.

28. See flowchart below.

29. Construct auxiliary $\overline{NH}$ so that $\overline{NH} \cong \overline{AB}$. $\angle NHB$ is a right angle by definition of perpendicular. $\overline{CE} \perp \overline{AB}$ and $\overline{CE} \perp \overline{MN}$ by definition of altitude and corresponding angles of parallel lines. $\angle CPN$ and $\angle CEB$ are right angles by definition of perpendicular, so $\angle CPN \cong \angle CEB$ because all right angles are congruent. $\overline{CD} \parallel \overline{AB}$ by definition of a trapezoid. $\overline{MN} \parallel \overline{AB}$ by Trapezoid Midsegment Conjecture. Therefore, $\angle CNP \cong \angle NBH$ by corresponding angles. $\overline{CN} \cong \overline{NB}$ by definition of midpoint. $\triangle CPN \cong \triangle NHB$ by AAS. $\overline{CP} \cong \overline{NH}$ by CPCTC. $\overline{PE} \cong \overline{NH}$ by definition of parallel lines. By substitution, $\overline{CP} \cong \overline{PE}$.

CHAPTER REVIEW

1. True   **2.** True   **3.** True
4. True   **5.** True   **6.** True

7. 6-fold rotational symmetry

8. Translational symmetry

9. Reflectional; color arrangements will vary, but the white candle must be in the middle.

10. The two towers are not the reflection (or even the translation) of each other. Each tower individually has bilateral symmetry. The center portion has bilateral symmetry.

11. Answers will vary.

12. Answers will vary.

13. Translate $\triangle A'BC$ by $\overrightarrow{BB''}$. For a sequence of transformations, draw $\overrightarrow{BB''}$. Construct the perpendicular bisector. Reflect $\triangle ABC$ across perpendicular bisector. Reflect across angle bisector of $\angle A'B''A''$.

14. $\triangle XYZ$ is reflected across the left side of the angle to form $\triangle X'Y'Z'$ which is then reflected across the right side of the angle. A rotation of 136° about the vertex of the angle.

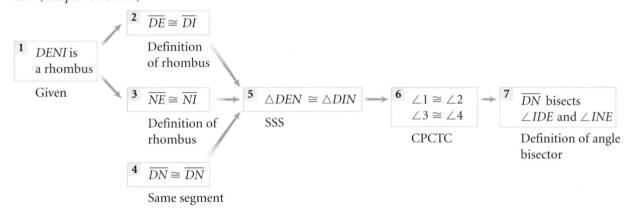

27. (*Chapter 5 Review*)

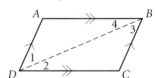

28. (*Chapter 5 Review*)

Given: Parallelogram ABCD
Show: $\overline{AB} \cong \overline{CD}$ and $\overline{AD} \cong \overline{CB}$
Flowchart Proof

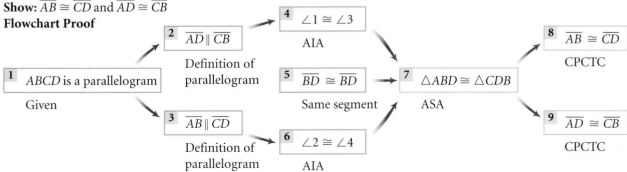

15. Draw $\overline{AA'}$ and $\overline{EE'}$. Construct the perpendicular bisector of $\overline{AA'}$ and $\overline{EE'}$. Mark the intersection as P. Rotate *ABCD* counterclockwise by $\angle APA'$ which is approximately 122°.

16. A' (−3, −3), B' (1, 0), C' (0, −7). Yes.

17a. $\triangle ABC \cong \triangle IGH \cong \triangle LKJ$. SAS

17b. $\triangle ABC$ to $\triangle IGH$: Reflection over the *y*-axis. $\triangle ABC$ to $\triangle LKJ$: 90° counterclockwise rotation about the origin.

17c. $\triangle ABC$ to $\triangle IGH$: $(x, y) \rightarrow (-x, y)$. $\triangle ABC$ to $\triangle LKJ$: $(x, y) \rightarrow (-y, x)$.

18. Answers will vary.

19. Use a grid of squares. Tessellate by translation.

20. Use a grid of equilateral triangles. Tessellate by rotation.

21. Use a grid of parallelograms. Tessellate by glide reflection.

22. Yes. It is a glide reflection for one pair of sides and midpoint rotation for the other two sides.

23. No. Because the shape is suitable for glide reflection, the rows of parallelograms should alternate the direction in which they lean (row 1 leans right, row 2 leans left, row 3 leans right, . . .).

24.

25. False. 20° + 20° + 140° = 180°. An angle with measure 140° is obtuse.

26. True   **27.** False

28. True   **29.** True   **30.** True

31. False. (7 − 2) · 180° = 900°. It could have seven sides.

32. False. The sum of the measures of any triangle is 180°.

33. False. The sum of the measures of one set of exterior angles for any polygon is 360°. The sum of the measures of the interior angles of a triangle is 180° and of a quadrilateral is 360°. Neither is greater than 360°, so these are two counterexamples.

34. False. The consecutive angles between the bases are supplementary.

35. False. 48° + 48° + 132° ≠ 180°

36. True

37. False. $\overline{AC}$ and $\overline{BD}$ bisect each other, but $\overline{AC}$ is not perpendicular to $\overline{BD}$.

38. False. It could be isosceles.

39. False. 100° + 100° + 100° + 60° = 360°

40. False.
24 + 24 + 48 + 48 ≠ 96

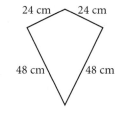

41. True

42. $a = 58°$, b = 61°, $c = 58°$, $d = 122°$, $e = 58°$, $f = 64°$, $g = 116°$, $h = 52°$, $i = 64°$, $k = 64°$, $l = 105°$, $m = 105°$, $n = 105°$, $p = 75°$, $q = 116°$, $r = 90°$, $s = 58°$, $t = 122°$, $u = 105°$, $v = 75°$, $w = 61°$, $x = 29°$, $y = 151°$

43. $\triangle TAR \cong \triangle YRA$ by SAS $\triangle TAE \cong \triangle YRE$ by SAA

44. $\triangle FTO \cong \triangle YTO$ by SAA, $\triangle FLO \cong \triangle YLO$ by SAA, $\triangle FTL \cong \triangle YTL$ by SSS

45. $\triangle PTR \cong \triangle ART$ by SAS, $\triangle TPA \cong \triangle RAP$ by SAS $\triangle TLP \cong \triangle RLA$ by SAA

46. ASA

47. Sample answer:

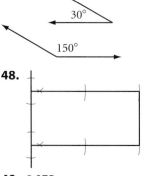

48.

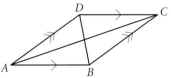

49. 9.375 cm

50.

51. Translation. $(x, y) \rightarrow (x + 1, y + 4)$

52. Reflection. $(x, y) \rightarrow (x, -y)$

53. Triangles are not congruent so there is no transformation.

CHAPTER REVIEW

1. False

2. True

3. True

4. True

5. True

6. Answers will vary. Dilation of 2:

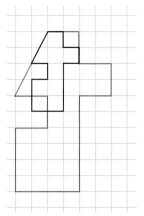

7. Answers will vary. Dilation of $\frac{3}{2}$:

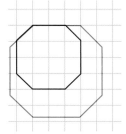

8. $(x, y) \rightarrow \left(\frac{1}{3}x, \frac{1}{3}y - 2\right)$. $(0, -3)$

9. $MNSR \cong EFGH$ and $BCDA \cong QMOP$ because they have congruent sides and angles. $MNSR \sim BCDA$, $MNSR \sim QMOP$, $EFGH \sim BCDA$, and $EFGH \sim QMOP$ because their sides are proportional and angles congruent.

10. They are not similar. The ratio of the lengths of the triangles, $\frac{LB}{LS} = \frac{5}{10}$ and $\frac{LD}{LZ} = \frac{5}{9}$, are not equal, therefore, they are not similar.

11. $4\frac{1}{6}$

12. $w = 6$ cm; $x = 4.5$ cm; $y = 7.5$ cm; $z = 3$ cm

13. $x = 4\frac{1}{6}$ cm; $y = 7\frac{1}{2}$ cm

14. XWV. The Alternate Interior Angles conjecture verifies that two sets of corresponding angles are congruent. Therefore, the triangles are similar by the AA Similarity Conjecture.

15. Yes. The angles are congruent and the sides proportional.

16. 21 feet

17. 13 ft 2 in.

18. It would still be a 20° angle.

19.

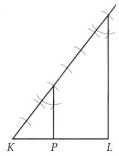

20. Yes. If two triangles are congruent, corresponding angles are congruent and corresponding sides are proportional with ratio $\frac{1}{1}$, so the triangles are similar.

21. Possible answer: You would measure the height and weight of the real ice cream cone and the height of the sculpture.

$$\frac{W_{\text{sculpture}}}{W_{\text{ice cream cone}}} = \left(\frac{H_{\text{sculpture}}}{H_{\text{ice cream cone}}}\right)^3$$

If you don't know the height of the sculpture, you could estimate it from this photo by setting up a ratio, for example

$$\frac{H_{\text{person}}}{H_{\text{person's photo}}} = \frac{H_{\text{sculpture}}}{H_{\text{sculpture's photo}}}$$

22. Since they share angle M and both triangles have a right angle, the triangles are similar by the AA Similarity conjecture. $h = 6.72$.

23. $\triangle LRP \sim \triangle TUP$ by AA Similarity conjecture. $x = 24$.

24. $(-2, 2)$. $(x, y) \rightarrow (4x + 6, 4y - 6)$.

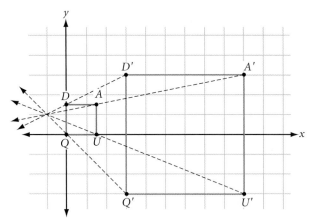

25. 15

26. $x = 4$. The Proportional Parts conjecture tells us that the median is also proportional. Since the sides are all proportional, $\triangle ABD \sim \triangle EFH$ and $\triangle BDC \sim \triangle FHG$.

27. $w = 32$; $x = 24$; $y = 40$; $z = 126$

8 CHAPTER REVIEW

1a. True
1b. False
1c. True
1d. True
1e. False
1f. True
1g. True
1h. Both
2. B (parallelogram)
3. A (triangle)
4. C (trapezoid)
5. E (kite)
6. F (regular polygon)
7. D (circle)
8. J (sector)
9. I (annulus)
10. G (cylinder)
11. H (cone)

12.

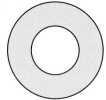

13.

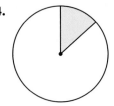

14.

15. Sample answer: Construct an altitude from the vertex of an obtuse angle to the base. Cut off the right triangle and move it to the opposite side, forming a rectangle. Because the parallelogram's area hasn't changed, its area equals the area of the rectangle. Because the area of the rectangle is given by the formula $A = bh$, the area of the parallelogram is also given by $A = bh$.

16. Sample answer: Make a copy of the trapezoid and put the two copies together to form a parallelogram with base $(b_1 + b_2)$ and height h. Thus the area of one trapezoid is given by the formula $A = \frac{1}{2}(b_1 + b_2)h$.

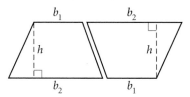

17. Sample answer: Cut a circular region into 16 wedges and arrange them into a shape that resembles a rectangle. The base length of this "rectangle" is πr and the height is r, so its area is πr^2. Thus the area of a circle is given by the formula $A = \pi r^2$.

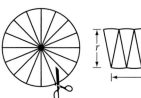

18. 800 cm^2
19. 5990.4 cm^2
20. 60π cm^2 or about 188.5 cm^2
21. 32 cm
22. 32 cm
23. 15 cm
24. 81π cm^2
25. 48π cm
26. 40°
27. 153.9 cm^2
28. 72 cm^2
29. 30.9 cm^2
30. 300 cm^2
31. 940 cm^2
32. 1356 cm^2

33. Area is 112 square units.

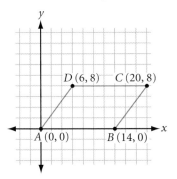

34. Area is 81 square units.

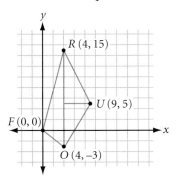

35. 6 cm

36. 172.5 cm^2

37. Sample answers:

38. 9:49 or $\frac{9}{49}$

39. $266.67

40. 1250 m^2

41. Circle. For the square, $100 = 4s$, $s = 25$, $A = 25^2 = 625$ ft^2. For the circle, $100 = 2\pi r$, $r \approx 15.9$, $A \approx \pi(15.9)^2 \approx 794$ ft^2.

42. A round peg in a square hole is a better fit. The round peg fills about 78.5% of area of the square hole, whereas the square peg fills only about 63.7% of the area of the round hole.

43. Giant

44. About 14 oz

45. One-eighth of a 12-inch diameter pie; one-fourth of a 6-inch pie and one-eighth of a 12-inch pie both have the same length of crust, and more than one-sixth of an 8-inch pie.

46. 1 to $\frac{\pi}{4}$ to $\frac{1}{2}$, or 4 to π to 2

47a. 96 ft; 40 ft

47b. 3290 ft^2

48. $3000

49. $4160

50. It's a bad deal. $2\pi r_1 = 44$ cm. $2\pi r_2 = 22$ cm, which implies $4\pi r_2 = 44$ cm. Therefore $r_1 = 2r_2$. The area of the large bundle is $4\pi(r_2)^2$ cm^2. The combined area of two small bundles is $2\pi(r_2)^2$ cm^2. Thus he is getting half as much for the same price.

51. ~$2000

52. $384 (16 gal)

CHAPTER REVIEW

1. Answers will vary.

2. Draw two nonparallel chords. The intersection of their perpendicular bisectors is the center of the circle.

Fold the paper so that two semicircles coincide. Repeat with two different semicircles. The center is the intersection of the two folds.

Place the outside or inside corner of the L in the circle so that it is an inscribed right angle. Trace the sides of the corner. Draw the hypotenuse of the right triangle (which is the diameter of the circle). Repeat. The center is the intersection of the two diameters.

3. The velocity vector is always perpendicular to the radius at the point of tangency to the object's circular path.

4. Sample answer: An arc measure is between 0° and 360°. An arc length is proportional to arc measure and depends on the radius of the circle.

5. 55°   **6.** 65°   **7.** 128°   **8.** 118°

9. 91°   **10.** 66°

11. 125.7 cm   **12.** 42.0 cm

13. 15π cm   **14.** 14π ft

15. $2 \cdot 57° + 2 \cdot 35° \neq 180°$

16. $84° + 56° + 56° + 158° \neq 360°$

17. $m\angle EKL = \frac{1}{2}m\widehat{EL} = \frac{1}{2}(180° - 108°) = 36° = m\angle KLY$. Therefore $\overline{KE} \parallel \overline{YL}$ by Converse of the Parallel Lines Conjecture.

18. $m\widehat{JI} = 360° - 56° - 152° = 152° = m\widehat{MI}$. Therefore $m\angle JMI = \frac{1}{2}m\widehat{JI} = \frac{1}{2}m\widehat{MI} = m\angle MJI$. By the Converse of the Isosceles Triangle Conjecture, $\triangle JIM$ is isosceles.

19. $m\widehat{KIM} = 2m\angle KEM = 140°$, so $m\widehat{KI} = 140° - 70° = 70° = m\widehat{MI}$. Therefore $m\angle IKM = \frac{1}{2}m\widehat{MI} = \frac{1}{2}m\widehat{KI} = m\angle IMK$. By the Converse of the Isosceles Triangle Conjecture, $\triangle KIM$ is isosceles.

20. Ertha can trace the incomplete circle on paper. She can lay the corner of the pad on the circle to trace an inscribed right angle. Then Ertha should mark the endpoints of the intercepted arc and use the pad to construct the hypotenuse of the right triangle, which is the diameter of the circle.

21. Sample answer: Construct perpendicular bisectors of two sides of the triangle. The point at which they intersect (the circumcenter) is the center of the circle. The distance from the circumcenter to each vertex is the radius.

22. Sample answer: Construct the incenter (from the angle bisectors) of the triangle. From the incenter, which is the center of the circle, construct a perpendicular to a side. The distance from the incenter to the foot of the perpendicular is the radius.

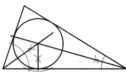

23. Sample answer: Construct a right angle and label the vertex R. Mark off $\overline{RE}$ and $\overline{RT}$ with any lengths. From point E, swing an arc with radius RT. From point T, swing an arc with radius RE. Label the intersection of the arcs as C. Construct the diagonals $\overline{ET}$ and $\overline{RC}$. Their intersection is the center of the circumscribed circle. The circle's radius is the distance from the center to a vertex. It is not possible to construct an inscribed circle in a rectangle unless it is a square.

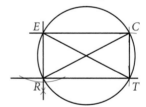

24. $\frac{3\pi}{4}$. The radian measure does not change because the radius cancels out in the calculation.

25a. $\frac{\pi}{3}$ **25b.** π

25c. $\frac{3\pi}{2}$ **25d.** $\frac{7\pi}{4}$

26. $(-3, 2)$ **27.** $d = 0.318$ m

28. Melanie: 151 m/min or 9 km/h; Melody: 94 m/min or 6 km/h.

29.

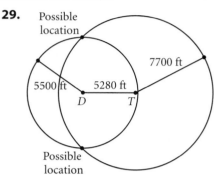

30. $\frac{200}{\pi}$ ft ≈ 63.7 ft   **31.** 8π m ≈ 25.1 m

32. The circumference is $\frac{48}{360} \cdot 2\pi(45) = 12\pi$; 12 cm is the diameter.

33. $\frac{2\pi(6357)}{360 \cdot 60} \approx 1.849 < 1.852 < 1.855$
$\approx \frac{2\pi(6378)}{360 \cdot 60}$

MIXED REVIEW

34.

35. 4; 0; 10. The rule is $\frac{n}{2}$ if n is even, but 0 if n is odd.

36. 4π, or approximately 12.6 in./s

37. True   **38.** True

39. False. Two sets of corresponding sides must be proportional and their included angle must be congruent.

40. True

41. False. You must also be able to see the shadow of the tree.

42. False. A glide reflection is a combination of a translation and a reflection.

43. False. Equilateral triangles, squares, and regular *hexagons* can be used to create monohedral tessellations.

44. True   **45.** A, B, C   **46.** B, C

47. C   **48.** C   **49.** D

50. Yes. Yes. $p = 52$. $q = 42$.

51. Angles U and A are congruent because they intersect the same arc. Angles T and S are congruent because they intersect the same arc. Therefore, they are similar by the AA Similarity conjecture. $r = 13$. $s = 20$.

52. See flowchart below.

53.

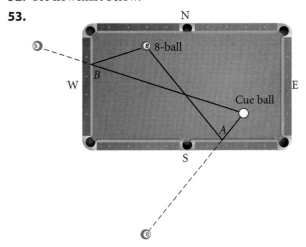

54. $\frac{40\pi}{3}$ cm²

55. 322 ft²

56. About 61.5 cm²

57. Yes they are similar. 2:1. 4:1

58. 118

59. Approximately 637 revolutions.

1. 20 cm   **2.** 10 cm   **3.** obtuse   **4.** 26 cm

5. $\left(\frac{\sqrt{3}}{2}, \frac{1}{2}\right)$ **6.** $\left(-\frac{1}{\sqrt{2}}, -\frac{1}{\sqrt{2}}\right)$

7. $200\sqrt{3}$ cm²   **8.** $d = 12\sqrt{2}$ cm

9. 246 cm²   **10.** 72π in²

11. 24π cm²   **12.** $(2\pi - 4)$ cm²

13. 222.8 cm²   **14.** isosceles right

15. No. The closest she can come to camp is 10 km.

16. No. The 15 cm diagonal is the longer diagonal.

17. 1.4 km; $8\frac{1}{2}$ min

18. Yes   **19.** 29 ft   **20.** ≈ 45 ft

21. Since the distance from the origin to (5,0) is 5, the radius of the circle is equal to 5. Since the distance from the origin to (−3, 4) is also 5, we can conclude that the point is on the circle.

22. 707 m²   **23.** $6\sqrt{3}$ and 18

24. 12 m   **25.** 42

26. Shearing the square into a parallelogram does not change the height or base of the quadrilateral, therefore the areas of the small squares remain the same. When they are added together, they form the large square and thus the areas combine to equal the area of the large square.

52. (*Chapter 9 Review*)

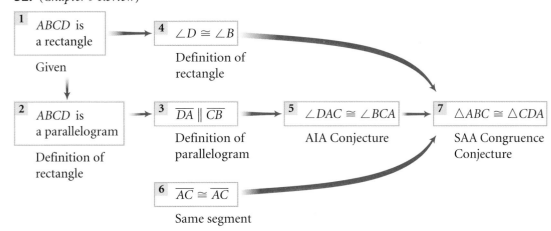

27. $(0,1)$, $(0, -5)$, and $(4, -1)$ are points on the circle because when you substitute each point into the equation, it creates a true statement.

28. $A = 25\pi$. $C = 10\pi$.

29. Rectangle

30. Rhombus

31. Square

32. $A = 4$. $P = 4\sqrt{5}$.

33. $C(-5, -3)$. $r = 2$.

34. No. If you reflect one of the right triangles into the center piece, you'll see that the area of the kite is almost half again as large as the area of each of the other triangles.

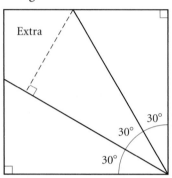

Or you might compare areas by assuming the short leg of the 30°-60°-90° triangle is 1. The area of each triangle is then $\frac{\sqrt{3}}{2}$ and the area of the kite is $3 - \sqrt{3}$.

35. $(x + 2)^2 + (y - 5)^2 = 4$

36. The quarter-circle gives the maximum area.

Triangle:

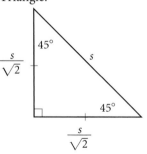

$$A = \frac{1}{2} \cdot \frac{s}{\sqrt{2}} \cdot \frac{s}{\sqrt{2}} = \frac{s^2}{4}$$

Square:

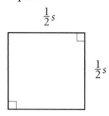

$$A = \frac{1}{2}s \cdot \frac{1}{2}s = \frac{s^2}{4}$$

Quarter-circle:

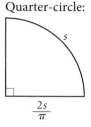

$$s = \frac{1}{4} \cdot 2\pi r$$
$$r = \frac{2s}{\pi}$$
$$A = \frac{1}{4}\pi\left(\frac{2s}{\pi}\right)^2 = \frac{s^2}{\pi}$$

$$\frac{s^2}{\pi} > \frac{s^2}{4}$$

37. 1.6 m

38a. $6\sqrt{3}$ cm **38b.** 6 cm

11

CHAPTER REVIEW

1. They have the same formula for volume: $V = BH$.

2. They have the same formula for volume: $V = \frac{1}{3}BH$.

3. 6240 cm³ **4.** 1029π cm³

5. 1200 cm³ **6.** 32 cm³

7. 100π cm³ **8.** 2250π cm³

9. $H = 12.8$ cm **10.** $h = 7$ cm

11. $r = 12$ cm **12.** $r = 8$ cm

13. For Exercise 11, rotate a right triangle, with legs equal to r and 36, 360° about the y-axis. For Exercise 12, rotate $\frac{1}{4}$ of a circle, with radius r, 270° about the y-axis.

14. 960 cm³ **15.** 9 m

16. 851 cm³ **17.** Four times as great

18a. $V_{\text{extra large}} = 54$ in³
$V_{\text{jumbo}} \approx 201.1$ in³
$V_{\text{colossal}} \approx 785.4$ in³

18b. 14.5 times as great

19. Cylinder B weighs $\frac{8}{3}$ times as much as cylinder A.

20. 2129 kg; 9 loads

21. $H = 2r$. $\frac{V_{\text{sphere}}}{V_{\text{box}}} = \frac{\frac{4}{3}\pi r^3}{(2r)^3} \approx 0.524$. Thus, 52.4% of the box is filled by the ball.

22. Approximately 358 yd^3

23. No. The unused volume is 98π in^3, and the volume of the meatballs is 32π in^3.

24. Platinum

25. No. The ball weighs 253 lb.

26. 256 lb

27. Approximately 3 in.

28. $\left(\frac{\pi}{8} - \frac{3\sqrt{3}}{32}\right)$ m$^3 \approx 0.23$ m^3

29. 160π cubic units

30. 4 pints. 8 times.

31. $\frac{5}{4}, \frac{125}{64}$

32a. 3 to 2 to 1

32b. Answers will vary.

33. Possible answer: If food is proportional to body volume, then $\frac{1}{8000}$ of the usual amount of food is required. If clothing is proportional to surface area, then $\frac{1}{400}$ of the usual amount of clothing is required. It would take 20 times longer to walk a given distance.

34. The ice cubes would melt faster because they have greater surface area.

12

1. 0.8387   **2.** 0.9877

3. 28.6363

4. $\sin A = \frac{a}{b}$; $\cos A = \frac{c}{b}$; $\tan A = \frac{a}{c}$

5. $\sin B = \frac{8}{17}$; $\cos B = \frac{15}{17}$; $\tan B = \frac{8}{15}$

6. $\sin\theta = s$; $\cos\theta = t$; $\tan\theta = \frac{s}{t}$

7. Several approaches are possible. One of the simplest: $\frac{a}{\sin A} = \frac{1}{\frac{\sin A}{a}} = \frac{1}{\frac{\sin B}{b}} = \frac{b}{\sin B}$.

8. $a^2 = b^2 + c^2 - 2bc\cos A$. $b^2 = a^2 + c^2 - 2ac\cos B$.

9. 33°   **10.** 86°

11. 71°   **12.** 1823 cm^2

13. 15,116 cm^3

14. Yes, the plan meets the act's requirements. The angle of ascent is approximately 4.3°.

15. Approximately 52 km

16. Approximately 7.3°

17. Approximately 22 ft

18. Approximately 6568 m

19. Approximately 2973 km/h

20. 393 cm^2 **21.** 30 cm

22. 78°   **23.** 105 cm

24. 51°   **25.** 759 cm^2

26. Approximately 25 cm

27. 72 cm^2

28. Approximately 15.7 cm

29. Approximately 33.5 cm^2

30. Approximately 10.1 km/h at an approximate bearing of 24.5°

31a. $4\sqrt{2}$ cm   **31b.** $2\sqrt{6}$ cm   **31c.** 120°

32. False; an octahedron is a polyhedron with eight faces.

33. False

34. True   **35.** True

36. False; the ratio of their areas is $\frac{m^2}{n^2}$.

37. True

38. False; tangent of $\angle T = \frac{\text{length of leg opposite }\angle T}{\text{length of leg adjacent to }\angle T}$

39. True   **40.** True

41. True   **42.** True

43. False; the slope of line ℓ_2 is $\frac{-1}{m}$.

44. False

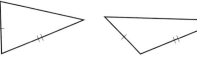

45. B   **46.** C   **47.** A   **48.** D

49. B   **50.** B   **51.** A   **52.** B

53. C   **54.** D   **55.** C   **56.** A

57. $\frac{100\pi}{3}$ cm^3 **58.** 28π cm^3

59. 30.5π cm^3 **60.** 33

61. $(x, y) \rightarrow (x + 1, y - 3)$

62. $w = 48$ cm, $x = 24$ cm, $y = 28.5$ cm

63. Approximately 18 cm

64. $(x-5)^2 + (y-1)^2 = 9$

65. Approximately 99.5 m

66. 30 ft   **67.** 4 cm

68.

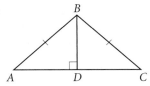

68a. $m\angle ABC = 2 \cdot m\angle ABD$

68b. Possible answers: $\overline{BD}$ is the perpendicular bisector of $\overline{AC}$. It is the angle bisector of $\angle ABC$; a median, and divides $\triangle ABC$ into two congruent right triangles.

69. $A = 14$

CHAPTER REVIEW

1. False. It could be an isosceles trapezoid.

2. True

3. False. It could be an isosceles trapezoid or a kite.

4. True

5. False. The angles are supplementary, but not necessarily congruent.

6. False. See Lesson 13.5, Example B.

7. True

8. False. The parallelogram could be any rhombus.

9. False. Possible counterexample:

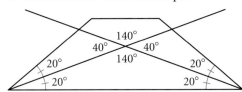

10. False. The sum of measures of the interior angles formed by the perpendicular bisectors is 540°, so $x + 90° + b + b + 90° = 540°$, which simplifies to $x = 360° - 2b$. So $x = 90°$ only if $b = 135°$.

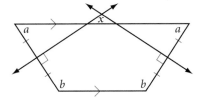

11. True (except in the special case of an isosceles right triangle, in which the segment is not defined because the feet coincide).

Given: Isosceles $\triangle ABC$ with $\overline{AC} \cong \overline{BC}$; altitudes $\overline{AD}$ and $\overline{BE}$; $\overline{ED}$

Show: $\overline{ED} \parallel \overline{AB}$

Paragraph Proof:

$\angle EAB \cong \angle DBA$ by the Isosceles Triangle Theorem. $\angle AEB \cong \angle BDA$ by the definition of altitude and the Right Angles Are Congruent Theorem. $\overline{AB} \cong \overline{AB}$ by the reflexive property of congruence. $\triangle AEB \cong \triangle BDA$ by SAA. Therefore $\overline{AE} \cong \overline{BD}$ by CPCTC. By the definition of congruence, $AC = BC$ and $AE = BD$, so $EC = DC$ by the subtraction property of equality. By the division property of equality, $\frac{EC}{AE} = \frac{DC}{BD}$, so $\overline{ED}$ divides the sides of $\triangle ABC$ proportionally. Therefore $\overline{ED} \parallel \overline{AB}$ by the Converse of the Parallel/Proportionality Theorem.

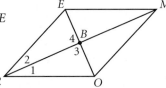

12. True

Given: Rhombus *ROME* with diagonals $\overline{RM}$ and $\overline{EO}$ intersecting at *B*

Show: $\overline{RM} \perp \overline{EO}$

Statement	Reason
1. $\angle 1 \cong \angle 2$	1. Rhombus Angles Theorem
2. $RO = RE$	2. Definition of rhombus
3. $\overline{RO} \cong \overline{RE}$	3. Definition of congruence
4. $\overline{RB} \cong \overline{RB}$	4. Reflexive property of congruence
5. $\triangle ROB \cong \triangle REB$	5. SAS Congruence Postulate
6. $\angle 3 \cong \angle 4$	6. CPCTC
7. $\angle 3$ and $\angle 4$ are a linear pair	7. Definition of linear pair
8. $\angle 3$ and $\angle 4$ are supplementary	8. Linear Pair Postulate
9. $\angle 3$ and $\angle 4$ are right angles	9. Congruent and Supplementary Theorem
10. $\overline{RM} \perp \overline{EO}$	10. Definition of perpendicular

13. True. See flowchart proof below.

NOTE: The answers to Exercises 8–13 are models of what a thorough proof should look like. The answers to Exercises 23–33 explain the logic of each proof without showing the details required for a thorough proof.

14. perpendicular

15. congruent

16. the center of the circle

17. four congruent triangles that are similar to the original triangle

18. an auxiliary theorem proven specifically to help prove other theorems

19. If a segment joins the midpoints of the diagonals of a trapezoid, then it is parallel to the bases.

20. Angle Bisector Postulate

21. Perpendicular Postulate

22. Assume the opposite of what you want to prove, then use valid reasoning to derive a contradiction.

23. Use the Inscribed Angle Theorem, the addition property, and the distributive property to get
$m\angle P + m\angle E + m\angle N + m\angle T + m\angle A = \frac{1}{2}(m\widehat{TN} + m\widehat{AT} + m\widehat{PA} + m\widehat{EP} + m\widehat{NE})$.
Because there are 360° in a circle, $m\angle P + m\angle E + m\angle N + m\angle T + m\angle A = 180°$.

24.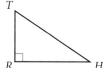

Assume $m\angle H > 45°$ and $m\angle T > 45°$. Use the Triangle Sum Theorem, the substitution property, and the subtraction property to get $m\angle H + m\angle T > 90°$, which creates a contradiction. Therefore $m\angle H \leq 45°$ or $m\angle T \leq 45°$.

25.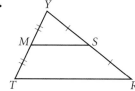

Use the definition of midpoint, the Segment Addition Postulate, the substitution property, and the division property to get $\frac{MY}{TY} = \frac{1}{2}$ and $\frac{YS}{YR} = \frac{1}{2}$. Then use the reflexive property and the SAS Similarity Theorem to get $\triangle MSY \sim \triangle TRY$. Therefore, $MS = \frac{1}{2}TR$ by CSSTP and the multiplication property and $\overline{MS} \parallel \overline{TR}$ by CASTC and the CA Postulate.

---

13. (*Chapter 13 Review*)

Given: Parallelogram $ABCD$; $\overline{AE}$ bisects $\angle BAD$; $\overline{CF}$ bisects $\angle BCD$
Show: $\overline{AE} \parallel \overline{CF}$
Flowchart Proof

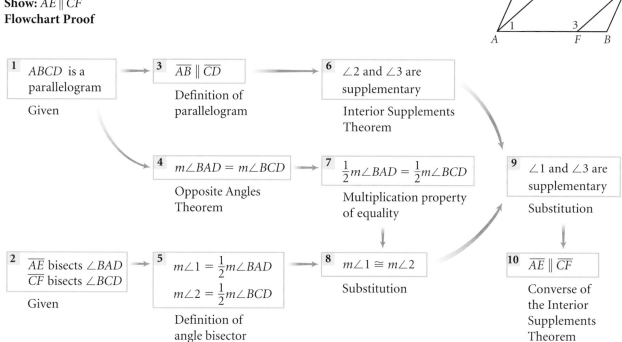

26.

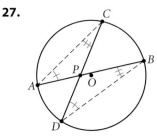

Use the Line Postulate to extend $\overline{ZO}$ and $\overline{DR}$. Then use the Line Intersection Postulate to label P as the intersection of $\overline{ZO}$ and $\overline{DR}$. $\triangle DYR \cong \triangle POR$ by the SAA Theorem; thus $\overline{DY} \cong \overline{OP}$ by CPCTC. Use the Triangle Midsegment Theorem and the substitution property to get $TR = \frac{1}{2}(ZO + DY)$.

27.

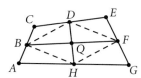

Use the Line Postulate to construct chords $\overline{DB}$ and $\overline{AC}$. Then use the Inscribed Angles Intercepting Arcs Theorem and the AA Similarity Postulate to get $\triangle APC \sim \triangle DPB$. Therefore, by CSSTP and the multiplication property, $AP \cdot PB = DP \cdot PC$.

28. $BGEC$ is an isosceles trapezoid. Using the definitions of an isosceles triangle and an equilateral triangle, prove that the two squares are congruent. The Squares Diagonals Theorem shows that $\overline{BG} \cong \overline{CE}$. Show that $\triangle BGF \cong \triangle CEF$ by the SSS Congruence Postulate. Using CPCTC and the definition of equilateral and isosceles triangles, show that $\angle BGE \cong \angle CEG$. Since $\triangle BGF \cong \triangle CEF$, use CPCTC, the definition of equilateral triangles, and algebra to show that $\angle CBG$ and $\angle BGE$ are supplementary and hence $\overline{BC} \| \overline{CE}$. Therefore, $BGEC$ is an isosceles trapezoid.

29. $AB = 2A'B'$. Since points A and B are midpoints, $AA' = PA$ and $BP = B'B$. Use proportions and the shared angle to show that $\triangle A'PB' \sim \triangle APB$. By corresponding parts of similar triangles, algebra, and substitution, show that $AB = 2A'B'$.

30. The points are collinear and form a line parallel to the initial parallel lines. Construct a perpendicular $\overleftrightarrow{KJ}$ to $\overleftrightarrow{AF}$ through point E. By the Transitive Property, $\overleftrightarrow{KJ} \perp \overleftrightarrow{CG}$. Use the Alternate Interior Angles Theorem to show that $\angle KDE \cong \angle JFE$. Use the Vertical Angles Theorem, definition of a midpoint, and the ASA Congruence Postulate to show that triangles DKE and FJE are congruent. Use the definition of a trapezoid and the Trapezoid Midsegment Theorem to show that $\overline{BE}$ is a midsegment of trapezoid $ACKJ$ and $\overline{BE} \| \overleftrightarrow{CK} \| \overleftrightarrow{AJ}$. Use similar reasoning to show that

$\overleftrightarrow{BH} \| \overleftrightarrow{CG} \| \overleftrightarrow{AI}$. Since there is only one line parallel to $\overleftrightarrow{CG}$ and $\overleftrightarrow{AF}$ through point B, points E and H must also be on that line and therefore the points are collinear.

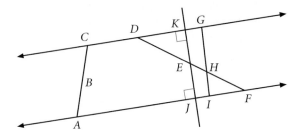

31. The midpoints are collinear and $\overleftrightarrow{KM} \| \overleftrightarrow{AE}$. Use the definition of a midpoint and the Triangle Midsegment Theorem to identify the midsegments of triangles BCP, DCP, and BDP, and establish that they are all parallel to $\overleftrightarrow{AE}$. Since $\overline{KL} \| \overleftrightarrow{AE}$ and $\overline{LM} \| \overleftrightarrow{AE}$ and $\overline{KM} \| \overleftrightarrow{AE}$ and there is a unique point parallel through points K, L, and M, all three points must be on the same line and hence collinear.

32. Rhombus. Use SAS Congruence to show that triangles ABH and GFH are congruent and $\overline{BH} \cong \overline{FH}$ by CPCTC. Repeat for triangles BCD and FED to show that $\overline{BD} \cong \overline{FD}$. By Varignon's Theorem from the Exploration, $BDFH$ is a parallelogram. Use the Parallelogram Diagonals Theorem and SAS Congruence to show that all four triangles within the parallelogram are congruent. Therefore, the hypotenuses of each triangle are congruent and the parallelogram is a rhombus.

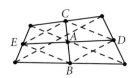

33. The segments bisect each other. Using Varignon's Theorem from the Exploration, the quadrilateral formed by the midpoints on the quadrilateral is a parallelogram. The segments connecting the midpoints, $\overline{ED}$ and $\overline{CB}$, are diagonals of a parallelogram. Following the Parallelogram Diagonals Theorem, the diagonals bisect each other, therefore, $\overline{EA} \cong \overline{AD}$ and $\overline{CA} \cong \overline{AB}$.

Glossary

The number in parentheses at the end of each definition gives the page where each term is introduced in the text. Some terms have multiple page numbers listed because they have different applications in different lessons. Most terms, including those that you define in investigations, include either a visual representation or a reference to a related definition that includes a visual representation.

A

acute angle

∠ABC is an acute angle.

You define this term in the Investigation Defining Angles. (44)

acute triangle

If ∠A, ∠B, and ∠C are acute angles, △ABC is an acute triangle.

You define this term in the Investigation Triangles. (56)

adjacent angles

∠1 and ∠2 are adjacent angles.

Two non-overlapping angles with a common vertex and one common side. (37)

adjacent interior angle The angle of a polygon that forms a linear pair with a given exterior angle of a polygon. See **remote interior angles.** (222)

adjacent leg (of an acute angle in a right triangle)

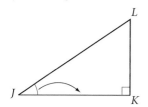

$\overline{JK}$ is the side adjacent to ∠J.

The side of the angle that is not the hypotenuse. (584)

adjacent sides See **consecutive sides.**

alternate exterior angles

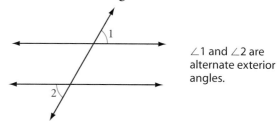

∠1 and ∠2 are alternate exterior angles.

A pair of angles, formed by a transversal intersecting two lines, that do not lie between the two lines and are on opposite sides of the transversal. (138)

alternate interior angles

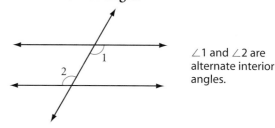

∠1 and ∠2 are alternate interior angles.

A pair of angles, formed by a transversal intersecting two lines, that lie between the two lines and are on opposite sides of the transversal. (138)

altitude (of a cone, pyramid, or triangle)

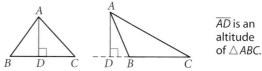

$\overline{AD}$ is an altitude of △ABC.

A perpendicular segment from a vertex to the base or to the line or plane containing the base. See **cone, pyramid,** and **triangle.** (162, 535)

altitude (of a parallelogram, trapezoid, prism, or cylinder)

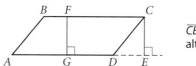

$\overline{CE}$ and $\overline{FG}$ are altitudes of ABCD.

A perpendicular segment from a base to the parallel base or to the line or plane containing the parallel base. See **cylinder, parallelogram, prism,** and **trapezoid.** (535)

angle

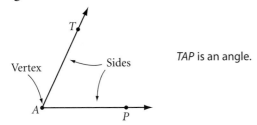

TAP is an angle.

Two noncollinear rays having a common endpoint. (33)

angle (of a polygon) An angle having two adjacent sides of the polygon as its sides. See **polygon.** (50)

angle addition A property that states if *D* is in the interior of $\angle CAB$, then $m\angle CAD + m\angle DAB = m\angle CAB$. (36)

angle bisector

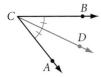

$\overrightarrow{CD}$ is the angle bisector of $\angle BCA$.

A ray that has its endpoint at the vertex of the angle and that divides the angle into two congruent angles. (35)

angle bisector (of a triangle)

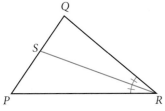

$\overline{RS}$ is an angle bisector of $\triangle PQR$.

A segment that lies on an angle bisector and that has one endpoint at the vertex and the other on the opposite side of the triangle. (35)

angle of depression The angle formed by a horizontal line and the line of sight of a viewer looking down. See **angle of elevation.** (590)

angle of elevation

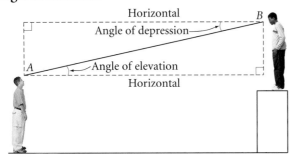

The angle formed by a horizontal line and the line of sight of a viewer looking up. (590)

angle of rotation

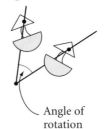

The image has been rotated by the angle of rotation.

The angle between a point and its image under a rotation, with its vertex at the center of the rotation and sides that go through the point and its image. (80)

angular velocity (of an object moving around a circle) The rate of change, with respect to time, of the measure of the arc between an object and its starting position. (485)

annulus

The shaded region between the circles is an annulus.

The region between two concentric circles of unequal radius. (425)

antecedent The first or "if" clause of a conditional statement. (609)

apothem (of a regular polygon)

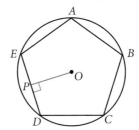

$\overline{OP}$ is an apothem of *ABCDE*.

A perpendicular segment from the center of the polygon's circumscribed circle to a side of the polygon. Also, the length of that segment. (420)

arc

$\overparen{AB}$ is an arc.

Two points on a circle and the continuous part of the circle between them. (67)

arc length The portion of the circumference of the circle described by an arc, measured in units of length. (481)

arc measure

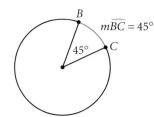

$m\widehat{BC} = 45°$

The measure of arc *BC* is 45°.

The measure of the central angle that intercepts an arc, measured in degrees. (68)

area The measure of the size of the interior of a figure, expressed in square units. (410)

assume To accept as true without facts or proof. (55)

auxiliary line

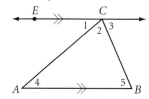

$\overleftrightarrow{EC}$ is an auxiliary line that helps prove that $m\angle 2 + m\angle 4 + m\angle 5$ equals 180°.

An extra line or line segment drawn in a figure to help with a proof. (205)

axis (of a cone or cylinder) The line segment connecting the center of the base to the vertex or center of the other base. See **cone** and **cylinder.** (536)

base (of a polygon) A side of the polygon used for reference to determine an altitude or other feature. See **parallelogram, trapezoid,** and **triangle.** (276, 410)

base (of a solid) A polygon or circle used for reference to determine an altitude or other feature of the solid, or to classify the solid. See **cone, cylinder, prism,** and **pyramid.** (432)

base angles (of an isosceles triangle) The two angles opposite the two congruent sides. See **isosceles triangle.** (57)

base angles (of a trapezoid) A pair of angles with a base of the trapezoid as a common side. See **trapezoid.** (276)

bearing The clockwise measure of the angle from due north to the path of travel. (605)

biconditional statement A statement that includes both a conditional statement and its converse, usually written in "if and only if" form. (212)

bilateral symmetry Reflectional symmetry with only one line of symmetry. (3)

bisect To divide into two congruent parts. (27)

Cavalieri's Principle If two solids have the same cross-sectional area whenever they are sliced at the same height, then the two solids have the same volume. (562)

center (of a circle) The coplanar point from which all points of the circle are the same distance. See **circle.** (65)

center (of a sphere) The point from which all points on the sphere are the same distance. See **sphere.** (537)

center of gravity The balancing point of an object. (191)

central angle

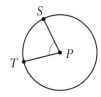

$\angle SPT$ is a central angle of circle *P*.

An angle whose vertex is the center of a circle and whose sides pass through the endpoints of an arc. (68, 458)

centroid

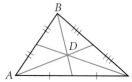

Point *D* is the centroid of △*ABC*.

The point of concurrency of a triangle's three medians. (190)

chord

$\overline{AB}$ is a chord of circle *Q*.

You define this term in the Investigation Defining Circle Terms. (65)

circle

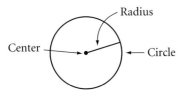

The set of all points in a plane at a given distance from a given point. (65)

circumcenter

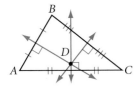

Point *D* is the circumcenter of △*ABC*.

The point of concurrency of a triangle's three perpendicular bisectors. (185)

circumference The perimeter of a circle, which is the distance around the circle. Also, the curved path of the circle itself. (67)

circumscribed (about a circle)

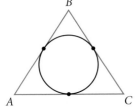

△*ABC* is circumscribed about the circle.

Having all sides tangent to the circle, such as a triangle circumscribed about a circle. (67)

circumscribed (about a polygon)

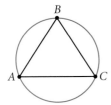

The circle is circumscribed about △*ABC*.

Passing through each vertex of the polygon, such as a circle circumscribed about a triangle. (67)

classify and differentiate Defining a term by categorizing it, then distinguishing it from other members of the same group, according to chosen characteristics. (43)

clinometer A tool for measuring an angle of elevation or depression, consisting of an edge to sight along, a plumb line, and a protractor. (594)

coincide To lie exactly on top of each other. (3)

collinear

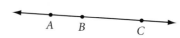

Points *A*, *B*, and *C* are collinear.

On the same line. (25)

compass A tool used to construct circles. (7)

complementary angles

∠1 and ∠2 are complementary angles.

You define this term in the Investigation Defining Angles. (45)

composition (of transformations) The single transformation that gives the same image as a transformation applied to a figure followed by a second transformation applied to the image of the first. (127)

concave polygon

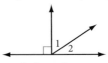

ABCDE is a concave polygon.

A polygon with at least one diagonal outside the polygon. (50)

concentric circles

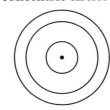

Three concentric circles

Circles that share the same center. (66)

concurrent lines

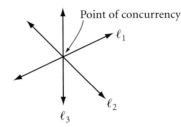

Lines ℓ₁, ℓ₂, and ℓ₃ are concurrent.

Two or more lines that intersect in a single point. (109, 184)

conditional proof A proof of a conditional statement. (609)

conditional statement A statement that can be expressed in "if-then" form. (609)

cone

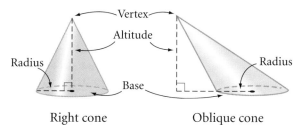

Right cone   Oblique cone

A solid consisting of a circle and its interior, a point not in the plane of the circle, and all points on line segments connecting that point to points on the circle. (72, 536)

congruent (angles, line segments, circles, or polygons)

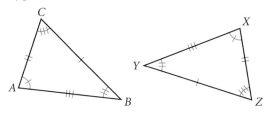

△ABC is congruent to △XYZ. All corresponding parts are congruent. For instance, $\overline{AB}$ is congruent to $\overline{XY}$, and ∠C is congruent to ∠Z.

Identical in shape and size. (26, 35, 51, 66)

conjecture A generalization resulting from inductive reasoning. (100)

consecutive (angles, sides, or vertices of a polygon)

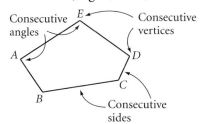

Two angles that share a common side, two sides that share a common vertex, or two vertices that are the endpoints of one side. Consecutive sides are also called adjacent sides. (50)

consequent The second or "then" clause of a conditional statement. (609)

contrapositive The statement formed by exchanging and negating the antecedent and the consequent of a conditional statement. (575)

converse The statement formed by exchanging the antecedent and the consequent of a conditional statement. (134)

convex polygon A polygon with no diagonal outside the polygon. See **concave polygon.** (50)

coordinate proof A proof using coordinates of points in a coordinate system. (660)

coplanar

Points D, E, and F are coplanar.

In the same plane. (25)

corollary A theorem that is the immediate consequence of another proven theorem. (637)

corresponding angles

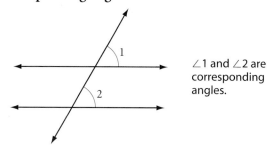

∠1 and ∠2 are corresponding angles.

Two angles formed by a transversal intersecting two lines that lie in the same position relative to the two lines and the transversal. (138)

cosine (of an acute angle in a right triangle)

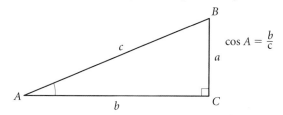

$\cos A = \dfrac{b}{c}$

The cosine of ∠A is the ratio of AC to AB.

The ratio of the length of the leg adjacent to the angle to the length of the hypotenuse. (585)

counterexample An example that shows a conjecture to be incorrect or a definition to be inadequate. (42)

cross-section The intersection of a solid and a plane. (75)

cube A regular polyhedron with six faces. See **hexahedron.** (74)

cyclic quadrilateral

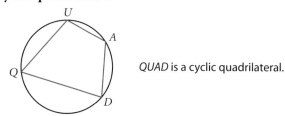

QUAD is a cyclic quadrilateral.

A quadrilateral that can be inscribed in a circle. (467)

cylinder

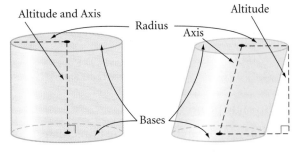

Right cylinder   Oblique cylinder

A solid consisting of two congruent, parallel circles and their interiors, and the segments having an endpoint on each circle that are parallel to the segment between the centers of the circles. (72, 536)

D

dart

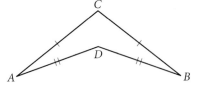

ACBD is a dart.

A concave kite. (299)

decagon A polygon with ten sides. (50)

deductive argument Support for a conjecture based on deductive reasoning. (119)

deductive reasoning The process of showing that certain statements follow logically from agreed-upon assumptions and proven facts. (119)

deductive system A set of premises and logical rules used to organize the properties of geometry, in which each theorem can be proved by deductive reasoning using only the premises and previous theorems, and in which each definition uses only terms that have been defined previously in the system. (622)

definition A statement that clarifies or explains the meaning of a word or phrase. (25)

degree A unit of measure for angles and arcs equivalent to $\frac{1}{360}$ of a rotation around a circle. (34)

density The ratio of the mass of an object to its volume. (558)

determine To provide the characteristics necessary to specify a figure. For example, three sides determine a triangle; three angles do not determine a triangle. (175)

diagonal

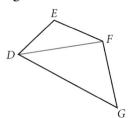

$\overline{DF}$ is a diagonal of *DEFG*.

A line segment connecting two nonconsecutive vertices of a polygon or polyhedron. (50)

diameter

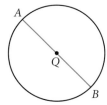

$\overline{AB}$ is a diameter of circle *Q*.

A chord of a circle that contains the center, or the length of that chord. (66)

dilation

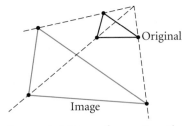

The image is a dilation of the original triangle.

A nonrigid transformation that enlarges or reduces a geometric figure by a scale factor relative to a point. (370)

direct proof A proof requiring a statement of premises and the use of valid forms of reasoning to arrive at a conclusion in the simplest way without need for any assumptions. (609)

directed two-column proof A form of proof in which each statement in the argument is written in the left column, and the reason for each statement is written directly across from it in the right column. (640)

displacement The volume of fluid that rises above the original fluid line when a solid object is submerged in the fluid. (558)

dissection The result of dividing a figure into pieces. (498)

distance (between two points) The length of the line segment between the two points. (514)

distance (from a point to a line or plane)

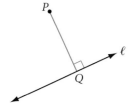

The distance from point *P* to line ℓ is the length of $\overline{PQ}$.

The length of the perpendicular line segment from the point to the line or plane. (161)

distance (of a translation) The length of the line segment between a point and its image in a translation. (79)

dodecagon A polygon with 12 sides. (50)

dodecahedron

The faces of this dodecahedron are regular pentagons.

A polyhedron with 12 faces. (534)

dual (of a tessellation)

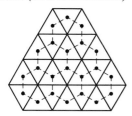

The new tessellation formed by constructing line segments between the centers of polygons having a common edge in a tessellation. (346)

E

edge The intersection of two faces in a polyhedron. See **polyhedron.** (534)

endpoint

A and *B* are endpoints.

The point at either end of a segment or an arc, or the first point of a ray. (27, 67)

enlargement A dilation in which the amount increases by a scale factor greater than 1. (371)

equiangular polygon

This octagon is equiangular.

You define this term in the Investigation Special Polygons. (52)

equidistant The same distance. (156)

equilateral polygon

This octagon is equilateral.

You define this term in the Investigation Special Polygons. (52)

equilateral triangle

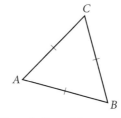

△*ABC* is an equilateral triangle.

You define this term in the Investigation Triangles. (10, 57)

Euler line The line through three of the four points of concurrency of a triangle. (195)

Euler segment The line segment on the Euler line determined by the three points of concurrency of the triangle. (195)

exterior angle

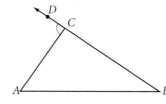

∠*ACD* is an exterior angle of △*ABC*.

An angle that forms a linear pair with one of the interior angles of a polygon. (222)

externally tangent circles Two tangent circles having centers on opposite sides of their common tangent. See **tangent circles.** (455)

F

face A surface of a polyhedron formed by a polygon and its interior. (534)

flowchart A concept map that shows a step-by-step process. Boxes represent the steps and arrows connect the boxes to show how they are sequenced. (243)

flowchart proof

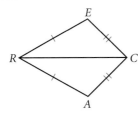

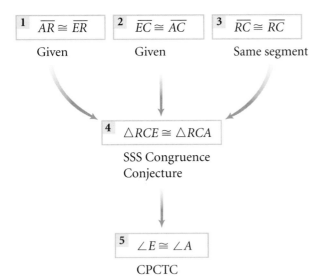

1 $\overline{AR} \cong \overline{ER}$	2 $\overline{EC} \cong \overline{AC}$	3 $\overline{RC} \cong \overline{RC}$
Given	Given	Same segment

4 $\triangle RCE \cong \triangle RCA$

SSS Congruence Conjecture

5 $\angle E \cong \angle A$

CPCTC

A logical argument presented in the form of a flowchart. (243)

frustum (of a cone or pyramid)

A solid formed by cutting a cone or pyramid with a plane parallel to the base and removing the vertex portion. Also called a truncated cone or truncated pyramid. (574)

glide reflection

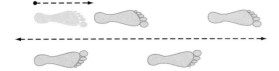

Footsteps are an example of a glide reflection.

An isometry that is a composition of a translation and a reflection across a line parallel to the translation vector. (320)

glide-reflectional symmetry The property that a figure coincides with its image under a glide reflection. (320)

golden cut

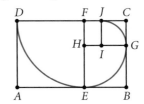

Point X is the golden cut of $\overline{AB}$.

$$\frac{AB}{AX} = \frac{AX}{XB}$$

The point that divides a line segment into two segments so that the ratio of their lengths is the golden ratio. (390)

golden ratio The ratio of two numbers whose ratio to each other equals the ratio of their sum to the larger number. (390)

golden rectangle A rectangle in which the ratio of the lengths of the sides is the golden ratio. (402)

golden spiral

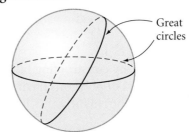

ABCD is a golden rectangle. The curve from *D* to *E* to *G* to *J* is the beginning of a golden spiral.

A spiral through vertices of nested golden rectangles. (403)

great circle

The intersection of a sphere with a plane that passes through its center. (537)

height The length of an altitude. See **cone, cylinder, parallelogram, prism, pyramid, trapezoid,** and **triangle.** (410, 535)

hemisphere

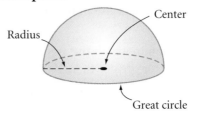

Half of a sphere and its great circle base. (72, 537)

heptagon A polygon with seven sides. (50)

hexagon

The first hexagon is a regular hexagon.

A polygon with six sides. (50)

hexahedron

The second hexahedron is a regular hexahedron.

A polyhedron with six faces. (534)

hypotenuse The side opposite the right angle in a right triangle. See **right triangle.** (498)

icosahedron

This is a regular icosahedron.

A polyhedron with 20 faces. (552)

if-then statement See **conditional statement.**

image The result of moving all points of a figure according to a transformation. (79)

incenter

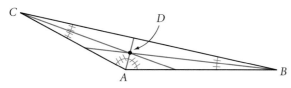

Point *D* is the incenter of △*ABC*.

The point of concurrency of a triangle's three angle bisectors. (185)

included angle

∠*A* is included by $\overline{AB}$ and $\overline{AC}$.

An angle formed between two consecutive sides of a polygon. (228)

included side

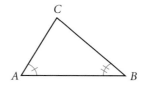

$\overline{AB}$ is included by ∠*A* and ∠*B*.

A side of a polygon between two consecutive angles. (233)

incoming angle

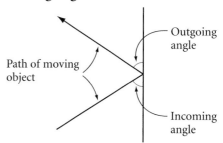

Outgoing angle

Path of moving object

Incoming angle

The angle formed between the path of an approaching object and the surface from which it rebounds, such as a billiard ball rolling toward a cushion or a ray of light traveling toward a mirror. (36)

indirect measurement Finding a distance or length by using properties of similar triangles or trigonometry. (387)

indirect proof A proof of a statement that begins by assuming that the statement is not true and then shows that this leads to a contradiction. (609, 647)

inductive reasoning The process of observing data, recognizing patterns, and making generalizations about those patterns. (100)

inscribed angle

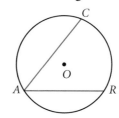

∠*CAR* is inscribed in circle *O*.

You define this term in the Investigation Defining Angles in a Circle. (458)

inscribed (in a circle)

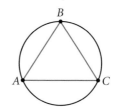

△*ABC* is inscribed in the circle.

Having each vertex on the circle, such as a triangle inscribed in a circle. (67)

inscribed (in a polygon)

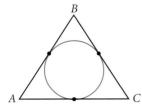

The circle is inscribed in △ABC.

Intersecting each side of the polygon exactly once, such as a circle inscribed in a triangle. (67)

intercepted arc

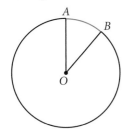

$\overparen{AB}$ is intercepted by ∠BOA.

An arc that lies in the interior of an angle with endpoints on the sides of the angle. (454)

interior angle An angle of a polygon that lies inside the polygon. (262)

internally tangent circles Two tangent circles having centers on the same side of their common tangent. See **tangent circles.** (455)

intersection

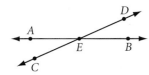

Point *E* is the intersection of $\overleftrightarrow{AB}$ and $\overleftrightarrow{CD}$.

The point or set of points common to two geometric figures. (46)

inverse cosine, sine, or **tangent** (of a number) A function that gives the measure of an acute angle whose cosine, sine, or tangent is the given number. (588)

inverse (of a conditional statement) The statement formed by negating the antecedent and the consequent. (575)

isometric drawing

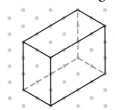

An isometric drawing of a prism using isometric dot paper.

A drawing of a three-dimensional object that shows three faces in one view. Also called an edge view. (71)

isometry See **rigid transformation.**

isosceles trapezoid

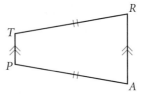

TRAP is an isosceles trapezoid.

A trapezoid whose two nonparallel sides are congruent. (188, 277)

isosceles triangle

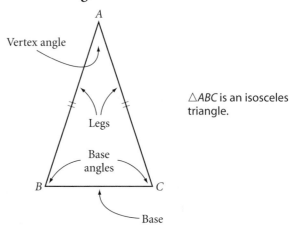

△ABC is an isosceles triangle.

You define this term in the Investigation Triangles. (57)

kite

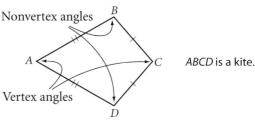

ABCD is a kite.

You define this term in the Investigation Special Quadrilaterals. (60, 275)

lateral edge The intersection of two lateral faces of a polyhedron. See **prism** and **pyramid.** (535)

lateral face A face of a polyhedron other than a base. See **prism** and **pyramid.** (432, 535)

Law of Contrapositive A type of valid reasoning that concludes the truth of a statement from the truth of its contrapositive. (575)

Law of Syllogism A type of valid reasoning that uses "if P then Q" and "if Q then R" to conclude that "if P then R." (575)

leg (of an isosceles triangle) One of the congruent sides of an isosceles triangle. See **isosceles triangle.** (210)

leg (of a right triangle) One of the perpendicular sides of a right triangle. See **right triangle.** (498)

lemma An auxiliary theorem used specifically to prove other theorems. (250)

line

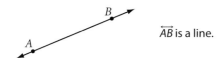

$\overleftrightarrow{AB}$ is a line.

An undefined term thought of as a straight, continuous arrangement of infinitely many points extending forever in two directions. A line has length, but no width or thickness, so it is one-dimensional. (24)

line of reflection The line over which every point of a figure is moved by a reflection. See **reflection.** (81)

line of symmetry

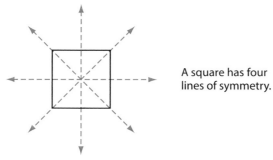

A square has four lines of symmetry.

The line of reflection of a figure having reflectional symmetry. (3, 318)

line segment

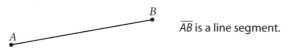

$\overline{AB}$ is a line segment.

Two points and all the points between them that are collinear with the two points. Also called a segment. The measure of a line segment is its length. (25)

linear pair (of angles)

∠1 and ∠2 are a linear pair of angles.

You define this term in the Investigation Defining Angles. (45)

locus The set of all points that satisfy some given conditions. (96)

logical argument A set of premises followed by statements, each of which relies on the premises or on previous statements, and ending with a final statement called a conclusion. An argument is valid if the conclusion has been arrived at through deductive reasoning. (119)

major arc

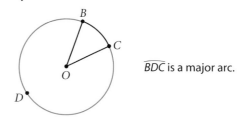

$\overset{\frown}{BDC}$ is a major arc.

An arc of a circle that is greater than a semicircle. (67)

mathematical model A mathematical way of representing a real-world situation, such as a geometric figure, graph, table, or equation. (105)

mean The number obtained by dividing the sum of the values in a data set by the number of values. Often called the average or the arithmetic mean. (217)

measure (of an angle)

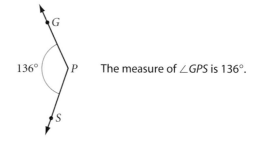

The measure of ∠GPS is 136°.

The smallest amount of rotation about the vertex from one ray to the other, measured in degrees. (34)

median

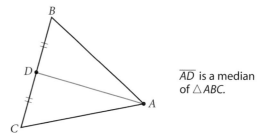

$\overline{AD}$ is a median of △ABC.

A line segment connecting a vertex of a triangle to the midpoint of the opposite side. (157)

midpoint

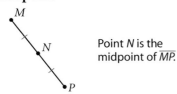

Point *N* is the midpoint of $\overline{MP}$.

The point on the line segment that is the same distance from both endpoints. The midpoint bisects the segment. (27)

midsegment (of a trapezoid)

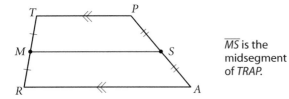

$\overline{MS}$ is the midsegment of *TRAP*.

The line segment connecting the midpoints of the two nonparallel sides of the trapezoid. (157)

midsegment (of a triangle)

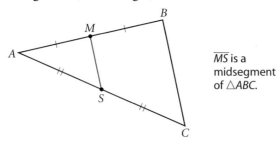

$\overline{MS}$ is a midsegment of △*ABC*.

A line segment connecting the midpoints of two sides of the triangle. (157)

minimal path The path of shortest length. (329)

minor arc

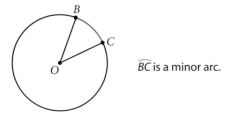

$\overparen{BC}$ is a minor arc.

An arc of a circle that is less than a semicircle. (67)

modular origami Origami art created by producing a number of identical origami pieces and assembling them. (226)

Modus Ponens The type of valid reasoning that uses "if *P* then *Q*" and the statement *P* to conclude that *Q* must be true. (525)

Modus Tollens The type of valid reasoning that uses "if *P* then *Q*" and the statement "not *Q*" to conclude that "not *P*" must be true. (526)

monohedral tessellation A tessellation that uses only one shape. See **regular tessellation.** (343)

negation (of a statement) A statement that is false if the original statement is true, and true if the original statement is false. The negation can usually be made by adding or removing the word *not* to the statement. (526)

net

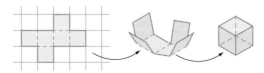

This net folds into a cube.

A two-dimensional pattern that can be folded to form a three-dimensional figure. (74)

network A collection of points connected by paths. (125)

n-**gon** A polygon with *n* sides. (50)

nonagon A polygon with nine sides. (50)

nonrigid transformation A transformation that does not preserve the size of the original figure, such as a dilation tranformed by a scale factor other than zero or one. (79)

nonvertex angle (of a kite) An angle formed by two noncongruent sides. See **kite.** (275)

oblique (cone, cylinder, prism) A cone or cylinder in which the axis is not perpendicular to the base(s), or a prism in which the lateral edges are not perpendicular to the bases. See **cone, cylinder,** and **prism.** (536)

obtuse angle

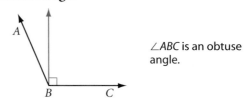

∠*ABC* is an obtuse angle.

You define this term in the Investigation Defining Angles. (44)

obtuse triangle

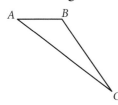

If ∠A or ∠B or ∠C is an obtuse angle, △ABC is an obtuse triangle.

You define this term in the Investigation Triangles. (56)

octagon A polygon with eight sides. (50)

octahedron

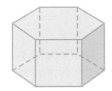

The first octahedron is a regular octahedron.

An polyhedron with eight faces. (582)

opposite angle or **side** (in a triangle)

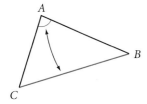

∠A is the angle opposite $\overline{BC}$, and $\overline{BC}$ is the side opposite ∠A.

The angle that does not contain a given side, or the side that is not a side of a given angle. (57)

opposite leg (of an acute angle in a right triangle)

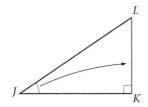

$\overline{KL}$ is the side opposite ∠J.

The side of the triangle that is not a side of the angle. (584)

opposite sides (of a quadrilateral) Two sides that do not share a vertex. (282)

ordered pair rule A rule that describes how to transform points on a coordinate plane. For example, the ordered pair rule $(x, y) \rightarrow (x + h, y + k)$ describes a translation horizontally by h units and vertically by k units. (112)

origami Traditional Japanese art of paper folding. (226)

Origamics Scientific origami developed by Dr. Kazuo Haga. (226)

orthocenter

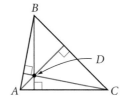

Point D is the orthocenter of △ABC.

The point of concurrency of a triangle's three altitudes (or of the lines containing the altitudes). (185)

orthographic drawing

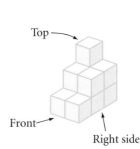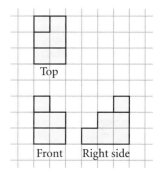

A drawing of the top, front, and right side views of a solid. (77)

outgoing angle The angle formed between the path of a rebounding object and the surface it collided with, such as a billiard ball bouncing off a cushion or a ray of light reflecting off a mirror. See **incoming angle.** (36)

paragraph proof A logical explanation presented in the form of a paragraph. (205)

parallel (lines, line segments, or rays)

Lines i and j are parallel.

Lines are parallel if they lie in the same plane and do not intersect. Line segments or rays are parallel if they lie on parallel lines. (43, 170)

parallel (planes or figures)

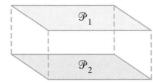

$\mathcal{P}_1$ and $\mathcal{P}_2$ are parallel planes.

Planes are parallel if they do not intersect. Figures are parallel if they lie in parallel planes. (76)

parallelogram

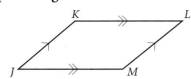

JKLM is a parallelogram.

You define this term in the Investigation Special Quadrilaterals. (61)

pentagon

PLATE and *HOMER* are both pentagons. *HOMER* is a regular pentagon.

A polygon with five sides. (50)

perimeter The length of the boundary of a two-dimensional figure. For a polygon, the perimeter is the sum of the lengths of its sides. (51)

perpendicular (lines, line segments, or rays)

Lines *k* and ℓ are perpendicular.

Lines are perpendicular if they meet at 90° angles. Line segments and rays are perpendicular if they lie on perpendicular lines. (43)

perpendicular bisector

Line ℓ is the perpendicular bisector of $\overline{AB}$.

A line that divides a line segment into two congruent parts and is perpendicular to the line segment. (155)

pi (π) The ratio of the circumference of a circle to its diameter. (476)

plane

$\mathcal{P}$ is a plane.

An undefined term thought of as a flat surface that extends infinitely along its edges. A plane has length and width but no thickness, so it is two-dimensional. (24)

Platonic solids The five regular polyhedrons. See **dodecahedron, hexahedron, icosahedron, octahedron,** and **tetrahedron.** (582)

point

P is a point.

An undefined term thought of as a location with no size or dimension. It is the most basic building block of geometry. In a two-dimensional coordinate system, a point's location is represented by an ordered pair of numbers (*x, y*). (24)

point of concurrency The point at which two or more lines, line segments, or rays intersect. See **concurrent lines.** (184)

point symmetry

This figure has point symmetry.

The property that a figure coincides with itself under a rotation of 180°. Also called two-fold rotational symmetry. (318)

point of tangency The point of intersection of a tangent line and a circle. See **tangent line.** (66)

polygon

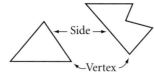

The triangle and pentagon are examples of polygons.

A closed figure in a plane, formed by connecting line segments endpoint to endpoint with each segment intersecting exactly two others. (50)

polyhedron

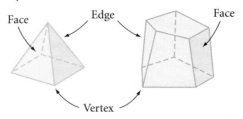

A solid formed by polygonal surfaces that enclose a single region of space. (534)

postulates A collection of simple and useful statements about geometry accepted without proof. (622)

premises (of a deductive system) A set of accepted facts, including undefined terms, definitions, properties of algebra and equality, and postulates, used to organize the properties of the system and to prove further conclusions. (622)

prism

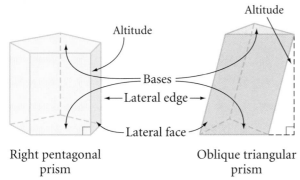

Right pentagonal prism   Oblique triangular prism

A polyhedron with two congruent, parallel bases connected by lateral faces that are parallelograms. (535)

proportion A statement of equality between two ratios. (375)

protractor

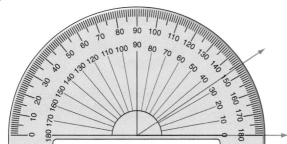

A tool used to measure the size of an angle in degrees. (34)

pyramid

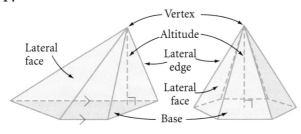

Trapezoidal pyramid   Hexagonal pyramid

A polyhedron consisting of a polygon base and triangular lateral faces that share a common vertex. (72, 535)

Pythagorean Theorem

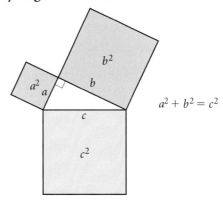

$$a^2 + b^2 = c^2$$

The relationship among the lengths of the sides of a right triangle in which the sum of the squares of the lengths of the legs equals the square of the length of the hypotenuse. (498)

Pythagorean triple Three positive integers with the property that the sum of the squares of two of the integers equals the square of the third. (500)

quadrilateral

QUAD is a quadrilateral.

A polygon with four sides. (50)

radian measure The ratio found by dividing the length of the arc by its radius. (482)

radius

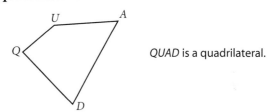

Segment *r* is a radius.

A line segment from the center of a circle or sphere to a point on the circle or sphere. Also, the length of that line segment. (65, 537)

ratio An expression that compares two quantities by division. (372)

ray

Endpoint

$\overrightarrow{AB}$ is a ray.

A point on a line, and all the points of the line that lie on one side of this point. (27)

rectangle

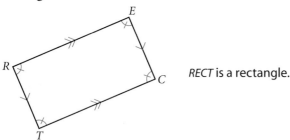

RECT is a rectangle.

You define this term in the Investigation Special Quadrilaterals. (61)

rectangular numbers Numbers that can be represented by a rectangular array of dots or squares. (108)

reduction A dilation in which the amount is decreased by a scale factor less than 1. (371)

reflection

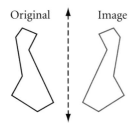

Original   Image

The image is a reflection of the original figure across the line of reflection.

Line of reflection

An isometry in which every point and its image are on opposite sides and the same distance from a fixed line. (81)

reflectional symmetry The property that a figure coincides with itself under a reflection. Also called line symmetry or mirror symmetry. (3, 318)

reflex measure (of an angle)

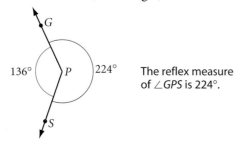

136°   P   224°

The reflex measure of ∠GPS is 224°.

The largest amount of rotation less than 360° about the vertex from one ray to the other measured in degrees. (34)

regular hexagon A polygon with six congruent sides and angles that can be constructed using a single compass setting. See **hexagon.** (10)

regular polygon

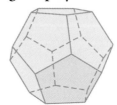

This octagon is a regular polygon.

You define this term in the Investigation Special Polygons. (52)

regular polyhedron

A polyhedron whose faces are enclosed by congruent regular polygons, which meet at all vertices in exactly the same way. (534)

regular tessellation

Equilateral triangles, squares, or regular hexagons form regular tessellations.

A tessellation of congruent regular polygons. (344)

remote interior angles (of a triangle)

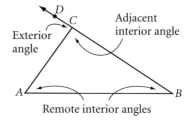

Exterior angle

Adjacent interior angle

∠A and ∠B are the remote interior angles of exterior angle ACD.

Remote interior angles

Interior angles of the triangle that do not share a vertex with a given exterior angle. (222)

rhombus

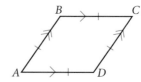

ABCD is a rhombus.

You define this term in the Investigation Special Quadrilaterals. (61)

right (cone, cylinder, or prism) A cone or cylinder in which the axis is perpendicular to the base(s), or a prism in which the lateral edges are perpendicular to the bases. See **cone, cylinder,** and **prism.** (536)

right angle

∠ABC is a right angle.

You define this term in the Investigation Defining Angles. (44)

right triangle

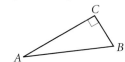

△ABC is a right triangle.

You define this term in the Investigation Triangles. (56)

rigid transformation A transformation that preserves size and shape. The image of a figure under an isometry is congruent to the original figure. Also called a rigid transformation. See **reflection, rotation,** and **translation.** (79)

rotation

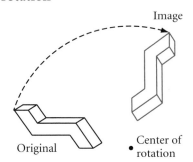

The image is a rotation of the original figure about the center of rotation.

An isometry in which each point is moved by the same angle measure in the same direction along a circular path about a fixed point. (80)

rotational symmetry The property that a figure coincides with itself under some rotation. If the angle of rotation is $\frac{360}{n}$ degrees for some positive integer n, the symmetry is called n-fold rotational symmetry. (3, 318)

scale factor The ratio of corresponding lengths in similar figures. (371)

scalene triangle

△ABC is a scalene triangle.

You define this term in the Investigation Triangles. (54)

secant

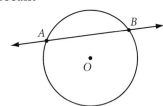

$\overleftrightarrow{AB}$ is a secant of circle O.

A line that intersects a circle in two points. (467)

sector of a circle

The shaded region bounded by $\overline{OA}$, $\overline{OB}$, and $\overparen{AB}$ is a sector of circle O.

The region between two radii and an arc of the circle. (425)

segment See **line segment.**

segment addition A property that states if A, B, and C are collinear and B is between A and C, then $AB + BC = AC$. (26)

segment bisector

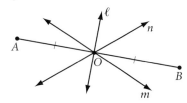

Lines ℓ, m, and n bisect $\overline{AB}$.

A line, ray, or segment that passes through the midpoint of a line segment in a plane. (155)

segment of a circle

The shaded region between $\overline{AB}$ and $\overparen{AB}$ is a segment of circle O.

The region between a chord and an arc of the circle. (425)

semicircle

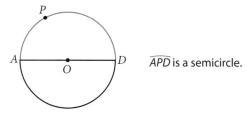

$\overset{\frown}{APD}$ is a semicircle.

An arc of a circle whose endpoints are the endpoints of a diameter. (67)

side (of a polygon) A line segment connecting consecutive vertices of the polygon. See **polygon.** (50)

side (of an angle) One of the two rays that form the angle. See **angle.** (34)

similar (figures, polygons, or solids)

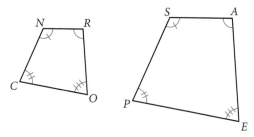

CORN is similar to *PEAS* if and only if $\frac{CO}{PE} = \frac{OR}{EA} = \frac{RN}{AS} = \frac{NC}{SP}$.

Identical in shape but not necessarily in size. Two figures are similar if and only if all corresponding angles are congruent and lengths of all corresponding sides, edges, or other one-dimensional measures are proportional. (374, 375)

sine (of an acute angle in a right triangle)

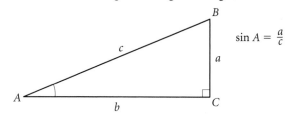

$\sin A = \frac{a}{c}$

The sine of $\angle A$ is the ratio of *BC* to *AB*.

The ratio of the length of the leg opposite the angle to the length of the hypotenuse. (585)

skew lines

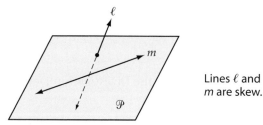

Lines ℓ and m are skew.

Lines that are not in the same plane and do not intersect. (43)

slant height

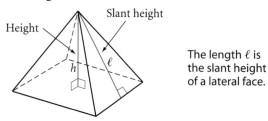

The length ℓ is the slant height of a lateral face.

The height of each triangular lateral face of a pyramid. (434)

slope In a two-dimensional coordinate system, the ratio of the vertical change to the horizontal change between two points on a line. (217)

solid A three-dimensional geometric figure that completely encloses a region of space. See **cone, cylinder, hemisphere, polyhedron, prism, pyramid,** and **sphere.** (71)

solid of revolution

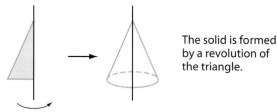

The solid is formed by a revolution of the triangle.

A solid formed by rotating a two-dimensional figure about a line. (111)

space An undefined term thought of as the set of all points. Space extends infinitely in all directions, so it is three-dimensional. (71)

sphere

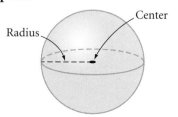

The set of all points in space at a given distance from a given point. (72, 537)

square

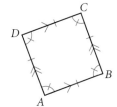

ABCD is a square.

You define this term in the Investigation Special Quadrilaterals. (61)

straightedge A tool used to construct lines, rays, and line segments. (7)

supplementary angles

∠1 and ∠2 are supplementary angles.

You define this term in the Investigation Defining Angles. (45)

surface area The sum of the areas of all the surfaces of a solid. (432)

symmetry The property that a figure coincides with itself under an isometry. (3)

tangent (of an acute angle in a right triangle)

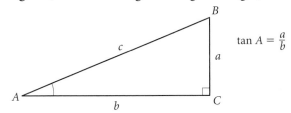

$\tan A = \frac{a}{b}$

The tangent of ∠*A* is the ratio of *BC* to *AC*.

The ratio of the length of the leg opposite the angle to the length of the leg adjacent to the angle. (584, 585)

tangent circles

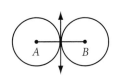

Circles *A* and *B* are externally tangent.
Circles *P* and *Q* are internally tangent.

Circles that are tangent to the same line at the same point. They can be internally tangent or externally tangent. (455)

tangent

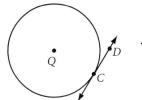

$\overleftrightarrow{CD}$ is a tangent of circle *Q*.

You define this term in the Investigation Defining Circle Terms. (66)

tangent segment

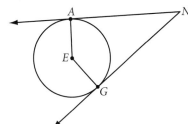

$\overline{AN}$ and $\overline{GN}$ are tangent segments from point *N* to circle *E*.

A line segment that lies on a tangent line with one endpoint at the point of tangency. (453)

tangential velocity The speed of an object at a point as it moves around the circumference of a circle. (485)

tessellation

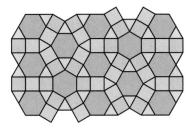

A pattern of shapes that completely cover a plane without overlaps or gaps. (18, 343)

tetrahedron

This is a regular tetrahedron.

A polyhedron with four faces. (534)

theorem A conjecture that has been proved within a deductive system. (499, 622)

tiling See **tessellation.**

transformation A rule that assigns to each point of a figure another point in the plane, called its image. See **dilation, reflection, rotation,** and **translation.** (79)

translation

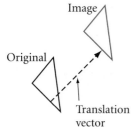

The image is a translation of the original triangle by the translation vector.

An isometry in which each point is moved by the same translation vector. (79)

translation vector A directed line segment from a point to its translated image. See **translation.** (79, 82)

translational symmetry The result of sliding a design repeatedly by the same translation vector. (320)

transversal

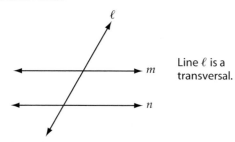

Line ℓ is a transversal.

A line that intersects two or more other coplanar lines. (138)

trapezoid

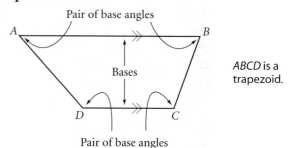

ABCD is a trapezoid.

You define this term in the Investigation Special Quadrilaterals. (60, 276)

triangle

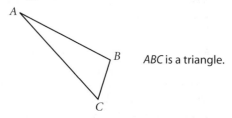

ABC is a triangle.

A polygon with three sides. (50)

triangular numbers Numbers that can be represented by a triangular array of dots or squares. (108)

trigonometry The study of the relationships between the measures of sides and angles of triangles. See **cosine, sine,** and **tangent.** (584)

truncated (cone or pyramid) See **frustum.**

undecagon A polygon with 11 sides. (50)

undefined term In a deductive system, terms whose general meaning is assumed and whose characteristics are understood only from the postulates or axioms that use them. See **line, plane, point,** and **space.** (623)

valid reasoning An argument that reaches its conclusion through accepted forms of reasoning. (525)

vector A quantity that has both magnitude and direction. A vector is represented by an arrow whose length and direction represent the magnitude and direction of the vector. (112)

Glossary

Venn diagram

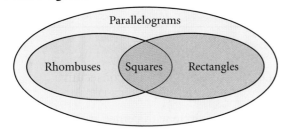

A Venn diagram showing the relationships among some quadrilaterals.

A concept map of overlapping circles or ovals that shows the relationships among members of different sets. (96)

vertex A point of intersection of two or more rays or line segments in a geometric figure. The plural of vertex is vertices. See **angle, polygon,** and **polyhedron.** (33, 50, 534)

vertex angle (of an isosceles triangle) The angle between the two congruent sides. See **isosceles triangle.** (57, 210)

vertex angles (of a kite) The angles between the pairs of congruent sides. See **kite.** (275)

vertical angles

∠1 and ∠2 are vertical angles.

You define this term in the Investigation Defining Angles. (45)

volume A measure of the amount of space contained in a solid, expressed in cubic units. (541)

work The measure of force applied over distance, calculated as the product of the force and the distance. (512)

Table of Symbols

$\overleftrightarrow{AB}$	line AB	$\triangle ABC$	triangle ABC
$\overrightarrow{AB}$	ray AB	$ABCD...$	polygon with consecutive vertices A, B, C, D,...
$\overline{AB}$	line segment AB	$\odot A$	circle with center at point A
AB or $m\overline{AB}$	length of line segment AB	π	pi, approximately equal to 3.14
$\angle A$	angle A	$\overparen{AB}$	arc AB
$\angle ABC$	angle with vertex at point B	$m\overparen{AB}$	measure of arc AB
$m\angle A$	measure of angle A	$m\overparen{ABC}$	measure of major arc ABC
°	degree(s)	(a, b)	ordered pair with x-coordinate a and y-coordinate b
$=$	is equal to	$\langle a, b \rangle$	vector with horizontal component a and vertical component b
$\approx$	is approximately equal to		
$\neq$	is not equal to	$\vec{A}$	vector A
$\stackrel{?}{=}$	is this equal to?	A′	image of point A resulting from a transformation
$>$	is greater than		
$<$	is less than	$\dfrac{a}{b}$ or $a{:}b$	ratio of a to b
$\cong$	is congruent to	$P \rightarrow Q$	if P then Q
$\sim$	is similar to	$\sim P$	not P
$\parallel$	is parallel to	$\therefore$	therefore
$\perp$	is perpendicular to	sin	sine
	j is parallel to k	cos	cosine
		tan	tangent
	j is perpendicular to k	$\sin^{-1}$	inverse sine
		$\cos^{-1}$	inverse cosine
	$\overline{AB}$ is congruent to $\overline{CD}$	$\tan^{-1}$	inverse tangent
		$\sqrt{a}$	nonnegative square root of a
	$\angle A$ is congruent to $\angle B$	$|a|$	absolute value of a

Index

D

Index

Index

Photo Credits

Abbreviations: top (**T**), center (**C**), bottom (**B**), left (**L**), right (**R**)

Cover

Background Ferris Wheel image: Ti_ser/Shutterstock.com

Front Matter

iii–x: All images are from M. C. Escher ©2014, The M. C. Escher Company—The Netherlands. All rights reserved. www.mcescher.com

Chapter 0

1: M. C. Escher's *Print Gallery* ©2014 The M. C. Escher Company—The Netherlands. All rights reserved. www.mcescher.com; **2 (TL):** Cheryl Fenton; **2 (TC):** NASA; **2 (TR):** ©Darios/Shutterstock.com; **2 (BL):** ©David Peter Robinson/Shutterstock.com; **2 (BR):** Cheryl Fenton; **3 (TR):** ©Sleeping cat/Shutterstock.com; **3 (BR):** ©Sigpoggy/Shutterstock.com; **4 (TL):** Cheryl Fenton; **4 (TC):** Cheryl Fenton; **4 (TR):** Cheryl Fenton; **4 (CL):** ©Marylia/Shutterstock.com; **4 (CR):** Hillary Turner; **4 (BL):** Cheryl Fenton; **5 (T, a–c):** Cheryl Fenton; **5 (C, d–f):** Cheryl Fenton; **5 (B):** ©Andy Goldsworthy. Reprinted by permission; **6 (C):** ©Ruth Choi/Shutterstock.com; **7 (L):** ©Kate Connes/Shutterstock.com; **7 (T):** ©Christopher Kolaczan/Shutterstock.com; **7 (B):** ©Ariy/Shutterstock.com; **9 (L):** ©hxdbzxy/Shutterstock.com; **9 (C):** ©Mikhaylova Liubov/Shutterstock.com; **9 (R):** ©viduka/Shutterstock.com; **11 (R):** ©Frances A. Miller/Shutterstock.com; **12 (L):** ©Neveshkin Nikolay/Shutterstock.com; **12 (R):** ©Neftali/Shutterstock.com; **13 (L):** ©Elenasz/Shutterstock.com; **13 (B):** ©Richard T. Nowitz/Corbis; **14 (TR):** ©Chantal de Bruijne/Shutterstock.com; **14 (CR):** ©SKABARCAT/Shutterstock.com; **15 (L):** Cheryl Fenton; **16 (CL):** ©Artem Efimov/Shutterstock.com; **16 (CR):** ©polosatik/Shutterstock.com; **16 (B):** M. C. Escher's *Snakes* ©2014 The M. C. Escher Company—The Netherlands. All rights reserved. www.mcescher.com; **17 (BL):** Cheryl Fenton; **17 (BR):** Cheryl Fenton; **18 (L):** ©Kobby Dagan/Shutterstock.com; **18 (R):** ©javarman/Shutterstock.com; **20 (T):** ©Azat1976/Shutterstock.com; **20 (CR):** Ken Karp Photography; **20 (BR):** ©littlewormy/Shutterstock.com; **21 (C):** ©Sigpoggy/Shutterstock.com; **22 (BL):** ©trappy76/Shutterstock.com; **22 (BR):** ©ilky/Shutterstock.com

Chapter 1

23: M. C. Escher's *Three Worlds* ©2014 The M. C. Escher Company—The Netherlands. All rights reserved. www.mcescher.com; **24 (TR):** Hillary Turner; **24 (CR):** Cheryl Fenton; **24 (BR):** ©schankz/Shutterstock.com; **27 (BR):** ©Alexander Gospodinov/Shutterstock.com; **28 (TR):** ©Lee Yiu Tung/Shutterstock.com; **28 (CL):** ©starD/Shutterstock.com; **28 (CR):** ©CHEN WS/Shutterstock.com; **30 (CR):** ©Tyler Olson/Shutterstock.com; **31 (BL):** ©Joao Virissimo/Shutterstock.com; **33 (TR):** ©Jirsak/Shutterstock.com; **33 (C):** ©Will Rodrigues/Shutterstock.com; **33 (BL):** ©Mixov/Shutterstock.com; **33 (BL):** ©antb/Shutterstock.com; **34 (B):** Ken Karp Photography; **36 (TR):** ©Pixelbliss/Shutterstock.com; **41 (C):** ©Sergiy Kuzmin/Shutterstock.com; **42 (C):** ©Morphart Creation/Shutterstock.com; **44 (CL):** ©SPYDER/Shutterstock.com; **45 (CL):** ©Zhukov Oleg/Shutterstock.com; **47 (CR):** ©PremiumVector/Shutterstock.com; **51 (CR):** ©Pack-Shot/Shutterstock.com; **53 (TR):** Hillary Turner; **53 (TC):** Hillary Turner; **53 (TC):** ©Robyn Mackenzie/Shutterstock.com; **53 (TR):** ©MarArt/Shutterstock.com; **55 (TR):** ©AC Rider/Shutterstock.com; **55 (TR):** ©Anita Patterson Peppers/Shutterstock.com; **56 (TL):** ©archetype/Shutterstock.com; **60 (TR):** ©f11photo/Shutterstock.com; **61 (CL):** Cheryl Fenton; **63 (BR):** ©Natalia Bratslavsky/Shutterstock.com; **63 (BR):** ©Subbotina Anna/Shutterstock.com; **65 (CR):** ©t50/Shutterstock.com; **65 (CL):** ©anyaivanova/Shutterstock.com; **66 (BL):** ©Jaroslaw Grudzinski/Shutterstock.com;

66 (BR): ©Dmitry Naumov/Shutterstock.com; **68 (CL):** ©Alex Pix/Shutterstock.com; **68 (CT):** ©Roberto Delamora/Shutterstock.com; **71 (CL):** Cheryl Fenton; **71 (C):** ©M. Unal Ozmen/Shutterstock.com; **71 (CR):** ©dean bertoncelj/Shutterstock.com; **72 (CR):** ©vadim kozlovsky/Shutterstock.com; **72 (BR):** ©archetype/Shutterstock.com; **73 (CR):** Cheryl Fenton; **74 (TR):** ©pisaphotography/Shutterstock.com; **75 (BL):** Ken Karp Photography; **75 (BR):** ©JoMo333/Shutterstock.com; **77 (TR):** Ken Karp Photography; **78 (CL):** Ken Karp Photography; **79 (TR):** ©JoeyPhoto/Shutterstock.com; **79 (BR):** Ken Karp Photography; **81 (CL):** ©Janaka Dharmasena/Shutterstock.com; **85 (CL):** ©testing/Shutterstock.com; **85 (CR):** ©testing/Shutterstock.com; **89 (BR):** ©Yanas/Shutterstock.com; **91 (CR):** Cheryl Fenton

Chapter 2

93: M. C. Escher's *Hand with Reflecting Sphere (Self Portrait in Spherical Mirror)* ©2014 The M. C. Escher Company—The Netherlands. All rights reserved. www.mcescher.com; **94 (CL):** ©PathDoc/Shutterstock.com; **94 (BR):** M. C. Escher's *Bookplate for Albert Ernst Bosman* ©2014 The M. C. Escher Company—The Netherlands. All rights reserved. www.mcescher.com; **99 (C):** Hillary Turner; **100 (TR):** Ken Karp Photography; **100 (BR):** ©Zern Liew/Shutterstock.com; **101 (TR):** ©Dainis Derics/Shutterstock.com; **105 (TR):** ©Flat Design/Shutterstock.com; **105 (C):** ©lucadp/Shutterstock.com; **106 (T):** Hillary Turner; **107 (TL):** ©Minimal_Pixel/Shutterstock.com; **107 (TR):** ©Mckyartstudio/Shutterstock.com; **108 (TL):** Cheryl Fenton; **109 (TR):** ©Rock and Wasp/Shutterstock.com; **109 (BL):** ©Destinyweddingstudio/Shutterstock.com; **118 (BR):** ©DVARG/Shutterstock.com; **119 (C):** ©bikeriderlondon/Shutterstock.com; **122 (BR):** ©Andrey Gontarev/Shutterstock.com; **123 (TR):** NASA; **125 (TR):** ©Georgios Kollidas/Shutterstock.com; **125 (BR):** Ken Karp Photography; **127 (TR):** ©Alexey Stiop/Shutterstock.com; **133 (CR):** Ken Karp Photography; **138 (CR):** ©Robert Crum/Shutterstock.com; **138 (BR):** Ken Karp Photography; **140 (TR):** Hillary Turner; **142 (BL):** ©Wolf Design/Shutterstock.com

Chapter 3

149: M. C. Escher's *Bookplate for Albert Ernst Bosman* ©2014 The M. C. Escher Company—The Netherlands. All rights reserved. www.mcescher.com; **150 (CL):** ©pavila/Shutterstock.com; **150 (B):** Hillary Turner; **151 (T):** Hillary Turner; **153 (CR):** ©pavila/Shutterstock.com; **155 (CL):** ©nex999/Shutterstock.com; **155 (C):** ©Koksharov Dmitry/Shutterstock.com; **162 (BR):** ©R. P. Visual/Shutterstock.com; **165 (BL):** ©lynnette/Shutterstock.com; **170 (TR):** ©photobank.ch/Shutterstock.com; **170 (CR):** ©karin claus/Shutterstock.com; **171 (CR):** ©Fotokostic/Shutterstock.com; **174 (TR):** ©Peter Gudella/Shutterstock.com; **174 (CR):** ©emran/Shutterstock.com; **178 (TL):** ©Shamleen/Shutterstock.com; **178 (TL):** ©David Huntley Creative/Shutterstock.com; **183 (B):** ©Mazzzur/Shutterstock.com; **184 (CR):** Ken Karp Photography; **192 (CL):** ©bikeriderlondon/Shutterstock.com; **192 (CR):** Ken Karp Photography; **193 (CR):** ©Alexandra Lande/Shutterstock.com; **195 (TR):** Ken Karp Photography

Chapter 4

203: M. C. Escher's *Symmetry Drawing* ©2014 The M. C. Escher Company—The Netherlands. All rights reserved. www.mcescher.com; **204 (TR):** ©michaeljung/Shutterstock.com; **204 (BR):** Ken Karp Photography; **209 (C):** Hillary Turner; **210 (CL):** ©Glenn W. Walker/Shutterstock.com; **210 (CR):** ©spirit of america/Shutterstock.com; **215 (TR):** ©Gwoeii/Shutterstock.com; **219 (B):** ©Michael D. Brown/Shutterstock.com; **220 (T):** ©Mark Baldwin/Shutterstock.com; **224 (CL):** ©SF photo/Shutterstock.com;